Study and Solutions Guide
Precalculus
FOURTH EDITION
Larson / Hostetler

Dianna L. Zook

Indiana University
Purdue University at Fort Wayne, Indiana

HOUGHTON MIFFLIN COMPANY Boston   New York

Sponsoring Editor: Christine B. Hoag
Senior Associate Editor: Maureen Brooks
Managing Editor: Catherine B. Cantin
Supervising Editor: Karen Carter
Associate Project Editor: Rachel D'Angelo Wimberly
Editorial Assistant: Caroline Lipscomb
Production Supervisor: Lisa Merrill
Art Supervisor: Gary Crespo
Marketing Associate: Ros Kane
Marketing Assistant: Kate Burden Thomas

Printed in the United States of America.

International Standard Book Number: 0-669-41743-2

3456789–VG 01 00 99 98

PREFACE

The *Study and Solutions Guide* for *Precalculus*, Fourth Edition, is a supplement to the text by Roland E. Larson and Robert P. Hostetler.

As a mathematics instructor, I often have students come to me with questions about assigned homework. When I ask to see their work, the reply often is "I didn't know where to start." The purpose of the *Study Guide* is to provide brief summaries of the topics covered in the textbook and enough detailed solutions to problems so that you will be able to work the remaining exercises.

A special thanks to Larson Texts, Inc. for typing this guide. Also I would like to thank my husband Edward L. Schlindwein for his support during the several months I worked on this project.

If you have any corrections or suggestions for improving this *Study Guide*, I would appreciate hearing from you.

Good luck with your study of precalculus.

Dianna L. Zook
Indiana University
Purdue University at
Fort Wayne, Indiana 46805

CONTENTS

PART 1 Solutions to Odd-Numbered Exercises

CHAPTER P
Prerequisites

CHAPTER P
Prerequisites

Section P.1   Real Numbers

■ You should know the following sets.

(a) The set of real numbers includes the rational numbers and the irrational numbers.

(b) The set of rational numbers includes all real numbers that can be written as the ratio p/q of two integers, where $q \neq 0$.

(c) The set of irrational numbers includes all real numbers which are not rational.

(d) The set of integers: $\{\ldots, -3, -2, -1, 0, 1, 2, 3, \ldots\}$

(e) The set of whole numbers: $\{0, 1, 2, 3, 4, \ldots\}$

(f) The set of natural numbers: $\{1, 2, 3, 4, \ldots\}$

■ The real number line is used to represent the real numbers.

■ Know the inequality symbols.

(a) $a < b$ means a is less than b.

(b) $a \leq b$ means a is less than or equal to b.

(c) $a > b$ means a is greater than b.

(d) $a \geq b$ means a is greater than or equal to b.

■ You should know that
$$|a| = \begin{cases} a, & \text{if } a \geq 0 \\ -a, & \text{if } a < 0. \end{cases}$$

■ Know the properties of absolute value.

(a) $|a| \geq 0$ (b) $|-a| = |a|$ (c) $|ab| = |a|\,|b|$ (d) $\left|\dfrac{a}{b}\right| = \dfrac{|a|}{|b|}$

■ The distance between a and b on the real line is $|b - a| = |a - b|$.

■ You should be able to identify the terms in an algebraic expression.

■ You should know and be able to use the basic rules of algebra.

■ Commutative Property

(a) Addition: $a + b = b + a$ (b) Multiplication: $a \cdot b = b \cdot a$

■ Associative Property

(a) Addition: $(a + b) + c = a + (b + c)$ (b) Multiplication: $(ab)c = a(bc)$

■ Identity Property

(a) Addition: 0 is the identity; $a + 0 = 0 + a = a$.

(b) Multiplication: 1 is the identity; $a \cdot 1 = 1 \cdot a = a$.

■ Inverse Property

(a) Addition: $-a$ is the inverse of a; $a + (-a) = -a + a = 0$.

(b) Multiplication: $1/a$ is the inverse of a, $a \neq 0$; $a(1/a) = (1/a)a = 1$.

■ Distributive Property

(a) Left: $a(b + c) = ab + ac$ (b) Right: $(a + b)c = ac + bc$

continued

- ■ Properties of Negatives
    - (a) $(-1)a = -a$
    - (b) $-(-a) = a$
    - (c) $(-a)b = a(-b) = -ab$
    - (d) $(-a)(-b) = ab$
    - (e) $-(a + b) = (-a) + (-b) = -a - b$
- ■ Properties of Zero
    - (a) $a \pm 0 = a$
    - (b) $a \cdot 0 = 0$
    - (c) $0 \div a = 0/a = 0, a \neq 0$
    - (d) If $ab = 0$, then $a = 0$ or $b = 0$.
    - (e) $a/0$ is undefined.
- ■ Properties of Fractions $(b \neq 0, d \neq 0)$
    - (a) Equivalent Fractions: $a/b = c/d$ if and only if $ad = bc$.
    - (b) Rule of Signs: $-a/b = a/-b = -(a/b)$ and $-a/-b = a/b$
    - (c) Equivalent Fractions: $a/b = ac/bc, c \neq 0$
    - (d) Addition and Subtraction
        1. Like Denominators: $(a/b) \pm (c/b) = (a \pm c)/b$
        2. Unlike Denominators: $(a/b) \pm (c/d) = (ad \pm bc)/bd$
    - (e) Multiplication: $(a/b) \cdot (c/d) = ac/bd$
    - (f) Division: $(a/b) \div (c/d) = (a/b) \cdot (d/c) = ad/bc$ if $c \neq 0$.
- ■ Properties of Equality
    - (a) If $a = b$, then $a + c = b + c$.
    - (b) If $a = b$, then $ac = bc$.
    - (c) If $a + c = b + c$, then $a = b$.
    - (d) If $ac = bc$ and $c \neq 0$, then $a = b$.

Solutions to Odd-Numbered Exercises

1. $-9, -\frac{7}{2}, 5, \frac{2}{3}, \sqrt{2}, 0, 1$
   - (a) Natural numbers: $5, 1$
   - (b) Integers: $-9, 5, 0, 1$
   - (c) Rational numbers: $-9, -\frac{7}{2}, 5, \frac{2}{3}, 0, 1$
   - (d) Irrational numbers: $\sqrt{2}$

3. $2.01, 0.666\ldots, -13, 0.010110111\ldots$
   - (a) Natural numbers: none
   - (b) Integers: -13
   - (c) Rational numbers: $2.01, 0.666\ldots, -13$
   - (d) Irrational numbers: $0.010110111\ldots$

5. $-\pi, -\frac{1}{3}, \frac{6}{3}, \frac{1}{2}\sqrt{2}, -7.5$
   - (a) Natural numbers: $\frac{6}{3}$ (since it equals 2)
   - (b) Integers: $\frac{6}{3}$
   - (c) Rational numbers: $-\frac{1}{3}, \frac{6}{3}, -7.5$
   - (d) Irrational numbers: $-\pi, \frac{1}{2}\sqrt{2}$

7. $\frac{5}{8} = 0.625$

9. $\frac{41}{333} = 0.\overline{123}$

11. $-1 < 2.5$

13. $\frac{3}{2} < 7$

15. $-4 > -8$

17. $\frac{5}{6} > \frac{2}{3}$

19. The inequality $x \leq 5$ is the set of all real numbers less than or equal to 5. The interval is unbounded.

21. The inequality $x < 0$ is the set of all negative real numbers. The interval is unbounded.

23. The inequality $x \geq 4$ is the set of all real numbers greater than or equal to 4. The interval is unbounded.

25. The inequality $-2 < x < 2$ is the set of all real numbers greater than -2 and less than 2. The interval is bounded.

27. The inequality $-1 \leq x < 0$ is the set of all negative real numbers greater than or equal to -1. The interval is bounded.

29. $\frac{127}{90} \approx 1.41111, \frac{584}{413} \approx 1.41404, \frac{7071}{5000} \approx 1.41420, \sqrt{2} \approx 1.41421, \frac{47}{33} \approx 1.42424$

31. $x < 0$ **33.** $y \geq 0$ **35.** $A \geq 30$

37. $|-10| = -(-10) = 10$ **39.** $|3 - \pi| = -(3 - \pi) = \pi - 3 \approx 0.1416$

41. $\dfrac{-5}{|-5|} = \dfrac{-5}{-(-5)} = \dfrac{-5}{5} = -1$ **43.** $-3|-3| = -3[-(-3)] = -9$

45. $-|16.25| + 20 = -16.25 + 20 = 3.75$ **47.** $|-3| > -|-3|$ since $3 > -3$.

49. $-5 = -|5|$ since $-5 = -5$.   **51.** $-|-2| = -|2|$ since $-2 = -2$.

53. $d(-1, 3) = |3 - (-1)| = |3 + 1| = 4$ **55.** $d\left(-\frac{5}{2}, 0\right) = \left|0 - \left(-\frac{5}{2}\right)\right| = \frac{5}{2}$

57. $d(126, 75) = |75 - 126| = 51$ **59.** $d\left(\frac{16}{5}, \frac{112}{75}\right) = \left|\frac{112}{75} - \frac{16}{5}\right| = \frac{128}{75}$

61. $d(x, 5) = |x - 5|$ and $d(x, 5) \leq 3$, thus $|x - 5| \leq 3$.

63. $d(7, 18) = |7 - 18| = 11$ miles

65. $d(y, 0) = |y - 0| = |y|$ and $d(y, 0) \geq 6$, thus $|y| \geq 6$.

67.

Budgeted Expense, b	*Actual Expense, a*	$|a - b|$	$0.05b$
$112,700	$113,356	$656	$5635

The actual expense difference is greater than $500 (but is less than 5% of the budget) so it does not pass the test.

69.

Budgeted Expense, b	*Actual Expense, a*	$|a - b|$	$0.05b$
$37,640	$37,335	$305	$1882

Since $305 < $500 and $305 < $1882, it passes the "budget variance test."

71. $|77.8 - 92.2| = \$14.4$ billion deficit for 1960

73. $|1031.3 - 1252.7| = \$221.4$ billion deficit for 1990

75. (a) $|u + v| \neq |u| + |v|$ if u is positive and v is negative or vice versa.

(b) $|u + v| \leq |u| + |v|$

They are equal when u and v have the same sign. If they differ in sign, $|u + v|$ is less than $|u| + |v|$.

77. $7x + 4$
Terms: $7x, 4$

79. $4x^3 + x - 5$
Terms: $4x^3, x, -5$

81. $4x - 6$
(a) $4(-1) - 6 = -4 - 6 = -10$
(b) $4(0) - 6 = 0 - 6 = -6$

83. $x^2 - 3x + 4$
(a) $(-2)^2 - 3(-2) + 4 = 4 + 6 + 4 = 14$
(b) $(2)^2 - 3(2) + 4 = 4 - 6 + 4 = 2$

85. $\dfrac{x + 1}{x - 1}$

(a) $\dfrac{1 + 1}{1 - 1} = \dfrac{2}{0}$ is undefined.

You cannot divide by zero.

(b) $\dfrac{-1 + 1}{-1 - 1} = \dfrac{0}{-2} = 0$

87. $x + 9 = 9 + x$

Commutative (addition)

89. $\dfrac{1}{(h + 6)}(h + 6) = 1, h \neq -6$
Inverse (multiplication)

91. $2(x + 3) = 2x + 6$

Distributive Property

93. $1 \cdot (1 + x) = 1 + x$

Identity (multiplication)

95. $x(3y) = (x \cdot 3)y$ Associative (multiplication)
$= (3x)y$ Commutative (multiplication)

97. $\dfrac{81 - (90 - 9)}{5} = \dfrac{81 - 81}{5} = \dfrac{0}{5} = 0$

99. $\dfrac{8 - 8}{-9 + (6 + 3)} = \dfrac{0}{-9 + 9} = \dfrac{0}{0}$ which is undefined.

101. $(4 - 7)(-2) = (-3)(-2) = 6$

103. $\frac{3}{16} + \frac{5}{16} = \frac{8}{16} = \frac{1}{2}$

105. $\frac{5}{8} - \frac{5}{12} + \frac{1}{6} = \frac{15}{24} - \frac{10}{24} + \frac{4}{24} = \frac{9}{24} = \frac{3}{8}$

107. $\frac{\not{4}}{5} \cdot \frac{1}{2} \cdot \frac{3}{\not{4}} \cdot = \frac{3}{10}$

109. $12 \div \frac{1}{4} = 12 \cdot \frac{4}{1} = 12 \cdot 4 = 48$

111. $-3 + \frac{3}{7} \approx -2.57$

113. $\dfrac{11.46 - 5.37}{3.91} \approx 1.56$

115.

n	1	0.5	0.01	0.0001	0.000001
$5/n$	5	10	500	50,000	5,000,000

117.

n	1	10	100	10,000	100,000
$5/n$	5	0.5	0.05	0.0005	0.00005

Section P.2   Exponents and Radicals

■ You should know the properties of exponents.

(a) $a^1 = a$

(b) $a^0 = 1, a \neq 0$

(c) $a^m a^n = a^{m+n}$

(d) $a^m/a^n = a^{m-n}, a \neq 0$

(e) $a^{-n} = 1/a^n, a \neq 0$

(f) $(a^m)^n = a^{mn}$

(g) $(ab)^n = a^n b^n$

(h) $(a/b)^n = a^n/b^n, b \neq 0$

(i) $(a/b)^{-n} = (b/a)^n, a \neq 0, b \neq 0$

(j) $|a^2| = |a|^2 = a^2$

■ You should be able to write numbers in scientific notation, $c \times 10^n$, where $1 \leq c < 10$ and n is an integer.

■ You should be able to use your calculator to evaluate expressions involving exponents.

■ You should know the properties of radicals.

(a) $\sqrt[n]{a^m} = \left(\sqrt[n]{a}\right)^m$

(b) $\sqrt[n]{a} \cdot \sqrt[n]{b} = \sqrt[n]{ab}$

(c) $\dfrac{\sqrt[n]{a}}{\sqrt[n]{b}} = \sqrt[n]{\dfrac{a}{b}}$

(d) $\sqrt[m]{\sqrt[n]{a}} = \sqrt[mn]{a}$

(e) $\left(\sqrt[n]{a}\right)^n = a$

(f) For n even, $\sqrt[n]{a^n} = |a|$.

For n odd, $\sqrt[n]{a^n} = a$.

(g) $a^{1/n} = \sqrt[n]{a}$

(h) $a^{m/n} = \left(\sqrt[n]{a}\right)^m = \sqrt[n]{a^m}, a \geq 0$

■ You should be able to simplify radicals.

(a) All possible factors have been removed from the radical sign.

(b) All fractions have radical-free denominators.

(c) The index for the radical has been reduced as far as possible

■ You should be able to use your calculator to evaluate radicals.

Solutions to Odd-Numbered Exercises

1. $-0.4^6 = -(0.4 \times 0.4 \times 0.4 \times 0.4 \times 0.4 \times 0.4)$

3. $(-10)(-10)(-10)(-10)(-10) = (-10)^5$

5. (a) $4^2 \cdot 3 = 16 \cdot 3 = 48$

(b) $3 \cdot 3^3 = 3^4 = 81$

7. (a) $(3^3)^2 = 3^6 = 729$

(b) $-3^2 = -9$

9. (a) $\dfrac{3}{3^{-4}} = 3^{1+4} = 3^5 = 243$

11. $(-4)^3(5^2) = (-64)(25) = -1600$

(b) $24(-2)^{-5} = \dfrac{24}{(-2)^5} = \dfrac{24}{-32} = -\dfrac{3}{4}$

13. $\dfrac{3^6}{7^3} = \dfrac{729}{343} \approx 2.125$

15. When $x = 2$, $-3x^3 = -3(2)^3 = -24$.

17. When $x = 10$, $6x^0 - (6x)^0 = 6(10)^0 - (60)^0 = 6(1) - 1 = 5$.

19. (a) $(-5z)^3 = (-5)^3 z^3 = -125z^3$

(b) $5x^4(x^2) = 5x^{4+2} = 5x^6$

21. (a) $6y^2(2y^4)^2 = 6y^2 2^2 y^8 = 6 \cdot 4y^{2+8} = 24y^{10}$

23. (a) $\dfrac{7x^2}{x^3} = 7x^{2-3} = 7x^{-1} = \dfrac{7}{x}$

(b) $\dfrac{3x^5}{x^3} = 3x^{5-3} = 3x^2$

(b) $\dfrac{12(x + y)^3}{9(x + y)} = \dfrac{4}{3}(x + y)^{3-1} = \dfrac{4}{3}(x + y)^2$

25. (a) $(x + 5)^0 = 1$, $x \neq -5$

27. (a) $(-2x^2)^3 (4x^3)^{-1} = \dfrac{-8x^6}{4x^3} = -2x^3$

(b) $(2x^2)^{-2} = \dfrac{1}{(2x^2)^2} = \dfrac{1}{4x^4}$

(b) $\left(\dfrac{x}{10}\right)^{-1} = \dfrac{10}{x}$

29. (a) $(4a^{-2}b^3)^{-3} = 4^{-3}a^6 b^{-9} = \dfrac{a^6}{4^3 b^9} = \dfrac{a^6}{64b^9}$

31. (a) $3^n \cdot 3^{2n} = 3^{n+2n} = 3^{3n}$

(b) $\left(\dfrac{5x^2}{y^{-2}}\right)^{-4} = (5x^2 y^2)^{-4} = \dfrac{1}{(5x^2 y^2)^4} = \dfrac{1}{625x^8 y^8}$

(b) $\left(\dfrac{a^{-2}}{b^{-2}}\right)\left(\dfrac{b}{a}\right)^3 = \left(\dfrac{b^2}{a^2}\right)\left(\dfrac{b^3}{a^3}\right) = \dfrac{b^5}{a^5}$

Radical Form	*Rational Exponent Form*
33. $\sqrt{9} = 3$ Given	$9^{1/2} = 3$ Answer
35. $\sqrt[5]{32} = 2$ Answer	$32^{1/5} = 2$ Given
37. $\sqrt{196} = 14$ Answer	$196^{1/2} = 14$ Given
39. $\sqrt[3]{-216} = -6$ Given	$(-216)^{1/3} = -6$ Answer
41. $\sqrt[3]{27^2} = \left(\sqrt[3]{27}\right)^2 = 9$ Answer	$27^{2/3} = 9$ Given
43. $\sqrt[4]{81^3} = 27$ Given	$81^{3/4} = 27$ Answer

45. (a) $\sqrt{9} = 3$

47. (a) $-\sqrt[3]{-27} = -(-3) = 3$

49. (a) $\left(\sqrt[3]{-125}\right)^3 = -125$

(b) $\sqrt[3]{8} = 2$

(b) $\dfrac{4}{\sqrt{64}} = \dfrac{4}{8} = \dfrac{1}{2}$

(b) $27^{1/3} = \sqrt[3]{27} = 3$

51. (a) $32^{-3/5} = \dfrac{1}{32^{3/5}} = \dfrac{1}{\left(\sqrt[5]{32}\right)^3} = \dfrac{1}{(2)^3} = \dfrac{1}{8}$

(b) $\left(\dfrac{16}{81}\right)^{-3/4} = \left(\dfrac{81}{16}\right)^{3/4} = \left(\sqrt[4]{\dfrac{81}{16}}\right)^3 = \left(\dfrac{3}{2}\right)^3 = \dfrac{27}{8}$

53. (a) $\left(-\dfrac{1}{64}\right)^{-1/3} = (-64)^{1/3} = \sqrt[3]{-64} = -4$

(b) $\left(\dfrac{1}{\sqrt{32}}\right)^{-2/5} = \left(\sqrt{32}\right)^{2/5} = \sqrt[5]{\left(\sqrt{32}\right)^2} = \sqrt[5]{32} = 2$

55. (a) $\sqrt{57} \approx 7.550$

(b) $\sqrt[5]{-27^3} = (-27)^{3/5} \approx -7.225$

57. (a) $(1.2^{-2})\sqrt{75} + 3\sqrt{8} \approx 14.499$

(b) $\dfrac{-3 + \sqrt{21}}{3} \approx 0.528$

59. (a) $\sqrt{8} = \sqrt{4 \cdot 2} = \sqrt{4}\sqrt{2} = 2\sqrt{2}$

(b) $\sqrt[3]{24} = \sqrt[3]{8 \cdot 3} = \sqrt[3]{8}\sqrt[3]{3} = 2\sqrt[3]{3}$

61. (a) $\sqrt{72x^3} = \sqrt{36x^2 \cdot 2x} = 6x\sqrt{2x}$

(b) $\sqrt{\dfrac{18^2}{z^3}} = \dfrac{\sqrt{18^2}}{\sqrt{z^2 \cdot z}} = \dfrac{18}{z\sqrt{z}}$

63. (a) $\sqrt[3]{16x^5} = \sqrt[3]{8x^3 \cdot 2x^2} = 2x\sqrt[3]{2x^2}$

(b) $\sqrt{75x^2y^{-4}} = \sqrt{\dfrac{75x^2}{y^4}} = \dfrac{\sqrt{25x^2 \cdot 3}}{\sqrt{y^4}} = \dfrac{5|x|\sqrt{3}}{y^2}$

65. $5^{4/3} \cdot 5^{8/3} = 5^{12/3} = 5^4 = 625$

67. $\dfrac{(2x^2)^{3/2}}{2^{1/2}x^4} = \dfrac{2^{3/2}(x^2)^{3/2}}{2^{1/2}x^4} = \dfrac{2^{3/2}x^3}{2^{1/2}x^4} = 2^{3/2-1/2}x^{3-4} = 2^1 x^{-1} = \dfrac{2}{x}$

69. $\dfrac{x^{-3} \cdot x^{1/2}}{x^{3/2} \cdot x^{-1}} = \dfrac{x^{1/2} \cdot x^1}{x^{3/2} \cdot x^3} = x^{1/2+1-3/2-3} = x^{-3} = \dfrac{1}{x^3}, x > 0$

71. (a) $\dfrac{1}{\sqrt{3}} = \dfrac{1}{\sqrt{3}} \cdot \dfrac{\sqrt{3}}{\sqrt{3}} = \dfrac{\sqrt{3}}{3}$

(b) $\dfrac{8}{\sqrt[3]{2}} = \dfrac{8}{\sqrt[3]{2}} \cdot \dfrac{\sqrt[3]{4}}{\sqrt[3]{4}} = \dfrac{8\sqrt[3]{4}}{2} = 4\sqrt[3]{4}$

73. (a) $\dfrac{2x}{5 - \sqrt{3}} = \dfrac{2x}{5 - \sqrt{3}} \cdot \dfrac{5 + \sqrt{3}}{5 + \sqrt{3}}$

$= \dfrac{2x(5 + \sqrt{3})}{25 - 3} = \dfrac{x(5 + \sqrt{3})}{11}$

(b) $\dfrac{3}{\sqrt{5} + \sqrt{6}} \cdot \dfrac{\sqrt{5} - \sqrt{6}}{\sqrt{5} - \sqrt{6}} = \dfrac{3(\sqrt{5} - \sqrt{6})}{5 - 6}$

$= -3(\sqrt{5} - \sqrt{6})$

$= 3(\sqrt{6} - \sqrt{5})$

75. (a) $\dfrac{\sqrt{8}}{2} = \dfrac{\sqrt{4 \cdot 2}}{2} = \dfrac{2\sqrt{2}}{2} = \dfrac{\sqrt{2}}{1} \cdot \dfrac{\sqrt{2}}{\sqrt{2}} = \dfrac{2}{\sqrt{2}}$

(b) $\sqrt[3]{\dfrac{9}{25}} = \dfrac{\sqrt[3]{9}}{\sqrt[3]{25}} \cdot \dfrac{\sqrt[3]{3}}{\sqrt[3]{3}} = \dfrac{\sqrt[3]{27}}{\sqrt[3]{75}} = \dfrac{3}{\sqrt[3]{75}}$

77. (a) $\dfrac{\sqrt{5} + \sqrt{3}}{3} = \dfrac{\sqrt{5} + \sqrt{3}}{3} \cdot \dfrac{\sqrt{5} - \sqrt{3}}{\sqrt{5} - \sqrt{3}} = \dfrac{5 - 3}{3\left(\sqrt{5} - \sqrt{3}\right)}$

$$= \dfrac{2}{3\left(\sqrt{5} - \sqrt{3}\right)}$$

(b) $\dfrac{\sqrt{7} - 3}{4} = \dfrac{\sqrt{7} - 3}{4} \cdot \dfrac{\sqrt{7} + 3}{\sqrt{7} + 3} = \dfrac{7 - 9}{4\left(\sqrt{7} + 3\right)}$

$$= \dfrac{-2}{4\left(\sqrt{7} + 3\right)}$$

$$= -\dfrac{1}{2\left(\sqrt{7} + 3\right)}$$

79. (a) $\sqrt[4]{3^2} = 3^{2/4} = 3^{1/2} = \sqrt{3}$

(b) $\sqrt[6]{(x + 1)^4} = (x + 1)^{4/6} = (x + 1)^{2/3} = \sqrt[3]{(x + 1)^2}$

81. (a) $\sqrt{\sqrt{32}} = (32^{1/2})^{1/2} = 32^{1/4} = \sqrt[4]{32} = \sqrt[4]{16 \cdot 2} = 2\sqrt[4]{2}$

(b) $\sqrt{\sqrt[4]{2x}} = ((2x)^{1/4})^{1/2} = (2x)^{1/8} = \sqrt[8]{2x}$

83. (a) $2\sqrt{50} + 12\sqrt{8} = 2\sqrt{25 \cdot 2} + 12\sqrt{4 \cdot 2}$

$$= 2\left(5\sqrt{2}\right) + 12\left(2\sqrt{2}\right) = 10\sqrt{2} + 24\sqrt{2} = 34\sqrt{2}$$

(b) $10\sqrt{32} - 6\sqrt{18} = 10\sqrt{16 \cdot 2} - 6\sqrt{9 \cdot 2}$

$$= 10\left(4\sqrt{2}\right) - 6\left(3\sqrt{2}\right) = 40\sqrt{2} - 18\sqrt{2} = 22\sqrt{2}$$

85. (a) $5\sqrt{x} - 3\sqrt{x} = 2\sqrt{x}$

(b) $-2\sqrt{9y} + 10\sqrt{y} = -2\left(3\sqrt{y}\right) + 10\sqrt{y} = -6\sqrt{y} + 10\sqrt{y} = 4\sqrt{y}$

87. $\sqrt{5} + \sqrt{3} \approx 3.968$ and $\sqrt{5 + 3} = \sqrt{8} \approx 2.828$
Thus, $\sqrt{5} + \sqrt{3} > \sqrt{5 + 3}$.

89. $\sqrt{3^2 + 2^2} = \sqrt{9 + 4} = \sqrt{13} \approx 3.606$
Thus, $5 > \sqrt{3^2 + 2^2}$.

91. $57{,}500{,}000 = 5.75 \times 10^7$ square miles

93. $0.0000899 = 8.99 \times 10^{-5}$

95. $5.24 \times 10^8 = 524{,}000{,}000$ servings

97. $4.8 \times 10^{-10} = 0.00000000048$ electrostatic units

99. (a) $750\left(1 + \dfrac{0.11}{365}\right)^{800} \approx 954.448$

(b) $\dfrac{67,000,000 + 93,000,000}{0.0052} = 30,769,230,769.2 \approx 3.077 \times 10^{10}$

101. (a) $\sqrt{4.5 \times 10^9} \approx 67,082.039$

(b) $\sqrt[3]{6.3 \times 10^4} \approx 39.791$

103. When any positive integer is squared, the units digit is 0, 1, 4, 5, 6, or 9. Therefore, $\sqrt{5233}$ is not an integer.

105. $T = 2\pi\sqrt{\dfrac{2}{32}} = 2\pi\sqrt{\dfrac{1}{16}} = 2\pi\left(\dfrac{1}{4}\right) = \dfrac{\pi}{2} \approx 1.57$ seconds

107. $r = 1 - \left(\dfrac{3225}{12,000}\right)^{1/4} \approx 0.280$ or 28%

109. Time $= \dfrac{\text{Distance}}{\text{Rate}} = \dfrac{93,000,000 \text{ miles}}{11,160,000 \text{ miles per minute}} = \dfrac{25}{3}$ minutes

Section P.3   Polynomials and Factoring

- Given a polynomial in x, $a_n x^n + a_{n-1} x^{n-1} + \ldots + a_1 x + a_0$, where $a_n \neq 0$, and n is a nonnegative integer, you should be able to identify the following.
  (a) Degree: n
  (b) Terms: $a_n x^n, a_{n-1} x^{n-1}, \ldots, a_1 x, a_0$
  (c) Coefficients: $a_n, a_{n-1}, \ldots, a_1, a_0$
  (d) Leading coefficient: a_n
  (e) Constant term: a
- You should be able to add and subtract polynomials.
- You should be able to multiply polynomials by the Distributive Properties
- You should know the special binomial products.
  (a) $(u + v)(u - v) = u^2 - v^2$
  (b) $(u \pm v)^2 = u^2 \pm 2uv + v^2$
  (c) $(u \pm v)^3 = u^3 \pm 3u^2 v + 3uv^2 \pm v^3$
- You should be able to factor out all common factors, the first step in factoring.
- You should be able to factor the following special polynomial forms.
  (a) $u^2 - v^2 = (u + v)(u - v)$
  (b) $u^2 \pm 2uv + v^2 = (u \pm v)^2$
  (c) $u^3 \pm v^3 = (u \pm v)(u^2 \mp uv + v^2)$
- You should be able to factor by grouping.
- You should be able to factor some trinomials by grouping.

Solutions to Odd-Numbered Exercises

1. $(6x + 5) - (8x + 15) = 6x + 5 - 8x - 15$
$$= (6x - 8x) + (5 - 15)$$
$$= -2x - 10$$

3. $-(x^3 - 2) + (4x^3 - 2x) = -x^3 + 2 + 4x^3 - 2x$
$$= (4x^3 - x^3) - 2x + 2$$
$$= 3x^3 - 2x + 2$$

5. $(15x^2 - 6) - (-8x^3 - 14x^2 - 17) = 15x^2 - 6 + 8x^3 + 14x^2 + 17$
$$= 8x^3 + (15x^2 + 14x^2) + (-6 + 17)$$
$$= 8x^3 + 29x^2 + 11$$

7. $5z - [3z - (10z + 8)] = 5z - (3z - 10z - 8)$
$$= 5z - 3z + 10z + 8$$
$$= (5z - 3z + 10z) + 8$$
$$= 12z + 8$$

9. $3x(x^2 - 2x + 1) = 3x(x^2) + 3x(-2x) + 3x(1)$
$$= 3x^3 - 6x^2 + 3x$$

11. $-5z(3z - 1) = -5z(3z) + (-5z)(-1)$
$$= -15z^2 + 5z$$

13. $(1 - x^3)(4x) = 1(4x) - x^3(4x) = 4x - 4x^4 = -4x^4 + 4x$

15. Add: $7x^3 - 2x^2 + 8$
$$\underline{-3x^3 \qquad\quad - 4}$$
$$4x^3 - 2x^2 + 4$$

17. Subtract: $5x^2 - 3x + 8$
$$\underline{-\qquad\quad (x - 3)}$$
$$5x^2 - 4x + 11$$

19. Multiply: $-6x^2 + 15x - 4$
$$\underline{\qquad\qquad 5x + 3}$$
$$-30x^3 + 75x^2 - 20x$$
$$\underline{\qquad\quad - 18x^2 + 45x - 12}$$
$$-30x^3 + 57x^2 + 25x - 12$$

21. Multiply: $x^2 - x - 4$
$$\underline{\qquad\quad x^2 + 9}$$
$$x^4 - x^3 - 4x^2$$
$$\underline{\qquad\qquad 9x^2 - 9x - 36}$$
$$x^4 - x^3 + 5x^2 - 9x - 36$$

23. Multiply: $x^2 - x + 1$
$$\underline{\quad x^2 + x + 1}$$
$$x^4 - x^3 + x^2$$
$$\quad x^3 - x^2 + x$$
$$\underline{\qquad\quad x^2 - x + 1}$$
$$x^4 - 0x^3 + x^2 + 0x + 1 = x^4 + x^2 + 1$$

25. $(x + 3)(x + 4) = x^2 + 4x + 3x + 12$ FOIL
$$= x^2 + 7x + 12$$

27. $(3x - 5)(2x + 1) = 6x^2 + 3x - 10x - 5$ FOIL
$$= 6x^2 - 7x - 5$$

29. $(2x + 3)^2 = (2x)^2 + 2(2x)(3) + 3^2$
$$= 4x^2 + 12x + 9$$

31. $(2x - 5y)^2 = 4x^2 - 2(5y)(2x) + 25y^2$
$$= 4x^2 - 20xy + 25y^2$$

33. $[(x - 3) + y]^2 = (x - 3)^2 + 2y(x - 3) + y^2$
$$= x^2 - 6x + 9 + 2xy - 6y + y^2$$
$$= x^2 + 2xy + y^2 - 6x - 6y + 9$$

35. $(x + 10)(x - 10) = x^2 - 100$

37. $(x + 2y)(x - 2y) = x^2 - (2y)^2 = x^2 - 4y^2$

39. $[(m - 3) + n][(m - 3) - n] = (m - 3)^2 - n^2$
$$= m^2 - 6m + 9 - n^2$$
$$= m^2 - n^2 - 6m + 9$$

41. $(2r^2 - 5)(2r^2 + 5) = (2r)^2 - 5^2 = 4r^4 - 25$

43. $(x + 1)^3 = x^3 + 3x^2(1) + 3x(1^2) + 1^3$
$$= x^3 + 3x^2 + 3x + 1$$

45. $(2x - y)^3 = (2x)^3 - 3(2x)^2 y + 3(2x)y^2 - y^3$
$$= 8x^3 - 12x^2 y + 6xy^2 - y^3$$

47. $(4x^3 - 3)^2 = (4x^3)^2 - 2(4x^3)(3) + (3)^2$
$$= 16x^6 - 24x^3 + 9$$

49. $5x(x + 1) - 3x(x + 1) = 2x(x + 1)$
$$= 2x^2 + 2x$$

51. $(u + 2)(u - 2)(u^2 + 4) = (u^2 - 4)(u^2 + 4)$
$$= u^4 - 16$$

53. No. $(x^2 + 1) + (-x^2 + 3) = 4$ which is not a second degree polynomial.

55. (a) $(x - 1)(x + 1) = x^2 - 1$

(b) $(x - 1)(x^2 + x + 1) = x^3 + x^2 + x - x^2 - x - 1 = x^3 - 1$

(c) $(x - 1)(x^3 + x^2 + x + 1) = x^4 + x^3 + x^2 + x - x^3 - x^2 - x - 1$
$$= x^4 - 1$$

From this pattern we have $(x - 1)(x^4 + x^3 + x^2 + x + 1) = x^5 - 1$.

57. (a) $500(1 + r)^2 = 500(r + 1)^2 = 500(r^2 + 2r + 1)$
$$= 500r^2 + 1000r + 500$$

(b)

r	$5\frac{1}{2}\%$	7%	8%	$8\frac{1}{2}\%$	9%
$500(1 + r)^2$	\$556.51	\$572.45	\$583.20	\$588.61	\$594.05

(c) As r increases, the amount increases.

59. $V = l \cdot w \cdot h$

$$= \left(\frac{45 - 3x}{2}\right)(15 - 2x)(x)$$

$$= \frac{3}{2}x(x - 15)(2x - 15)$$

When $x = 3$: $V = (18)(9)(3) = 486$ cubic cm

When $x = 5$: $V = (15)(5)(5) = 375$ cubic cm

When $x = 7$: $V = (12)(1)(7) = 84$ cubic cm

61. (a) $T = R + B = 1.1x + (0.14x^2 - 4.43x + 58.40)$

$$= 0.14x^2 - 3.33x + 58.40$$

(b)

x mi/hr	30	40	55
T feet	84.50	149.20	298.75

(c) As the speed increases, the total stopping distance increases.

63. $(x + 1)(x + 4) = x(x + 4) + 1(x + 4)$

$$= x^2 + 4x + x + 4$$

This illustrates the Distributive Property.

65. $3x + 6 = 3(x + 2)$

67. $2x^3 - 6x = 2x(x^2 - 3)$

69. $x^2 - 36 = x^2 - 6^2 = (x + 6)(x - 6)$

71. $16y^2 - 9 = (4y + 3)(4y - 3)$

73. $(x - 1)^2 - 4 = [(x - 1) + 2][(x - 1) - 2]$

$$= (x + 1)(x - 3)$$

75. $x^2 - 4x + 4 = x^2 - 2(2)x + 2^2 = (x - 2)^2$

77. $4t^2 + 4t + 1 = (2t)^2 + 2(2t)(1) + 1^2$

$$= (2t + 1)^2$$

79. $x^2 + x - 2 = (x + 2)(x - 1)$

81. $s^2 - 5s + 6 = (s - 3)(s - 2)$

83. $20 - y - y^2 = (5 + y)(4 - y)$ or $-(y + 5)(y - 4)$

85. $3x^2 - 5x + 2 = (3x - 2)(x - 1)$

87. $5x^2 + 26x + 5 = (5x + 1)(x + 5)$

89. $x^3 - 8 = x^3 - 2^3 = (x - 2)(x^2 + 2x + 4)$

91. $y^3 + 64 = y^3 + 4^3 = (y + 4)(y^2 - 4y + 16)$

93. $x^3 - x^2 + 2x - 2 = x^2(x - 1) + 2(x - 1)$

$$= (x - 1)(x^2 + 2)$$

95. $2x^3 - x^2 - 6x + 3 = x^2(2x - 1) - 3(2x - 1)$

$$= (2x - 1)(x^2 - 3)$$

97. $x^3 - 9x = x(x^2 - 9) = x(x + 3)(x - 3)$

99. $x^3 - 4x^2 = x^2(x - 4)$

101. $x^2 - 2x + 1 = (x - 1)^2$

103. $1 - 4x + 4x^2 = (1 - 2x)^2$

105. $2x^2 + 4x - 2x^3 = -2x(-x - 2 + x^2)$

$$= -2x(x^2 - x - 2)$$

$$= -2x(x + 1)(x - 2)$$

107. $9x^2 + 10x + 1 = (9x + 1)(x + 1)$

109. $3x^3 + x^2 + 15x + 5 = x^2(3x + 1) + 5(3x + 1)$

$$= (3x + 1)(x^2 + 5)$$

111. $x^4 - 4x^3 + x^2 - 4x = x(x^3 - 4x^2 + x - 4)$

$$= x[x^2(x - 4) + (x - 4)]$$

$$= x(x - 4)(x^2 + 1)$$

113. $25 - (z + 5)^2 = [5 + (z + 5)][5 - (z + 5)]$

$$= -z(z + 10)$$

115. $(x^2 + 1)^2 - 4x^2 = [(x^2 + 1) + 2x][(x^2 + 1) - 2x]$

$$= (x^2 + 2x + 1)(x^2 - 2x + 1)$$

$$= (x + 1)^2(x - 1)^2$$

117. $2t^3 - 16 = 2(t^3 - 8) = 2(t - 2)(t^2 + 2t + 4)$

119. $4x(2x - 1) + (2x - 1)^2 = (2x - 1)[4x + (2x - 1)]$

$$= (2x - 1)(6x - 1)$$

121. $2(x + 1)(x - 3)^2 - 3(x + 1)^2(x - 3) = (x + 1)(x - 3)[2(x - 3) - 3(x + 1)]$

$$= (x + 1)(x - 3)[2x - 6 - 3x - 3]$$

$$= (x + 1)(x - 3)(-x - 9)$$

$$= -(x + 1)(x - 3)(x + 9)$$

123. $7x(2)(x^2 + 1)(2x) - (x^2 + 1)^2(7) = 7(x^2 + 1)[4x^2 - (x^2 + 1)]$

$$= 7(x^2 + 1)(3x^2 - 1)$$

125. $2x(x - 5)^4 - x^2(4)(x - 5)^3 = 2x(x - 5)^3[(x - 5) - 2x]$

$$= 2x(x - 5)^3(-x - 5)$$

$$= -2x(x - 5)^3(x + 5)$$

127. $\dfrac{x^2}{2}(x^2 + 1)^4 - (x^2 + 1)^5 = (x^2 + 1)^4\left[\dfrac{x^2}{2} - (x^2 + 1)\right]$

$$= (x^2 + 1)^4\left(-\dfrac{x^2}{2} - 1\right)$$

$$= -(x^2 + 1)^4\left(\dfrac{x^2}{2} + 1\right)$$

129. $a^2 - b^2 = (a + b)(a - b)$

Matches model (b).

131. $a^2 + 2a + 1 = (a + 1)^2$

Matches model (a).

133. $3x^2 + 7x + 2 = (3x + 1)(x + 2)$

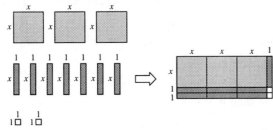

135. $2x^2 + 7x + 3 = (2x + 1)(x + 3)$

137. $A = \pi(r + 2)^2 - \pi r^2$

$\quad = \pi[(r + 2)^2 - r^2]$

$\quad = \pi[r^2 + 4r + 4 - r^2]$

$\quad = \pi(4r + 4)$

$\quad = 4\pi(r + 1)$

139. $A = 8(18) - 4x^2$

$\quad = 4(36 - x^2)$

$\quad = 4(6 - x)(6 + x)$

141. For $x^2 + bx - 15$ to be factorable, b must equal $m + n$ where $mn = -15$.

Factors of -15	Sum of factors
$(15)(-1)$	$15 + (-1) = 14$
$(-15)(1)$	$-15 + 1 = -14$
$(3)(-5)$	$3 + (-5) = -2$
$(-3)(5)$	$-3 + 5 = 2$

The possible b values are 14, -14, -2, or 2.

143. For $2x^2 + 5x + c$ to be factorable, the factors of $2c$ must add up to 5.

Possible c values	$2c$	Factors of $2c$ that add up to 5
2	4	$(1)(4) = 4$ and $1 + 4 = 5$
3	6	$(2)(3) = 6$ and $2 + 3 = 5$
-3	-6	$(6)(-1) = -6$ and $6 + (-1) = 5$
-7	-14	$(7)(-2) = -14$ and $7 + (-2) = 5$
-12	-24	$(8)(-3) = -24$ and $8 + (-3) = 5$

These are a few possible c values. There are *many* correct answers.

If $c = \quad 2 : 2x^2 + 5x + 2 = (2x + 1)(x + 2)$
If $c = \quad 3 : 2x^2 + 5x + 3 = (2x + 3)(x + 1)$
If $c = -3 : 2x^2 + 5x - 3 = (2x - 1)(x + 3)$
If $c = -7 : 2x^2 + 5x - 7 = (2x + 7)(x - 1)$
If $c = -12: 2x^2 + 5x - 12 = (2x - 3)(x + 4)$

145. $9x^2 - 9x - 54 = 9(x^2 - x - 6) = 9(x + 2)(x - 3)$

The error in the problem in the book was that 3 was factored out of the first binomial but not out of the second binomial.

$$(3x + 6)(3x - 9) = 3(x + 2)(3)(x - 3) = 9(x + 2)(x - 3)$$

147. (a) $V = \pi R^2 h - \pi r^2 h$

$= \pi h(R^2 - r^2)$

$= \pi h(R - r)(R + r)$

(b) The average radius is $\dfrac{R + r}{2}$.

The thickness of the shell is $R - r$.

$$V = \pi h(R - r)(R + r) = 2\pi\left(\frac{R + r}{2}\right)(R - r)h$$

Section P.4   Fractional Expressions

- You should be able to find the domain of a fractional expression.
- You should know that a rational expression is the quotient of two polynomials.
- You should be able to simplify rational expressions by reducing them to lowest terms. This may involve factoring both the numerator and the denominator.
- You should be able to add, subtract, multiply, and divide rational expressions.
- You should be able to simplify compound fractions.

Solutions to Odd-Numbered Exercises

1. The domain of the polynomial $3x^2 - 4x + 7$ is the set of all real numbers.

3. The domain of the polynomial $4x^3 + 3, x \ge 0$ is the set of non-negative real numbers, since the polynomial is restricted to that set.

5. The domain of $\dfrac{1}{x - 2}$ is the set of all real numbers x such that $x \ne 2$.

7. The domain of $\dfrac{x - 1}{x(x - 4)}$ is the set of all real numbers x such that $x \ne 0$ and $x \ne 4$.

9. The domain of $\sqrt{x + 1}$ is the set of all real numbers x such that $x \ge -1$.

11. $\dfrac{5}{2x} = \dfrac{5(3x)}{(2x)(3x)} = \dfrac{5(3x)}{6x^2}, \quad x \ne 0$

The missing factor is $3x, x \ne 0$.

13. $\dfrac{x + 1}{x} = \dfrac{(x + 1)(x - 2)}{x(x - 2)}, \quad x \ne 2$

The missing factor is $x - 2, x \ne 2$.

15. $\dfrac{3x}{x - 3} = \dfrac{3x(x)}{(x - 3)(x)} = \dfrac{3x^2}{x^2 - 3x}, \quad x \ne 0$

The missing factor is $x, x \ne 0$.

17. $\dfrac{15x^2}{10x} = \dfrac{5x(3x)}{5x(2)} = \dfrac{3x}{2}, \quad x \ne 0$

19. $\dfrac{3xy}{xy + x} = \dfrac{x(3y)}{x(y + 1)} = \dfrac{3y}{y + 1}, \quad x \ne 0$

21. $\dfrac{x - 5}{10 - 2x} = \dfrac{x - 5}{-2(x - 5)} = -\dfrac{1}{2}, \quad x \ne 5$

23. $\dfrac{x^3 + 5x^2 + 6x}{x^2 - 4} = \dfrac{x(x + 2)(x + 3)}{(x + 2)(x - 2)} = \dfrac{x(x + 3)}{x - 2}, \quad x \ne -2$

25. $\dfrac{y^2 - 7y + 12}{y^2 + 3y - 18} = \dfrac{(y - 3)(y - 4)}{(y + 6)(y - 3)} = \dfrac{y - 4}{y + 6}, \quad y \neq 3$

27. $\dfrac{2 - x + 2x^2 - x^3}{x - 2} = \dfrac{(2 - x) + x^2(2 - x)}{-(2 - x)} = \dfrac{(2 - x)(1 + x^2)}{-(2 - x)} = -(1 + x^2), \quad x \neq 2$

29. $\dfrac{z^3 - 8}{z^2 + 2z + 4} = \dfrac{(z - 2)(z^2 + 2z + 4)}{z^2 + 2z + 4} = z - 2$

31.

x	0	1	2	3	4	5	6
$\dfrac{x^2 - 2x - 3}{x - 3}$	1	2	3	undef.	5	6	7
$x + 1$	1	2	3	4	5	6	7

The expressions are equivalent except at $x = 3$.

33. $\dfrac{5x^3}{2x^3 + 4} = \dfrac{5x^3}{2(x^3 + 2)}$. There are no common factors so this expression is in reduced form. In this case factors of terms were incorrectly cancelled.

35. $\dfrac{\pi r^2}{(2r)^2} = \dfrac{\pi r^2}{4r^2} = \dfrac{\pi}{4}, \quad r \neq 0$

37. $\dfrac{5}{x - 1} \cdot \dfrac{x - 1}{25(x - 2)} = \dfrac{1}{5(x - 2)}, \quad x \neq 1$

39. $\dfrac{(x + 5)(x - 3)}{x + 2} \cdot \dfrac{1}{(x + 5)(x + 2)} = \dfrac{x - 3}{(x + 2)^2}, \quad x \neq -5$

41. $\dfrac{r}{r - 1} \cdot \dfrac{r^2 - 1}{r^2} = \dfrac{r(r + 1)(r - 1)}{r^2(r - 1)} = \dfrac{r + 1}{r}, \quad r \neq 1$

43. $\dfrac{t^2 - t - 6}{t^2 + 6t + 9} \cdot \dfrac{t + 3}{t^2 - 4} = \dfrac{(t - 3)(t + 2)(t + 3)}{(t + 3)^2(t + 2)(t - 2)} = \dfrac{t - 3}{(t + 3)(t - 2)}, \quad t \neq -2$

45. $\dfrac{x^2 + xy - 2y^2}{x^3 + x^2y} \cdot \dfrac{x}{x^2 + 3xy + 2y^2} = \dfrac{(x + 2y)(x - y)}{x^2(x + y)} \cdot \dfrac{x}{(x + 2y)(x + y)}$

$$= \dfrac{x - y}{x(x + y)^2}, \quad x \neq -2y$$

47. $\dfrac{3(x + y)}{4} \div \dfrac{x + y}{2} = \dfrac{3(x + y)}{4} \cdot \dfrac{2}{x + y} = \dfrac{3}{2}, \quad x \neq -y$

49. $\dfrac{\left[\dfrac{x^2}{(x + 1)^2}\right]}{\left[\dfrac{x}{(x + 1)^3}\right]} = \dfrac{x^2}{(x + 1)^2} \cdot \dfrac{(x + 1)^3}{x} = x(x + 1), \quad x \neq -1, 0$

51. $\dfrac{5}{x - 1} + \dfrac{x}{x - 1} = \dfrac{5 + x}{x - 1} = \dfrac{x + 5}{x - 1}$

53. $6 - \dfrac{5}{x + 3} = \dfrac{6(x + 3)}{(x + 3)} - \dfrac{5}{x + 3} = \dfrac{6(x + 3) - 5}{x + 3} = \dfrac{6x + 13}{x + 3}$

55. $\dfrac{3}{x-2} + \dfrac{5}{2-x} = \dfrac{3}{x-2} - \dfrac{5}{x-2} = -\dfrac{2}{x-2}$

57. $\dfrac{2}{x^2-4} - \dfrac{1}{x^2-3x+2} = \dfrac{2}{(x+2)(x-2)} - \dfrac{1}{(x-1)(x-2)}$

$$= \dfrac{2(x-1) - (x+2)}{(x+2)(x-2)(x-1)} = \dfrac{x-4}{(x+2)(x-2)(x-1)}$$

59. $\dfrac{1}{x^2-x-2} - \dfrac{x}{x^2-5x+6} = \dfrac{1}{(x-2)(x+1)} - \dfrac{x}{(x-2)(x-3)}$

$$= \dfrac{(x-3) - x(x+1)}{(x+1)(x-2)(x-3)}$$

$$= \dfrac{-x^2-3}{(x+1)(x-2)(x-3)} = -\dfrac{x^2+3}{(x+1)(x-2)(x-3)}$$

61. $-\dfrac{1}{x} + \dfrac{2}{x^2+1} + \dfrac{1}{x^3+x} = \dfrac{-(x^2+1)}{x(x^2+1)} + \dfrac{2x}{x(x^2+1)} + \dfrac{1}{x(x^2+1)}$

$$= \dfrac{-x^2-1+2x+1}{x(x^2+1)} = \dfrac{-x^2+2x}{x(x^2+1)} = \dfrac{-x(x-2)}{x(x^2+1)}$$

$$= -\dfrac{x-2}{x^2+1} = \dfrac{2-x}{x^2+1}, \quad x \neq 0$$

63. $x^2(x^2+1)^{-5} - (x^2+1)^{-4} = (x^2+1)^{-5}[x^2 - (x^2+1)]$

$$= -\dfrac{1}{(x^2+1)^5}$$

65. $\dfrac{x+4}{x+2} - \dfrac{3x-8}{x+2} = \dfrac{(x+4) - (3x-8)}{x-2}$

$$= \dfrac{x+4-3x+8}{x-2}$$

$$= \dfrac{-2x+12}{x-2}$$

$$= \dfrac{-2(x-6)}{x-2}$$

67. $\dfrac{\left(\dfrac{x}{2}-1\right)}{(x-2)} = \dfrac{\left(\dfrac{x}{2}-\dfrac{2}{2}\right)}{\left(\dfrac{x-2}{1}\right)}$

$$= \dfrac{x-2}{2} \cdot \dfrac{1}{x-2}$$

$$= \dfrac{1}{2}, \quad x \neq 2$$

The error was an incorrect subtraction in the numerator.

69. $\dfrac{\left(\dfrac{1}{x}-\dfrac{1}{x+1}\right)}{\left(\dfrac{1}{x+1}\right)} = \dfrac{\dfrac{(x+1)-x}{x(x+1)}}{\dfrac{1}{x+1}} = \dfrac{1}{x(x+1)} \cdot \dfrac{x+1}{1} = \dfrac{1}{x}, \quad x \neq -1$

71. $\dfrac{\left(\dfrac{x+3}{x-3}\right)^2}{\dfrac{1}{x+3}+\dfrac{1}{x-3}}=\dfrac{\dfrac{(x+3)^2}{(x-3)^2}}{\dfrac{(x-3)+(x+3)}{(x+3)(x-3)}}$

$$=\frac{(x+3)^2}{(x-3)^2}\cdot\frac{(x+3)(x-3)}{2x}=\frac{(x+3)^3}{2x(x-3)},\quad x\neq-3$$

73. $\dfrac{\left[\dfrac{1}{(x+h)^2}-\dfrac{1}{x^2}\right]}{h}=\dfrac{\left[\dfrac{1}{(x+h)^2}-\dfrac{1}{x^2}\right]}{h}\cdot\dfrac{x^2(x+h)^2}{x^2(x+h)^2}$

$$=\frac{x^2-(x+h)^2}{hx^2(x+h)^2}$$

$$=\frac{x^2-(x^2+2xh+h^2)}{hx^2(x+h)^2}$$

$$=\frac{-h(2x+h)}{hx^2(x+h)^2}$$

$$=-\frac{2x+h}{x^2(x+h)^2},\quad h\neq0$$

75. $\dfrac{\left(\sqrt{x}-\dfrac{1}{2\sqrt{x}}\right)}{\sqrt{x}}=\dfrac{\left(\sqrt{x}-\dfrac{1}{2\sqrt{x}}\right)}{\sqrt{x}}\cdot\dfrac{2\sqrt{x}}{2\sqrt{x}}=\dfrac{2x-1}{2x},\quad x>0$

77. $\dfrac{\dfrac{t^2}{\sqrt{t^2+1}}-\sqrt{t^2+1}}{t^2}=\dfrac{\left[\dfrac{t^2}{\sqrt{t^2+1}}-\sqrt{t^2+1}\right]}{t^2}\cdot\dfrac{\sqrt{t^2+1}}{\sqrt{t^2+1}}$

$$=\frac{t^2-(t^2+1)}{t^2\sqrt{t^2+1}}=-\frac{1}{t^2\sqrt{t^2+1}}$$

79. $\dfrac{x(x+1)^{-3/4}-(x+1)^{1/4}}{x^2}=\dfrac{x(x+1)^{-3/4}-(x+1)^{1/4}}{x^2}\cdot\dfrac{(x+1)^{3/4}}{(x+1)^{3/4}}$

$$=\frac{x(x+1)^0-(x+1)^1}{x^2(x+1)^{3/4}}$$

$$=\frac{x-x-1}{x^2(x+1)^{3/4}}$$

$$=-\frac{1}{x^2(x+1)^{3/4}}$$

81. $\dfrac{\sqrt{x+2}-\sqrt{x}}{2}=\dfrac{\sqrt{x+2}-\sqrt{x}}{2}\cdot\dfrac{\sqrt{x+2}+\sqrt{x}}{\sqrt{x+2}+\sqrt{x}}$

$$=\frac{(x+2)-x}{2\left(\sqrt{x+2}+\sqrt{x}\right)}=\frac{2}{2\left(\sqrt{x+2}+\sqrt{x}\right)}$$

$$=\frac{1}{\sqrt{x+2}+\sqrt{x}}$$

83. (a) $\dfrac{1}{16}$ minute

(b) $x\left(\dfrac{1}{16}\right) = \dfrac{x}{16}$ minutes

(c) $\dfrac{60}{16} = \dfrac{15}{4}$ minutes

85. Average $= \dfrac{\left(\dfrac{x}{3} + \dfrac{2x}{5}\right)}{2} = \dfrac{\left(\dfrac{x}{3} + \dfrac{2x}{5}\right)}{2} \cdot \dfrac{15}{15} = \dfrac{5x + 6x}{30} = \dfrac{11x}{30}$

87. (a) $r = \dfrac{\left(\dfrac{24[48(400) - 15{,}000]}{48}\right)}{\left[15{,}000 + \dfrac{48(400)}{12}\right]} \approx 0.1265 = 12.65\%$

(b) $r = \dfrac{\left[\dfrac{24(NM - P)}{N}\right]}{\left(P + \dfrac{NM}{12}\right)} = \dfrac{24(NM - P)}{N} \cdot \dfrac{12}{12P + NM} = \dfrac{288(NM - P)}{N(12P + NM)}$

$r = \dfrac{288[48(400) - 15{,}000]}{48[12(15{,}000) + 48(400)]} \approx 0.1265 = 12.65\%$

89. $T = 10\left(\dfrac{4t^2 + 16t + 75}{t^2 + 4t + 10}\right)$

(a)

t	0	1	2	3	4	5
T	75°	63.3°	55.9°	51.3°	48.3°	46.4°

(b)

91. $\dfrac{x\left(\dfrac{x}{2}\right)}{x(2x + 1)} = \dfrac{\dfrac{x}{2}}{2x + 1} \cdot \dfrac{2}{2} = \dfrac{x}{2(2x + 1)}$

Section P.5   Solving Equations

- You should know how to solve linear equations.
  $ax + b = 0$
- An identity is an equation whose solution consists of every real number in its domain.
- To solve an equation you can:
  (a) Add or subtract the same quantity from both sides.
  (b) Multiply or divide both sides by the same nonzero quantity.
- To solve an equation that can be simplified to a linear equation:
  (a) Remove all symbols of grouping and all fractions.
  (b) Combine like terms.
  (c) Solve by algebra.
  (d) Check the answer.
- A "solution" that does not satisfy the original equation is called an extraneous solution.
- You should be able to solve a quadratic equation by factoring, if possible.
- You should be able to solve a quadratic equation of the form $u^2 = d$ by extracting square roots.
- You should be able to solve a quadratic equation by completing the square.
- You should know and be able to use the Quadratic Formula: For $ax^2 + bx + c = 0, a \neq 0,$

  $$x = \frac{-b \pm \sqrt{b^2 - 4ac}}{2a}.$$

- You should be able to solve polynomials of higher degree by factoring.
- For equations involving radicals or fractional powers, raise both sides to the same power.
- For equations with fractions, multiply both sides by the least common denominator to clear the fractions.
- For equations involving absolute value, remember that the expression inside the absolute value can be positive or negative.
- Always check for extraneous solutions.

Solutions to Odd-Numbered Exercises

1. $5x - 3 = 3x + 5$

  (a) $5(0) - 3 \overset{?}{=} 3(0) + 5$

        $-3 \neq 5$

     $x = 0$ *is not* a solution.

  (b) $5(-5) - 3 \overset{?}{=} 3(-5) + 5$

        $-28 \neq -10$

     $x = -5$ *is not* a solution.

  (c) $5(4) - 3 \overset{?}{=} 3(4) + 5$

        $17 = 17$

     $x = 4$ *is* a solution.

  (d) $5(10) - 3 \overset{?}{=} 3(10) + 5$

        $47 \neq 35$

     $x = 10$ *is not* a solution.

3. $3x^2 + 2x - 5 = 2x^2 - 2$

(a) $3(-3) + 2(-3) - 5 \stackrel{?}{=} 2(-3)^2 - 2$

$$16 = 16$$

$x = -3$ *is* a solution.

(b) $3(1)^2 + 2(1) - 5 \stackrel{?}{=} 2(1)^2 - 2$

$$0 = 0$$

$x = 1$ *is* a solution.

(c) $3(4)^2 + 2(4) - 5 \stackrel{?}{=} 2(4)^2 - 2$

$$51 \neq 30$$

$x = 4$ *is not* a solution.

(d) $3(-5)^2 + 2(-5) - 5 \stackrel{?}{=} 2(-5)^2 - 2$

$$60 \neq 48$$

$x = -5$ *is not* a solution.

5. $\dfrac{5}{2x} - \dfrac{4}{x} = 3$

(a) $\dfrac{5}{2(-1/2)} - \dfrac{5}{(-1/2)} \stackrel{?}{=} 3$

$$3 = 3$$

$x = -\frac{1}{2}$ *is* a solution.

(b) $\dfrac{5}{2(4)} - \dfrac{4}{4} \stackrel{?}{=} 3$

$$-\dfrac{3}{8} \neq 3$$

$x = 4$ *is not* a solution.

(c) $\dfrac{5}{2(0)} - \dfrac{4}{0}$ is undefined.

$x = 0$ *is not* a solution.

(d) $\dfrac{5}{2(1/4)} - \dfrac{4}{1/4} \stackrel{?}{=} 3$

$$-6 \neq 3$$

$x = \frac{1}{4}$ *is not* a solution.

7. $2(x - 1) = 2x - 2$ is an *identity* by the Distributive Property. It is true for all real values of x.

9. $-6(x - 3) + 5 = -2x + 10$ is *conditional*. There are real values of x for which the equation is not true.

11. $x^2 - 8x + 5 = (x - 4)^2 - 11$ is an *identity* since $(x - 4)^2 - 11 = x^2 - 8x + 16 - 11 = x^2 - 8x + 5$.

13. (a) Equivalent equations are derived from the substitution principle and simplification techniques. They have the same solution(s).

$2x + 3 = 8$ and $2x = 5$ are equivalent equations.

(b) Equivalent equations are produced by removing symbols of grouping, adding or subtracting the same quantity from both sides of the equation, multiplying or dividing both sides of the equation by the same nonzero quantity, or by interchanging the two sides of the equation.

15. $2(x + 5) - 7 = 3(x - 2)$

$$2x + 10 - 7 = 3x - 6$$

$$2x + 3 = 3x - 6$$

$$-x = -9$$

$$x = 9$$

17. $\dfrac{5x}{4} + \dfrac{1}{2} = x - \dfrac{1}{2}$

$$4\left(\dfrac{5x}{4}\right) + 4\left(\dfrac{1}{2}\right) = 4(x) - 4\left(\dfrac{1}{2}\right)$$

$$5x + 2 = 4x - 2$$

$$x = -4$$

19.
$$0.25x + 0.75(10 - x) = 3$$
$$4(0.25x) + 4(0.75)(10 - x) = 4(3)$$
$$x + 3(10 - x) = 12$$
$$x + 30 - 3x = 12$$
$$-2x = -18$$
$$x = 9$$

21. $x + 8 = 2(x - 2) - x$
$$x + 8 = 2x - 4 - x$$
$$x + 8 = x - 4$$
$$8 = -4$$

Contradiction: no solution

23.
$$\frac{100 - 4u}{3} = \frac{5u + 6}{4} + 6$$
$$12\left(\frac{100 - 4u}{3}\right) = 12\left(\frac{5u + 6}{4}\right) + 12(6)$$
$$4(100 - 4u) = 3(5u + 6) + 72$$
$$400 - 16u = 15u + 18 + 72$$
$$-31u = -310$$
$$u = 10$$

25.
$$\frac{5x - 4}{5x + 4} = \frac{2}{3}$$
$$3(5x - 4) = 2(5x + 4)$$
$$15x - 12 = 10x + 8$$
$$5x = 20$$
$$x = 4$$

27.
$$10 - \frac{13}{x} = 4 + \frac{5}{x}$$
$$\frac{10x - 13}{x} = \frac{4x + 5}{x}$$
$$10x - 13 = 4x + 5$$
$$6x = 18$$
$$x = 3$$

29.
$$\frac{1}{x - 3} + \frac{1}{x + 3} = \frac{10}{x^2 - 9}$$
$$\frac{(x + 3) + (x - 3)}{x^2 - 9} = \frac{10}{x^2 - 9}$$
$$2x = 10$$
$$x = 5$$

31.
$$\frac{x}{x + 4} + \frac{4}{x + 4} + 2 = 0$$
$$\frac{x + 4}{x + 4} + 2 = 0$$
$$1 + 2 = 0$$
$$3 = 0$$

Contradiction : no solution

33.
$$\frac{7}{2x + 1} - \frac{8x}{2x - 1} = -4$$
$$7(2x - 1) - 8x(2x + 1) = -4(2x + 1)(2x - 1)$$
$$14x - 7 - 16x^2 - 8x = -16x^2 + 4$$
$$6x = 11$$
$$x = \frac{11}{6}$$

35.
$$(x + 2)^2 + 5 = (x + 3)^2$$
$$x^2 + 4x + 4 + 5 = x^2 + 6x + 9$$
$$4x + 9 = 6x + 9$$
$$-2x = 0$$
$$x = 0$$

37.
$$(x + 2)^2 - x^2 = 4(x + 1)$$
$$x^2 + 4x + 4 - x^2 = 4x + 4$$
$$4 = 4$$

The equation is an identity; every real number is a solution.

39. $4 - 2(x - 2b) = ax + 3$

$4 - 2x + 4b = ax + 3$

$1 + 4b = ax + 2x$

$1 + 4b = x(a + 2)$

$\dfrac{1 + 4b}{a + 2} = x, \; a \neq -2$

41. (a)

x	-1	0	1	2	3	4
$3.2x - 5.8$	-9	-5.8	-2.6	0.6	3.8	7

(b) Since the sign changes from negative at 1 to positive at 2, the root is somewhere between 1 and 2.
$1 < x < 2$

(c)

x	1.5	1.6	1.7	1.8	1.9	2
$3.2x - 5.8$	-1	-0.68	-0.36	-0.04	0.28	0.6

(d) Since the sign changes from negative at 1.8 to positive at 1.9, the root is somewhere between 1.8 and 1.9.
$1.8 < x < 1.9$.

To improve accuracy, evaluate the expression in this interval and determine where the sign changes.

43. $6x^2 + 3x = 0$

$3x(2x + 1) = 0$

$3x = 0 \quad \text{or} \quad 2x + 1 = 0$

$x = 0 \quad \text{or} \qquad x = -\frac{1}{2}$

45. $x^2 - 2x - 8 = 0$

$(x - 4)(x + 2) = 0$

$x - 4 = 0 \quad \text{or} \quad x + 2 = 0$

$x = 4 \quad \text{or} \qquad x = -2$

47. $3 + 5x - 2x^2 = 0$

$(3 - x)(1 + 2x) = 0$

$3 - x = 0 \quad \text{or} \quad 1 + 2x = 0$

$x = 3 \quad \text{or} \qquad x = -\frac{1}{2}$

49. $2x^2 = 19x + 33$

$2x^2 - 19x - 33 = 0$

$(2x + 3)(x - 11) = 0$

$2x + 3 = 0 \quad \text{or} \quad x - 11 = 0$

$x = -\frac{3}{2} \quad \text{or} \qquad x = 11$

51. $2x^4 - 18x^2 = 0$

$2x^2(x^2 - 9) = 0$

$2x^2(x + 3)(x - 3) = 0$

$2x^2 = 0 \quad \text{or} \quad x + 3 = 0 \quad \text{or} \quad x - 3 = 0$

$x = 0 \quad \text{or} \qquad x = -3 \quad \text{or} \qquad x = 3$

53. $x^3 - 2x^2 - 3x = 0$

$x(x^2 - 2x - 3) = 0$

$x(x + 1)(x - 3) = 0$

$x = 0 \quad \text{or} \quad x + 1 = 0 \quad \text{or} \quad x - 3 = 0$

$x = 0 \quad \text{or} \qquad x = -1 \quad \text{or} \qquad x = 3$

55. $2x^4 - 15x^3 + 18x^2 = 0$

$x^2(2x^2 - 15x + 18) = 0$

$x^2(2x - 3)(x - 6) = 0$

$x^2 = 0 \quad \text{or} \quad 2x - 3 = 0 \quad \text{or} \quad x - 6 = 0$

$x = 0 \quad \text{or} \qquad x = \frac{3}{2} \quad \text{or} \qquad x = 6$

57. $x^2 = 16$

$\quad x = \pm 4$

$\qquad = \pm 4.00$

59. $3x^2 = 36$

$\quad\ x^2 = 12$

$\qquad x = \pm 2\sqrt{3}$

$\qquad\ \approx \pm 3.46$

61. $(x - 12)^2 = 18$

$\quad x - 12 = \pm 3\sqrt{2}$

$\qquad\ \ x = 12 \pm 3\sqrt{2}$

$\qquad\ \ x \approx 16.24 \quad \text{or} \quad \approx 7.76$

63. $(x + 2)^2 = 12$

$\quad x + 2 = \pm 2\sqrt{3}$

$\qquad\ \ x = -2 \pm 2\sqrt{3}$

$\qquad\ \ x \approx 1.46 \quad \text{or} \quad x \approx -5.46$

65. $\qquad x^2 - 2x = 0$

$x^2 - 2x + 1^2 = 0 + 1$

$\ x^2 - 2x + 1 = 1$

$\qquad (x - 1)^2 = 1$

$\qquad\ \ x - 1 = \pm \sqrt{1}$

$\qquad\qquad x = 1 \pm 1$

$\qquad\qquad x = 0 \quad \text{or} \quad x = 2$

67. $x^2 + 6x + 2 = 0$

$\qquad x^2 + 6x = -2$

$x^2 + 6x + 3^2 = -2 + 3^2$

$\qquad (x + 3)^2 = 7$

$\qquad\ \ x + 3 = \pm \sqrt{7}$

$\qquad\qquad x = -3 \pm \sqrt{7}$

69. $\quad 8 + 4x - x^2 = 0$

$\quad\ -x^2 + 4x + 8 = 0$

$\qquad x^2 - 4x - 8 = 0$

$\qquad\quad x^2 - 4x = 8$

$x^2 - 4x + 2^2 = 8 + 2^2$

$\qquad (x - 2)^2 = 12$

$\qquad\ \ x - 2 = \pm \sqrt{12}$

$\qquad\qquad x = 2 \pm 2\sqrt{3}$

71. $2x^2 + x - 1 = 0$

$$x = \frac{-b \pm \sqrt{b^2 - 4ac}}{2a}$$

$$= \frac{-1 \pm \sqrt{1^2 - 4(2)(-1)}}{2(2)}$$

$$= \frac{-1 \pm 3}{4} = \frac{1}{2}, -1$$

73. $x^2 + 8x - 4 = 0$

$$x = \frac{-b \pm \sqrt{b^2 - 4ac}}{2a}$$

$$= \frac{-8 \pm \sqrt{8^2 - 4(1)(-4)}}{2(1)}$$

$$= \frac{-8 \pm 4\sqrt{5}}{2}$$

$$= -4 \pm 2\sqrt{5}$$

75. $\qquad 12x - 9x^2 = -3$

$\quad -9x^2 + 12x + 3 = 0$

$$x = \frac{-b \pm \sqrt{b^2 - 4ac}}{2a}$$

$$= \frac{-12 \pm \sqrt{12^2 - 4(-9)(3)}}{2(-9)}$$

$$= \frac{-12 \pm 6\sqrt{7}}{-18} = \frac{2}{3} \pm \frac{\sqrt{7}}{3}$$

77. $3x + x^2 - 1 = 0$

$\quad x^2 + 3x - 1 = 0$

$$x = \frac{-b \pm \sqrt{b^2 - 4ac}}{2a}$$

$$= \frac{-3 \pm \sqrt{3^2 - 4(1)(-1)}}{2(1)}$$

$$= \frac{-3 \pm \sqrt{13}}{2}$$

$$= -\frac{3}{2} \pm \frac{\sqrt{13}}{2}$$

79.
$$28x - 49x^2 = 4$$
$$-49x^2 + 28x - 4 = 0$$
$$x = \frac{-b \pm \sqrt{b^2 - 4ac}}{2a}$$
$$= \frac{-28 \pm \sqrt{28^2 - 4(-49)(-4)}}{2(-49)}$$
$$= \frac{-28 \pm 0}{-98} = \frac{2}{7}$$

81.
$$8t = 5 + 2t^2$$
$$-2t^2 + 8t - 5 = 0$$
$$t = \frac{-b \pm \sqrt{b^2 - 4ac}}{2a}$$
$$= \frac{-8 \pm \sqrt{8^2 - 4(-2)(-5)}}{2(-2)}$$
$$= \frac{-8 \pm 2\sqrt{6}}{-4} = 2 \pm \frac{\sqrt{6}}{2}$$

83. False. The product must equal zero to use the Zero-Factor Property.

85. (a)
$$ax^2 + bx = 0$$
$$x(ax + b) = 0$$
$$x = 0 \quad \text{or} \quad x = -\frac{b}{a}$$

(b)
$$ax^2 - ax = 0$$
$$ax(x - 1) = 0$$
$$x = 0 \quad \text{or} \quad x = 1$$

87.
$$x^4 - 4x^2 + 3 = 0$$
$$(x^2 - 3)(x^2 - 1) = 0$$
$$\left(x + \sqrt{3}\right)\left(x - \sqrt{3}\right)(x + 1)(x - 1) = 0$$
$$x + \sqrt{3} = 0 \Longrightarrow x = -\sqrt{3}$$
$$x - \sqrt{3} = 0 \Longrightarrow x = \sqrt{3}$$
$$x + 1 = 0 \quad \Longrightarrow \quad x = -1$$
$$x - 1 = 0 \quad \Longrightarrow \quad x = 1$$

89.
$$\frac{1}{t^2} + \frac{8}{t} + 15 = 0$$
$$1 + 8t + 15t^2 = 0$$
$$(1 + 3t)(1 + 5t) = 0$$
$$1 + 3t = 0 \quad \Longrightarrow \quad t = -\frac{1}{3}$$
$$1 + 5t = 0 \quad \Longrightarrow \quad t = -\frac{1}{5}$$

91.
$$2x + 9\sqrt{x} - 5 = 0$$
$$\left(2\sqrt{x} - 1\right)\left(\sqrt{x} + 5\right) = 0$$
$$\sqrt{x} = \frac{1}{2} \Longrightarrow x = \frac{1}{4}$$
$$\left(\sqrt{x} = -5 \text{ is not a solution.}\right)$$

93.
$$3x^{1/3} + 2x^{2/3} = 5$$
$$2x^{2/3} + 3x^{1/3} - 5 = 0$$
$$(2x^{1/3} + 5)(x^{1/3} - 1) = 0$$
$$2x^{1/3} + 5 = 0 \quad \Longrightarrow \quad x^{1/3} = -\frac{5}{2} \quad \Longrightarrow \quad x = \left(-\frac{5}{2}\right)^3 = -\frac{125}{8}$$
$$x^{1/3} - 1 = 0 \quad \Longrightarrow \quad x^{1/3} = 1 \quad \Longrightarrow \quad x = (1)^3 = 1$$

95. $\sqrt{x-10}-4=0$

$\sqrt{x-10}=4$

$x-10=16$

$x=26$

97. $\sqrt[3]{2x+5}+3=0$

$\sqrt[3]{2x+5}=-3$

$2x+5=-27$

$2x=-32$

$x=-16$

99. $\qquad x=\sqrt{11x-30}$

$x^2=11x-30$

$x^2-11x+30=0$

$(x-5)(x-6)=0$

$x-5=0 \implies x=5$

$x-6=0 \implies x=6$

101. $\sqrt{x+1}-3x=1$

$\sqrt{x+1}=3x+1$

$x+1=9x^2+6x+1$

$0=9x^2+5x$

$0=x(9x+5)$

$x=0$

$9x+5=0 \implies x=-\frac{5}{9}$, extraneous

103. $\sqrt{x}-\sqrt{x-5}=1$

$\sqrt{x}=1+\sqrt{x-5}$

$\left(\sqrt{x}\right)^2=\left(1+\sqrt{x-5}\right)^2$

$x=1+2\sqrt{x-5}+x-5$

$4=2\sqrt{x-5}$

$2=\sqrt{x-5}$

$4=x-5$

$9=x$

105. $2\sqrt{x+1}-\sqrt{2x+3}=1$

$2\sqrt{x+1}=\sqrt{2x+3}+1$

$\left(2\sqrt{x+1}\right)^2=\left(\sqrt{2x+3}+1\right)^2$

$4(x+1)=2x+3+2\sqrt{2x+3}+1$

$4x+4=2x+4+2\sqrt{2x+3}$

$2x=2\sqrt{2x+3}$

$x=\sqrt{2x+3}$

$x^2=2x+3$

$x^2-2x-3=0$

$(x-3)(x+1)=0$

$x-3=0 \implies x=3$

$x+1=0 \implies x=-1$, extraneous

107. $(x-5)^{2/3}=16$

$x-5=\pm 16^{3/2}$

$x-5=\pm 64$

$x=69,\ -59$

109. $\qquad 37.55=40-\sqrt{0.01x+1}$

$\sqrt{0.01x+1}=2.45$

$0.01x+1=6.0025$

$0.01x=5.0025$

$x=500.25$

Rounding x to the nearest whole unit yields $x \approx 500$ units.

111.
$$S = \pi r \sqrt{r^2 + h^2}$$
$$S^2 = \pi^2 r^2 (r^2 + h^2)$$
$$S^2 = \pi^2 r^4 + \pi^2 r^2 h^2$$
$$\frac{S^2 - \pi^2 r^4}{\pi^2 r^2} = h^2$$
$$h = \frac{\sqrt{S^2 - \pi^2 r^4}}{\pi r}$$

113. $20 + \sqrt{20 - a} = b$

$$\sqrt{20 - a} = b - 20$$
$$20 - a = b^2 - 40b + 400$$
$$-a = b^2 - 40b + 380$$
$$a = -b^2 + 40b - 380$$

This formula gives the relationship between a and b. From the original equation we know that $a \le 20$ and $b \ge 20$. Choose a b value, where $b \ge 20$ and then solve for a, keeping in mind that $a \le 20$.

Some possibilities are:

$b = 20, \quad a = 20$

$b = 21, \quad a = 19$

$b = 22, \quad a = 16$

$b = 23, \quad a = 11$

$b = 24, \quad a = 4 \quad \leftarrow \left(\begin{array}{l}\text{This is the one given}\\\text{in your textbook.}\end{array}\right)$

$b = 25, \quad a = -5$

115. $|x + 1| = 2$

$x + 1 = 2 \quad \Rightarrow \quad x = 1$

$-(x + 1) = 2 \quad \Rightarrow \quad x = -3$

117. $|2x - 1| = 5$

$2x - 1 = 5 \quad \Rightarrow \quad x = 3$

$-(2x - 1) = 5 \quad \Rightarrow \quad x = -2$

119.
$$|x^2 + 6x| = 3x + 18$$

$x^2 + 6x = 3x + 18$ or $-(x^2 + 6x) = 3x + 18$

$x^2 + 3x - 18 = 0$	$-x^2 - 6x = 3x + 18$
$(x + 6)(x - 3) = 0$	$0 = x^2 + 9x + 18$
$x + 6 = 0 \Rightarrow x = -6$	$0 = (x + 3)(x + 6)$
$x - 3 = 0 \Rightarrow x = 3$	$x + 3 = 0 \Rightarrow x = -3$
	$x + 6 = 0 \Rightarrow x = -6$

The solutions are $x = -6$ and $x = \pm 3$.

121. $[x - (-3)](x - 5) = 0$

$$(x + 3)(x - 5) = 0$$
$$x^2 - 2x - 15 = 0$$

This equation has $x = -3$ and $x = 5$ as solutions, as does any nonzero multiple of this equation.

123.
$$4x + 3y = 100$$
$$3y = 100 - 4x$$
$$y = \tfrac{1}{3}(100 - 4x)$$
$$\text{Area} = \text{length} \cdot \text{width}$$
$$350 = (2x)(y)$$
$$350 = 2x\left[\tfrac{1}{3}(100 - 4x)\right]$$
$$350 = \tfrac{2}{3}x(100 - 4x)$$
$$1050 = 2x(100 - 4x)$$
$$1050 = 200x - 8x^2$$
$$8x^2 - 200x + 1050 = 0$$
$$2(4x^2 - 100x + 525) = 0$$
$$2(2x - 35)(2x - 15) = 0$$
$$2x - 35 = 0 \quad \text{or} \quad 2x - 15 = 0$$
$$x = \tfrac{35}{2} \qquad\qquad x = \tfrac{15}{2}$$
$$y = 10 \qquad\qquad y = \tfrac{70}{3}$$

There are two different possible dimensions:

$x = \tfrac{35}{2} = 17.5$ meters and $y = 10$ meters

or $x = \tfrac{15}{2} = 7.5$ meters and $y = \tfrac{70}{3} = 23\tfrac{1}{3}$ meters

Section P.6   Solving Inequalities

■ You should know the properties of inequalities.

(a) Transitive: $a < b$ and $b < c$ implies $a < c$.

(b) Addition: $a < b$ and $c < d$ implies $a + c < b + d$.

(c) Adding or Subtracting a Constant: $a \pm c < b \pm c$ if $a < b$.

(d) Multiplying or Dividing a Constant: For $a < b$,

    1. If $c > 0$, then $ac < bc$ and $\dfrac{a}{c} < \dfrac{b}{c}$.

    2. If $c < 0$, then $ac > bc$ and $\dfrac{a}{c} > \dfrac{b}{c}$.

■ You should be able to solve absolute value or rational inequalities.

(a) $|x| < a$ if and only if $-a < x < a$.   (b) $|x| > a$ if and only if $x < -a$ or $x > a$.

■ You should be able to solve polynomial inequalities.

(a) Find the critical number.

    1. Values that make the expression zero

    2. Values that make the expression undefined

(b) Test one value in each interval on the real number line resulting from the critical numbers.

(c) Determine the solution intervals.

Solutions to Odd-Numbered Exercises

1. Interval: $[-1, 3]$

   Inequality: $-1 \le x \le 3$

   The interval is bounded.

3. Interval: $(10, \infty)$

   Inequality: $x > 10$ or $10 < x < \infty$

   The interval is unbounded.

5. $x < 3$

   Matches (c).

7. $-3 < x \le 4$

   Matches (f).

9. $|x| < 3 \implies -3 < x < 3$

   Matches (g).

11. $|x - 4| > 2 \implies x - 4 < -2$ or $x - 4 > 2$

    $$x < 2 \text{ or } x > 6$$

    Matches (b).

13. (a) $x = 3$

$$5(3) - 12 \overset{?}{>} 0$$

$$3 > 0$$

Yes, $x = 3$ is a solution.

(b) $x = -3$

$$5(-3) - 12 \overset{?}{>} 0$$

$$-27 \not> 0$$

No, $x = -3$ is not a solution.

(c) $x = \frac{5}{2}$

$$5\left(\frac{5}{2}\right) - 12 \overset{?}{>} 0$$

$$\frac{1}{2} > 0$$

Yes, $x = \frac{5}{2}$ is a solution.

(d) $x = \frac{3}{2}$

$$5\left(\frac{3}{2}\right) - 12 \overset{?}{>} 0$$

$$-\frac{9}{2} \not> 0$$

No, $x = \frac{3}{2}$ is not a solution.

15. (a) $x = 4$

$$0 \overset{?}{<} \frac{4 - 2}{4} \overset{?}{<} 2$$

$$0 < \frac{1}{2} < 2$$

Yes, $x = 4$ is a solution.

(b) $x = 10$

$$0 \overset{?}{<} \frac{10 - 2}{4} \overset{?}{<} 2$$

$$0 < 2 \not< 2$$

No, $x = 10$ is not a solution.

(c) $x = 0$

$$0 \overset{?}{<} \frac{0 - 2}{4} \overset{?}{<} 2$$

$$0 \not< -\frac{1}{2} < 2$$

No, $x = 0$ is not a solution.

(d) $x = \frac{7}{2}$

$$0 \overset{?}{<} \frac{(7/2) - 2}{4} \overset{?}{<} 2$$

$$0 < \frac{3}{8} < 2$$

Yes, $x = \frac{7}{2}$ is a solution.

17. $x^2 - 3 < 0$

(a) $x = 3$

$$(3)^2 - 3 \overset{?}{<} 0$$

$$6 \not< 0$$

No, $x = 3$ is not a solution.

(b) $x = 0$

$$(0)^2 - 3 \overset{?}{<} 0$$

$$-3 < 0$$

Yes, $x = 0$ is a solution.

(c) $x = \frac{3}{2}$

$$\left(\frac{3}{2}\right)^2 - 3 \overset{?}{<} 0$$

$$-\frac{3}{4} < 0$$

Yes, $x = \frac{3}{2}$ is a solution.

(d) $x = -5$

$$(-5)^2 - 3 \overset{?}{<} 0$$

$$22 \not< 0$$

No, $x = -5$ is not a solution.

19. $\dfrac{x+2}{x-4} \geq 3$

(a) $x = 5$

$$\dfrac{5+2}{5-4} \overset{?}{\geq} 3$$

$$7 \geq 3$$

Yes, $x = 5$ is a solution.

(b) $x = 4$

$$\dfrac{4+2}{4-4} \overset{?}{\geq} 3$$

$\dfrac{6}{0}$ is undefined.

No, $x = 4$ is not a solution.

(c) $x = -\dfrac{9}{2}$

$$\dfrac{-\frac{9}{2}+2}{-\frac{9}{2}-4} \overset{?}{\geq} 3$$

$$\dfrac{5}{17} \not\geq 3$$

No, $x = -\frac{9}{2}$ is not a solution.

(d) $x = \dfrac{9}{2}$

$$\dfrac{\frac{9}{2}+2}{\frac{9}{2}-4} \overset{?}{\geq} 3$$

$$13 \geq 3$$

Yes, $x = \frac{9}{2}$ is a solution.

21. $4x < 12$

$\frac{1}{4}(4x) < \frac{1}{4}(12)$

$x < 3$

23. $-10x < 40$

$-\frac{1}{10}(-10) > -\frac{1}{10}(40)$

$x > -4$

25. $x - 5 \geq 7$

$x \geq 12$

27. $4(x+1) < 2x + 3$

$4x + 4 < 2x + 3$

$2x < -1$

$x < -\frac{1}{2}$

29. $4 - 2x < 3$

$-2x < -1$

$x > \frac{1}{2}$

31. $1 < 2x + 3 < 9$

$-2 < 2x < 6$

$-1 < x < 3$

33. $-4 < \dfrac{2x-3}{3} < 4$

$-12 < 2x - 3 < 12$

$-9 < 2x < 15$

$-\dfrac{9}{2} < x < \dfrac{15}{2}$

35. $\dfrac{3}{4} > x + 1 > \dfrac{1}{4}$

$-\dfrac{1}{4} > x > -\dfrac{3}{4}$

$-\dfrac{3}{4} < x < -\dfrac{1}{4}$

37. $|x| < 5$

$-5 < x < 5$

39. $\left|\dfrac{x}{2}\right| > 3$

$\dfrac{x}{2} < -3 \quad$ or $\quad \dfrac{x}{2} > 3$

$x < -6 \qquad\qquad x > 6$

41. $|x - 20| \le 4$

$-4 \le x - 20 \le 4$

$16 \le x \le 24$

43. $|x - 20| \ge 4$

$x - 20 \le -4 \quad$ or $\quad x - 20 \ge 4$

$x \le 16 \qquad\qquad\qquad x \ge 24$

45. $\left|\dfrac{x - 3}{2}\right| \ge 5$

$\dfrac{x - 3}{2} \le -5 \quad$ or $\quad \dfrac{x - 3}{2} \ge 5$

$x - 3 \le -10 \qquad\qquad x - 3 \ge 10$

$x \le -7 \qquad\qquad\qquad x \ge 13$

47. $|9 - 2x| - 2 < -1$

$|9 - 2x| < 1$

$-1 < 9 - 2x < 1$

$-10 < -2x < -8$

$5 > x > 4$

$4 < x < 5$

49. $2|x + 10| \ge 9$

$|x + 10| \ge \dfrac{9}{2}$

$x + 10 \le -\dfrac{9}{2} \quad$ or $\quad x + 10 \ge \dfrac{9}{2}$

$x \le -\dfrac{29}{2} \qquad\qquad\qquad x \ge -\dfrac{11}{2}$

51. $|x - 5| < 0$

No solution. The absolute value of a number can never be less than zero.

53. The midpoint of the interval $[-3, 3]$ is 0. The interval represents all real numbers x no more than 3 units from 0.

$|x - 0| \le 3$

$|x| \le 3$

55. The graph shows all real numbers at least 3 units from 7.

$|x - 7| \ge 3$

57. All real numbers within 10 units of 12.

$|x - 12| < 10$

59. All real numbers more than 5 units from -3.

$|x - (-3)| > 5$

$|x + 3| > 5$

61. $|x - 10| < 8$ represents all real numbers within 8 units of 10.

63.
$$x^2 \le 9$$
$$x^2 - 9 \le 0$$
$$(x + 3)(x - 3) \le 0$$

Critical numbers: $x = \pm 3$

Test intervals: $(-\infty, -3), (-3, 3), (3, \infty)$

Test: Is $(x + 3)(x - 3) \le 0$?

Solution set: $[-3, 3]$

65.
$$x^2 > 4$$
$$x^2 - 4 > 0$$
$$(x + 2)(x - 2) > 0$$

Critical numbers: $x = \pm 2$

Test intervals: $(-\infty, -2), (-2, 2), (2, \infty)$

Test: Is $x^2 - 4 > 0$?

Solution set: $(-\infty, -2) \cup (2, \infty)$

67.
$$(x + 2)^2 < 25$$
$$x^2 + 4x + 4 < 25$$
$$x^2 + 4x - 21 < 0$$
$$(x + 7)(x - 3) < 0$$

Critical numbers: $x = -7, x = 3$

Test intervals: $(-\infty, -7), (-7, 3), (3, \infty)$

Test: Is $(x + 7)(x - 3) < 0$?

Solution set: $(-7, 3)$

69.
$$x^2 + 4x + 4 \ge 9$$
$$x^2 + 4x - 5 \ge 0$$
$$(x + 5)(x - 1) \ge 0$$

Critical numbers: $x = -5, x = 1$

Test intervals: $(-\infty, -5), (-5, 1), (1, \infty)$

Test: Is $(x + 5)(x - 1) \ge 0$?

Solution set: $(-\infty, -5] \cup [1, \infty)$

71. $3(x - 1)(x + 1) > 0$

Critical numbers: $x = \pm 1$

Test intervals: $(-\infty, -1), (-1, 1), (1, \infty)$

Test: Is $3(x - 1)(x + 1) > 0$?

Solution set: $(-\infty, -1) \cup (1, \infty)$

Solution set: $(-3, 2)$

73. $x^2 + 2x - 3 < 0$
$$(x + 3)(x - 1) < 0$$

Critical numbers: $x = -3, x = 1$

Test intervals: $(-\infty, -3), (-3, 1), (1, \infty)$

Test: Is $(x + 3)(x - 1) < 0$?

Solution set: $(-3, 1)$

75. $4x^3 - 6x^2 < 0$
$$2x^2(2x - 3) < 0$$

Critical numbers: $x = 0, x = \frac{3}{2}$

Test intervals: $(-\infty, 0), \left(0, \frac{3}{2}\right), \left(\frac{3}{2}, \infty\right)$

Test: Is $2x^2(2x - 3) < 0$?

Solution set: $(-\infty, 0) \cup \left(0, \frac{3}{2}\right)$

77. $(x - 1)^2(x + 2)^3 \ge 0$

Critical numbers: $x = 1, x = -2$

Test intervals: $(-\infty, -2), (-2, 1), (1, \infty)$

Test: Is $(x - 1)^2(x + 3)^3 \ge 0$?

Solution set: $[-2, \infty)$

79. $\dfrac{1}{x} - x > 0$

$\dfrac{1 - x^2}{x} > 0$

Critical numbers: $x = 0, x = \pm 1$

Test intervals: $(-\infty, -1), (-1, 0), (0, 1), (1, \infty)$

Test: Is $\dfrac{1 - x^2}{x} > 0$?

Solution set: $(-\infty, -1) \cup (0, 1)$

81. $\dfrac{x + 6}{x + 1} - 2 < 0$

$\dfrac{x + 6 - 2(x + 1)}{x + 1} < 0$

$\dfrac{4 - x}{x + 1} < 0$

Critical numbers: $x = -1, x = 4$

Test intervals: $(-\infty, -1), (-1, 4), (4, \infty)$

Test: Is $\dfrac{4 - x}{x + 1} < 0$?

Solution set: $(-\infty, -1) \cup (4, \infty)$

83. $\dfrac{4}{x + 5} > \dfrac{1}{2x + 3}$

$\dfrac{4}{x + 5} - \dfrac{1}{2x + 3} > 0$

$\dfrac{4(2x + 3) - (x + 5)}{(x + 5)(2x + 3)} > 0$

$\dfrac{7x + 7}{(x + 5)(2x + 3)} > 0$

Critical numbers: $x = -1, x = -5, x = -\dfrac{3}{2}$

Test intervals: $(-\infty, -5), \left(-5, -\dfrac{3}{2}\right), \left(-\dfrac{3}{2}, -1\right), (-1, \infty)$

Test: Is $\dfrac{7(x + 1)}{(x + 5)(2x + 3)} > 0$?

Solution set: $\left(-5, -\dfrac{3}{2}\right) \cup (-1, \infty)$

85. $x - 5 \geq 0$

$x \geq 5$

Domain: $[5, \infty)$

87. $4 - x^2 \geq 0$

$(2 + x)(2 - x) \geq 0$

Critical numbers: $x = \pm 2$

Test intervals: $(-\infty, -2), (-2, 2), (2, \infty)$

Test: Is $4 - x^2 \geq 0$?

Domain: $[-2, 2]$

89. $x^2 - 7x + 12 \geq 0$

$(x - 3)(x - 4) \geq 0$

Critical numbers: $x = 3, x = 4$

Test intervals: $(-\infty, 3), (3, 4), (4, \infty)$

Test: Is $(x - 3)(x - 4) \geq 0$?

Domain: $(-\infty, 3] \cup [4, \infty)$

91. $1250 < 1000[1 + r(2)]$

$1.250 < 1 + 2r$

$0.250 < 2r$

$0.125 < r$

$r > 12.5\%$

93. $R > C$

$115.95x > 95x + 750$

$20.95x > 750$

$x > 35.7995$

$x \geq 36$ units

95. $|h - 50| \leq 30$

$-30 \leq h - 50 \leq 30$

$20 \leq h \leq 80$

Minimum: $h = 20$

Maximum: $h = 80$

97. $7.34 + 0.41t + 0.002t^2 \geq 25$

$0.002t^2 + 0.41t - 17.66 \geq 0$

By the Quadratic Formula, the critical numbers are $t \approx -241.55$ and $t \approx 36.55$. The only one that makes sense here is $t \approx 36.55$. This corresponds to the year 1996.

99. $|ax - b| \leq c \implies c$ must be greater than or equal to zero.

$-c \leq ax - b \leq c$

$b - c \leq ax \leq b + c$

Let $a = 1$, then $b - c = 0$ and $b + c = 10$. This is true when $b = c = 5$. One set of values is : $a = 1$, $b = 5$, $c = 5$

(Note: This solution is not unique. Any positive multiple of these values will also work, such as:

$a = 2$, $b = c = 10$

$a = 3$, $b = c = 15$).

101. $x(50 - 0.0002x) - (12x + 150,000) \geq 1,650,000$

$-0.0002x^2 + 38x - 1,800,000 \geq 0$

By the Quadratic Formula, the critical numbers are $x = 90,000$ and $x = 100,000$.

The profit is at least \$1,650,000 when $90,000 \leq x \leq 100,000$ units

103.

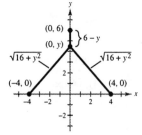

(a) $L = (6 - y) + 2\sqrt{16 + y^2}$

(b) $0 \leq y \leq 6$

When $y = 0$: $L = 14$

When $y = 6$: $L = 2\sqrt{52} = 4\sqrt{13} \approx 14.4$

(c)

(d) $6 - y + 2\sqrt{16 + y^2} < 13$

$2\sqrt{16 + y^2} - y - 7 < 0$

To find the critical numbers, set:

$2\sqrt{16 + y^2} - y - 7 = 0$

$2\sqrt{16 + y^2} = y + 7$

$4(16 + y^2) = y^2 + 14y + 49$

$64 + 4y^2 = y^2 + 14y + 49$

$3y^2 - 14y + 15 = 0$

$(3y - 5)(y - 3) = 0$

$y = \frac{5}{3}, y = 3$

By testing, the solution set is $\frac{5}{3} < y < 3$.

Section P.7   Errors and the Algebra of Calculus

- You should be able to recognize and avoid the common algebraic errors involving parentheses, fractions, exponents, radicals, and cancellation.
- You should be able to "unsimplify" algebraic expressions by the following methods.
  - (a) Unusual Factoring
  - (b) Inserting Factors or Terms
  - (c) Rewriting with Negative Exponents
  - (d) Writing a Fraction as a Sum of Terms

Solutions to Odd-Numbered Exercises

1. $2x - (3y + 4) = 2x - 3y - 4$

Distribute the minus sign.

3. $5z + 3(x - 2) = 5z + 3x - 6$

Use the Distributive Property.

5. $-\dfrac{x - 3}{x - 1} = \dfrac{-(x - 3)}{x - 1}$

$\qquad = \dfrac{3 - x}{x - 1}$

Only the numerator is multiplied by (-1).

7. $a\left(\dfrac{x}{y}\right) = \dfrac{a}{1} \cdot \dfrac{x}{y} = \dfrac{ax}{y}$

Only the numerator is multiplied by a.

9. $(4x)^2 = 4^2x^2 = 16x^2$

Square both factors.

11. $\sqrt{x + 9}$ does not simplify.

Do not apply the radical to the terms.

13. $\dfrac{6x + y}{6x - y}$ does not simplify.

Reduce common factors, not common factors of terms.

15. $\dfrac{1}{x + y^{-1}} = \dfrac{1}{x + (1/y)} \cdot \dfrac{y}{y} = \dfrac{y}{xy + 1}$

The negative exponent is on a term of the denominator, not a factor.

17. $x(2x + 1)^2 = x(4x^2 + 4x + 1)$

Exponents are applied before multiplying.

19. $\sqrt[3]{x^3 + 7x^2} = \sqrt[3]{x^2(x + 7)} = \sqrt[3]{x^2}\sqrt[3]{x + 7}$

Radicals apply to every factor of the radicand.

21. $\dfrac{3}{x} + \dfrac{4}{y} = \dfrac{3}{x} \cdot \dfrac{y}{y} + \dfrac{4}{y} \cdot \dfrac{x}{x} = \dfrac{3y + 4x}{xy}$

To add fractions, they must have a common denominator.

23. $\dfrac{1}{2y} = \dfrac{1}{2} \cdot \dfrac{1}{y}$

Use the definition for multiplying fractions.

25. $\dfrac{3x + 2}{5} = \dfrac{1}{5}(3x + 2)$

The required factor is $3x + 2$.

27. $\dfrac{2}{3}x^2 + \dfrac{1}{3}x + 5 = \dfrac{2}{3}x^2 + \dfrac{1}{3}x + \dfrac{15}{3} = \dfrac{1}{3}(2x^2 + x + 15)$

The required factor is $2x^2 + x + 15$.

29. $\frac{1}{3}x^3 + 5 = \frac{1}{3}x^3 + \frac{15}{3} = \frac{1}{3}(x^3 + 15)$

The required factor is $\frac{1}{3}$.

31. $x(2x^2 + 15) = \dfrac{2x}{2}(2x^2 + 15) = \left(\dfrac{1}{2}\right)(2x)(2x^2 + 15)$

$\qquad = \left(\dfrac{1}{2}\right)(2x^2 + 15)(2x)$

The required factor is $\frac{1}{2}$.

33. $x(1 - 2x^2)^3 = \dfrac{-4x}{-4}(1 - 2x^2)^3 = \left(-\dfrac{1}{4}\right)(-4x)(1 - 2x^2)^3$

$\qquad = \left(-\dfrac{1}{4}\right)(1 - 2x^2)^3(-4x)$

The required factor is $-\frac{1}{4}$.

35. $\dfrac{1}{\sqrt{x}\left(1 + \sqrt{x}\right)^2} = \dfrac{1}{\sqrt{x}} \cdot \dfrac{1}{\left(1 + \sqrt{x}\right)^2} = (2)\left(\dfrac{1}{2\sqrt{x}}\right)\dfrac{1}{\left(1 + \sqrt{x}\right)^2}$

$\qquad = (2)\dfrac{1}{\left(1 + \sqrt{x}\right)^2}\left(\dfrac{1}{2\sqrt{x}}\right)$

The required factor is 2.

37. $\dfrac{x + 1}{(x^2 + 2x - 3)^2} = \dfrac{1}{2} \cdot \dfrac{2(x + 1)}{(x^2 + 2x - 3)^2} = \left(\dfrac{1}{2}\right)\left(\dfrac{1}{(x^2 + 2x - 3)^2}\right)(2x + 2)$

The required factor is $\frac{1}{2}$.

39. $\dfrac{3}{x} + \dfrac{5}{2x^2} - \dfrac{3}{2}x = \dfrac{6x}{2x^2} + \dfrac{5}{2x^2} - \dfrac{3x^3}{2x^2} = \left(\dfrac{1}{2x^2}\right)(6x + 5 - 3x^3)$

The required factor is $\dfrac{1}{2x^2}$.

41. $\dfrac{9x^2}{25} + \dfrac{16y^2}{49} = \dfrac{9}{25} \cdot \dfrac{x^2}{1} + \dfrac{16}{49} \cdot \dfrac{y^2}{1}$

$\qquad\qquad = \dfrac{1}{25/9} \cdot \dfrac{x^2}{1} + \dfrac{1}{49/16} \cdot \dfrac{y^2}{1}$

$\qquad\qquad = \dfrac{x^2}{(25/9)} + \dfrac{y^2}{(49/16)}$

The required factors are $\frac{25}{9}$ and $\frac{49}{16}$.

43. $\dfrac{x^2}{1/12} - \dfrac{y^2}{2/3} = x^2\left(\dfrac{12}{1}\right) - y^2\left(\dfrac{3}{2}\right) = \dfrac{12x^2}{1} - \dfrac{3y^2}{2}$

The required factors are 1 and 2.

45. $\sqrt{x} + \left(\sqrt{x}\right)^3 = \sqrt{x}\left(1 + \left(\sqrt{x}\right)^2\right) = \sqrt{x}\,(1 + x)$

The required factor is $1 + x$.

47. $3(2x + 1)x^{1/2} + 4x^{3/2} = x^{1/2}[3(2x + 1) + 4x]$

$\qquad\qquad\qquad\qquad = x^{1/2}(6x + 3 + 4x)$

$\qquad\qquad\qquad\qquad = x^{1/2}(10x + 3)$

The required factor is $10x + 3$.

49. $\dfrac{x^2}{\sqrt{x^2 + 1}} - \sqrt{x^2 + 1} = \dfrac{x^2}{\sqrt{x^2 + 1}} - \dfrac{\sqrt{x^2 + 1}}{1} \cdot \dfrac{\sqrt{x^2 + 1}}{\sqrt{x^2 + 1}}$

$\qquad\qquad\qquad\qquad = \dfrac{x^2 - (x^2 + 1)}{\sqrt{x^2 + 1}} = \dfrac{-1}{\sqrt{x^2 + 1}}$

$\qquad\qquad\qquad\qquad = \dfrac{1}{\sqrt{x^2 + 1}}(-1)$

The required factor is -1.

51. $\frac{1}{10}(2x + 1)^{5/2} - \frac{1}{6}(2x + 1)^{3/2} = \frac{3}{30}(2x + 1)^{3/2}(2x + 1)^1 - \frac{5}{30}(2x + 1)^{3/2}$

$\qquad\qquad\qquad\qquad\qquad = \frac{1}{30}(2x + 1)^{3/2}[3(2x + 1) - 5]$

$\qquad\qquad\qquad\qquad\qquad = \frac{1}{30}(2x + 1)^{3/2}(6x - 2)$

$\qquad\qquad\qquad\qquad\qquad = \frac{1}{30}(2x + 1)^{3/2}2(3x - 1)$

$\qquad\qquad\qquad\qquad\qquad = \frac{1}{15}(2x + 1)^{3/2}(3x - 1)$

The required factor is $3x - 1$.

53. $\dfrac{16 - 5x - x^2}{x} = \dfrac{16}{x} - \dfrac{5x}{x} - \dfrac{x^2}{x} = \dfrac{16}{x} - 5 - x$

55. $\dfrac{4x^3 - 7x^2 + 1}{x^{1/3}} = \dfrac{4x^3}{x^{1/3}} - \dfrac{7x^2}{x^{1/3}} + \dfrac{1}{x^{1/3}}$

$\qquad\qquad = 4x^{3-1/3} - 7x^{2-1/3} + \dfrac{1}{x^{1/3}}$

$\qquad\qquad = 4x^{8/3} - 7x^{5/3} + \dfrac{1}{x^{1/3}}$

57. $\dfrac{3 - 5x^2 - x^4}{\sqrt{x}} = \dfrac{3}{\sqrt{x}} - \dfrac{5x^2}{\sqrt{x}} - \dfrac{x^4}{\sqrt{x}}$

$\qquad\qquad = \dfrac{3}{\sqrt{x}} - 5x^{2-1/2} - x^{4-1/2}$

$\qquad\qquad = \dfrac{3}{\sqrt{x}} - 5x^{3/2} - x^{7/2}$

59. $\dfrac{-2(x^2 - 3)^{-3}(2x)(x + 1)^3 - 3(x + 1)^2(x^2 - 3)^{-2}}{[(x + 1)^3]^2} = \dfrac{(x^2 - 3)^{-3}(x + 1)^2[-4x(x + 1) - 3(x^2 - 3)]}{(x + 1)^6}$

$\qquad\qquad\qquad\qquad\qquad = \dfrac{-4x^2 - 4x - 3x^2 + 9}{(x^2 - 3)^3(x + 1)^4}$

$\qquad\qquad\qquad\qquad\qquad = \dfrac{-7x^2 - 4x + 9}{(x^2 - 3)^3(x + 1)^4}$

61. $\dfrac{(6x + 1)^3(27x^2 + 2) - (9x^3 + 2x)(3)(6x + 1)^2(6)}{[(6x + 1)^3]^2} = \dfrac{(6x + 1)^2[(6x + 1)(27x^2 + 2) - 18(9x^3 + 2x)]}{(6x + 1)^6}$

$\qquad\qquad\qquad\qquad\qquad = \dfrac{162x^3 + 12x + 27x^2 + 2 - 162x^3 - 36x}{(6x + 1)^4}$

$\qquad\qquad\qquad\qquad\qquad = \dfrac{27x^2 - 24x + 2}{(6x + 1)^4}$

63. $\dfrac{(x + 2)^{3/4}(x + 3)^{-2/3} - (x + 3)^{1/3}(x + 2)^{-1/4}}{[(x + 2)^{3/4}]^2} = \dfrac{(x + 2)^{-1/4}(x + 3)^{-2/3}[(x + 2) - (x + 3)]}{(x + 2)^{6/4}}$

$\qquad\qquad\qquad\qquad\qquad = \dfrac{x + 2 - x - 3}{(x + 2)^{1/4}(x + 3)^{2/3}(x + 2)^{6/4}}$

$\qquad\qquad\qquad\qquad\qquad = -\dfrac{1}{(x + 3)^{2/3}(x + 2)^{7/4}}$

65. $\dfrac{2(3x - 1)^{1/3} - (2x + 1)\left(\frac{1}{3}\right)(3x - 1)^{-2/3}(3)}{(3x - 1)^{2/3}} = \dfrac{(3x - 1)^{-2/3}[2(3x - 1) - (2x + 1)]}{(3x - 1)^{2/3}}$

$\qquad\qquad\qquad\qquad\qquad = \dfrac{6x - 2 - 2x - 1}{(3x - 1)^{2/3}(3x - 1)^{2/3}}$

$\qquad\qquad\qquad\qquad\qquad = \dfrac{4x - 3}{(3x - 1)^{4/3}}$

67. (a) $y_1 = x^2\left(\dfrac{1}{3}\right)(x^2 + 1)^{-2/3}(2x) + (x^2 + 1)^{1/3}(2x)$

$$= 2x(x^2 + 1)^{-2/3}\left[\dfrac{x^2}{3} + (x^2 + 1)\right]$$

$$= 2x(x^2 + 1)^{-2/3}\left(\dfrac{4x^2}{3} + \dfrac{3}{3}\right)$$

$$= \dfrac{2x}{(x^2 + 1)^{2/3}} \cdot \dfrac{4x^2 + 3}{3}$$

$$= \dfrac{2x(4x^2 + 3)}{3(x^2 + 1)^{2/3}}$$

$$= y_2$$

(b)

x	-2	-1	$-\frac{1}{2}$	0	1	2	$\frac{5}{2}$
y_1	-8.7	-2.9	-1.1	0	2.9	8.7	12.5
y_2	-8.7	-2.9	-1.1	0	2.9	8.7	12.5

69. $y_1 = 2x\sqrt{1 - x^2} - \dfrac{x^3}{\sqrt{1 - x^2}}$ $\qquad$ $y_2 = \dfrac{2 - 3x^2}{\sqrt{1 - x^2}}$

When $x = 0$, $y_1 = 0$. $\qquad\qquad$ When $x = 0$, $y_2 = 1$.

Thus, $y_1 \neq y_2$.

$$y_1 = \dfrac{2x\sqrt{1 - x^2}}{1} - \dfrac{x^3}{\sqrt{1 - x^2}} = \dfrac{2x\sqrt{1 - x^2}}{1} \cdot \dfrac{\sqrt{1 - x^2}}{\sqrt{1 - x^2}} - \dfrac{x^3}{\sqrt{1 - x^2}}$$

$$= \dfrac{2x(1 - x^2) - x^3}{\sqrt{1 - x^2}} = \dfrac{2x - 2x^3 - x^3}{\sqrt{1 - x^2}}$$

$$= \dfrac{2x - 3x^3}{\sqrt{1 - x^2}}$$

Let $y_2 = \dfrac{2x - 3x^3}{\sqrt{1 - x^2}}$. Then $y_1 = y_2$.

Section P.8   Graphical Representation of Data

- ■ You should be able to plot points.
- ■ You should know that the distance between (x_1, y_1) and (x_2, y_2) in the plane is

$$d = \sqrt{(x_2 - x_1)^2 + (y_2 - y_1)^2}.$$

- ■ You should know that the midpoint of the line segment joining (x_1, y_1) and (x_2, y_2) is

$$\left(\frac{x_1 + x_2}{2}, \frac{y_1 + y_2}{2} \right).$$

Solutions to Odd-Numbered Exercises

1.

3.

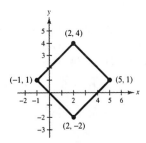

5. $A: (2, 6),$ $B: (-6, -2),$ $C: (4, -4),$ $D: (-3, 2)$

7. $(-3, 4)$

9. $(-5, -5)$

11. On the x-axis, $y = 0$.
On the y-axis, $x = 0$.

13. $x > 0$ and $y < 0$ in Quadrant IV.

15. $x = -4$ and $y > 0$ in Quadrant II.

17. $y < -5$ in Quadrants III and IV.

19. $(x, -y)$ is in the second Quadrant means that (x, y) is in Quadrant III.

21. $(x, y), xy > 0$ means x and y have the same signs. This occurs in Quadrants I and III.

23. $(-2 + 2, -4 + 5) = (0, 1)$
$(2 + 2, -3 + 5) = (4, 2)$
$(-1 + 2, -1 + 5) = (1, 4)$

25.

27. $y = 2 - \frac{1}{2}x$

x	-2	-1	$-\frac{1}{2}$	0	$\frac{1}{2}$	1	2
y	3	$\frac{5}{2}$	$\frac{9}{4}$	2	$\frac{7}{4}$	$\frac{3}{2}$	1

29. The highest price of milk is approximately $13.70 per 100 lb. This occurred in 1990.

31. $\left(\dfrac{1200}{1995} \div \dfrac{51}{1967}\right)100 \approx 2300\%$

33. The minimum wage increased most rapidly in the 1970s.

35. The point $(65, 83)$ represents an entrance exam score of 65.

37. $d = |5 - (-3)| = 8$ **39.** $d = |2 - (-3)| = 5$

41. (a) The distance between $(0, 2)$ and $(4, 2)$ is 4.
The distance between $(4, 2)$ and $(4, 5)$ is 3.
The distance between $(0, 2)$ and $(4, 5)$ is

$$\sqrt{(4 - 0)^2 + (5 - 2)^2} = \sqrt{16 + 9} = \sqrt{25} = 5.$$

(b) $4^2 + 3^2 = 16 + 9 = 25 = 5^2$

43. (a) The distance between $(-1, 1)$ and $(9, 1)$ is 10.
The distance between $(9, 1)$ and $(9, 4)$ is 3.
The distance between $(-1, 1)$ and $(9, 4)$ is

$$\sqrt{(9 - (-1))^2 + (4 - 1)^2} = \sqrt{100 + 9} = \sqrt{109}.$$

(b) $10^2 + 3^2 = 109 = \left(\sqrt{109}\right)^2$

45. (a)

(b) $d = \sqrt{(9 - 1)^2 + (7 - 1)^2}$

$= \sqrt{64 + 36} = 10$

(c) $\left(\dfrac{9 + 1}{2}, \dfrac{7 + 1}{2}\right) = (5, 4)$

47. (a)

(b) $d = \sqrt{(4 + 4)^2 + (-5 - 10)^2}$

$= \sqrt{64 + 225} = 17$

(c) $\left(\dfrac{4 - 4}{2}, \dfrac{-5 + 10}{2}\right) = \left(0, \dfrac{5}{2}\right)$

49. (a)

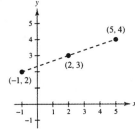

(b) $d = \sqrt{(5+1)^2 + (4-2)^2}$

$= \sqrt{36+4} = 2\sqrt{10}$

(c) $\left(\dfrac{-1+5}{2}, \dfrac{2+4}{2}\right) = (2, 3)$

51. (a)

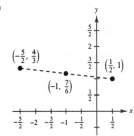

(b) $d = \sqrt{\left(\dfrac{1}{2}+\dfrac{5}{2}\right)^2 + \left(1-\dfrac{4}{3}\right)^2}$

$d = \sqrt{9+\dfrac{1}{9}} = \dfrac{\sqrt{82}}{3}$

(c) $\left(\dfrac{-\frac{5}{2}+\frac{1}{2}}{2}, \dfrac{\frac{4}{3}+1}{2}\right) = \left(-1, \dfrac{7}{6}\right)$

53. (a)

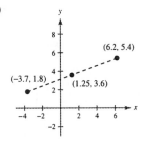

(b) $d = \sqrt{(6.2+3.7)^2 + (5.4-1.8)^2}$

$= \sqrt{98.01 + 12.96}$

$= \sqrt{110.97}$

(c) $\left(\dfrac{6.2-3.7}{2}, \dfrac{5.4+1.8}{2}\right) = (1.25, 3.6)$

55. (a)

(b) $d = \sqrt{(48+36)^2 + (-72+18)^2}$

$= \sqrt{7056 + 2916}$

$= \sqrt{9972} = 6\sqrt{277}$

(c) $\left(\dfrac{-36+48}{2}, \dfrac{-18-72}{2}\right) = (6, -45)$

57. $\left(\dfrac{1991+1995}{2}, \dfrac{\$520{,}000 + \$740{,}000}{2}\right) = (1993, \$630{,}000)$

In 1993 the sales were $630,000.

59. $d_1 = \sqrt{(4-2)^2 + (0-1)^2} = \sqrt{5}$

$d_2 = \sqrt{(4+1)^2 + (0+5)^2} = \sqrt{50}$

$d_3 = \sqrt{(2+1)^2 + (1+5)^2} = \sqrt{45}$

$\left(\sqrt{5}\right)^2 + \left(\sqrt{45}\right)^2 = \left(\sqrt{50}\right)^2$

61. $d_1 = \sqrt{(0-1)^2 + (0-2)^2} = \sqrt{5}$

$d_2 = \sqrt{(0-2)^2 + (0-1)^2} = \sqrt{5}$

$d_3 = \sqrt{(3-1)^2 + (3-2)^2} = \sqrt{5}$

$d_4 = \sqrt{(3-2)^2 + (3-1)^2} = \sqrt{5}$

$d_1 = d_2 = d_3 = d_4$

63. $d_1 = \sqrt{(0-2)^2 + (9-5)^2} = \sqrt{4+16} = \sqrt{20} = 2\sqrt{5}$

$d_2 = \sqrt{(-2-0)^2 + (0-9)^2} = \sqrt{4+81} = \sqrt{85}$

$d_3 = \sqrt{(0-(-2))^2 + (-4-0)^2} = \sqrt{4+16} = \sqrt{20} = 2\sqrt{5}$

$d_4 = \sqrt{(0-2)^2 + (-4-5)^2} = \sqrt{4+81} = \sqrt{85}$

Opposite sides have equal lengths of $2\sqrt{5}$ and $\sqrt{85}$.

65. Since $x_m = \dfrac{x_1 + x_2}{2}$ and $y_m = \dfrac{y_1 + y_2}{2}$ we have:

$$2x_m = x_1 + x_2 \qquad\qquad 2y_m = y_1 + y_2$$

$$2x_m - x_1 = x_2 \qquad\qquad 2y_m - y_1 = y_2$$

Thus, $(x_2, y_2) = (2x_m - x_1, 2y_m - y_1)$.

67. The midpoint of the given line segment is $\left(\dfrac{x_1 + x_2}{2}, \dfrac{y_1 + y_2}{2}\right)$.

The midpoint between (x_1, y_1) and $\left(\dfrac{x_1 + x_2}{2}, \dfrac{y_1 + y_2}{2}\right)$ is

$$\left(\dfrac{x_1 + \dfrac{x_1 + x_2}{2}}{2}, \dfrac{y_1 + \dfrac{y_1 + y_2}{2}}{2}\right) = \left(\dfrac{3x_1 + x_2}{4}, \dfrac{3y_1 + y_2}{4}\right).$$

The midpoint between $\left(\dfrac{x_1 + x_2}{2}, \dfrac{y_1 + y_2}{2}\right)$ and (x_2, y_2) is

$$\left(\dfrac{\dfrac{x_1 + x_2}{2} + x_2}{2}, \dfrac{\dfrac{y_1 + y_2}{2} + y_2}{2}\right) = \left(\dfrac{x_1 + 3x_2}{4}, \dfrac{y_1 + 3y_2}{4}\right).$$

Thus, the three points are

$$\left(\dfrac{3x_1 + x_2}{4}, \dfrac{3y_1 + y_2}{4}\right), \left(\dfrac{x_1 + x_2}{2}, \dfrac{y_1 + y_2}{2}\right), \text{ and } \left(\dfrac{x_1 + 3x_2}{4}, \dfrac{y_1 + 3y_2}{4}\right).$$

69. $d = \sqrt{(45-10)^2 + (40-15)^2} = \sqrt{35^2 + 25^2} = \sqrt{1850} = 5\sqrt{74} \approx 43$ yards

71.

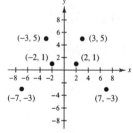

The points are reflected through the y-axis.

73. (a) It appears that the number of artists elected alternates between 7 and 8 per year in the 1990s. If this pattern continues, 8 would be elected in 1996.

(b) Since 1986 and 1987 were the first two years that artists were elected, there was a larger number of artists chosen.

❏ Review Exercises for Chapter P

Solutions to Odd-Numbered Exercises

1. $\{11, -14, -\frac{8}{9}, \frac{5}{2}, \sqrt{6}, 0.4\}$

(a) Natural numbers: 11

(b) Integers: $11, -14$

(c) Rational numbers: $11, -14, -\frac{8}{9}, \frac{5}{2}, 0.4$

(d) Irrational numbers: $\sqrt{6}$

3. (a) $\frac{5}{6} = 0.8\overline{3}$

(b) $\frac{7}{8} = 0.875$

5. $x \le 7$
The set consists of all real numbers less than or equal to 7.

7. $d(x, 7) = |x - 7|$ and $d(x, 7) \ge 4$, thus $|x - 7| \ge 4$.

9. $d(y, -30) = |y - (-30)| = |y + 30|$ and $d(y, -30) < 5$, thus $|y + 30| < 5$.

11. $2x + (3x - 10) = (2x + 3x) - 10$
Illustrates the Associative Property of Addition

13. $0 + (a - 5) = a - 5$
Illustrates the Additive Identity Property

15. (a) $(-2z)^3 = (-2)^3 z^3 = -8z^3$

(b) $(a^2 b^4)(3ab^{-2}) = 3a^{2+1}b^{4+(-2)} = 3a^3 b^2$

17. (a) $\dfrac{6^2 u^3 v^{-3}}{12 u^{-2} v} = \dfrac{36 u^{3-(-2)} v^{-3-1}}{12} = 3u^5 v^{-4} = \dfrac{3u^5}{v^4}$

(b) $\dfrac{3^{-4} m^{-1} n^{-3}}{9^{-2} mn^{-3}} = \dfrac{9^2 n^3}{3^4 mmn^3} = \dfrac{81}{81 m^2} = \dfrac{1}{m^2} = m^{-2}$

19. $30,296,000,000 = 3.0296 \times 10^{10}$

21. $4.833 \times 10^8 = 483,300,000$

23. (a) $1800(1 + 0.08)^{24} \approx 11,414.125$

(b) $0.0024 \, (7,658,400) = 18,380.160$

25. Radical form: $\sqrt{16} = 4$

Rational exponent form: $16^{1/2} = 4$

27. (a) $\sqrt{4x^4} = 2x^2$

(b) $\sqrt{\dfrac{18u^2}{b^3}} = \sqrt{\dfrac{9u^2}{b^2} \cdot \dfrac{2}{b}} = \dfrac{3|u|}{b} \sqrt{\dfrac{2}{b}}$

29. $\dfrac{1}{2 - \sqrt{3}} = \dfrac{1}{2 - \sqrt{3}} \cdot \dfrac{2 + \sqrt{3}}{2 + \sqrt{3}} = \dfrac{2 + \sqrt{3}}{4 - 3} = \dfrac{2 + \sqrt{3}}{1} = 2 + \sqrt{3}$

31. $\sqrt{50} - \sqrt{18} = \sqrt{25 \cdot 2} - \sqrt{9 \cdot 2} = 5\sqrt{2} - 3\sqrt{2} = 2\sqrt{2}$

33. $A = wh = 8\sqrt{3}\ \sqrt{24^2 - \left(8\sqrt{3}\right)^2} = 8\sqrt{3}\ \sqrt{384}$

$\qquad = 8\sqrt{3}\left(8\sqrt{6}\right) = 64\sqrt{18} = 64\left(3\sqrt{2}\right) = 192\sqrt{2}$

35. $10(4 \cdot 7) = 10(28) = 280$

The error in $40 \cdot 70$ is an improper use of the Distributive Property.

37. $4\left(\dfrac{3}{7}\right) = \dfrac{4}{1}\left(\dfrac{3}{7}\right) = \dfrac{12}{7}$

Only the numerator is multiplied by 4.

39. $\dfrac{x - 1}{1 - x} = \dfrac{x - 1}{-(x - 1)} = -1, x \neq 1$

The error is an improper cancellation.

41. $(-x)^6 = x^6$

The exponent is to be applied to the whole quantity inside the parentheses.

43. $\sqrt{3^2 + 4^2} = \sqrt{9 + 16} = \sqrt{25} = 5$

Do not apply radicals term–by–term.

45. $\sqrt{10x} = \sqrt{10}\sqrt{x}$

Radicals apply to each factor.

47. $-(3x^2 + 2x) + (1 - 5x) = -3x^2 - 2x + 1 - 5x$

$\qquad\qquad\qquad\qquad\qquad\quad = -3x^2 - 7x + 1$

49. $(2x - 3)^2 = (2x)^2 - 2(2x)(3) + 3^2$

$\qquad\qquad\quad = 4x^2 - 12x + 9$

51. $(x^3 - 3x)(2x^2 + 3x + 5) = x^3(2x^2 + 3x + 5) - 3x(2x^2 + 3x + 5)$

$\qquad\qquad\qquad\qquad\qquad\quad = 2x^5 + 3x^4 + 5x^3 - 6x^3 - 9x^2 - 15x$

$\qquad\qquad\qquad\qquad\qquad\quad = 2x^5 + 3x^4 - x^3 - 9x^2 - 15x$

53. $x^3 - x = x(x^2 - 1) = x(x + 1)(x - 1)$

55. $2x^2 + 21x + 10 = (2x + 1)(x + 10)$

57. $x^3 - x^2 + 2x - 2 = x^2(x - 1) + 2(x - 1)$

$\qquad\qquad\qquad\qquad = (x - 1)(x^2 + 2)$

59. (a)

The surface area is the sum of the area of the side, $2\pi rh$, and the areas of the top and bottom which are each πr^2.

$S = 2\pi rh + \pi r^2 + \pi r^2 = 2\pi rh + 2\pi r^2$

(b) $S = 2\pi rh + 2\pi r^2 = 2\pi r(r + h)$

61. $\dfrac{2}{3}x^4 - \dfrac{3}{8}x^3 + \dfrac{5}{6}x^2 = \dfrac{16}{24}x^4 - \dfrac{9}{24}x^3 + \dfrac{20}{24}x^2$

$\qquad\qquad\qquad\qquad = \dfrac{1}{24}x^2(16x^2 - 9x + 20)$

The missing factor is $16x^2 - 9x + 20$.

63. $\dfrac{x^2 - 4}{x^4 - 2x^2 - 8} \cdot \dfrac{x^2 + 2}{x^2} = \dfrac{(x + 2)(x - 2)}{(x^2 + 2)(x^2 - 4)} \cdot \dfrac{x^2 + 2}{x^2}$

$$= \dfrac{(x + 2)(x - 2)}{(x^2 + 2)(x + 2)(x - 2)} \cdot \dfrac{x^2 + 2}{x^2}$$

$$= \dfrac{1}{x^2}$$

65. $2x + \dfrac{3}{2(x - 4)} - \dfrac{1}{2(x + 2)} = \dfrac{2x(2)(x - 4)(x + 2) + 3(x + 2) - (x - 4)}{2(x - 4)(x + 2)}$

$$= \dfrac{4x(x^2 - 2x - 8) + 3x + 6 - x + 4}{2(x - 4)(x + 2)}$$

$$= \dfrac{4x^3 - 8x^2 - 32x + 2x + 10}{2(x - 4)(x + 2)}$$

$$= \dfrac{4x^3 - 8x^2 - 30x + 10}{2(x - 4)(x + 2)}$$

$$= \dfrac{2(2x^3 - 4x^2 - 15x + 5)}{2(x - 4)(x + 2)}$$

$$= \dfrac{2x^3 - 4x^2 - 15x + 5}{(x - 4)(x + 2)}$$

67. $\dfrac{1}{x - 1} + \dfrac{1 - x}{x^2 + x + 1} = \dfrac{(x^2 + x + 1) + (1 - x)(x - 1)}{(x - 1)(x^2 + x + 1)}$

$$= \dfrac{x^2 + x + 1 - x^2 + 2x - 1}{(x - 1)(x^2 + x + 1)}$$

$$= \dfrac{3x}{(x - 1)(x^2 + x + 1)}$$

$$= \dfrac{3x}{x^3 - 1}$$

69. $\dfrac{\left[\dfrac{3a}{(a^2/x) - 1}\right]}{\left(\dfrac{a}{x} - 1\right)} = \dfrac{\dfrac{3ax}{a^2 - x}}{\dfrac{a - x}{x}}$

$$= \dfrac{3ax}{a^2 - x} \cdot \dfrac{x}{a - x}$$

$$= \dfrac{3ax^2}{(a^2 - x)(a - x)}$$

$$= \dfrac{3ax^2}{(a + x)(a - x)(a - x)}$$

$$= \dfrac{3ax^2}{(a + x)(a - x)^2}$$

71. $3x - 2(x + 5) = 10$

$$3x - 2x - 10 = 10$$

$$x = 20$$

73. $4(x + 3) - 3 = 2(4 - 3x) - 4$

$4x + 12 - 3 = 8 - 6x - 4$

$4x + 9 = -6x + 4$

$10x = -5$

$x = -\dfrac{1}{2}$

75. $3\left(1 - \dfrac{1}{5t}\right) = 0$

$1 - \dfrac{1}{5t} = 0$

$1 = \dfrac{1}{5t}$

$5t = 1$

$t = \dfrac{1}{5}$

77. $6x = 3x^2$

$0 = 3x^2 - 6x$

$0 = 3x(x - 2)$

$3x = 0 \implies x = 0$

$x - 2 = 0 \implies x = 2$

79. $(x + 4)^2 = 18$

$x + 4 = \pm\sqrt{18}$

$x = -4 \pm 3\sqrt{2}$

81. $x^2 - 12x + 30 = 0$

$x^2 - 12x = -30$

$x^2 - 12x + 36 = -30 + 36$

$(x - 6)^2 = 6$

$x - 6 = \pm\sqrt{6}$

$x = 6 \pm \sqrt{6}$

83. $5x^4 - 12x^3 = 0$

$x^3(5x - 12) = 0$

$x^3 = 0 \quad\text{or}\quad 5x - 12 = 0$

$x = 0 \quad\text{or}\qquad\quad x = \frac{12}{5}$

85. $\dfrac{4}{(x - 4)^2} = 1$

$4 = (x - 4)^2$

$\pm 2 = x - 4$

$4 \pm 2 = x$

$x = 6 \quad\text{or}\quad x = 2$

87. $\sqrt{x + 4} = 3$

$\left(\sqrt{x + 4}\right)^2 = (3)^2$

$x + 4 = 9$

$x = 5$

89. $2\sqrt{x} - 5 = 0$

$2\sqrt{x} = 5$

$4x = 25$

$x = \frac{25}{4}$

91. $\sqrt{2x + 3} + \sqrt{x - 2} = 2$

$\left(\sqrt{2x + 3}\right)^2 = \left(2 - \sqrt{x - 2}\right)^2$

$2x + 3 = 4 - 4\sqrt{x - 2} + x - 2$

$x + 1 = -4\sqrt{x - 2}$

$(x + 1)^2 = \left(-4\sqrt{x - 2}\right)^2$

$x^2 + 2x + 1 = 16(x - 2)$

$x^2 - 14x + 33 = 0$

$(x - 3)(x - 11) = 0$

$x = 3, \text{extraneous} \quad\text{or}\quad x = 11, \text{extraneous}$

No solution

93. $(x - 1)^{2/3} - 25 = 0$

$$(x - 1)^{2/3} = 25$$

$$(x - 1)^2 = 25^3$$

$$x - 1 = \pm\sqrt{25^3}$$

$$x = 1 \pm 125$$

$$x = 126 \quad \text{or} \quad x = -124$$

95. $(x + 4)^{1/2} + 5x(x + 4)^{3/2} = 0$

$$(x + 4)^{1/2}[1 + 5x(x + 4)] = 0$$

$$(x + 4)^{1/2}(5x^2 + 20x + 1) = 0$$

$$(x + 4)^{1/2} = 0 \qquad \text{OR} \quad 5x^2 + 20x + 1 = 0$$

$$x = -4 \qquad\qquad\qquad x = \frac{-20 \pm \sqrt{400 - 20}}{10}$$

$$x = \frac{-20 \pm 2\sqrt{95}}{10}$$

$$x = -2 \pm \frac{\sqrt{95}}{5}$$

97. $|x - 5| = 10$

$$x - 5 = -10 \quad \text{or} \quad x - 5 = 10$$

$$x = -5 \qquad\qquad x = 15$$

99. $|x^2 - 3| = 2x$

$$x^2 - 3 = 2x \quad \text{or} \qquad x^2 - 3 = -2x$$

$$x^2 - 2x - 3 = 0 \qquad\qquad x^2 + 2x - 3 = 0$$

$$(x - 3)(x + 1) = 0 \qquad (x + 3)(x - 1) = 0$$

$$x = 3 \quad \text{or} \quad x = -1 \qquad x = -3 \quad \text{or} \quad x = 1$$

The only solutions to the original equation are $x = 3$ or $x = 1$.
($x = -3$ and $x = -1$ are extraneous.)

101. $V = \dfrac{1}{3}\pi r^2 h$

$$3V = \pi r^2 h$$

$$\frac{3V}{\pi h} = r^2$$

$$r = \sqrt{\frac{3V}{\pi h}}$$

Since r represents the radius of a cone, r is positive only.

103. $L = \dfrac{k}{3\pi r^2 p}$

$$3\pi r^2 p L = k$$

$$p = \frac{k}{3\pi r^2 L}$$

105.
$$x^2 - 2x \geq 3$$
$$x^2 - 2x - 3 \geq 0$$
$$(x + 1)(x - 3) \geq 0$$
Critical numbers: $x = -1, x = 3$

Test intervals: $(-\infty, -1), (-1, 3), (3, \infty)$

Test: Is $(x + 1)(x - 3) \geq 0$?

Solution set: $(-\infty, -1] \cup [3, \infty)$

107. $\dfrac{x - 5}{3 - x} < 0$

Critical numbers: $x = 5, x = 3$

Test intervals: $(-\infty, 3), (3, 5), (5, \infty)$

Test: Is $\dfrac{x - 5}{3 - x} < 0$?

Solution set: $(-\infty, 3) \cup (5, \infty)$

109.
$$|x - 2| < 1$$
$$-1 < x - 2 < 1$$
$$1 < x < 3,$$
which can be written as $(1, 3)$.

111. $\left| x - \dfrac{3}{2} \right| \geq \dfrac{3}{2}$

$$x - \frac{3}{2} \leq -\frac{3}{2} \quad \text{or} \quad x - \frac{3}{2} \geq \frac{3}{2}$$
$$x \leq 0 \qquad \text{or} \qquad x \geq 3,$$
which can be written as $(-\infty, 0] \cup [3, \infty)$.

113.
$$\frac{x}{5} - 6 \leq -\frac{x}{2} + 6$$
$$10\left(\frac{x}{5} - 6 \right) \leq 10\left(-\frac{x}{2} + 6 \right)$$
$$2x - 60 \leq -5x + 60$$
$$7x \leq 120$$
$$x \leq \frac{120}{7}$$

115. $(x - 4)|x| > 0$

Critical numbers: $x = 4, x = 0$

Test intervals: $(-\infty, 0), (0, 4), (4, \infty)$

Test: Is $(x - 4)|x| > 0$?

Solution set: $(4, \infty)$

117. $2x - 10 \geq 0$
$$2x \geq 10$$
$$x \geq 5$$
Domain: $[5, \infty)$

119.

$$d_1 = \sqrt{(13 - 5)^2 + (11 - 22)^2} = \sqrt{8^2 + (-11)^2} = \sqrt{64 + 121} = \sqrt{185}$$
$$d_2 = \sqrt{(2 - 13)^2 + (3 - 11)^2} = \sqrt{(-11)^2 + (-8)^2} = \sqrt{121 + 64} = \sqrt{185}$$
$$d_3 = \sqrt{(2 - 5)^2 + (3 - 22)^2} = \sqrt{(-3)^2 + (-19)^2} = \sqrt{9 + 361} = \sqrt{370}$$
$$d_1^2 + d_2^2 = 185 + 185 = 370 = d_3^2$$

The points form a right triangle.

121. $x > 0$ and $y = -2$ is in Quadrant IV

123. $(-x, y)$ is in Quadrant III $\Longrightarrow (x, y)$ is in Quadrant IV.

125. (a)

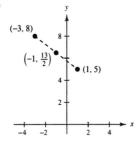

(b) $d = \sqrt{(1 - (-3))^2 + (5 - 8)^2}$

$= \sqrt{4^2 + (-3)^2}$

$= \sqrt{16 + 9}$

$= \sqrt{25}$

$= 5$

(c) $\left(\dfrac{-3 + 1}{2}, \dfrac{8 + 5}{2}\right) = \left(-1, \dfrac{13}{2}\right)$

127. Each corner has a length of $2\sqrt{2}$ by the Pythagorean Theorem.

$P = 2\left(8\frac{1}{2} - 4\right) + 2(11 - 4) + 4\left(2\sqrt{2}\right)$

$= 9 + 14 + 8\sqrt{2}$

$= 23 + 8\sqrt{2} \approx 34.3$ inches

129. (a) $2m + 2n = 2(m + n)$ which is even.

(b) $(2m + 1) + (2n + 1) = 2m + 2n + 2 = 2(m + n + 1)$ which is even.

(c) $(2n)(m) = 2nm$ which is even.

131. Original Price: $340 + 85 = 425$

Percent Discount: $85/425 = 0.20 = 20\%$

133. $2\pi(r + 1) - 2\pi r = 2\pi r + 2\pi - 2\pi r$

$= 2\pi$ meters longer

135.

$\dfrac{90,000}{x} = \dfrac{90,000}{x + 3} + 2500$

$90,000(x + 3) = 90,000x + 2500x(x + 3)$

$90,000x + 270,000 = 90,000x + 2500x^2 + 7500x$

$0 = 2500x^2 + 7500x - 270,000$

$0 = 2500(x^2 + 3x - 108)$

$0 = 2500(x + 12)(x - 9)$

$x = -12$, extraneous

$x = 9$

There are 9 people in the original group.

❑ Practice Test for Chapter P

1. Evaluate $\dfrac{|-42| - 20}{15 - |-4|}$.

2. Simplify $\dfrac{x}{z} - \dfrac{z}{y}$.

3. The distance between x and 7 is no more than 4. Use absolute value notation to describe this expression.

4. Evaluate $10(-x)^3$ for $x = 5$.

5. Simplify $(-4x^3)\,(-2x^{-5})\,\left(\tfrac{1}{16}x\right)$.

6. Change 0.0000412 to scientific notation.

7. Evaluate $125^{2/3}$.

8. Simplify $\sqrt[4]{64x^7y^9}$.

9. Rationalize the denominator and simplify $\dfrac{6}{\sqrt{12}}$.

10. Simplify $3\sqrt{80} - 7\sqrt{500}$.

11. Simplify $(8x^4 - 9x^2 + 2x - 1) - (3x^3 + 5x + 4)$.

12. Multiply $(x - 3)(x^2 + x - 7)$.

13. Multiply $[(x - 2) - y]^2$.

14. Factor $16x^4 - 1$.

15. Factor $6x^2 + 5x - 4$.

16. Factor $x^3 - 64$.

17. Combine and simplify $-\dfrac{3}{x} + \dfrac{x}{x^2 + 2}$.

18. Combine and simplify $\dfrac{x - 3}{4x} \div \dfrac{x^2 - 9}{x^2}$.

19. Simplify $\dfrac{1 - (1/x)}{1 - \dfrac{1}{1 - (1/x)}}$.

20. (a) Plot the points $(-3, 7)$ and $(5, -1)$,

    (b) find the distance between the points, and

    (c) find the midpoint of the line segment joining the points.

21. Solve $x^2 - 2x - 35 = 0$.

    (a) by factoring.

    (b) by completing the square.

    (c) by the Quadratic Formula.

22. Solve $x^5 - 5x^3 + 4x = 0$ by factoring.

23. Solve $x = 2\sqrt{x + 3}$.

24. Solve $x^2 - 16 \le 0$.

25. Solve $\left|\dfrac{4 - x}{3}\right| > 2$.

CHAPTER 1
Functions and Their Graphs

CHAPTER 1
Functions and Their Graphs

Section 1.1   Graphs and Graphing Utilities

- ■ You should be able to use the point-plotting method of graphing.
- ■ You should be able to find x- and y-intercepts.
  - (a) To find the x-intercepts, let $y = 0$ and solve for x.
  - (b) To find the y-intercepts, let $x = 0$ and solve for y.
- ■ You should be able to test for symmetry.
  - (a) To test for x-axis symmetry, replace y with $-y$.
  - (b) To test for y-axis symmetry, replace x with $-x$.
  - (c) To test for origin symmetry, replace x with $-x$ and y with $-y$.
- ■ You should know the standard equation of a circle with center (h, k) and radius r:

$$(x - h)^2 + (y - k)^2 = r^2$$

Solutions to Odd-Numbered Exercises

1. $y = \sqrt{x + 4}$

   (a) $(0, 2)$: $2 \overset{?}{=} \sqrt{0 + 4}$

      $2 = 2\ 3$

      Yes, the point *is* on the graph.

   (b) $(5, 3)$: $3 \overset{?}{=} \sqrt{5 + 4}$

      $3 = \sqrt{9}\ 3$

      Yes, the point *is* on the graph.

3. $y = 4 - |x - 2|$

   (a) $(1, 5)$: $5 \overset{?}{=} 4 - |1 - 2|$

      $5 \neq 4 - 1$

      No, the point *is not* on the graph.

   (b) $(6, 0)$: $0 \overset{?}{=} 4 - |6 - 2|$

      $0 = 4 - 4\ 3$

      Yes, the point *is* on the graph.

5. $2x - y - 3 = 0$

   (a) $(1, 2)$: $2(1) - (2) - 3 \overset{?}{=} 0$

      $-3 \neq 0$

      No, the point *is not* on the graph.

   (b) $(1, -1)$: $2(1) - (-1) - 3 \overset{?}{=} 0$

      $2 + 1 - 3 = 0\ 3$

      Yes, the point *is* on the graph.

7. $x^2 y - x^2 + 4y = 0$

   (a) $\left(1, \tfrac{1}{5}\right)$: $(1)^2 \left(\tfrac{1}{5}\right) - (1)^2 + 4\left(\tfrac{1}{5}\right) \overset{?}{=} 0$

      $\tfrac{1}{5} - 1 + \tfrac{4}{5} = 0\ 3$

      Yes, the point *is* on the graph.

   (b) $\left(2, \tfrac{1}{2}\right)$: $(2)^2\left(\tfrac{1}{2}\right) - (2)^2 + 4\left(\tfrac{1}{2}\right) \overset{?}{=} 0$

      $2 - 4 + 2 = 0\ 3$

      Yes, the point *is* on the graph.

9. $y = -2x + 3$

x	-1	0	1	$\frac{3}{2}$	2
y	5	3	1	0	-1

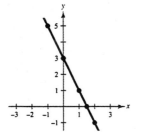

11. $y = x^2 - 2x$

x	-1	0	1	2	3
y	3	0	-1	0	3

13.

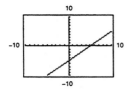

$y = x - 5$

Intercepts: $(5, 0), (0, -5)$

15.

$y = x^2 + x - 2$

Intercepts: $(1, 0), (-2, 0), (0, -2)$

17.

$y = x\sqrt{x + 6}$

Intercepts: $(0, 0), (-6, 0)$

19.

$y = \dfrac{2x}{x - 1}$

Intercept: $(0, 0)$

21. $(-x)^2 - y = 0 \implies x^2 - y = 0$

y-axis symmetry

23. $x - (-y)^2 = 0 \implies x - y^2 = 0$

x-axis symmetry

25. $-y = (-x)^3 \implies y = x^3$

Origin symmetry

27. $-y = \dfrac{-x}{(-x)^2 + 1} \implies y = \dfrac{x}{x^2 + 1}$

Origin symmetry

29. y-axis symmetry

31. Origin symmetry

33. $y = 1 - x$ has intercepts $(1, 0)$ and $(0, 1)$. Matches graph (c).

35. $y = \sqrt{9 - x^2}$ has intercepts $(\pm 3, 0)$ and $(0, 3)$. Matches graph (f).

37. $y = x^3 - x + 1$ has a y-intercept of $(0, 1)$ and the points $(1, 1)$ and $(-2, -5)$ are on the graph. Matches graph (b).

39. $y = -3x + 2$
No symmetry

41. $y = 1 - x^2$
y-axis symmetry

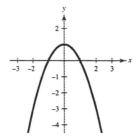

43. $y = x^2 - 3x$
No symmetry

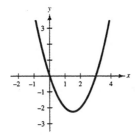

45. $y = x^3 + 2$
No symmetry

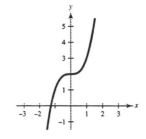

47. $y = \sqrt{x - 3}$
No symmetry
Domain: $x \geq 3$

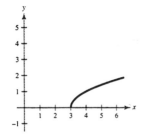

49. $y = |x - 2|$
No symmetry

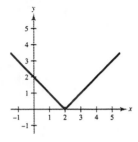

51. $x = y^2 - 1$
x-axis symmetry

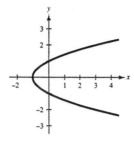

53. $y = 3 - \frac{1}{2}x$

Intercepts: (6,0), (0, 3)

55. $y = x^2 - 4x + 3$

Intercepts: (3, 0), (1, 0), (0, 3)

57. $y = x(x - 2)^2$

Intercepts: (0, 0), (2, 0)

59. $y = \sqrt[3]{x}$

Intercepts: (0, 0)

61. $y = \frac{5}{2}x + 5$

The standard setting gives a more complete graph.

63. $y = -x^2 + 10x - 5$

The specified setting gives a more complete graph.

65. $y = 4x^2 - 25$

Range/Window

Xmin = -5
Xmax = 5
Xscl = 1
Ymin = -30
Ymax = 30
Yscl = 10

67. $y = |x| + |x + 10|$

Range/Window

Xmin = -10
Xmax = 20
Xscl = 5
Ymin = -5
Ymax = 30
Yscl = 5

69. $x^2 + y^2 = 3^2$

$x^2 + y^2 = 9$

71. $(x - 2)^2 + [y - (-1)]^2 = 4^2$

$(x - 2)^2 + (y + 1)^2 = 16$

73. $r = \sqrt{(0 - (-1))^2 + (0 - 2)^2} = \sqrt{1 + 4} = \sqrt{5}$

$[x - (-1)]^2 + (y - 2)^2 = \left(\sqrt{5}\right)^2$

$(x + 1)^2 + (y - 2)^2 = 5$

75. $r = \dfrac{1}{2}\sqrt{(6 - 0)^2 + (8 - 0)^2} = 5$

$\text{Center} = \left(\dfrac{0 + 6}{2}, \dfrac{0 + 8}{2}\right) = (3, 4)$

$(x - 3)^2 + (y - 4)^2 = 25$

77. Center: $(-2, -3)$; radius: 2

$[x - (-2)]^2 + [y - (-3)]^2 = 2^2$

$(x + 2)^2 + (y + 3)^2 = 4$

79. $x^2 + y^2 = 4$

Center: $(0, 0)$; radius: 2

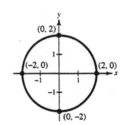

81. $(x - 1)^2 + (y + 3)^2 = 4$

$(x - 1)^2 + [y - (-3)]^2 = 2^2$

Center: $(1, -3)$; radius: 2

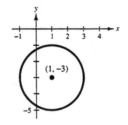

83. $\left(x - \frac{1}{2}\right)^2 + \left(y - \frac{1}{2}\right)^2 = \frac{9}{4}$

Center: $\left(\frac{1}{2}, \frac{1}{2}\right)$; radius: $\frac{3}{2}$

85. $y_1 = \sqrt{9 - x^2}$

$y_2 = -\sqrt{9 - x^2}$

A circle is bounded by their graphs.

87. $y_1 = \frac{1}{4}(x^2 - 8)$

$y_2 = \frac{1}{4}x^2 - 2$

The graphs are identical. The Distributive Property is illustrated.

89. $y_1 = \frac{1}{5}[10(x^2 - 1)]$

$y_2 = 2(x^2 - 1)$

The graphs are identical. The Associative Property of Multiplication is illustrated.

91. $y = 225{,}000 - 20{,}000t, \ 0 \le t \le 8$

93. Most likely you would need to change the viewing window. For example, let $y_1 = x^2 + 12$. This graph would not show up on the standard window. Change the range/window to the following setting and try again.

Xmin = -5
Xmax = 5
Xscl = 1
Ymin = -5
Ymax = 40
Yscl = 5

95. (a)

Year	1920	1930	1940	1950	1960	1970	1980	1990
Life Expectancy	54.1	59.7	62.9	68.2	69.7	70.8	73.7	75.4
Model	52.8	58.7	63.3	66.9	69.9	72.4	74.6	76.4

(b) When $t = 48$, $y \approx 77.7$ years.

(c) When $t = 50$, $y \approx 78.0$ years.

97. $y = 0.086t + 0.872$, $0 \leq t \leq 4$

Year	1990	1991	1992	1993	1994
t	0	1	2	3	4
y	0.872	0.958	1.044	1.130	1.216

99. $9x^5 + 4x^3 - 7$

Terms: $9x^5, 4x^3, -7$

101. $\dfrac{1}{3 \cdot 4^{-1}} = \dfrac{4}{3} \neq 3 \cdot 4$ False

103. $\sqrt{18x} - \sqrt{2x} = 3\sqrt{2x} - \sqrt{2x} = 2\sqrt{2x}$

105. $\dfrac{70}{\sqrt{7x}} = \dfrac{70}{\sqrt{7x}} \cdot \dfrac{\sqrt{7x}}{\sqrt{7x}} = \dfrac{70\sqrt{7x}}{7x} = \dfrac{10\sqrt{7x}}{x}$

107. $\sqrt[6]{t^2} = t^{2/6} = |t|^{1/3} = \sqrt[3]{|t|}$

Section 1.2   Lines in the Plane and Slope

You should know the following important facts about lines.

- The graph of $y = mx + b$ is a straight line. It is called a linear equation.
- The slope of the line through (x_1, y_1) and (x_2, y_2) is

$$m = \frac{y_2 - y_1}{x_2 - x_1}.$$

- (a) If $m > 0$, the line rises from left to right.

  (b) If $m = 0$, the line is horizontal.

  (c) If $m < 0$, the line falls from left to right.

  (d) If m is undefined, the line is vertical.

- Equations of Lines

  (a) Slope-Intercept: $y = mx + b$

  (b) Point-Slope: $y - y_1 = m(x - x_1)$

  (c) Two-Point: $y - y_1 = \dfrac{y_2 - y_1}{x_2 - x_1}(x - x_1)$

  (d) General: $Ax + By + C = 0$

  (e) Vertical: $x = a$

  (f) Horizontal: $y = b$

- Given two distinct nonvertical lines

$$L_1: y = m_1 x + b_1 \quad \text{and} \quad L_2: y = m_2 x + b_2$$

  (a) L_1 is parallel to L_2 if and only if $m_1 = m_2$ and $b_1 \neq b_2$.

  (b) L_1 is perpendicular to L_2 if and only if $m_1 = -1/m_2$.

Solutions to Odd-Numbered Exercises

1. (a) $m = \frac{2}{3}$. Since the slope is positive, the line rises. Matches L_2.

   (b) m is undefined. The line is vertical. Matches L_3.

   (c) $m = -2$. The line falls. Matches L_1.

5. Slope $= \dfrac{\text{rise}}{\text{run}} = \dfrac{8}{5}$

7. Slope $= \dfrac{\text{rise}}{\text{run}} = \dfrac{0}{1} = 0$

3.

9. Slope $= \dfrac{\text{rise}}{\text{run}} = \dfrac{-8}{2} = -4$

11.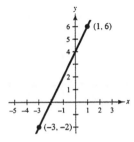

$$\text{slope} = \frac{6 + 2}{1 + 3} = 2$$

13.

Slope is undefined.

15.

$$\text{slope} = \frac{2 + 2}{1 + 2} = \frac{4}{3}$$

17. Since $m = 0$, y does not change. Three points are $(0, 1)$, $(3, 1)$, and $(-1, 1)$.

19. Since $m = 1$, y increases by 1 for every one unit increase in x. Three points are $(6, -5)$, $(7, -4)$, and $(8, -3)$.

21. Since m is undefined, x does not change. Three points are $(-8, 0)$, $(-8, 2)$, and $(-8, 3)$.

23. Slope of L_1: $m = \dfrac{9 + 1}{5 - 0} = 2$

Slope of L_2: $m = \dfrac{1 - 3}{4 - 0} = -\dfrac{1}{2}$

L_1 and L_2 are perpendicular.

25. Slope of L_1: $m = \dfrac{0 - 6}{-6 - 3} = \dfrac{2}{3}$

Slope of L_2: $m = \dfrac{\frac{7}{3} + 1}{5 - 0} = \dfrac{2}{3}$

L_1 and L_2 are parallel.

27. Yes, any pair of points on a line can be used to calculate the slope of the line. The rate of change remains the same on a line.

29. (a) $m = 135$. The sales are increasing 135 units per year.

(b) $m = 0$. There is no change in sales.

(c) $m = -40$. The sales are decreasing 40 units per year.

31. (a) The slope is negative and steep in 1989 to 1990.

(b) The slope is positive and steep in 1988 to 1989.

33. Slope $= \dfrac{\text{rise}}{\text{run}}$

$-\dfrac{12}{100} = -\dfrac{2000}{y}$

$-12y = -200{,}000$

$y = 16{,}666\frac{2}{3}$ feet ≈ 3.16 miles

35. $5x - y + 3 = 0$

$y = 5x + 3$

Slope: $m = 5$

y-intercept: $(0, 3)$

37. $5x - 2 = 0$

$x = \frac{2}{5}$

Slope: undefined

No y-intercept

39. $7x + 6y - 30 = 0$

$y = -\frac{7}{6}x + 5$

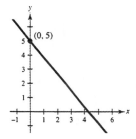

Slope: $m = -\frac{7}{6}$

y-intercept: $(0, 5)$

41. $y + 1 = \dfrac{5 + 1}{-5 - 5}(x - 5)$

$y = -\dfrac{3}{5}(x - 5) - 1$

$y = -\dfrac{3}{5}x + 2 \implies 3x + 5y - 10 = 0$

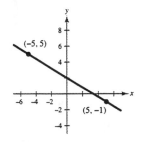

43. $y - \dfrac{1}{2} = \dfrac{\frac{5}{4} - \frac{1}{2}}{\frac{1}{2} - 2}(x - 2)$

$y = -\dfrac{1}{2}(x - 2) + \dfrac{1}{2}$

$y = -\dfrac{1}{2}x + \dfrac{3}{2} \implies x + 2y - 3 = 0$

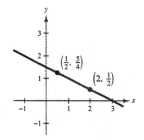

45. Since both points have $x = -8$, the slope is undefined.

$x = -8 \implies x + 8 = 0$

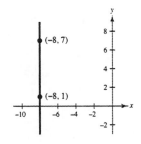

47. $y - 0.6 = \dfrac{-0.6 - 0.6}{-2 - 1}(x - 1)$

$y = 0.4(x - 1) + 0.6$

$y = 0.4x + 0.2 \implies 2x - 5y + 1 = 0$

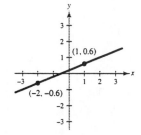

49. $y + 2 = 3(x - 0)$

$y = 3x - 2 \implies 3x - y - 2 = 0$

51. $y - 6 = -2(x + 3)$

$y = -2x \implies 2x + y = 0$

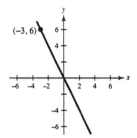

53. $y - 0 = -\frac{1}{3}(x - 4)$

$y = -\frac{1}{3}x + \frac{4}{3} \implies x + 3y - 4 = 0$

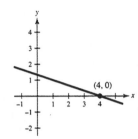

55. $x = 6$

$x - 6 = 0$

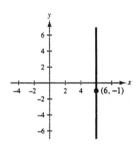

57. $y - \frac{5}{2} = \frac{4}{3}(x - 4)$

$y = \frac{4}{3}x - \frac{17}{6} \implies 8x - 6y - 17 = 0$

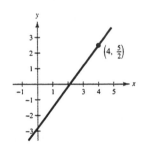

59. $\dfrac{x}{2} + \dfrac{y}{3} = 1$

$3x + 2y - 6 = 0$

61. $\dfrac{x}{-1/6} + \dfrac{y}{-2/3} = 1$

$6x + \dfrac{3}{2}y = -1$

$12x + 3y + 2 = 0$

63. $\dfrac{x}{a} + \dfrac{y}{a} = 1, \; a \neq 0$

$x + y = a$

$1 + 2 = a$

$3 = a$

$x + y = 3$

$x + y - 3 = 0$

65. $4x - 2y = 3$

$$y = 2x - \frac{3}{2}$$

slope: $m = 2$

(a) $y - 1 = 2(x - 2)$

$$y = 2x - 3 \implies 2x - y - 3 = 0$$

(b) $y - 1 = -\frac{1}{2}(x - 2)$

$$y = -\frac{1}{2}x + 2 \implies x + 2y - 4 = 0$$

67. $3x + 4y = 7$

$$y = -\frac{3}{4}x + \frac{7}{4}$$

slope: $m = -\frac{3}{4}$

(a) $y - 4 = -\frac{3}{4}(x + 6)$

$$y = -\frac{3}{4}x - \frac{1}{2} \implies 3x + 4y + 2 = 0$$

(b) $y - 4 = \frac{4}{3}(x + 6)$

$$y = \frac{4}{3}x + 12 \implies 4x - 3y + 36 = 0$$

69. $y = -3$

slope: $m = 0$

(a) $y = 0$

(b) $x = -1 \implies x + 1 = 0$

71. $L_1: y = \frac{1}{3}x - 2$

$L_2: y = \frac{1}{3}x + 3$

The lines are parallel.

73. $L_1: y = \frac{1}{2}x - 3$

$L_2: y = -\frac{1}{2}x + 1$

Neither parallel nor perpendicular

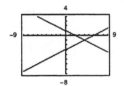

75. $L_1: y = \frac{2}{3}x - 3$

$L_2: y = -\frac{3}{2}x + 2$

The lines are perpendicular.

77. $y = 0.5x - 3$

The second setting shows the x- and y-intercepts more clearly.

79. (a) $y = 2x$ (b) $y = -2x$ (c) $y = \frac{1}{2}x$

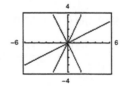

(b) and (c) are perpendicular.

81. (a) $y = -\frac{1}{2}x$ (b) $y = -\frac{1}{2}x + 3$ (c) $y = 2x - 4$

(a) and (b) are parallel.

(c) is perpendicular to (a) and (b).

83. $(6, 2540), m = 125$

$$V - 2540 = 125(t - 6)$$

$$V - 2540 = 125t - 750$$

$$V = 125t + 1790$$

85. The slope is $m = -20$. This represents the decrease in the amount of the loan each week. Matches graph (b).

87. The slope is $m = 0.32$. This represents the increase in travel cost for each mile driven. Matches graph (a).

89. Set the distance between $(4, -1)$ and (x, y) equal to the distance between $(-2, 3)$ and (x, y).

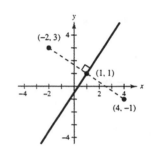

$$\sqrt{(x - 4)^2 + [y - (-1)]^2} = \sqrt{[x - (-2)]^2 + (y - 3)^2}$$

$$(x - 4)^2 + (y + 1)^2 = (x + 2)^2 + (y - 3)^2$$

$$x^2 - 8x + 16 + y^2 + 2y + 1 = x^2 + 4x + 4 + y^2 - 6y + 9$$

$$-8x + 2y + 17 = 4x - 6y + 13$$

$$0 = 12x - 8y - 4$$

$$0 = 4(3x - 2y - 1)$$

$$0 = 3x - 2y - 1$$

This line is the perpendicular bisector of the line segment connecting $(4, -1)$ and $(-2, 3)$.

91. Using the points $(0, 32)$ and $(100, 212)$, we have

$$m = \frac{212 - 32}{100 - 0} = \frac{180}{100} = \frac{9}{5}$$

$$F - 32 = \frac{9}{5}(C - 0)$$

$$F = \frac{9}{5}C + 32.$$

93. Using the points $(1995, 28{,}500)$ and $(1997, 32{,}900)$, we have

$$m = \frac{32{,}900 - 28{,}500}{1997 - 1995} = \frac{4400}{2} = 2200$$

$$S - 28{,}500 = 2200(t - 1995)$$

$$S = 2200t - 4{,}360{,}500$$

When $t = 2000$ we have $S = 2200(2000) - 4{,}360{,}500$ or $\$39{,}500$.

95. Using the points $(0, 875)$ and $(5, 0)$, where the first coordinate represents the year t and the second coordinate represents the value V, we have

$$m = \frac{0 - 875}{5 - 0} = -175$$

$$V = -175t + 875, \ 0 \le t \le 5.$$

97. Sale price = List price − 15% of the list price

$$S = L - 0.15L$$

$$S = 0.85L$$

99. (a) $C = 36,500 + 5.25t + 11.50t$

$= 16.75t + 36,500$

(b) $R = 27t$

(c) $P = R - C$

$= 27t - (16.75t + 36,500)$

$= 10.25t - 36,500$

(d) $\quad 0 = 10.25t - 36,500$

$36,500 = 10.25t$

$t \approx 3561$ hours

101. (a)

(b) $y = 2(15 + 2x) + 2(10 + 2x)$

$= 8x + 50$

(c) 150

0 ⌐ 0 ⌐ 10

(d) Since $m = 8$, each 1 meter increase in x will increase y by 8 meters.

103. $C = 120 + 0.26x$

105. Two approximate points on this line are $(6, 710)$ and $(10, 1075)$.

$$m = \frac{1075 - 710}{10 - 6} \approx 91$$

$$y - 710 = 91(x - 6)$$

$$y = 91x + 164$$

This answer may vary depending on the points used.

107. $y = 8 - 3x$ is a linear equation with slope $m = -3$. Matches graph (d).

109. $y = \frac{1}{2}x^2 + 2x + 1$ is a quadratic equation. Its graph is a parabola.
Matches graph (a).

Section 1.3   Functions

■ Given a set or an equation, you should be able to determine if it represents a function.

■ Given a function, you should be able to do the following.

(a) Find the domain.

(b) Evaluate it at specific values.

Solutions to Odd-Numbered Exercises

1. Yes, it does represent a function. Each domain value is matched with only one range value.

3. No, it does not represent a function. The domain values are each matched with three range values.

5. Yes, it does represent a function. Each input value is matched with only one output value.

7. No, it does not represent a function. The input values of 10 and 7 are each matched with two output values.

9. (a) Each element of A is matched with exactly one element of B, so it does represent a function.

    (b) The element 1 in A is matched with two elements, -2 and 1 of B, so it does not represent a function.

    (c) Each element of A is matched with exactly one element of B, so it does represent a function.

    (d) The element 2 in A is not matched with an element of B, so it does not represent a function.

11. Each is a function. For each year there corresponds one and only one circulation.

13. $x^2 + y^2 = 4 \implies y = \pm\sqrt{4 - x^2}$

    No, y *is not* a function of x.

15. $x^2 + y = 4 \implies y = 4 - x^2$

    Yes, y *is* a function of x.

17. $2x + 3y = 4 \implies y = \frac{1}{3}(4 - 2x)$

    Yes, y *is* a function of x.

19. $y^2 = x^2 - 1 \implies y = \pm\sqrt{x^2 - 1}$

    No, y *is not* a function of x.

21. $y = |4 - x|$

    Yes, y is a function of x.

23. $f(s) = \dfrac{1}{s + 1}$

    (a) $f(4) = \dfrac{1}{(4) + 1} = \dfrac{1}{5}$

    (b) $f(0) = \dfrac{1}{(0) + 1} = 1$

    (c) $f(4x) = \dfrac{1}{(4x) + 1} = \dfrac{1}{4x + 1}$

    (d) $f(x + c) = \dfrac{1}{(x + c) + 1} = \dfrac{1}{x + c + 1}$

25. $f(x) = 2x - 3$

    (a) $f(1) = 2(1) - 3 = -1$

    (b) $f(-3) = 2(-3) - 3 = -9$

    (c) $f(x - 1) = 2(x - 1) - 3 = 2x - 5$

27. $h(t) = t^2 - 2t$

    (a) $h(2) = 2^2 - 2(2) = 0$

    (b) $h(1.5) = (1.5)^2 - 2(1.5) = -0.75$

    (c) $h(x + 2) = (x + 2)^2 - 2(x + 2) = x^2 + 2x$

29. $f(y) = 3 - \sqrt{y}$

    (a) $f(4) = 3 - \sqrt{4} = 1$

    (b) $f(0.25) = 3 - \sqrt{0.25} = 2.5$

    (c) $f(4x^2) = 3 - \sqrt{4x^2} = 3 - 2|x|$

31. $q(x) = \dfrac{1}{x^2 - 9}$

    (a) $q(0) = \dfrac{1}{0^2 - 9} = -\dfrac{1}{9}$

    (b) $q(3) = \dfrac{1}{3^2 - 9}$ is undefined.

    (c) $q(y + 3) = \dfrac{1}{(y + 3)^2 - 9} = \dfrac{1}{y^2 + 6y}$

33. $f(x) = \dfrac{|x|}{x}$

    (a) $f(2) = \dfrac{|2|}{2} = 1$

    (b) $f(-2) = \dfrac{|-2|}{-2} = -1$

    (c) $f(x - 1) = \dfrac{|x - 1|}{x - 1}$

35. $f(x) = \begin{cases} 2x + 1, & x < 0 \\ 2x + 2, & x \geq 0 \end{cases}$

    (a) $f(-1) = 2(-1) + 1 = -1$

    (b) $f(0) = 2(0) + 2 = 2$

    (c) $f(2) = 2(2) + 2 = 6$

37. $f(x) = x^2 - 3$

x	-2	-1	0	1	2
$f(x)$	1	-2	-3	-2	1

39. $h(t) = \frac{1}{2}|t + 3|$

t	-5	-4	-3	-2	-1
$h(t)$	1	$\frac{1}{2}$	0	$\frac{1}{2}$	1

41. $f(x) = \begin{cases} -\frac{1}{2}x + 4, & x \leq 0 \\ (x - 2)^2, & x > 0 \end{cases}$

x	-2	-1	0	1	2
$f(x)$	5	$\frac{9}{2}$	4	1	0

43. $15 - 3x = 0$

        $3x = 15$

         $x = 5$

45. $x^2 - 9 = 0$

         $x^2 = 9$

        $x = \pm 3$

47. $f(x) = g(x)$

                $x^2 = x + 2$

        $x^2 - x - 2 = 0$

    $(x + 1)(x - 2) = 0$

    $x = -1$ or $x = 2$

49. $f(x) = g(x)$

      $\sqrt{3x} + 1 = x + 1$

         $\sqrt{3x} = x$

           $3x = x^2$

            $0 = x^2 - 3x$

            $0 = x(x - 3)$

       $x = 0$ or $x = 3$

51. $f(x) = 5x^2 + 2x - 1$

    Since $f(x)$ is a polynomial, the domain is all real numbers x.

53. $h(t) = \dfrac{4}{t}$

    Domain: All real numbers except $t = 0$

55. $g(y) = \sqrt{y - 10}$

Domain: $y - 10 \geq 0$

$\quad\quad\quad\quad y \geq 10$

57. $f(x) = \sqrt[4]{1 - x^2}$

Domain: $1 - x^2 \geq 0$

$\quad\quad\quad -x^2 \geq -1$

$\quad\quad\quad\quad x^2 \leq 1$

$\quad\quad\quad x^2 - 1 \leq 0$

$\quad\quad -1 \leq x \leq 1$ (See Section 1.8.)

59. $g(x) = \dfrac{1}{x} - \dfrac{1}{x + 2}$

Domain: All real numbers except
$x = 0, \; x = -2$

61. $f(x) = x^2$

$\{(-2, 4), (-1, 1), (0, 0), (1, 1), (2, 4)\}$

63. $f(x) = \sqrt{x + 2}$

$\left\{(-2, 0), (-1, 1), \left(0, \sqrt{2}\right), \left(1, \sqrt{3}\right), (2, 2)\right\}$

65. The domain is the set of inputs of the function and the range is the set of corresponding outputs.

67. By plotting the points, we have a parabola, so $g(x) = cx^2$. Since $(-4, -32)$ is on the graph, we have $-32 = c(-4)^2 \implies c = -2$. Thus, $g(x) = -2x^2$.

69. Since the function is undefined at 0, we have $r(x) = c/x$. Since $(-8, -4)$ is on the graph, we have $-4 = c/-8 \implies c = 32$. Thus, $r(x) = 32/x$.

71.
$$f(x) = x^2 - x + 1$$
$$f(2 + h) = (2 + h)^2 - (2 + h) + 1$$
$$= 4 + 4h + h^2 - 2 - h + 1$$
$$= h^2 + 3h + 3$$
$$f(2) = (2)^2 - 2 + 1 = 3$$
$$f(2 + h) - f(2) = h^2 + 3h$$
$$\cdot \frac{f(2 + h) - f(2)}{h} = h + 3, \; h \neq 0$$

73. $f(x) = x^3$
$$f(x + c) = (x + c)^3 = x^3 + 3x^2c + 3xc^2 + c^3$$
$$\frac{f(x + c) - f(x)}{c} = \frac{(x^3 + 3x^2c + 3xc^2 + c^3) - x^3}{c}$$
$$= \frac{c(3x^2 + 3xc + c^2)}{c}$$
$$= 3x^2 + 3xc + c^2, \; c \neq 0$$

75. $g(x) = 3x - 1$

$$\frac{g(x) - g(3)}{x - 3} = \frac{(3x - 1) - 8}{x - 3} = \frac{3x - 9}{x - 3} = \frac{3(x - 3)}{x - 3} = 3, \; x \neq 3$$

77. $A = \pi r^2, \; C = 2\pi r$

$$r = \frac{C}{2\pi}$$

$$A = \pi \left(\frac{C}{2\pi}\right)^2 = \frac{C^2}{4\pi}$$

79. (a)

Height, x	Width	Volume, V
1	$24 - 2(1)$	$1[24 - 2(1)]^2 = 484$
2	$24 - 2(2)$	$2[24 - 2(2)]^2 = 800$
3	$24 - 2(3)$	$3[24 - 2(3)]^2 = 972$
4	$24 - 2(4)$	$4[24 - 2(4)]^2 = 1024$
5	$24 - 2(5)$	$5[24 - 2(5)]^2 = 980$
6	$24 - 2(6)$	$6[24 - 2(6)]^2 = 864$

The volume is maximum when $x = 4$.

(b)

(c) $V = x(24 - 2x)^2$

Domain: $0 < x < 12$

V is a function of x.

81. $A = \dfrac{1}{2}bh = \dfrac{1}{2}xy$

Since $(0, y)$, $(2, 1)$, and $(x, 0)$ all lie on the same line, the slopes between any pair are equal.

$$\frac{1 - y}{2 - 0} = \frac{0 - 1}{x - 2}$$

$$\frac{1 - y}{2} = \frac{-1}{x - 2}$$

$$y = \frac{2}{x - 2} + 1$$

$$y = \frac{x}{x - 2}$$

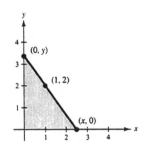

Therefore,

$$A = \frac{1}{2}x\left(\frac{x}{x - 2}\right) = \frac{x^2}{2(x - 2)}.$$

The domain of A includes x-values such that $x^2/[2(x - 2)] > 0$. Using methods of Section 1.8 we find that the domain is $x > 2$.

83. $V = l \cdot w \cdot h = x \cdot y \cdot x = x^2y$ where $4x + y = 108$.

Thus, $y = 108 - 4x$ and $V = x^2(108 - 4x) = 108x^2 - 4x^3$ where $0 < x < 27$.

85. (a) Cost = variable costs + fixed costs

$$C = 12.30x + 98,000$$

(b) Revenue = price per unit × number of units

$$R = 17.98x$$

(c) Profit = Revenue − Cost

$$P = 17.98x − (12.30x + 98,000)$$

$$P = 5.68x − 98,000$$

87. (a) $R = n(\text{rate}) = n[8.00 − 0.05(n − 80)]$, $n \geq 80$

$$R = 12.00n − 0.05n^2 = 12n − \frac{n^2}{20} = \frac{240n − n^2}{20}, \quad n \geq 80$$

(b)

n	90	100	110	120	130	140	150
$R(n)$	\$675	\$700	\$715	\$720	\$715	\$700	\$675

The revenue is maximum when 120 people take the trip.

89. (a)

d h

3000 ft

(b) $(3000)^2 + h^2 = d^2$

$$h = \sqrt{d^2 − (3000)^2}$$

Domain: $[3000, \infty)$

(since both $d \geq 0$ and $d^2 − (3000)^2 \geq 0$)

91. $\dfrac{t}{3} + \dfrac{t}{5} = 1$

$$15\left(\frac{t}{3} + \frac{t}{5}\right) = 15(1)$$

$$5t + 3t = 15$$

$$8t = 15$$

$$t = \frac{15}{8}$$

93. $\dfrac{3}{x(x + 1)} − \dfrac{4}{x} = \dfrac{1}{x + 1}$

$$x(x + 1)\left[\frac{3}{x(x + 1)} − \frac{4}{x}\right] = x(x + 1)\left(\frac{1}{x + 1}\right)$$

$$3 − 4(x + 1) = x$$

$$3 − 4x − 4 = x$$

$$−1 = 5x$$

$$−\frac{1}{5} = x$$

Section 1.4   Analyzing Graphs of Functions

■ You should be able to determine the domain and range of a function from its graph.

■ You should be able to use the vertical line test for functions.

■ You should be able to determine when a function is constant, increasing, or decreasing.

■ You should know that f is

(a) odd if $f(-x) = -f(x)$.

(b) even if $f(-x) = f(x)$.

Solutions to Odd-Numbered Exercises

1. $f(x) = 1 - x^2$

Domain: All real numbers

Range: $(-\infty, 1]$

3. $f(x) = \sqrt{x^2 - 1}$

Domain: $(-\infty, -1] \cup [1, \infty)$

Range: $[0, \infty)$

5. $h(x) = \sqrt{16 - x^2}$

Domain: $[-4, 4]$

Range: $[0, 4]$

7. $y = \frac{1}{2}x^2$

A vertical line intersects the graph just once, so y is a function of x.

9. $x - y^2 = 1 \implies y = \pm\sqrt{x - 1}$

y is not a function of x.

11. $x^2 = 2xy - 1$

A vertical line intersects the graph just once, so y is a function of x.

13. Yes, the graph in Exercise 9 does represent x as a function of y. For each y-value there corresponds one and only one x-value.

15. $f(x) = -0.2x^2 + 3x + 32$

The second setting shows the most complete graph.

17. $f(x) = 4x^3 - x^4$

The first setting shows the most complete graph.

19. $f(x) = \frac{3}{2}x$

(a) f is increasing on $(-\infty, \infty)$.

(b) Since $f(-x) = -f(x)$, f is odd.

21. $f(x) = x^3 - 3x^2 + 2$

(a) f is increasing on $(-\infty, 0)$ and $(2, \infty)$.

f is decreasing on $(0, 2)$.

(b) $f(-x) \neq -f(x)$

$f(-x) \neq f(x)$

f is neither odd nor even.

23. $f(x) = 3x^4 - 6x^2$

(a)

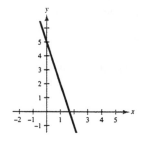

(b) Increasing on $(-1, 0)$ and $(1, \infty)$

Decreasing on $(-\infty, -1)$ and $(0, 1)$

(c) Since $f(-x) = f(x)$, f is even.

25. $f(x) = x\sqrt{x + 3}$

(a)

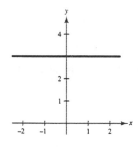

(b) Increasing on $(-2, \infty)$

Decreasing on $(-3, -2)$

(c) $f(-x) \neq -f(x)$

$f(-x) \neq f(x)$

f is neither odd nor even.

27. $f(-x) = (-x)^6 - 2(-x)^2 + 3$

$= x^6 - 2x^2 + 3$

$= f(x)$

f is even.

29. $g(-x) = (-x)^3 - 5(-x)$

$= -x^3 + 5x$

$= -g(x)$

g is odd.

31. $f(-t) = (-t)^2 + 2(-t) - 3$

$= t^2 - 2t - 3$

$\neq f(t) \neq -f(t)$

f is neither even nor odd.

33. $\left(-\frac{3}{2}, 4\right)$

(a) If f is even, another point is $\left(\frac{3}{2}, 4\right)$.

(b) If f is odd, another point is $\left(\frac{3}{2}, -4\right)$.

35. $f(x) = 3$, even

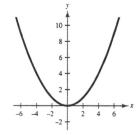

37. $f(x) = 5 - 3x$, neither even nor odd

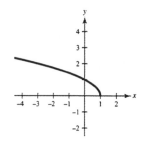

39. $g(s) = \dfrac{s^2}{4}$, even

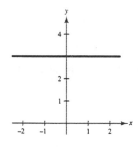

41. $f(x) = \sqrt{1 - x}$, neither even nor odd

43. $g(t) = \sqrt[3]{t-1}$, neither even nor odd

45. $f(x) = \begin{cases} x+3, & x \le 0 \\ 3, & 0 < x \le 2 \\ 2x-1, & x > 2 \end{cases}$

Neither even nor odd

47. $f(x) = 4 - x$

$f(x) \ge 0$ on $(-\infty, 4]$.

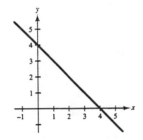

49. $f(x) = x^2 - 9$

$f(x) \ge 0$ on $(-\infty, -3]$ and $[3, \infty)$.

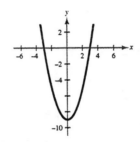

51. $f(x) = 1 - x^4$

$f(x) \ge 0$ on $[-1, 1]$.

53. $f(x) = x^2 + 1$

$f(x) \ge 0$ on $(-\infty, \infty)$.

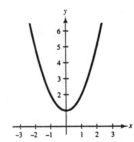

55. $f(x) = -5$, $f(x) < 0$ for all x.

57. $f(x) = \begin{cases} 2x + 3, & x < 0 \\ 3 - x, & x \geq 0 \end{cases}$

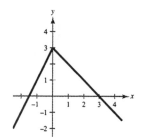

59. $f(x) = \begin{cases} x^2 + 5, & x \leq 1 \\ -x^2 + 4x + 3, & x > 1 \end{cases}$

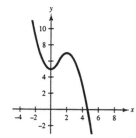

61. $f(x) = |x + 3|$

Domain: All real numbers or $(-\infty, \infty)$

Range: $[0, \infty)$

63. $s(x) = 2\left(\frac{1}{4}x - \left[\!\left[\frac{1}{4}x\right]\!\right]\right)$

Domain: $(-\infty, \infty)$

Range: $[0, 2)$

Sawtooth pattern

65. (a) $y = x$

(b) $y = x^2$

(c) $y = x^3$

(d) $y = x^4$

(e) $y = x^5$

(f) $y = x^6$

All the graphs pass through the origin. The graphs of the odd powers of x are symmetric to the origin and the graphs of the even powers are symmetric to the y-axis. As the powers increase, the graphs become narrower in the interval $-1 < x < 1$.

67. (a) $C_2(t) = 0.65 - 0.4\left[\!\left[-(t - 1)\right]\!\right]$ is the appropriate model since the cost does not increase until after the next minute of conversation has started.

(b)

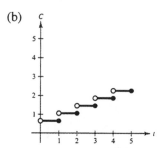

$C = 0.65 + 0.40(18) = \$7.85$

69. $P = R - C = xp - C = x(100 - 0.0001x) - (350,000 + 30x)$

$$= -0.0001x^2 + 70x - 350,000, \ 0 \le x$$

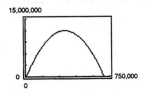

This function is maximized when $x = 350,000$ units.

71. $h = \text{top} - \text{bottom}$

$$= (-x^2 + 4x - 1) - 2$$

$$= -x^2 + 4x - 3$$

73. $h = \text{top} - \text{bottom}$

$$= (4x - x^2) - 2x$$

$$= 2x - x^2$$

75. $L = \text{right} - \text{left}$

$$= \tfrac{1}{2}y^2 - 0$$

$$= \tfrac{1}{2}y^2$$

77. $L = \text{right} - \text{left}$

$$= 4 - y^2$$

79. $y = -87.49 + 16.28t - 4.82t^2 - 1.20t^3$

(a) Domain: $-4 \le t \le 3$

(b)

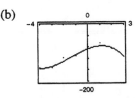

(c) Most accurate in 1986

Least accurate in 1990

(d) The balance would continue to decrease.

81. (a) For average salaries of college professors, a scale of \$10,000 would be appropriate.

(b) For the population of the United States, use a scale of 50,000,000.

(c) For the percent of the civilian workforce that is unemployed, use a scale of 1%.

83. $f(x) = a_{2n+1}x^{2n+1} + a_{2n-1}x^{2n-1} + \cdots + a_3x^3 + a_1x$

$f(-x) = a_{2n+1}(-x)^{2n+1} + a_{2n-1}(-x)^{2n-1} + \cdots + a_3(-x)^3 + a_1(-x)$

$$= -a_{2n+1}x^{2n+1} - a_{2n-1}x^{2n-1} - \cdots - a_3x^3 - a_1x = -f(x)$$

Therefore, $f(x)$ is odd.

85. $x^2 - 10x = 0$

$x(x - 10) = 0$

$x = 0 \quad \text{or} \quad x = 10$

87. $x^3 + x = 0$

$x(x^2 + 1) = 0$

$x = 0 \quad \text{or} \quad x^2 + 1 = 0$

$$x^2 = -1$$

$$x = \pm\sqrt{-1} = \pm i$$

Section 1.5   Translations and Combinations

■   You should know the basic types of transformations.

Let $y = f(x)$ and let c be a positive real number.

1. $h(x) = f(x) + c$ Vertical shift c units upward
2. $h(x) = f(x) - c$ Vertical shift c units downward
3. $h(x) = f(x - c)$ Horizontal shift c units to the right
4. $h(x) = f(x + c)$ Horizontal shift c units to the left
5. $h(x) = -f(x)$ Reflection in the x-axis
6. $h(x) = f(-x)$ Reflection in the y-axis
7. $h(x) = cf(x), c > 1$ Vertical stretch
8. $h(x) = cf(x), 0 < c < 1$ Vertical shrink

■   Given two functions, f and g, you should be able to form the following functions (if defined):

1. Sum: $(f + g)(x) = f(x) + g(x)$
2. Difference: $(f - g)(x) = f(x) - g(x)$
3. Product: $(fg)(x) = f(x)g(x)$
4. Quotient: $(f/g)(x) = f(x)/g(x), g(x) \neq 0$
5. Composition of f with g: $(f \circ g)(x) = f(g(x))$
6. Composition of g with f: $(g \circ f)(x) = g(f(x))$

Solutions to Odd-Numbered Exercises

1. (a) $f(x) = x^3 + c$ (b) $f(x) = (x - c)^3$

3. (a) $f(x) = |x + c|$ (b) $f(x) = |x - c|$ (c) $f(x) = |x + 4| + c$

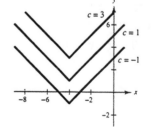

5. (a) $y = f(x) + 2$

(b) $y = -f(x)$

(c) $y = f(x - 2)$

(d) $y = f(x + 3)$

(e) $y = f(2x)$

(f) $y = f(-x)$

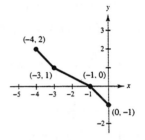

7. (a) Vertical shift one unit downward

$$y = x^2 - 1$$

(b) Vertical shift one unit upward, horizontal shift one unit to the left, and a reflection in the x-axis

$$y = 1 - (x + 1)^2$$

9. Horizontal shift two units to the right of $y = x^3$

$$y = (x - 2)^3$$

11. Reflection in the x-axis of $y = x^2$

$$y = -x^2$$

13. Reflection in the x-axis and a vertical shift one unit upward of $y = \sqrt{x}$

$$y = 1 - \sqrt{x}$$

15.

x	0	1	2	3
$f(x)$	2	3	1	2
$g(x)$	-1	0	$\frac{1}{2}$	0
$h(x) = f(x) + g(x)$	1	3	$\frac{3}{2}$	2

17.

x	-2	-1	0	1	2	3
$f(x)$	2	1	0	1	2	3
$g(x)$	4	3	2	1	0	1
$h(x) = f(x) + g(x)$	6	4	2	2	2	4

19. $f(x) = x + 1, g(x) = x - 1$

$(f + g)(x) = f(x) + g(x) = (x + 1) + (x - 1) = 2x$

$(f - g)(x) = f(x) - g(x) = (x + 1) - (x - 1) = 2$

$(fg)(x) = f(x) \cdot g(x) = (x + 1)(x - 1) = x^2 - 1$

$\left(\dfrac{f}{g}\right)(x) = \dfrac{f(x)}{g(x)} = \dfrac{x + 1}{x - 1}, \ x \neq 1$

21. $f(x) = x^2, g(x) = 1 - x$

$(f + g)(x) = f(x) + g(x) = x^2 + (1 - x) = x^2 - x + 1$

$(f - g)(x) = f(x) - g(x) = x^2 - (1 - x) = x^2 + x - 1$

$(fg)(x) = f(x) \cdot g(x) = x^2(1 - x) = x^2 - x^3$

$\left(\dfrac{f}{g}\right)(x) = \dfrac{f(x)}{g(x)} = \dfrac{x^2}{1 - x}, x \neq 1$

23. $f(x) = x^2 + 5, g(x) = \sqrt{1 - x}$

$(f + g)(x) = f(x) + g(x) = (x^2 + 5) + \sqrt{1 - x}$

$(f - g)(x) = f(x) - g(x) = (x^2 + 5) - \sqrt{1 - x}$

$(fg)(x) = f(x) \cdot g(x) = (x^2 + 5)\sqrt{1 - x}$

$\left(\dfrac{f}{g}\right)(x) = \dfrac{f(x)}{g(x)} = \dfrac{x^2 + 5}{\sqrt{1 - x}}, \ x < 1$

25. $f(x) = \dfrac{1}{x}, g(x) = \dfrac{1}{x^2}$

$(f + g)(x) = f(x) + g(x) = \dfrac{1}{x} + \dfrac{1}{x^2} = \dfrac{x + 1}{x^2}$

$(f - g)(x) = f(x) - g(x) = \dfrac{1}{x} - \dfrac{1}{x^2} = \dfrac{x - 1}{x^2}$

$(fg)(x) = f(x) \cdot g(x) = \dfrac{1}{x}\left(\dfrac{1}{x^2}\right) = \dfrac{1}{x^3}$

$\left(\dfrac{f}{g}\right)(x) = \dfrac{f(x)}{g(x)} = \dfrac{1/x}{1/x^2} = \dfrac{x^2}{x} = x, \ x \neq 0$

27. $(f + g)(3) = f(3) + g(3) = (3^2 + 1) + (3 - 4) = 9$

29. $(f - g)(0) = f(0) - g(0) = [0^2 + 1] - (0 - 4) = 5$

31. $(f - g)(2t) = f(2t) - g(2t) = [(2t)^2 + 1] - (2t - 4) = 4t^2 - 2t + 5$

33. $(fg)(4) = f(4)g(4) = (4^2 + 1)(4 - 4) = 0$

35. $\left(\dfrac{f}{g}\right)(5) = \dfrac{f(5)}{g(5)} = \dfrac{5^2 + 1}{5 - 4} = 26$

37. $\left(\dfrac{f}{g}\right)(-1) - g(3) = \dfrac{f(-1)}{g(-1)} - g(3)$

$$= \dfrac{(-1)^2 + 1}{-1 - 4} - (3 - 4)$$

$$= -\dfrac{2}{5} + 1 = \dfrac{3}{5}$$

39. $f(x) = \frac{1}{2}x, g(x) = x - 1, (f + g)(x) = \frac{3}{2}x - 1$

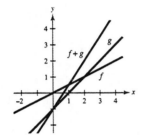

41. $f(x) = x^2, g(x) = -2x, (f + g)(x) = x^2 - 2x$

43. $f(x) = 3x, g(x) = -\dfrac{x^3}{10}, (f + g)(x) = 3x - \dfrac{x^3}{10}$

For $0 \le x \le 2$, $f(x)$ contributes most to the magnitude.
For $x > 6$, $g(x)$ contributes most to the magnitude.

45. $T(x) = R(x) + B(x) = \frac{3}{4}x + \frac{1}{15}x^2$

47.

49. (a) T is a function of t since for each time t there corresponds one and only one temperature T.

(b) $T(4) = 60°$
   $T(15) = 72°$

(c) $H(t) = T(t - 1)$; All the temperature changes would be one hour later.

(d) $H(t) = T(t) - 1$; The temperature would be decreased by one degree.

51. $f(x) = x^2, g(x) = x - 1$

    (a) $(f \circ g)(x) = f(g(x)) = f(x - 1) = (x - 1)^2$

    (b) $(g \circ f)(x) = g(f(x)) = g(x^2) = x^2 - 1$

    (c) $(f \circ f)(x) = f(f(x)) = f(x^2) = (x^2)^2 = x^4$

53. $f(x) = 3x + 5, g(x) = 5 - x$

    (a) $(f \circ g)(x) = f(g(x)) = f(5 - x) = 3(5 - x) + 5 = 20 - 3x$

    (b) $(g \circ f)(x) = g(f(x)) = g(3x + 5) = 5 - (3x + 5) = -3x$

    (c) $(f \circ f)(x) = f(f(x)) = f(3x + 5) = 3(3x + 5) + 5 = 9x + 20$

55. (a) $(f \circ g)(x) = f(g(x)) = f(x^2) = \sqrt{x^2 + 4}$

    (b) $(g \circ f)(x) = g(f(x)) = g(\sqrt{x + 4}) = (\sqrt{x + 4})^2 = x + 4, \; x \geq 4$

57. (a) $(f \circ g)(x) = f(g(x)) = f(3x + 1) = \frac{1}{3}(3x + 1) - 3 = x - \frac{8}{3}$

    (b) $(g \circ f)(x) = g(f(x)) = g(\frac{1}{3}x - 3) = 3(\frac{1}{3}x - 3) + 1 = x - 8$

59. (a) $(f \circ g)(x) = f(g(x)) = f(\sqrt{x}) = (x^{1/2})^{1/2} = x^{1/4} = \sqrt[4]{x}$

    (b) Since $f(x) = g(x), (g \circ f)(x) = (f \circ g)(x) = \sqrt[4]{x}$.

61. (a) $(f \circ g)(x) = f(g(x)) = f(x + 6) = |x + 6|$

    (b) $(g \circ f)(x) = g(f(x)) = g(|x|) = |x| + 6$

63. (a) $(f + g)(3) = f(3) + g(3) = 2 + 1 = 3$

    (b) $\left(\dfrac{f}{g}\right)(2) = \dfrac{f(2)}{g(2)} = \dfrac{0}{2} = 0$

65. (a) $(f \circ g)(2) = f(g(2)) = f(2) = 0$

    (b) $(g \circ f)(2) = g(f(2)) = g(0) = 4$

67. $g(x) = f(x) + 2$

Vertical shift 2 units upward

69. $g(x) = f(-x)$

Reflection in the y-axis

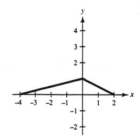

71. Let $f(x) = x^2$ and $g(x) = 2x + 1$, then $(f \circ g)(x) = h(x)$. This is not a unique solution.
For example, if $f(x) = (x + 1)^2$ and $g(x) = 2x$, then $(f \circ g)(x) = h(x)$ as well.

73. Let $f(x) = \sqrt[3]{x}$ and $g(x) = x^2 - 4$, then $(f \circ g)(x) = h(x)$.
This answer is not unique. Other possibilities may be:

$$f(x) = \sqrt[3]{x - 4} \text{ and } g(x) = x^2$$
$$\text{or } f(x) = \sqrt[3]{-x} \text{ and } g(x) = 4 - x^2$$
$$\text{or } f(x) = \sqrt[9]{x} \text{ and } g(x) = (4 - x^2)^3$$

75. Let $f(x) = 1/x$ and $g(x) = x + 2$, then $(f \circ g)(x) = h(x)$. Again, this is not a
unique solution. Other possibilities may be:

$$f(x) = \frac{1}{x + 2} \text{ and } g(x) = x$$

$$\text{or } f(x) = \frac{1}{x + 1} \text{ and } g(x) = x + 1$$

$$\text{or } f(x) = \frac{1}{x^2 + 2} \text{ and } g(x) = \sqrt{x}$$

77. (a) The domain of $f(x) = \sqrt{x}$ is $x \geq 0$.

(b) The domain of $g(x) = x^2 + 1$ is all real numbers.

(c) $(f \circ g)(x) = f(g(x)) = f(x^2 + 1) = \sqrt{x^2 + 1}$

The domain of $f \circ g$ is all real numbers.

79. (a) The domain of $f(x) = \dfrac{3}{x^2 - 1}$ is all real numbers except $x = \pm 1$.

(b) The domain of $g(x) = x + 1$ is all real numbers.

(c) $(f \circ g)(x) = f(g(x)) = f(x + 1) = \dfrac{3}{(x + 1)^2 - 1} = \dfrac{3}{x^2 + 2x} = \dfrac{3}{x(x + 2)}$

This domain of $f \circ g$ is all real numbers except $x = 0$ and $x = -2$.

81. $f(x) = 3x - 4$

$$\frac{f(x + h) - f(x)}{h} = \frac{[3(x + h) - 4] - (3x - 4)}{h}$$

$$= \frac{3x + 3h - 4 - 3x + 4}{h}$$

$$= \frac{3h}{h}$$

$$= 3$$

83. $f(x) = \dfrac{4}{x}$

$$\frac{f(x+h) - f(x)}{h} = \frac{\dfrac{4}{x+h} - \dfrac{4}{x}}{h} = \frac{\dfrac{4x - 4(x+h)}{x(x+h)}}{\dfrac{h}{1}}$$

$$= \frac{4x - 4x - 4h}{x(x+h)} \cdot \frac{1}{h}$$

$$= \frac{-4\!\!\not h}{x(x+h)} \cdot \frac{1}{\not h}$$

$$= \frac{-4}{x(x+h)}$$

85. (a) $r(x) = \dfrac{x}{2}$

(b) $A(r) = \pi r^2$

(c) $(A \circ r)(x) = A(r(x)) = A\!\left(\dfrac{x}{2}\right) = \pi\!\left(\dfrac{x}{2}\right)^2$

$(A \circ r)(x)$ represents the area of the circular base of the tank on the square foundation with side length y.

87. $(C \circ x)(t) = C(x(t))$

$$= 60(50t) + 750$$

$$= 3000t + 750$$

$(C \circ x)(t)$ represents the cost after t production hours.

89. (a) $R = p - 1200$

(b) $S = p - 0.08p = 0.92p$

(c) $(R \circ S)(p) = R(S(p)) = R(0.92p) = 0.92p - 1200$

$(S \circ R)(p) = S(R(p)) = S(p - 1200) = 0.92(p - 1200)$

$R \circ S$ represents taking a discount of 8% of the retail price and then receiving a $1200 rebate. $S \circ R$ represents taking the $1200 rebate first and then receiving an 8% discount on the difference.

(d) $(R \circ S)(18{,}400) = 0.92(18{,}400) - 1200 = \$15{,}728$

$(S \circ R)(18{,}400) = 0.92(18{,}400 - 1200) = \$15{,}824$

$R \circ S$ is a better deal. $S \circ R$ takes an 8% discount on a smaller amount.

91. Let $f(x)$ be an odd function, $g(x)$ be an even function and define $h(x) = f(x)g(x)$. Then

$$h(-x) = f(-x)g(-x)$$

$$= [-f(x)]g(x) \qquad \text{Since } f \text{ is odd and } g \text{ is even.}$$

$$= -f(x)g(x)$$

$$= -h(x)$$

Thus, h is odd.

Section 1.6   Inverse Functions

> ■ Two functions f and g are inverses of each other if $f(g(x)) = x$ for every x in the domain of g and $g(f(x)) = x$ for every x in the domain of f.
>
> ■ Be able to find the inverse of a function, if it exists.
>
> 1. Replace $f(x)$ with y.
>
> 2. Interchange x and y.
>
> 3. Solve for y. If this equation represents y as a function of x, then you have found $f^{-1}(x)$. If this equation does not represent y as a function of x, then f does not have an inverse function.
>
> ■ A function f has an inverse function if and only if no **horizontal** line crosses the graph of f at more than one point.

Solutions to Odd-Numbered Exercises

1. The inverse is a line through $(-1, 0)$. Matches graph (c).

3. The inverse is half a parabola starting at $(1, 0)$. Matches graph (a).

5. $f^{-1}(x) = \dfrac{x}{8} = \dfrac{1}{8}x$

$f(f^{-1}(x)) = f\left(\dfrac{x}{8}\right) = 8\left(\dfrac{x}{8}\right) = x$

$f^{-1}(f(x)) = f^{-1}(8x) = \dfrac{8x}{8} = x$

7. $f^{-1}(x) = x - 10$

$f(f^{-1}(x)) = f(x - 10) = (x - 10) + 10 = x$

$f^{-1}(f(x)) = f^{-1}(x + 10) = (x + 10) - 10 = x$

9. $f^{-1}(x) = x^3$

$f(f^{-1}(x)) = f(x^3) = \sqrt[3]{x^3} = x$

$f^{-1}(f(x)) = f^{-1}(\sqrt[3]{x}) = (\sqrt[3]{x})^3 = x$

11. (a) $f(g(x)) = f\left(\dfrac{x}{2}\right) = 2\left(\dfrac{x}{2}\right) = x$

$g(f(x)) = g(2x) = \dfrac{2x}{2} = x$

(b)

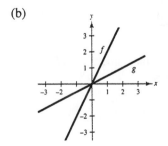

13. (a) $f(g(x)) = f\left(\dfrac{x-1}{5}\right) = 5\left(\dfrac{x-1}{5}\right) + 1 = x$

$g(f(x)) = g(5x + 1) = \dfrac{(5x + 1) - 1}{5} = x$

(b)

15. (a) $f(g(x)) = f\left(\sqrt[3]{x}\right) = \left(\sqrt[3]{x}\right)^3 = x$

$g(f(x)) = g(x^3) = \sqrt[3]{x^3} = x$

(b)

17. (a) $f(g(x)) = f(x^2 + 4),\ x \ge 0$

$= \sqrt{(x^2 + 4) - 4} = x$

$g(f(x)) = g\left(\sqrt{x - 4}\right)$

$= \left(\sqrt{x - 4}\right)^2 + 4 = x$

(b)

19. (a) $f(g(x)) = f\left(\sqrt{9 - x}\right),\ x \le 9$

$= 9 - \left(\sqrt{9 - x}\right)^2 = x$

$g(f(x)) = g(9 - x^2),\ x \ge 0$

$= \sqrt{9 - (9 - x^2)} = x$

(b)

21. No, $\{(-2, -1), (1, 0), (2, 1), (1, 2), (-2, 3), (-6, 4)\}$ does not represent a function.

23. Since no horizontal line crosses the graph of f at more than one point, f **has** an inverse.

25. Since some horizontal lines cross the graph of f twice, f does **not** have an inverse.

27. $g(x) = \dfrac{4 - x}{6}$

g passes the horizontal line test, so g **has** an inverse.

29. $h(x) = |x + 4| - |x - 4|$

h does not pass the horizontal line test, so h does **not** have an inverse.

31. $f(x) = -2x\sqrt{16 - x^2}$

f does not pass the horizontal line test, so f does **not** have an inverse.

33. $f(x) = 2x - 3$

$y = 2x - 3$

$x = 2y - 3$

$y = \dfrac{x + 3}{2}$

$f^{-1}(x) = \dfrac{x + 3}{2}$

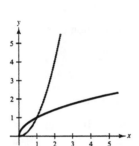

35. $f(x) = x^5$

$y = x^5$

$x = y^5$

$y = \sqrt[5]{x}$

$f^{-1}(x) = \sqrt[5]{x}$

37. $f(x) = \sqrt{x}$

$y = \sqrt{x}$

$x = \sqrt{y}$

$y = x^2$

$f^{-1}(x) = x^2,\ x \ge 0$

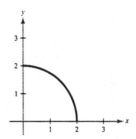

39. $f(x) = \sqrt{4 - x^2},\ 0 \le x \le 2$

$y = \sqrt{4 - x^2}$

$x = \sqrt{4 - y^2}$

$f^{-1}(x) = \sqrt{4 - x^2},\ 0 \le x \le 2$

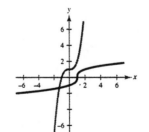

41. $f(x) = \sqrt[3]{x - 1}$

$y = \sqrt[3]{x - 1}$

$x = \sqrt[3]{y - 1}$

$x^3 = y - 1$

$y = x^3 + 1$

$f^{-1}(x) = x^3 + 1$

43. $f(x) = x^4$

$y = x^4$

$x = y^4$

$y = \pm\sqrt[4]{x}$

This does not represent y as a function of x.
f does not have an inverse.

45. $g(x) = \dfrac{x}{8}$

$y = \dfrac{x}{8}$

$x = \dfrac{y}{8}$

$y = 8x$

This is a function of x, so g has an inverse.
$g^{-1}(x) = 8x$

47. $p(x) = -4$

$y = -4$

Since $y = -4$ for all x, the graph is a horizontal line and fails the horizontal line test. p does not have an inverse.

49. $f(x) = (x + 3)^2, \ x \geq -3 \ \Rightarrow \ y \geq 0$

$y = (x + 3)^2, \ x \geq -3, \ y \geq 0$

$x = (y + 3)^2, \ y \geq -3, \ x \geq 0$

$\sqrt{x} = y + 3, \ y \geq -3, \ x \geq 0$

$y = \sqrt{x} - 3, \ x \geq 0, \ y \geq -3$

This is a function of x, so f has an inverse.
$f^{-1}(x) = \sqrt{x} - 3, \ x \geq 0$

51. $h(x) = \dfrac{1}{x}$

$y = \dfrac{1}{x}$

$xy = 1$

$y = \dfrac{1}{x}$

This is a function of x, so h has an inverse.
$h^{-1}(x) = \dfrac{1}{x}$

53. $f(x) = \sqrt{2x + 3} \ \Rightarrow \ x \geq -\dfrac{3}{2}, \ y \geq 0$

$y = \sqrt{2x + 3}, \ x \geq -\dfrac{3}{2}, \ y \geq 0$

$x = \sqrt{2y + 3}, \ y \geq -\dfrac{3}{2}, \ x \geq 0$

$x^2 = 2y + 3, \ x \geq 0, \ y \geq -\dfrac{3}{2}$

$y = \dfrac{x^2 - 3}{2}, \ x \geq 0, \ y \geq -\dfrac{3}{2}$

This is a function of x, so f has an inverse.

$f^{-1}(x) = \dfrac{x^2 - 3}{2}, \ x \geq 0$

55. $g(x) = x^2 - x^4$

The graph fails the horizontal line test, so g does not have an inverse.

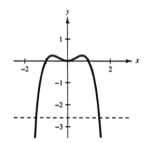

57. $f(x) = 25 - x^2, \ x \leq 0 \ \Rightarrow \ y \leq 25$

$y = 25 - x^2, \ x \leq 0, \ y \leq 25$

$x = 25 - y^2, \ y \leq 0, \ x \leq 25$

$y^2 = 25 - x, \ x \leq 25, \ y \leq 0$

$y = -\sqrt{25 - x}, \ x \leq 25, \ y \leq 0$

This is a function of x, so f has an inverse.

$f^{-1}(x) = -\sqrt{25 - x}, \ x \leq 25$

59. If we let $f(x) = (x - 2)^2$, $x \geq 2$, then f has an inverse. [Note: we could also let $x \leq 2$.]

$$f(x) = (x - 2)^2, \; x \geq 2 \implies y \geq 0$$
$$y = (x - 2)^2, \; x \geq 2, \; y \geq 0$$
$$x = (y - 2)^2, \; x \geq 0, \; y \geq 2$$
$$\sqrt{x} = y - 2, \; x \geq 0, \; y \geq 2$$
$$\sqrt{x} + 2 = y, \; x \geq 0, \; y \geq 2$$

Thus, $f^{-1}(x) = \sqrt{x} + 2$, $x \geq 0$.

61. If we let $f(x) = |x + 2|$, $x \geq -2$, then f has an inverse. [Note: we could also let $x \leq -2$.]

$$f(x) = |x + 2|, \; x \geq -2$$
$$f(x) = x + 2 \text{ when } x \geq -2.$$
$$y = x + 2, \; x \geq -2, \; y \geq 0$$
$$x = y + 2, \; x \geq 0, \; y \geq -2$$
$$x - 2 = y, \; x \geq 0, \; y \geq -2$$

Thus, $f^{-1}(x) = x - 2$, $x \geq 0$.

63.

x	$f(x)$
-2	-4
-1	-2
1	2
3	3

x	$f^{-1}(x)$
-4	-2
-2	-1
2	1
3	3

65. False, $f(x) = x^2$ is even and does not have an inverse.

67. True

In Exercises 69, 71, and 73, $f(x) = \frac{1}{8}x - 3$, $f^{-1}(x) = 8(x + 3)$, $g(x) = x^3$, $g^{-1}(x) = \sqrt[3]{x}$.

69. $(f^{-1} \circ g^{-1})(1) = f^{-1}(g^{-1}(1)) = f^{-1}(\sqrt[3]{1}) = 8(\sqrt[3]{1} + 3) = 32$

71. $(f^{-1} \circ f^{-1})(6) = f^{-1}(f^{-1}(6)) = f^{-1}(8[6 + 3]) = 8[8(6 + 3) + 3] = 600$

73. $(f \circ g)(x) = f(g(x)) = f(x^3) = \frac{1}{8}x^3 - 3$

$$y = \frac{1}{8}x^3 - 3$$
$$x = \frac{1}{8}y^3 - 3$$
$$x + 3 = \frac{1}{8}y^3$$
$$8(x + 3) = y^3$$
$$\sqrt[3]{8(x + 3)} = y$$
$$(f \circ g)^{-1}(x) = 2\sqrt[3]{x + 3}$$

In Exercises 75 and 77, $f(x) = x + 4$, $f^{-1}(x) = x - 4$, $g(x) = 2x - 5$, $g^{-1}(x) = \dfrac{x + 5}{2}$.

75. $(g^{-1} \circ f^{-1})(x) = g^{-1}(f^{-1}(x)) = g^{-1}(x - 4) = \dfrac{(x - 4) + 5}{2} = \dfrac{x + 1}{2}$

77. $(f \circ g)(x) = f(g(x)) = f(2x - 5) = (2x - 5) + 4 = 2x - 1$

$$(f \circ g)^{-1}(x) = \frac{x + 1}{2}$$

Note: Comparing Exercises 75 and 77, we see that $(f \circ g)^{-1}(x) = (g^{-1} \circ f^{-1})(x)$.

79. (a)
$$y = 8 + 0.75x$$
$$x = 8 + 0.75y$$
$$x - 8 = 0.75y$$
$$\frac{x - 8}{0.75} = y$$
$$f^{-1}(x) = \frac{x - 8}{0.75}$$

(b) x = hourly wage

y = number of units produced

(c) $y = \dfrac{22.25 - 8}{0.75} = 19$ units

81. (a)
$$y = 0.03x^2 + 254.50, \quad 0 < x < 100$$
$$x = 0.03y^2 + 254.50$$
$$x - 254.50 = 0.03y^2$$
$$\frac{x - 254.50}{0.03} = y^2$$
$$\sqrt{\frac{x - 254.50}{0.03}} = y, \quad 254.5 < x < 545.5$$
$$f^{-1}(x) = \sqrt{\frac{x - 254.50}{0.03}}$$

x = temperature in degrees Fahrenheit

y = percent load for a diesel engine

(b)

(c)
$$0.03x^2 + 254.50 < 500$$
$$0.03x^2 < 245.5$$
$$x^2 < 8183\tfrac{1}{3}$$
$$x < 90.46$$

Thus, $0 < x < 90.46$.

83. (a) Yes, since no y-value is paired with two different x-values, f^{-1} does exist.

(b) f^{-1} yields the year for a given average fuel consumption.

(c) $f^{-1}(19.95) = 8$

85. $x^2 = 64$

$x = \pm\sqrt{64} = \pm 8$

87. $4x^2 - 12x + 9 = 0$

$(2x - 3)^2 = 0$

$2x - 3 = 0$

$x = \tfrac{3}{2}$

89. $x^2 - 6x + 4 = 0$

$x^2 - 6x = -4$

$x^2 - 6x + 9 = -4 + 9$

$(x - 3)^2 = 5$

$x - 3 = \pm\sqrt{5}$

$x = 3 \pm \sqrt{5}$

91. $50 + 5x = 3x^2$

$0 = 3x^2 - 5x - 50$

$0 = (3x + 10)(x - 5)$

$3x + 10 = 0 \implies x = -\frac{10}{3}$

$x - 5 = 0 \implies x = 5$

93. Let $2n$ = first positive even integer. Then $2n + 2$ = next positive even integer.

$2n(2n + 2) = 288$

$4n^2 + 4n - 288 = 0$

$4(n^2 + n - 72) = 0$

$4(n + 9)(n - 8) = 0$

$n + 9 = 0 \implies n = -9$ Not a solution since the integers are positive.

$n - 8 = 0 \implies n = 8$

Thus, $2n = 16$ and $2n + 2 = 18$.

95.

Given $b = h$ and $A = 10$ sq ft:

$A = \frac{1}{2}bh$

$10 = \frac{1}{2}bb$

$20 = b^2$

$\sqrt{20} = b$

$2\sqrt{5} = b$

Thus, $b = h = 2\sqrt{5}$ feet.

Section 1.7   Mathematical Modeling

You should know the following the following terms and formulas.

■   Direct Variation (varies directly, directly proportional)

    (a) $y = mx$

    (b) $y = kx^n$ (as nth power)

■   Inverse Variation (varies inversely, inversely proportional)

    (a) $y = k/x$

    (b) $y = k/(x^n)$ (as nth power)

■   Joint Variation (varies jointly, jointly proportional)

    (a) $z = kxy$

    (b) $z = kx^n y^m$ (as nth power of x and mth power of y)

■ k is called the constant of proportionality.

■   Least Squares Regression Line $y = ax + b$ where

$$a = \frac{n\sum_{i=1}^{n} x_i y_i - \sum_{i=1}^{n} x_i \sum_{i=1}^{n} y_i}{n\sum_{i=1}^{n} x_i^2 - \left(\sum_{i=1}^{n} x_i\right)^2}$$

$$b = \frac{1}{n}\left(\sum_{i=1}^{n} y_i - a\sum_{i=1}^{n} x_i\right).$$

Solutions to Odd-Numbered Exercises

1. $y = 113,336.2 + 1265t, \ 7 \le t \le 13$

$t = 0$ represents 1980.

Year	1987	1988	1989	1990	1991	1992	1993
Actual Number	121,602	123,378	125,557	126,424	126,867	128,548	129,525
Model	122,191	123,456	124,721	125,986	127,251	128,516	129,781

The model is a "good fit" for the actual data.

3. The graph appears to represent $y = 4/x$ which is an inverse variation.

5.

x	2	4	6	8	10
$y = x^2$	4	16	36	64	100

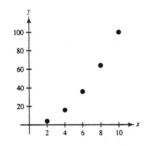

7.

x	2	4	6	8	10
$y = \frac{1}{2}x^2$	2	8	18	32	50

9.

x	2	4	6	8	10
$y = \dfrac{2}{x^2}$	$\dfrac{1}{2}$	$\dfrac{1}{8}$	$\dfrac{1}{18}$	$\dfrac{1}{32}$	$\dfrac{1}{50}$

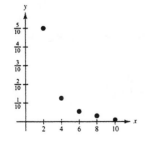

11.

x	2	4	6	8	10
$y = \dfrac{10}{x^2}$	$\dfrac{5}{2}$	$\dfrac{5}{8}$	$\dfrac{5}{18}$	$\dfrac{5}{32}$	$\dfrac{1}{10}$

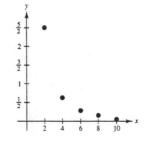

13. The chart represents the equation $y = \dfrac{5}{x}$.

15. $y = kx$

$-7 = k(10)$

$-\dfrac{7}{10} = k$

$y = -\dfrac{7}{10}x$

This equation checks with the other points given in the chart.

17. $y = mx$

$12 = m(5)$

$\dfrac{12}{5} = m$

$y = \dfrac{12}{5}x$

19. $y = mx$

$2050 = m(10)$

$205 = m$

$y = 205x$

21. $I = kP$

$187.59 = k(2500)$

$0.075 = k$

$I = 0.075P$

23. $y = kx$

$1840 = k(50{,}000)$

$0.0368 = k$

$y = 0.0368x$

When $x = 85{,}000$ we have

$y = 0.0368(85{,}000) = \$3128.$

25. $y = kx$

$33 = k(13)$

$\dfrac{33}{13} = k$

$y = \dfrac{33}{13}x$

Inches	5	10	20	25	30
Centimeters	12.7	25.4	50.8	63.5	76.2

27. $d = kF$

$0.15 = k(265)$

$\dfrac{3}{5300} = k$

$d = \dfrac{3}{5300}F$

(a) $d = \dfrac{3}{5300}(90) \approx 0.05$ meter

(b) $0.1 = \dfrac{3}{5300}F$

$\dfrac{530}{3} = F$

$F = 176\frac{2}{3}$ newtons

29. $d = kF$

$1.9 = k(25) \implies k = 0.076$

$d = 0.076F$

When the distance compressed is 3 inches, we have

$3 = 0.076F$

$F \approx 39.47.$

No child over 39.47 pounds should use the toy.

31. $A = kr^2$

33. $y = \dfrac{k}{x^2}$

35. $z = k\sqrt[3]{u}$

37. $z = kuv$

39. $F = \dfrac{kg}{r^2}$

41. $P = \dfrac{k}{V}$

43. $F = \dfrac{km_1m_2}{r^2}$

45. $A = \frac{1}{2}bh$

The area of a triangle is jointly proportional to the magnitude of the base and the height.

47. $V = \frac{4}{3}\pi r^3$

The volume of a sphere varies directly as the cube of its radius.

49. $r = \frac{d}{t}$

Average speed is directly proportional to the distance and inversely proportional to the time.

51. $A = kr^2$

$9\pi = k(3)^2$

$\pi = k$

$A = \pi r^2$

53. $y = \frac{k}{x}$

$3 = \frac{k}{25}$

$75 = k$

$y = \frac{75}{x}$

55. $h = \frac{k}{t^3}$

$\frac{3}{16} = \frac{k}{(4)^3}$

$\frac{3}{16} = \frac{k}{64}$

$k = 12$

$h = \frac{12}{t^3}$

57. $z = kxy$

$64 = k(4)(8)$

$2 = k$

$z = 2xy$

59. $F = krs^3$

$4158 = k(11)(3)^3$

$k = 14$

$F = 14rs^3$

61. $z = \frac{kx^2}{y}$

$6 = \frac{k(6)^2}{4}$

$\frac{24}{36} = k$

$\frac{2}{3} = k$

$z = \frac{(2/3)x^2}{y} = \frac{2x^2}{3y}$

63. $S = \frac{kL}{L - S}$

$4 = \frac{k(6)}{6 - 4}$

$4 = 3k$

$k = \frac{4}{3}$

$S = \frac{4/3L}{L - S} = \frac{4L}{3(L - S)}$

65. $d = kv^2$

$0.02 = k\left(\frac{1}{4}\right)^2$

$k = 0.32$

$d = 0.32v^2$

$0.12 = 0.32v^2$

$v^2 = \frac{0.12}{0.32} = \frac{3}{8}$

$v = \frac{\sqrt{3}}{2\sqrt{2}} = \frac{\sqrt{6}}{4} \approx 0.61$ mi/hr

67. $r = \frac{kl}{A}, \ A = \pi r^2 = \frac{\pi d^2}{4}$

$r = \frac{4kl}{\pi d^2}$

$66.17 = \frac{4(1000)k}{\pi(0.0126/12)^2}$

$k \approx 5.73 \times 10^{-8}$

$r = \frac{4(5.73 \times 10^{-8})l}{\pi(0.0126/12)^2}$

$33.5 = \frac{4(5.73 \times 10^{-8})l}{\pi(0.0126/12)^2}$

$\frac{33.5\pi(0.0126/12)^2}{4(5.73 \times 10^{-8})} = l$

$l \approx 506$ feet

69. $S = kt^2$

$144 = k(3)^2$

$16 = k$

$S = 16t^2$

$S = 16(5)^2 = 400$ feet

71. $P = kA = k(\pi r^2) = k\pi\left(\dfrac{d}{2}\right)^2$

$8.78 = k\pi\left(\dfrac{9}{2}\right)^2$

$\dfrac{4(8.78)}{81\pi} = k$

$k \approx 0.138$

However, we do not obtain \$11.78 when $d = 12$ inches.

$P = 0.138\pi\left(\dfrac{12}{2}\right)^2 \approx \$15.61$

Instead, $k = \dfrac{11.78}{36\pi} \approx 0.104$.

For the 15 inch pizza, we have $k = \dfrac{4(14.18)}{225\pi} \approx 0.080$.

The price is not directly proportional to the surface area. The best buy is the 15-inch pizza.

73. $v = \dfrac{k}{A}$

(a) $v = \dfrac{k}{0.75A} = \dfrac{4}{3}\left(\dfrac{k}{A}\right)$

The velocity is four-thirds the original.

(b) $v = \dfrac{k}{\left(1 + \frac{1}{3}\right)A} = \dfrac{k}{\frac{4}{3}A} = \dfrac{3}{4}\left(\dfrac{k}{A}\right)$

The velocity is decreased by one-fourth.

75. (a)

(b) It appears to fit Hooke's Law.

$k \approx \left|\dfrac{12.00 - 4.84}{0 - 300}\right| \approx |-0.0238| = 0.0238$

(c) $x = kF$

$9 = 0.0238F$

$F \approx 378$ grams

77. $y = \dfrac{262.76}{x^{2.12}}$

(a)

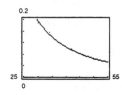

(b) $y = \dfrac{262.76}{(25)^{2.12}} \approx 0.2857$ microwatts per square centimeter

79. The data shown could be represented by a linear model which would be a good fit.

81. The points do not follow a linear pattern. A linear model would not be a good approximation.

83.

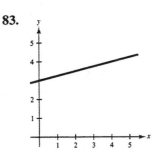

Using the points $(0, 3)$ and $(4, 4)$, we have
$y = \frac{1}{4}x + 3$.

85.

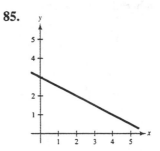

Using the points $(2, 2)$ and $(4, 1)$, we have
$y = -\frac{1}{2}x + 3$.

87. (a) $(7, 203)$, $(8, 239)$, $(9, 295)$, $(10, 352)$, $(11, 415)$, and $(12, 488)$

$$a = \frac{6(19929) - (57)(1992)}{6(559) - (57)^2} \approx 57.4$$

$$b = \frac{1}{6}[1992 - a(57)] \approx -213.6$$

$$y \approx 57.4t - 213.6$$

(b)

(c)

Year	t	y
1994	14	590.0
1995	15	647.4
1996	16	704.8

89. (a) Using the linear regression capabilities of a calculator yields $y \approx 1.145t + 124.425$.

(b)

(c) Using the model with $t = 96$ yields 234.345 feet.

91. (a) Using the linear regression capabilities of a calculator yields $y \approx -0.74x + 106$.

(b)

(c) Using the model with $x = 62$ yields 60.12 pounds.

(d) For each 1 pound increase in per capita consumption of poultry, the per capita consumption of beef decreases by an average of 0.74 pounds.

❏ **Review Exercises for Chapter 1**

Solutions to Odd-Numbered Exercises

1. $y - 2x - 3 = 0$

$y = 2x + 3$

Line with x-intercept $\left(-\frac{3}{2}, 0\right)$ and y-intercept $(0, 3)$

3. $x - 5 = 0$

$x = 5$ is a vertical line through $(5, 0)$.

5. $y = \sqrt{5 - x}$

Domain: $(-\infty, 5]$

x	5	4	1	-4
y	0	1	2	3

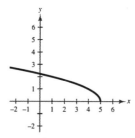

7. $y + 2x^2 = 0$

$y = -2x^2$ is a parabola

x	0	± 1	± 2
y	0	-2	-8

9. $y = \sqrt{25 - x^2}$

Domain: $-5 \le x \le 5$

x	0	± 3	± 4	± 5
y	5	4	3	0

11. $y = \frac{1}{4}(x + 1)^3$

Intercepts: $(-1, 0), \left(0, \frac{1}{4}\right)$

13. $y = \frac{1}{4}x^4 - 2x^2$

Intercepts: $(0, 0), \left(\pm 2\sqrt{2}, 0\right)$

15. $y = x\sqrt{9 - x^2}$

Intercepts: $(0, 0), (\pm 3, 0)$

17. $y = |x - 4| - 4$

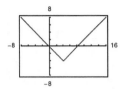

Intercepts: $(0, 0), (8, 0)$

19. $y^2 = 25 - x^2$

$y = \pm\sqrt{25 - x^2}$

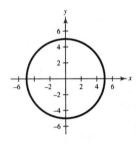

21. $y = 10x^3 - 21x^2$

Xmin = -2
Xmax = 3
Xscl = 1
Ymin = -20
Ymax = 15
Yscl = 5

23. $(x - 3)^2 + (y + 1)^2 = 9$

$(x - 3)^2 + [y - (-1)]^2 = 3^2$

Center: $(3, -1)$

Radius: $r = 3$

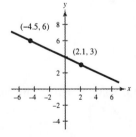

25. (a) $m = \frac{3}{2} > 0 \implies$ The line rises. Matches L_2.

(b) $m = 0 \implies$ The line is horizontal. Matches L_3.

(c) $m = -3 < 0 \implies$ The line falls. Matches L_1.

27. $(-4.5, 6), (2.1, 3)$

$$m = \frac{3 - 6}{2.1 - (-4.5)} = \frac{-3}{6.6} = -\frac{30}{66} = -\frac{5}{11}$$

29. $(-2, 5), (0, t), (1, 1)$ are collinear.

$$\frac{t - 5}{0 - (-2)} = \frac{1 - 5}{1 - (-2)}$$

$$\frac{t - 5}{2} = \frac{-4}{3}$$

$$3(t - 5) = -8$$

$$3t - 15 = -8$$

$$3t = 7$$

$$t = \frac{7}{3}$$

31. $(0, 0), (0, 10)$

$$m = \frac{10 - 0}{0 - 0} = \frac{10}{0} \text{ undefined.}$$

The line is vertical.

$$x = 0$$

33. $y - (-5) = \frac{3}{2}(x - 0)$

$$y + 5 = \frac{3}{2}x$$

$$y = \frac{3}{2}x - 5 \text{ or } 0 = 3x - 2y - 10$$

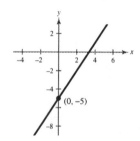

35. $5x - 4y = 8 \implies y = \frac{5}{4}x - 2$ and $m = \frac{5}{4}$

(a) Parallel slope: $m = \frac{5}{4}$

$$y - (-2) = \frac{5}{4}(x - 3)$$

$$4y + 8 = 5x - 15$$

$$0 = 5x - 4y - 23$$

(b) Perpendicular slope: $m = -\frac{4}{5}$

$$y - (-2) = -\frac{4}{5}(x - 3)$$

$$5y + 10 = -4x + 12$$

$$4x + 5y - 2 = 0$$

37. $(6, 12{,}500) \quad m = 850$

$$y - 12{,}500 = 850(t - 6)$$

$$y = 850t - 5100 + 12{,}500$$

$$y = 850t + 7400$$

39. $(2, \ 160{,}000), \ (3, \ 185{,}000)$

$$m = \frac{185{,}000 - 160{,}000}{3 - 2} = 25{,}000$$

$$S - 160{,}000 = 25{,}000(t - 2)$$

$$S = 25{,}000t + 110{,}000$$

For the fourth quarter let $t = 4$. Then we have

$$S = 25{,}000(4) + 110{,}000 = \$210{,}000.$$

41. $A = \{10, 20, 30, 40\}$ and $B = \{0, 2, 4, 6\}$

(a) 20 is matched with two elements in the range so it is not a function.

(b) function

(c) function

(d) 30 is not matched with any element of B so it is not a function.

43. $16x - y^4 = 0$

$$y^4 = 16x$$

$$y = \pm 2\sqrt[4]{x}$$

y is **not** a function of x. Some x-values correspond to two y-values.

45. $y = \sqrt{1 - x}$

Each x-value, $x \le 1$, corresponds to only one y-value so y **is** a function of x.

47. $f(x) = x^2 + 1$

(a) $f(2) = (2)^2 + 1 = 5$

(b) $f(-4) = (-4)^2 + 1 = 17$

(c) $f(t^2) = (t^2)^2 + 1 = t^4 + 1$

(d) $-f(x) = -(x^2 + 1) = -x^2 - 1$

49. $g(s) = \dfrac{5}{3s - 9} = \dfrac{5}{3(s - 3)}$

Domain: All real numbers except $s = 3$.

51. $f(x) = \sqrt{x^2 + 8x}$

Domain: $x^2 + 8x \geq 0$

$\qquad x(x + 8) \geq 0$

Critical numbers: $x = 0, -8$

Test intervals: $(-\infty, -8), (-8, 0), (0, \infty)$

Solution set: $(-\infty, -8] \cup [0, \infty)$

53. $f(x) = (x^2 - 4)^2$

(a) Increasing on $(-2, 0)$ and $(2, \infty)$

Decreasing on $(-\infty, -2)$ and $(0, 2)$

(b) The graph has y-axis symmetry so the function is even.

55. $g(x) = |x + 2| - |x - 2|$

(a) Increasing on $(-2, 2)$

Constant on $(-\infty, -2] \cup [2, \infty)$

(b) The graph has origin symmetry so the function is odd

57. $v(t) = -32t + 48$

(a) $v(1) = 16$ ft/sec

(b) $0 = -32t + 48$

$\qquad t = \frac{48}{32} = 1.5$ sec

(c) $v(2) = -16$ ft/sec

59. $(f - g)(4) = f(4) - g(4)$

$\qquad = [3 - 2(4)] - \sqrt{4}$

$\qquad = -5 - 2$

$\qquad = -7$

61. $(h \circ g)(7) = h(g(7))$

$\qquad = h\left(\sqrt{7}\right)$

$\qquad = 3\left(\sqrt{7}\right)^2 + 2$

$\qquad = 23$

63. (a)

$$f(x) = \tfrac{1}{2}x - 3$$

$$y = \tfrac{1}{2}x - 3$$

$$x = \tfrac{1}{2}y - 3$$

$$x + 3 = \tfrac{1}{2}y$$

$$2(x + 3) = y$$

$$f^{-1}(x) = 2x + 6$$

(b)

(c)

$$f^{-1}(f(x)) = f^{-1}\left(\tfrac{1}{2}x - 3\right)$$

$$= 2\left(\tfrac{1}{2}x - 3\right) + 6$$

$$= x - 6 + 6$$

$$= x$$

$$f(f^{-1}(x)) = f(2x + 6)$$

$$= \tfrac{1}{2}(2x + 6) - 3$$

$$= x + 3 - 3$$

$$= x$$

65. (a)

$$f(x) = \sqrt{x + 1}$$

$$y = \sqrt{x + 1}$$

$$x = \sqrt{y + 1}$$

$$x^2 = y + 1$$

$$x^2 - 1 = y$$

$$f^{-1}(x) = x^2 - 1, \ x \geq 0$$

(b)

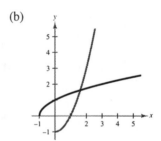

Note: The inverse must have a restricted domain.

(c)

$$f^{-1}(f(x)) = f^{-1}\left(\sqrt{x + 1}\right)$$

$$= \left(\sqrt{x + 1}\right)^2 - 1$$

$$= x + 1 - 1$$

$$= x$$

$$f(f^{-1}(x)) = f(x^2 - 1)$$

$$= \sqrt{(x^2 - 1) + 1}$$

$$= \sqrt{x^2} = x \ \text{for} \ x \geq 0.$$

67.

$$F = c\,x\sqrt{y}$$

$$6 = c\,(9)\sqrt{4}$$

$$6 = 18c$$

$$\tfrac{1}{3} = c$$

$$F = \tfrac{1}{3}x\sqrt{y}$$

69.

$$z = \frac{cx^2}{y}$$

$$16 = \frac{c(5)^2}{2}$$

$$32 = 25c$$

$$\frac{32}{25} = c$$

$$z = \frac{32x^2}{25y}$$

71. (0, 13.52), (5, 13.52), (10, 15.46), (15, 18.20), (20, 21.02)

(a) $y = 0.3936 + 12.408$

(b)

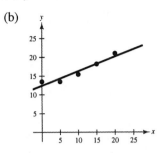

(c) The slope represents the increase per year in miles per gallon

(d) When $t = 30$, $y \approx 24.22$ miles per gallon

❑ Practice Test for Chapter 1

1. Graph $y = \sqrt{7 - x}$

2. Find the domain $y = \sqrt{25 - x^2}$

3. Write the standard equation of the circle with center $(-3, 5)$ and radius 6.

4. Find the equation of the line through $(2, 4)$ and $(3, -1)$.

5. Find the equation of the line with slope $m = 4/3$ and y-intercept $b = -3$.

6. Find the equation of the line through $(4, 1)$ perpendicular to the line $2x + 3y = 0$.

7. If it costs a company \$32 to produce 5 units of a product and \$44 to produce 9 units, how much does it cost to produce 20 units? (Assume that the cost function is linear.)

8. Given $f(x) = x^2 - 2x + 1$, find $f(x - 3)$.

9. Given $f(x) = 4x - 11$, find $\dfrac{f(x) - f(3)}{x - 3}$

10. Find the domain and range of $f(x) = \sqrt{36 - x^2}$.

11. Which equations determine y as a function of x?

    (a) $6x - 5y + 4 = 0$

    (b) $x^2 + y^2 = 9$

    (c) $y^3 = x^2 + 6$

12. Sketch the graph of $f(x) = x^2 - 5$.

13. Sketch the graph of $f(x) = |x + 3|$.

14. Sketch the graph of $f(x) = \begin{cases} 2x + 1 & \text{if } x \geq 0, \\ x^2 - x & \text{if } x < 0. \end{cases}$

15. Use the graph of $f(x) = |x|$ to graph the following:

    (a) $f(x + 2)$

    (b) $-f(x) + 2$

16. Given $f(x) = 3x + 7$ and $g(x) = 2x^2 - 5$, find the following:

    (a) $(g - f)(x)$

    (b) $(fg)(x)$

17. Given $f(x) = x^2 - 2x + 16$ and $g(x) = 2x + 3$, find $f(g(x))$.

18. Given $f(x) = x^3 + 7$, find $f^{-1}(x)$.

19. Which of the following functions have inverses?

    (a) $f(x) = |x - 6|$

    (b) $f(x) = ax + b,\ a \neq 0$

    (c) $f(x) = x^3 - 19$

20. Given $f(x) = \sqrt{\dfrac{3-x}{x}}$, $0 < x \leq 3$, find $f^{-1}(x)$.

Exercises 21–23, true or false?

21. $y = 3x + 7$ and $y = \frac{1}{3}x - 4$ are perpendicular.

22. $(f \circ g)^{-1} = g^{-1} \circ f^{-1}$

23. If a function has an inverse, then it must pass both the vertical line test and the horizontal line test.

24. If z varies directly as the cube of x and inversely as the square root of y, and $z = -1$ when $x = -1$ and $y = 25$, find z in terms of x and y.

25. Find the least square regression line for the data.

x	-2	-1	0	1	2	3
y	1	2.4	3	3.1	4	4.7

CHAPTER 2
Polynomial and Rational Functions

C H A P T E R   2
Polynomial and Rational Functions

Section 2.1   Quadratic Functions

You should know the following facts about parabolas.

- $f(x) = ax^2 + bx + c,\ a \neq 0$, is a quadratic function, and its graph is a parabola.
- If $a > 0$, the parabola opens upward and the vertex is the minimum point. If $a < 0$, the parabola opens downward and the vertex is the maximum point.
- The vertex is $(-b/2a, f(-b/2a))$.
- To find the x-intercepts (if any), solve
    $$ax^2 + bx + c = 0.$$
- The standard form of the equation of a parabola is
    $$f(x) = a(x - h)^2 + k$$
    where $a \neq 0$.
    (a) The vertex is (h, k).
    (b) The axis is the vertical line $x = h$.

Solutions to Odd-Numbered Exercises

1. $f(x) = (x - 2)^2$ opens upward and has vertex $(2, 0)$. Matches graph (g).

3. $f(x) = x^2 - 2$ opens upward and has vertex $(0, -2)$. Matches graph (b).

5. $f(x) = 4 - (x - 2)^2 = -(x - 2)^2 + 4$ opens downward and has vertex $(2, 4)$. Matches graph (f).

7. $f(x) = x^2 + 3$ opens upward and has vertex $(0, 3)$. Matches graph (e).

9. (a) $y = \frac{1}{2}x^2$

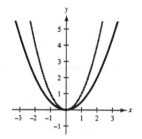

Vertical shrink

(b) $y = -\frac{1}{8}x^2$

Vertical shrink and reflection in the x-axis

(c) $y = \frac{3}{2}x^2$

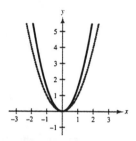

Vertical stretch

(d) $y = -3x^2$

Vertical stretch and reflection in the x-axis

11. (a) $y = (x - 1)^2$

Horizontal translation one unit to the right

(b) $y = (x + 1)^2$

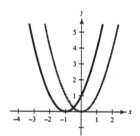

Horizontal translation one unit to the left

(c) $y = (x - 3)^2$

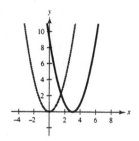

Horizontal translation three units to the right

(d) $y = (x + 3)^2$

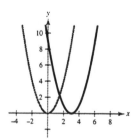

Horizontal translation three units to the left

13. $f(x) = x^2 - 5$

Vertex: $(0, -5)$

Intercepts: $\left(-\sqrt{5}, 0\right),\ (0, -5),\ \left(\sqrt{5}, 0\right)$

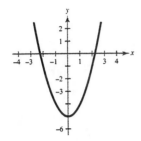

15. $f(x) = 16 - x^2$

Vertex: $(0, 16)$

Intercepts: $(-4, 0),\ (0, 16),\ (4, 0)$

17. $f(x) = (x + 5)^2 - 6$

Vertex: $(-5, -6)$

Intercepts: $\left(-5 - \sqrt{6}, 0\right),\ \left(-5 + \sqrt{6}, 0\right),$
$(0, 19)$

19. $h(x) = x^2 - 8x + 16 = (x - 4)^2$

Vertex: $(4, 0)$

Intercepts: $(0, 16),\ (4, 0)$

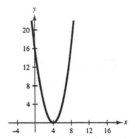

21. $f(x) = x^2 - x + \frac{5}{4} = \left(x - \frac{1}{2}\right)^2 + 1$

Vertex: $\left(\frac{1}{2}, 1\right)$

Intercept: $\left(0, \frac{5}{4}\right)$

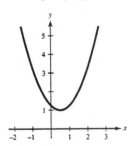

23. $f(x) = -x^2 + 2x + 5 = -(x - 1)^2 + 6$

Vertex: $(1, 6)$

Intercepts: $\left(1 - \sqrt{6}, 0\right),\ (0, 5),\ \left(1 + \sqrt{6}, 0\right)$

25. $h(x) = 4x^2 - 4x + 21 = 4\left(x - \frac{1}{2}\right)^2 + 20$

Vertex: $\left(\frac{1}{2}, 20\right)$

Intercept: $(0, 21)$

27. $f(x) = -(x^2 + 2x - 3) = -(x + 1)^2 + 4$

Vertex: $(-1, 4)$

Intercepts: $(-3, 0),\ (0, 3),\ (1, 0)$

29. $f(x) = 2x^2 - 16x + 31$

$\quad = 2(x - 4)^2 - 1$

Vertex: $(4, -1)$

Intercepts: $\left(4 \pm \frac{1}{2}\sqrt{2}, 0\right),\ (0, 31)$

31. $(1, 0)$ is the vertex.

$f(x) = a(x - 1)^2 + 0 = a(x - 1)^2$

Since the graph passes through the point $(0, 1)$ we have:

$1 = a(0 - 1)^2$

$1 = a$

$f(x) = 1(x - 1)^2 = (x - 1)^2$

33. $(-1, 4)$ is the vertex.

$f(x) = a(x + 1)^2 + 4$

Since the graph passes through the point $(1, 0)$, we have:

$0 = a(1 + 1)^2 + 4$

$-4 = 4a$

$-1 = a$

$f(x) = -1(x + 1)^2 + 4 = -(x + 1)^2 + 4.$

35. $(-2, 2)$ is the vertex.

$f(x) = a(x + 2)^2 + 2$

Since the graph passes through the point $(-1, 0)$, we have:

$0 = a(-1 + 2)^2 + 2$

$-2 = a$

$f(x) = -2(x + 2)^2 + 2$

37. $(-2, 5)$ is the vertex.

$f(x) = a(x + 2)^2 + 5$

Since the graph passes through the point $(0, 9)$, we have:

$9 = a(0 + 2)^2 + 5$

$4 = 4a$

$1 = a$

$f(x) = 1(x + 2)^2 + 5 = (x + 2)^2 + 5$

39. $(3, 4)$ is the vertex.

$f(x) = a(x - 3)^2 + 4$

Since the graph passes through the point $(1, 2)$, we have:

$2 = a(1 - 3)^2 + 4$

$-2 = 4a$

$-\frac{1}{2} = a$

$f(x) = -\frac{1}{2}(x - 3)^2 + 4$

41. $(5, 12)$ is the vertex.

$f(x) = a(x - 5)^2 + 12$

Since the graph passes through the point $(7, 15)$, we have:

$15 = a(7 - 5)^2 + 12$

$3 = 4a \implies a = \frac{3}{4}$

$f(x) = \frac{3}{4}(x - 5)^2 + 12$

43. $y = x^2 - 16$ $\qquad$ $0 = x^2 - 16$

$\quad$ x-intercepts: $(\pm 4, 0)$ $\quad$ $x^2 = 16$

$\qquad\qquad\qquad\qquad\qquad x = \pm 4$

45. $y = x^2 - 4x - 5$ $\qquad$ $0 = x^2 - 4x - 5$

$\quad$ x-intercepts: $(5, 0),\ (-1, 0)$ $\quad$ $0 = (x - 5)(x + 1)$

$\qquad\qquad\qquad\qquad\qquad\qquad x = 5 \text{ or } x = -1$

47. $y = x^2 - 4x$

x-intercepts: $(0, 0)$, $(4, 0)$

$0 = x^2 - 4x$

$0 = x(x - 4)$

$x = 0$ or $x = 4$

49. $y = 2x^2 - 7x - 30$

x-intercepts: $\left(-\frac{5}{2}, 0\right)$, $(6, 0)$

$0 = 2x^2 - 7x - 30$

$0 = (2x + 5)(x - 6)$

$x = -\frac{5}{2}$ or $x = 6$

51. $f(x) = [x - (-1)](x - 3)$ opens upward

$ = (x + 1)(x - 3)$

$ = x^2 - 2x - 3$

$f(x) = -[x - (-1)](x - 3)$ opens downward

$ = -(x + 1)(x - 3)$

$ = -(x^2 - 2x - 3)$

$ = -x^2 + 2x + 3$

Note: $f(x) = a(x + 1)(x - 3)$ has x-intercepts $(-1, 0)$ and $(3, 0)$ for all real numbers $a \neq 0$.

53. $f(x) = (x - 0)(x - 10)$ opens upward

$ = x^2 - 10x$

$f(x) = -(x - 0)(x - 10)$ opens downward

$ = -x^2 + 10x$

Note: $f(x) = a(x - 0)(x - 10) = ax(x - 10)$ has x-intercepts $(0, 0)$ and $(10, 0)$ for all real numbers $a \neq 0$.

55. $f(x) = [x - (-3)]\left[x - \left(-\frac{1}{2}\right)\right](2)$ opens upward

$ = (x + 3)\left(x + \frac{1}{2}\right)(2)$

$ = (x + 3)(2x + 1)$

$ = 2x^2 + 7x + 3$

$f(x) = -(2x^2 + 7x + 3)$ opens downward

$ = -2x^2 - 7x - 3$

Note: $f(x) = a(x + 3)(2x + 1)$ has x-intercepts $(-3, 0)$ and $\left(-\frac{1}{2}, 0\right)$ for all real numbers $a \neq 0$.

57. Let x = the first number and y = the second number. Then the sum is

$$x + y = 110 \implies y = 110 - x.$$

The product is $P(x) = xy = x(110 - x) = 110x - x^2$.

$P(x) = -x^2 + 110x$

$ = -(x^2 - 110x + 3025 - 3025)$

$ = -[(x - 55)^2 - 3025]$

$ = -(x - 55)^2 + 3025$

The maximum value of the product occurs at the vertex of $P(x)$ and is 3025. This happens when $x = y = 55$.

59. Let x = the first number and y = the second number. Then the sum is

$$x + 2y = 24 \implies y = \frac{24 - x}{2}.$$

The product is $P(x) = xy = x\left(\dfrac{24 - x}{2}\right)$.

$P(x) = \dfrac{1}{2}(-x^2 + 24x)$

$ = -\dfrac{1}{2}(x^2 - 24x + 144 - 144)$

$ = -\dfrac{1}{2}[(x - 12)^2 - 144] = -\dfrac{1}{2}(x - 12)^2 + 72$

The maximum value of the product occurs at the vertex of $P(x)$ and is 72. This happens when $x = 12$ and $y = (24 - 12)/2 = 6$. Thus, the numbers are 12 and 6.

61.

$$2x + 2y = 100$$
$$y = 50 - x$$

(a) $A(x) = xy = x(50 - x)$

     Domain: $0 < x < 50$

(b)

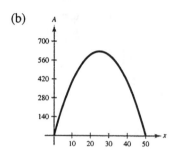

(c)   The area is maximum (625 square feet) when $x = y = 25$. The rectangle has dimensions 25 ft × 25 ft.

63. (a) $4x + 3y = 200 \implies y = \frac{1}{3}(200 - 4x)$

x	y	Area
2	$\frac{1}{3}[200 - 4(2)]$	$2xy = 256$
4	$\frac{1}{3}[200 - 4(4)]$	$2xy \approx 491$
6	$\frac{1}{3}[200 - 4(6)]$	$2xy = 704$
8	$\frac{1}{3}[200 - 4(8)]$	$2xy = 896$
10	$\frac{1}{3}[200 - 4(10)]$	$2xy \approx 1067$
12	$\frac{1}{3}[200 - 4(12)]$	$2xy = 1216$

(b)

x	y	Area
20	$\frac{1}{3}[200 - 4(20)]$	$2xy = 1600$
22	$\frac{1}{3}[200 - 4(22)]$	$2xy \approx 1643$
24	$\frac{1}{3}[200 - 4(24)]$	$2xy = 1664$
26	$\frac{1}{3}[200 - 4(26)]$	$2xy = 1664$
28	$\frac{1}{3}[200 - 4(28)]$	$2xy \approx 1643$
30	$\frac{1}{3}[200 - 4(30)]$	$2xy = 1600$

(c) $A = 2xy = 2x\left(\dfrac{200 - 4x}{3}\right) = \dfrac{2x(4)(50 - x)}{3}$

$= \dfrac{8x(50 - x)}{3}$

(d)

This area is maximum when $x = 25$ feet and $y = \frac{100}{3} = 33\frac{1}{3}$ feet.

(e) $A = \frac{8}{3}x(50 - x)$

$= -\frac{8}{3}(x^2 - 50x)$

$= -\frac{8}{3}(x^2 - 50x + 625 - 625)$

$= -\frac{8}{3}[(x - 25)^2 - 625]$

$= -\frac{8}{3}(x - 25)^2 + \frac{5000}{3}$

The maximum area occurs at the vertex and is 5000/3 square feet. This happens when $x = 25$ feet and $y = (200 - 4(25))/3 = 100/3$ feet. The dimensions are $2x = 50$ feet by $33\frac{1}{3}$ feet.

65. $R = 900x - 0.1x^2 = -0.1x^2 + 900x$

The vertex occurs at $x = -\dfrac{b}{2a} = -\dfrac{900}{2(-0.1)} = 4500$. The revenue is maximum when $x = 4500$ units.

67. $C = 800 - 10x + 0.25x^2 = 0.25x^2 - 10x + 800$

The vertex occurs at $x = -\dfrac{b}{2a} = -\dfrac{-10}{2(0.25)} = 20$. The cost is minimum when $x = 20$ fixtures.

69. $P = -0.0002x^2 + 140x - 250,000$

The vertex occurs at $x = -\dfrac{b}{2a} = -\dfrac{140}{2(-0.0002)} = 350,000$.

The profit is maximum when $x = 350,000$ units.

71. $y = -\dfrac{1}{12}x^2 + 2x + 4$

(a) When $x = 0$, $y = 4$ feet.

(b) The vertex occurs at $x = -\dfrac{b}{2a} = -\dfrac{2}{2\left(-\frac{1}{12}\right)} = 12$. The maximum height is

$$y = -\frac{1}{12}(12)^2 + 2(12) + 4 = 16 \text{ feet.}$$

(c) When the ball strikes the ground, $y = 0$.

$$0 = -\frac{1}{12}x^2 + 2x + 4$$

$$0 = x^2 - 24x - 48 \quad \text{Multiply both sides by } -12.$$

$$x = \frac{-(-24) \pm \sqrt{(-24)^2 - 4(1)(-48)}}{2(1)}$$

$$= \frac{24 \pm \sqrt{768}}{2} = \frac{24 \pm 16\sqrt{3}}{2} = 12 \pm 8\sqrt{3}$$

Using the positive value for x, we have $x = 12 + 8\sqrt{3} \approx 25.86$ feet.

73. $V = 0.77x^2 - 1.32x - 9.31, \ 5 \le x \le 40$

(a)

Number of board feet — Diameter (in inches)

(b) $V(16) = 166.69$ board feet

(c) $500 = 0.77x^2 - 1.32x - 9.31$

$0 = 0.77x^2 - 1.32x - 509.31$

Using the Quadratic Formula and selecting the positive value for x, we have $x \approx 26.6$ inches in diameter.

75. $C = 4024.5 + 51.4t - 3.1t^2,\ -10 \le t \le 30$

(a)

(b) $-\dfrac{b}{2a} = \dfrac{-51.4}{2(-3.1)} \approx 8.29$

The vertex occurs when $y \approx 4238$ which is the maximum average annual consumption. The warnings may not have had an immediate effect, but over time they and other findings about the health risks of cigarettes have had an effect.

(c) $C(0) = 4024.5$; annually $= \dfrac{116{,}530{,}000(4024.5)}{48{,}500{,}000} \approx 9670$; daily $= \dfrac{9670}{366} \approx 26$

77. If $f(x) = ax^2 + bx + c$ has two real zeros, then by the Quadratic Formula they are

$$x = \frac{-b \pm \sqrt{b^2 - 4ac}}{2a}.$$

The average of the zeros of f is

$$\frac{\dfrac{-b - \sqrt{b^2 - 4ac}}{2a} + \dfrac{-b + \sqrt{b^2 - 4ac}}{2a}}{2} = \frac{\dfrac{-2b}{2a}}{2} = -\frac{b}{2a}.$$

This is the x-coordinate of the vertex of the graph.

79. $(-4, 3)$ and $(2, 1)$

$$m = \frac{1 - 3}{2 - (-4)} = \frac{-2}{6} = -\frac{1}{3}$$

$$y - 1 = -\frac{1}{3}(x - 2)$$

$$3y - 3 = -x + 2$$

$$x + 3y - 5 = 0$$

81. $4x + 5y = 10 \implies y = -\frac{4}{5}x + 2$ and $m = -\frac{4}{5}$

The slope of the perpendicular line through $(0, 3)$ is $m = \frac{5}{4}$ and the y-intercept is $b = 3$.

$$y = \frac{5}{4}x + 3$$

$$0 = 5x - 4y + 12$$

Section 2.2   Polynomial Functions of Higher Degree

- You should know the following basic principles about polynomials.
- $f(x) = a_n x^n + a_{n-1}x^{n-1} + \cdots + a_2 x^2 + a_1 x + a_0$ is a polynomial function of degree n.
- If f is of odd degree and
  - (a) $a_n > 0$, then
    1. $f(x) \to \infty$ as $x \to \infty$.
    2. $f(x) \to -\infty$ as $x \to -\infty$.
  - (b) $a_n < 0$, then
    1. $f(x) \to -\infty$ as $x \to \infty$.
    2. $f(x) \to \infty$ as $x \to -\infty$.
- If f is of even degree and
  - (a) $a_n > 0$, then
    1. $f(x) \to \infty$ as $x \to \infty$.
    2. $f(x) \to \infty$ as $x \to -\infty$.
  - (b) $a_n < 0$, then
    1. $f(x) \to -\infty$ as $x \to \infty$.
    2. $f(x) \to -\infty$ as $x \to -\infty$.
- The following are equivalent for a polynomial function.
  - (a) $x = a$ is a zero of a function.
  - (b) $x = a$ is a solution of the polynomial equation $f(x) = 0$.
  - (c) $(x - a)$ is a factor of the polynomial.
  - (d) $(a, 0)$ is an x-intercept of the graph of f.
- A polynomial of degree n has at most n distinct zeros.
- If f is a polynomial function such that $a < b$ and $f(a) \neq f(b)$, then f takes on every value between $f(a)$ and $f(b)$ in the interval $[a, b]$.
- If you can find a value where a polynomial is positive and another value where it is negative, then there is at least one real zero between the values.

Solutions to Odd-Numbered Exercises

1. $f(x) = -2x + 3$ is a line with y-intercept $(0, 3)$. Matches graph (c).

3. $f(x) = -2x^2 - 5x$ is a parabola with x-intercepts $(0, 0)$ and $\left(-\frac{5}{2}, 0\right)$ and opens downward. Matches graph (h).

5. $f(x) = -\frac{1}{4}x^4 + 3x^2$ has intercepts $(0, 0)$ and $\left(\pm 2\sqrt{3}, 0\right)$. Matches graph (a).

7. $f(x) = x^4 + 2x^3$ has intercepts $(0, 0)$ and $(-2, 0)$. Matches graph (d).

9. $y = x^3$

(a) $f(x) = (x - 2)^3$

Horizontal shift two units to the right

(b) $f(x) = x^3 - 2$

Vertical shift two units downward

(c) $f(x) = -\frac{1}{2}x^3$

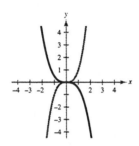

Reflection in the *x*-axis and a vertical shrink

(d) $f(x) = (x - 2)^3 - 2$

Horizontal shift two units to the right and a vertical shift two units downward

11. $y = x^4$

(a) $f(x) = (x + 3)^4$

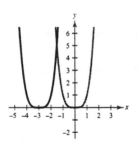

Horizontal shift three units to the left

(b) $f(x) = x^4 - 3$

Vertical shift three units downward

(c) $f(x) = 4 - x^4$

Reflection in the *x*-axis and then a vertical shift four units upward

(d) $f(x) = \frac{1}{2}(x - 1)^4$

Horizontal shift one unit to the right and a vertical shrink

13. $f(x) = \frac{1}{3}x^3 + 5x$

Degree: 3

Leading coefficient: $\frac{1}{3}$

The degree is odd and the leading coefficient is positive. The graph falls to the left and rises to the right.

15. $g(x) = 5 - \frac{7}{2}x - 3x^2$

Degree: 2

Leading coefficient: -3

The degree is even and the leading coefficient is negative. The graph falls to the left and right.

17. $f(x) = -2.1x^5 + 4x^3 - 2$

Degree: 5

Leading coefficient: -2.1

The degree is odd and the leading coefficient is negative. The graph rises to the left and falls to the right.

19. $f(x) = 6 - 2x + 4x^2 - 5x^3$

Degree: 3

Leading coefficient: -5

The degree is odd and the leading coefficient is negative. The graph rises to the left and falls to the right.

21. $h(t) = -\frac{2}{3}(t^2 - 5t + 3)$

Degree: 2

Leading coefficient: $-\frac{2}{3}$

The degree is even and the leading coefficient is negative. The graph falls to the left and right.

23. $f(x) = 3x^3 - 9x + 1$; $g(x) = 3x^3$

25. $f(x) = -(x^4 - 4x^3 + 16x)$; $g(x) = -x^4$

27. $f(x) = x^2 - 25$

$0 = (x + 5)(x - 5)$

$x = \pm 5$

29. $h(t) = t^2 - 6t + 9$

$0 = (t - 3)^2$

$t = 3$

31. $f(x) = x^2 + x - 2$

$0 = (x + 2)(x - 1)$

$x = -2, 1$

33. $f(x) = 3x^2 - 12x + 3$

$0 = 3(x^2 - 4x + 1)$

$x = \dfrac{4 \pm \sqrt{16 - 4}}{2} = 2 \pm \sqrt{3}$

35. $f(t) = t^3 - 4t^2 + 4t$

$0 = t(t - 2)^2$

$t = 0, 2$

37. $g(t) = \frac{1}{2}t^4 - \frac{1}{2}$

$0 = \frac{1}{2}(t + 1)(t - 1)(t^2 + 1)$

$t = \pm 1$

39. $f(x) = 2x^4 - 2x^2 - 40$

$0 = 2(x^2 + 4)(x + \sqrt{5})(x - \sqrt{5})$

$x = \pm\sqrt{5}$

41. $f(x) = 5x^4 + 15x^2 + 10$

$0 = 5(x^4 + 3x^2 + 2)$

$0 = 5(x^2 + 2)(x^2 + 1)$

No real zeros

43. $y = 4x^3 - 20x^2 + 25x$

$0 = 4x^3 - 20x^2 + 25x$

$0 = x(2x - 5)^2$

$x = 0$ or $x = \frac{5}{2}$

x-intercepts: $(0, 0), \left(\frac{5}{2}, 0\right)$

45. $y = x^5 - 5x^3 + 4x$

$0 = x^5 - 5x^3 + 4x$

$0 = x(x^2 - 1)(x^2 - 4)$

$0 = x(x + 1)(x - 1)(x + 2)(x - 2)$

$x = 0, \pm 1, \pm 2$

x-intercepts: $(0, 0), (\pm 1, 0), (\pm 2, 0)$

47. $f(x) = (x - 0)(x - 10)$

$f(x) = x^2 - 10x$

Note: $f(x) = a(x - 0)(x - 10) = ax(x - 10)$
has zeros 0 and 10 for all real numbers $a \neq 0$.

49. $f(x) = (x - 2)(x - (-6))$

$= (x - 2)(x + 6)$

$= x^2 + 4x - 12$

Note: $f(x) = a(x - 2)(x + 6)$ has zeros 2 and -6
for all real numbers $a \neq 0$.

51. $f(x) = (x - 0)(x - (-2))(x - (-3))$

$= x(x + 2)(x + 3)$

$= x^3 + 5x^2 + 6x$

Note: $f(x) = ax(x + 2)(x + 3)$ has zeros
$0, -2, -3$ for all real numbers $a \neq 0$.

53. $f(x) = (x - 4)(x + 3)(x - 3)(x - 0)$

$= (x - 4)(x^2 - 9)x$

$= x^4 - 4x^3 - 9x^2 + 36x$

Note: $f(x) = a(x^4 - 4x^3 - 9x^2 + 36x)$ has these
zeros for all real numbers $a \neq 0$.

55. $f(x) = \left[x - \left(1 + \sqrt{3}\right)\right]\left[x - \left(1 - \sqrt{3}\right)\right]$

$= \left[(x - 1) - \sqrt{3}\right]\left[(x - 1) + \sqrt{3}\right]$

$= (x - 1)^2 - \left(\sqrt{3}\right)^2$

$= x^2 - 2x + 1 - 3$

$= x^2 - 2x - 2$

Note: $f(x) = a(x^2 - 2x - 2)$ has these zeros for all real numbers $a \neq 0$.

57. $f(x) = x^3 - 3x^2 + 3$

The functions has three zeros. They are
in the intervals $(-1, 0), (1, 2)$ and $(2, 3)$.

59. $g(x) = 3x^4 + 4x^3 - 3$

The function has two zeros. They are in the
intervals $(-2, -1)$ and $(0, 1)$.

61. $f(x) = -\frac{3}{2}$

Horizontal line

63. $f(t) = \frac{1}{4}(t^2 - 2t + 15)$

$\qquad = \frac{1}{4}(t-1)^2 + \frac{7}{2}$

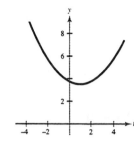

Parabola; opens upward

Vertex: $\left(1, \frac{7}{2}\right)$

65. $f(x) = x^3 - 3x^2 = x^2(x-3)$

Zeros: 0 and 3

Right: Moves up

Left: Moves down

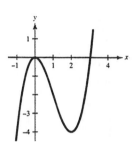

x	0	1	2	3	-1
$f(x)$	0	-2	-4	0	-4

67. $g(t) = -\frac{1}{4}(t-2)^2(t+2)^2$

Zeros: 2 and -2

Right: Moves down

Left: Moves down

t	-3	-2	-1	0	1	2	3
$g(t)$	$-\frac{25}{4}$	0	$-\frac{9}{4}$	-4	$-\frac{9}{4}$	0	$-\frac{25}{4}$

69. $h(x) = \frac{1}{3}x^3(x-4)^2$

Zeros: 0 and 4

Right: Moves up

Left: Moves down

x	-1	0	1	2	3	4	5
$h(x)$	$-\frac{25}{3}$	0	3	$\frac{32}{3}$	9	0	$\frac{125}{3}$

71. $f(x) = 1 - x^6$

x-intercepts: $(\pm 1, 0)$

y-intercept: $(0, 1)$

x	0	± 1	± 2
$f(x)$	1	0	-63

73. $f(x) = x^3 - 4x = x(x + 2)(x - 2)$

75. $g(x) = \frac{1}{5}(x + 1)^2(x - 3)(2x - 9)$

77. (a) $y_1 = -\frac{1}{3}(x - 2)^5 + 1$ is decreasing.

   $y_2 = \frac{3}{5}(x + 2)^5 - 3$ is increasing.

   (b) If $a > 0$, $g(x)$ will always be increasing.

   If $a < 0$, $g(x)$ will always be decreasing.

   (c) $H(x) = x^5 - 3x^3 + 2x + 1$

   Since $H(x)$ is not always increasing
   or always decreasing, $H(x) \neq a(x - h)^5 + k$.

   (d) $g(x) = a(x - h)^n + k$ is always increasing or
   always decreasing if n is an odd natural number.

79. $f(x) = x^4$; $f(x)$ is even.

(a) $g(x) = f(x) + 2$

Vertical shift two units upward

$g(-x) = f(-x) + 2$

$= f(x) + 2$

$= g(x)$

Even

(b) $g(x) = f(x + 2)$

Horizontal shift two units to the left

Neither odd nor even

(c) $g(x) = f(-x) = (-x)^4 = x^4$

Reflection in the y-axis. The graph
looks the same.
Even

(d) $g(x) = -f(x) = -x^4$

Reflection in the x-axis
Even

(e) $g(x) = f\left(\frac{1}{2}x\right) = \frac{1}{16}x^4$

Horizontal stretch

Even

(f) $g(x) = \frac{1}{2}f(x) = \frac{1}{2}x^4$

Vertical shrink

Even

(g) $g(x) = f(x^{3/4}) = (x^{3/4})^4 = x^3$

Odd

(h) $g(x) = (f \circ f)(x) = f(f(x)) = f(x^4) = (x^4)^4 = x^{16}$

Even

81. The point of diminishing returns (where the graph changes from curving
upward to curving downward) occurs when $x = 200$. The point is $(200, 160)$
which corresponds to spending $2,000,000 on advertising to obtain a revenue
of $160 million.

83. (a) $(f \circ g)(3) = f(g(3)) = f(1) = 0$

(b) The graph does not pass the horizontal line test.

(c) Since $g(3) = 1$, $g^{-1}(1) = 3$.

(d) $(g^{-1} \circ f)(0) = g^{-1}(f(0)) = g^{-1}(0) = 1$, since $g(1) = 0$.

85. $3x^2 - y = 4$

$y = 3x^2 - 4$

Yes, y is a function of x. Each x-value
corresponds to only one y-value.

87. $g(x) = x^2 - 1$

$$\frac{g(x) - g(4)}{x - 4} = \frac{(x^2 - 1) - 15}{x - 4}$$

$$= \frac{x^2 - 16}{x - 4}$$

$$= \frac{(x + 4)(x - 4)}{x - 4}$$

$$= x + 4, \quad x \neq 4$$

Section 2.3   Polynomial and Synthetic Division

You should know the following basic techniques and principles of polynomial division.

■   The Division Algorithm (Long Division of Polynomials)

■   Synthetic Division

■ $f(k)$ is equal to the remainder of $f(x)$ divided by $(x - k)$.

■ $f(k) = 0$ if and only if $(x - k)$ is a factor of $f(x)$.

Solutions to Odd-Numbered Exercises

1. $y_2 = 4 + \dfrac{4}{x - 1}$

$= \dfrac{4(x - 1) + 4}{x - 1}$

$= \dfrac{4x - 4 + 4}{x - 1}$

$= \dfrac{4x}{x - 1}$

$= y_1$

3. $y_2 = x - 2 + \dfrac{4}{x + 2}$

$= \dfrac{(x - 2)(x + 2) + 4}{x + 2}$

$= \dfrac{x^2 - 4 + 4}{x + 2}$

$= \dfrac{x^2}{x + 2}$

$= y_1$

5. $y_2 = x^3 - 4x + \dfrac{4x}{x^2 + 1}$

$= \dfrac{(x^3 - 4x)(x^2 + 1) + 4x}{x^2 + 1}$

$= \dfrac{x^5 + x^3 - 4x^3 - 4x + 4x}{x^2 + 1}$

$= \dfrac{x^5 - 3x^3}{x^2 + 1}$

7.

$$
\begin{array}{r}
2x + 4 \\
x + 3 \overline{)\ 2x^2 + 10x + 12} \\
-(2x^2 + 6x) \\
\hline
4x + 12 \\
-(4x + 12) \\
\hline
0
\end{array}
$$

$\dfrac{2x^2 + 10x + 12}{x + 3} = 2x + 4$

9.

$$
\begin{array}{r}
x^2 - 3x + 1 \\
4x + 5 \overline{)\ 4x^3 - 7x^2 - 11x + 5} \\
-(4x^3 + 5x^2) \\
\hline
-12x^2 - 11x \\
-(-12x^2 - 15x) \\
\hline
4x + 5 \\
-(4x + 5) \\
\hline
0
\end{array}
$$

$\dfrac{4x^3 - 7x^2 - 11x + 5}{4x + 5} = x^2 - 3x + 1$

11.

$$
\begin{array}{r}
x^3 + 3x^2 - 1 \\
x + 2 \overline{)\ x^4 + 5x^3 + 6x^2\ -x - 2} \\
-(x^4 + 2x^3) \\
\hline
3x^3 + 6x^2 \\
-(3x^3 + 6x^2) \\
\hline
-x - 2 \\
-(-x - 2) \\
\hline
0
\end{array}
$$

$$\frac{x^4 + 5x^3 + 6x^2 - x - 2}{x + 2} = x^3 + 3x^2 - 1$$

13.

$$
\begin{array}{r}
7 \\
x + 2 \overline{)\ 7x + 3} \\
-(7x + 14) \\
\hline
-11
\end{array}
$$

$$\frac{7x + 3}{x + 2} = 7 - \frac{11}{x + 2}$$

15.

$$
\begin{array}{r}
3x + 5 \\
2x^2 + 0x + 1 \overline{)\ 6x^3 + 10x^2 + x + 8} \\
-(6x^3 + 0x^2 + 3x) \\
\hline
10x^2 - 2x + 8 \\
-(10x^2 + 0x + 5) \\
\hline
-2x + 3
\end{array}
$$

$$\frac{6x^3 + 10x^2 + x + 8}{2x^2 + 1} = 3x + 5 - \frac{2x - 3}{2x^2 + 1}$$

17.

$$
\begin{array}{r}
x^2 + 2x + 4 \\
x^2 - 2x + 3 \overline{)\ x^4 + 0x^3 + 3x^2 + 0x + 1} \\
-(x^4 - 2x^3 + 3x^2) \\
\hline
2x^3 + 0x^2 + 0x \\
-(2x^3 - 4x^2 + 6x) \\
\hline
4x^2 - 6x + 1 \\
-(4x^2 - 8x + 12) \\
\hline
2x - 11
\end{array}
$$

$\Rightarrow$

$$\frac{x^4 + 3x^2 + 1}{x^2 - 2x + 3} = x^2 + 2x + 4 + \frac{2x - 11}{x^2 - 2x + 3}$$

19.

$$
\begin{array}{r}
x + 3 \\
x^3 - 3x^2 + 3x - 1 \overline{)\ x^4 + 0x^3 + 0x^2 + 0x + 0} \\
-(x^4 - 3x^3 + 3x^2 - x) \\
\hline
3x^3 - 3x^2 + x + 0 \\
-(3x^3 - 9x^2 + 9x - 3) \\
\hline
6x^2 - 8x + 3
\end{array}
$$

$$\frac{x^4}{(x - 1)^3} = x + 3 + \frac{6x^2 - 8x + 3}{(x - 1)^3}$$

21.

$$
\begin{array}{r}
x^{2n} + 6x^n + 9 \\
x^n + 3\overline{)\ x^{3n} + 9x^{2n} + 27x^n + 27} \\
-\ (x^{3n} + 3x^{2n}) \\
\hline
6x^{2n} + 27x^n \\
-\ (6x^{2n} + 18x^n) \\
\hline
9x^n + 27 \\
-\ (9x^n\ + 27) \\
\hline
0
\end{array}
$$

$$
\frac{x^{3n} + 9x^{2n} + 27x^n + 27}{x^n + 3} = x^{2n} + 6x^n + 9
$$

23.

$$
\begin{array}{r|rrrr}
5 & 3 & -17 & 15 & -25 \\
  &   & 15 & -10 & 25 \\
\hline
  & 3 & -2 & 5   & 0
\end{array}
$$

$$
\frac{3x^3 - 17x^2 + 15x - 25}{x - 5} = 3x^2 - 2x + 5
$$

25.

$$
\begin{array}{r|rrrr}
-2 & 4 & 8 & -9 & -18 \\
   &   & -8 & 0 & 18 \\
\hline
   & 4 & 0 & -9 & 0
\end{array}
$$

$$
\frac{4x^3 + 8x^2 - 9x - 18}{x + 2} = 4x^2 - 9
$$

27.

$$
\begin{array}{r|rrrr}
-10 & -1 & 0 & 75 & -250 \\
    &   & 10 & -100 & 250 \\
\hline
    & -1 & 10 & -25 & 0
\end{array}
$$

$$
\frac{-x^3 + 75x - 250}{x + 10} = -x^2 + 10x - 25
$$

29.

$$
\begin{array}{r|rrrr}
4 & 5 & -6 & 0 & 8 \\
  &   & 20 & 56 & 224 \\
\hline
  & 5 & 14 & 56 & 232
\end{array}
$$

$$
\frac{5x^3 - 6x^2 + 8}{x - 4} = 5x^2 + 14x + 56 + \frac{232}{x - 4}
$$

31.

$$
\begin{array}{r|rrrrr}
6 & 10 & -50 & 0 & 0 & -800 \\
  &   & 60 & 60 & 360 & 2160 \\
\hline
  & 10 & 10 & 60 & 360 & 1360
\end{array}
$$

$$
\frac{10^4 - 50x^3 - 800}{x - 6} = 10x^3 + 10x^2 + 60x + 360 + \frac{1360}{x - 6}
$$

33.

$$
\begin{array}{r|rrrr}
-8 & 1 & 0 & 0 & 512 \\
   &   & -8 & 64 & -512 \\
\hline
   & 1 & -8 & 64 & 0
\end{array}
$$

$$
\frac{x^3 + 512}{x + 8} = x^2 - 8x + 64
$$

35.

$$
\begin{array}{r|rrrrr}
2 & -3 & 0 & 0 & 0 & 0 \\
  &   & -6 & -12 & -24 & -48 \\
\hline
  & -3 & -6 & -12 & -24 & -48
\end{array}
$$

$$
\frac{-3x^4}{x - 2} = -3x^3 - 6x^2 - 12x - 24 - \frac{48}{x - 2}
$$

37.

$$
\begin{array}{r|rrrrr}
6 & -1 & 0 & 0 & 180 & 0 \\
  &   & -6 & -36 & -216 & -216 \\
\hline
  & -1 & -6 & -36 & -36 & -216
\end{array}
$$

$$\frac{180x - x^4}{x - 6} = -x^3 - 6x^2 - 36x - 36 - \frac{216}{x - 6}$$

39.

$$
\begin{array}{r|rrrr}
-\frac{1}{2} & 4 & 16 & -23 & -15 \\
            &   & -2 & -7 & 15 \\
\hline
            & 4 & 14 & -30 & 0
\end{array}
$$

$$\frac{4x^3 + 16x^2 - 23x - 15}{x + \frac{1}{2}} = 4x^2 + 14x - 30$$

41. A divisor divided evenly into the dividend if the remainder is zero.

43.

$$
\begin{array}{r|rrrr}
5 & 1 & 4 & -3 & c \\
  &   & 5 & 45 & 210 \\
\hline
  & 1 & 9 & 42 & c + 210
\end{array}
$$

For $c + 210$ to equal zero, c must equal -210.

45. $f(x) = x^3 - x^2 - 14x + 11$, $k = 4$

$$
\begin{array}{r|rrrr}
4 & 1 & -1 & -14 & 11 \\
  &   & 4 & 12 & -8 \\
\hline
  & 1 & 3 & -2 & 3
\end{array}
$$

$f(x) = (x - 4)(x^2 + 3x - 2) + 3$

$f(4) = (0)(26) + 3 = 3$

47. $f(x) = x^3 + 3x^2 - 2x - 14$, $k = \sqrt{2}$

$$
\begin{array}{r|rrrr}
\sqrt{2} & 1 & 3 & -2 & -14 \\
         &   & \sqrt{2} & 2 + 3\sqrt{2} & 6 \\
\hline
         & 1 & 3 + \sqrt{2} & 3\sqrt{2} & -8
\end{array}
$$

$f(x) = (x - \sqrt{2})\left[x^2 + (3 + \sqrt{2})x + 3\sqrt{2}\right] - 8$

$f(\sqrt{2}) = (0)(4 + 6\sqrt{2}) - 8 = -8$

49. $f(x) = 4x^3 - 13x + 10$

(a)
$$
\begin{array}{r|rrrr}
1 & 4 & 0 & -13 & 10 \\
  &   & 4 & 4 & -9 \\
\hline
  & 4 & 4 & -9 & \underline{1} = f(1)
\end{array}
$$

(b)
$$
\begin{array}{r|rrrr}
-2 & 4 & 0 & -13 & 10 \\
   &   & -8 & 16 & -6 \\
\hline
   & 4 & -8 & 3 & 4 & \underline{4} = f(-2)
\end{array}
$$

(c)
$$
\begin{array}{r|rrrr}
\frac{1}{2} & 4 & 0 & -13 & 10 \\
            &   & 2 & 1 & -6 \\
\hline
            & 4 & 2 & -12 & \underline{4} = f\left(\frac{1}{2}\right)
\end{array}
$$

(d)
$$
\begin{array}{r|rrrr}
8 & 4 & 0 & -13 & 10 \\
  &   & 32 & 256 & 1944 \\
\hline
  & 4 & 32 & 243 & \underline{1954} = f(8)
\end{array}
$$

51. $h(x) = 3x^3 + 5x^2 - 10x + 1$

(a)
$$
\begin{array}{r|rrrr}
3 & 3 & 5 & -10 & 1 \\
  &   & 9 & 42 & 96 \\
\hline
  & 3 & 14 & 32 & \underline{97} = h(3)
\end{array}
$$

(b)
$$
\begin{array}{r|rrrr}
\frac{1}{3} & 3 & 5 & -10 & 1 \\
            &   & 1 & 2 & -\frac{8}{3} \\
\hline
            & 3 & 6 & -8 & \underline{-\frac{5}{3}} = h\left(\frac{1}{3}\right)
\end{array}
$$

(c)
$$
\begin{array}{r|rrrr}
-2 & 3 & 5 & -10 & 1 \\
   &   & -6 & 2 & 16 \\
\hline
   & 3 & -1 & -8 & \underline{17} = h(-2)
\end{array}
$$

(d)
$$
\begin{array}{r|rrrr}
-5 & 3 & 5 & -10 & 1 \\
   &   & -15 & 50 & -200 \\
\hline
   & 3 & -10 & 40 & \underline{-199} = h(-5)
\end{array}
$$

53. $f(x) = (x + 3)^2(x - 3)(x + 1)^3$

The remainder when $k = -3$ is zero since $(x + 3)$ is a factor of $f(x)$.

55.

$$
\begin{array}{r|rrrr}
2 & 1 & 0 & -7 & 6 \\
  &   & 2 & 4 & -6 \\
\hline
  & 1 & 2 & -3 & 0
\end{array}
$$

$x^3 - 7x + 6 = (x - 2)(x^2 + 2x - 3)$
$\qquad\qquad\quad = (x - 2)(x + 3)(x - 1)$

Zeros: $2, -3, 1$

57.

$$
\begin{array}{r|rrrr}
\frac{1}{2} & 2 & -15 & 27 & -10 \\
  &   & 1 & -7 & 10 \\
\hline
  & 2 & -14 & 20 & 0
\end{array}
$$

$2x^3 - 15x^2 + 27x - 10$
$\qquad = \left(x - \tfrac{1}{2}\right)(2x^2 - 14x + 20)$
$\qquad = (2x - 1)(x - 2)(x - 5)$

Zeros: $\frac{1}{2}, 2, 5$

59.

$$
\begin{array}{r|rrrr}
\sqrt{3} & 1 & 2 & -3 & -6 \\
  &   & \sqrt{3} & 3 + 2\sqrt{3} & 6 \\
\hline
  & 1 & 2 + \sqrt{3} & 2\sqrt{3} & 0
\end{array}
$$

$$
\begin{array}{r|rrr}
-\sqrt{3} & 1 & 2 + \sqrt{3} & 2\sqrt{3} \\
  &   & -\sqrt{3} & -2\sqrt{3} \\
\hline
  & 1 & 2 & 0
\end{array}
$$

$x^3 + 2x^2 - 3x - 6 = \left(x - \sqrt{3}\right)\left(x + \sqrt{3}\right)(x + 2)$

Zeros: $\pm\sqrt{3}, -2$

61.

$$
\begin{array}{r|rrrr}
1 + \sqrt{3} & 1 & -3 & 0 & 2 \\
  &   & 1 + \sqrt{3} & 1 - \sqrt{3} & -2 \\
\hline
  & 1 & -2 + \sqrt{3} & 1 - \sqrt{3} & 0
\end{array}
$$

$$
\begin{array}{r|rrr}
1 - \sqrt{3} & 1 & -2 + \sqrt{3} & 1 - \sqrt{3} \\
  &   & 1 - \sqrt{3} & -1 + \sqrt{3} \\
\hline
  & 1 & -1 & 0
\end{array}
$$

$x^3 - 3x^2 + 2 = \left[x - \left(1 + \sqrt{3}\right)\right]\left[x - \left(1 - \sqrt{3}\right)\right](x - 1)$
$\qquad\qquad\quad = (x - 1)\left(x - 1 - \sqrt{3}\right)\left(x - 1 + \sqrt{3}\right)$

Zeros: $1, 1 \pm \sqrt{3}$

63. $f(x) = x^3 - 2x^2 - 5x + 10$

   (a) The zeros of f are 2 and $\approx \pm 2.236$.

   (b)

$$
\begin{array}{r|rrrr}
2 & 1 & -2 & -5 & 10 \\
  &   & 2 & 0 & -10 \\
\hline
  & 1 & 0 & -5 & 0
\end{array}
$$

$f(x) = (x - 2)(x^2 - 5)$

      $= (x - 2)(x - \sqrt{5})(x + \sqrt{5})$

65. $h(t) = t^3 - 2t^2 - 7t + 2$

   (a) The zeros of h are -2, ≈ 3.732, ≈ 0.268.

   (b)

$$
\begin{array}{r|rrrr}
-2 & 1 & -2 & -7 & 2 \\
   &   & -2 & 8 & -2 \\
\hline
   & 1 & -4 & 1 & 0
\end{array}
$$

$h(t) = (t + 2)(t^2 - 4t + 1)$

By the Quadratic Formula, the zeros of

     $t^2 - 4t + 1$ are $2 \pm \sqrt{3}$.

Thus, $h(t) = (t + 2)\left[t - \left(2 + \sqrt{3}\right)\right]\left[t - \left(2 - \sqrt{3}\right)\right]$.

67.

$$
\begin{array}{r|rrrr}
\frac{3}{2} & 4 & -8 & 1 & 3 \\
            &   & 6 & -3 & -3 \\
\hline
            & 4 & -2 & -2 & 0
\end{array}
$$

$4x^3 - 8x^2 + x + 3 = \left(x - \frac{3}{2}\right)(4x^2 - 2x - 2)$

                      $= \left(x - \frac{3}{2}\right)(2)(2x^2 - x - 1)$

                      $= (2x - 3)(2x^2 - x - 1)$

Thus,

$$\frac{4x^3 - 8x^2 + x + 3}{2x - 3} = 2x^2 - x - 1 = (2x + 1)(x - 1).$$

69.

$$
\begin{array}{r|rrrr}
-1 & 1 & 3 & -1 & -3 \\
   &   & -1 & -2 & 3 \\
\hline
   & 1 & 2 & -3 & 0
\end{array}
$$

$\dfrac{x^3 + 3x^2 - x - 3}{x + 1} = x^2 + 2x - 3$

                   $= (x + 3)(x - 1)$

71.

$$
\begin{array}{r|rrrrr}
-1 & 1 & 6 & 11 & 6 & 0 \\
   &   & -1 & -5 & -6 & 0 \\
\hline
   & 1 & 5 & 6 & 0 & 0
\end{array}
$$

$$
\begin{array}{r|rrrr}
-2 & 1 & 5 & 6 & 0 \\
   &   & -2 & -6 & 0 \\
\hline
   & 1 & 3 & 0 & 0
\end{array}
$$

$\dfrac{x^4 + 6x^3 + 11x^2 + 6x}{(x + 1)(x + 2)} = x^2 + 3x$

                      $= x(x + 3)$

73. Since $y = 110$ when $x = 5$, we have $x = 5$ as a zero to the equation $f(x) = y - 110$.

$$f(x) = y - 110, \ 1 \leq x \leq 5$$
$$= -1.42x^3 + 5.04x^2 + 32.45x - 110.75$$

$$5 \ \underline{\big|} \ \begin{array}{ccccc} -1.42 & 5.04 & 32.45 & -110.75 \\ & -7.10 & -10.30 & 110.75 \\ \hline -1.42 & -2.06 & 22.15 & 0 \end{array}$$

Thus, $f(x) = (x - 5)(-1.42x^2 - 2.06x + 22.15)$. Using the Quadratic Formula to find the other two zeros yields

$$x = \frac{-(-2.06) \pm \sqrt{(-2.06)^2 - 4(-1.42)(22.15)}}{2(-1.42)}$$

$$= \frac{2.06 \pm \sqrt{130.0556}}{-2.84}$$

$$x \approx -4.74 \text{ or } x \approx 3.29.$$

Since $1 \leq x \leq 5$, we choose $x = 3.29$ which corresponds to 3290 rpm.

75. $f(x) = (x - k)q(x) + r$

(a) $k = 2, \ r = 5, \ q(x) = $ any quadratic $ax^2 + bx + c$ where $a > 0$.

One example: $f(x) = (x - 2)x^2 + 5 = x^3 - 2x^2 + 5$

(b) $k = -3, \ r = 1, \ q(x) = $ any quadratic $ax^2 + bx + c$ where $a < 0$.

One example: $f(x) = (x + 3)(-x^2) + 1 = -x^3 - 3x^2 + 1$

77. $f(x) = \sqrt[3]{x + 2}$

$$y = \sqrt[3]{x + 2}$$

$$x = \sqrt[3]{y + 2}$$

$$x^3 = y + 2$$

$$x^3 - 2 = y$$

$$f^{-1}(x) = x^3 - 2$$

79. $f(x) = \sqrt{x}, \ g(x) = x^2 - 25$

$(f \circ g)(x) = f(g(x)) = f(x^2 - 25) = \sqrt{x^2 - 25}$

Domain: $x^2 - 25 \geq 0$

$(x + 5)(x - 5) \geq 0$

Critical numbers: $x = \pm 5$

Test intervals: $(-\infty, -5)(-5, \ 5)(5, \ \infty)$

Test: Is $x^2 - 25 \geq 0$?

Solution set: $[-\infty, -5] \cup [5, \infty)$ or $x \leq -5, x \geq 5$

2.4   Real Zeros of Polynomial Functions

■ You should know Descartes's Rule of Signs.

(a) The number of positive real zeros of f is either equal to the number of variations of sign of f or is less than that number by an even integer.

(b) The number of negative real zeros of f is either equal to the number of variations in sign of $f(-x)$ or is less than that number by an even integer.

(c) When there is only one variation in sign, there is exactly one positive (or negative) real zero.

■ You should know the Rational Zero Test.

■ You should know shortcuts for the Rational Zero Test.

(a) Use a graphing or programmable calculator.

(b) Sketch a graph.

(c) After finding a root, use synthetic division to reduce the degree of the polynomial.

■ You should be able to observe the last row obtained from synthetic division in order to determine upper or lower bounds.

(a) If the test value is positive and all of the entries in the last row are positive or zero, then the test value is an upper bound.

(b) If the test value is negative and the entries in the last row alternate from positive to negative, then the test value is a lower bound. (Zero entries count as positive or negative.)

Solutions to Odd-Numbered Exercises

1. $f(x) = x^3 + 3$

Sign variations: 0, positive zeros: 0

$f(-x) = -x^3 + 3$

Sign variations: 1, negative zeros: 1

3. $g(x) = 5x^5 + 10x = 5x(x^4 + 2)$

Let $f(x) = x^4 + 2$.

Sign variations: 0, positive zeros: 0

$f(-x) = x^4 + 2$

Sign variations: 0, negative zeros: 0

5. $h(x) = 3x^4 + 2x^2 + 1$

Sign variations: 0, positive zeros: 0

$h(-x) = 3x^4 + 2x^2 + 1$

Sign variations: 0, negative zeros: 0

7. $g(x) = 2x^3 - 3x^2 - 3$

Sign variations: 1, positive zeros: 1

$g(-x) = -2x^3 - 3x^2 - 3$

Sign variations: 0, negative zeros: 0

9. $f(x) = -5x^3 + x^2 - x + 5$

Sign variations: 3, positive zeros: 3 or 1

$f(-x) = 5x^3 + x^2 + x + 5$

Sign variations: 0, negative zeros: 0

11. $f(x) = x^3 + 3x^2 - x - 3$

Possible rational zeros: $\pm 1, \pm 3$

Zeros shown on graph: $-3, -1, 1$

13. $f(x) = 2x^4 - 17x^3 + 35x^2 + 9x - 45$

Possible rational zeros: $\pm 1, \pm 3, \pm 5, \pm 9, \pm 15, \pm 45, \pm\frac{1}{2}, \pm\frac{3}{2}, \pm\frac{5}{2}, \pm\frac{9}{2}, \pm\frac{15}{2}, \pm\frac{45}{2}$

Zeros shown on graph: $-1, \frac{3}{2}, 3, 5$

15. $f(x) = 20x^4 + 144x^3 - 253x^2 - 900x + 800$

Possible rational zeros: $\pm 1, \pm 2, \pm 4, \pm 5, \pm 8, \pm 10, \pm 16, \pm 20, \pm 25,$

$\pm 32, \pm 40, \pm 50, \pm 80, \pm 100, \pm 160, \pm 200, \pm 400,$

$\pm 800, \pm\frac{1}{2}, \pm\frac{5}{2}, \pm\frac{25}{2}, \pm\frac{1}{4}, \pm\frac{5}{4}, \pm\frac{25}{4}, \pm\frac{1}{5}, \pm\frac{2}{5}, \pm\frac{4}{5},$

$\pm\frac{8}{5}, \pm\frac{16}{5}, \pm\frac{32}{5}, \pm\frac{1}{10}, \pm\frac{1}{20}$

Zeros shown on graph: $-8, -\frac{5}{2}, \frac{4}{5}, \frac{5}{2}$

17. $f(x) = x^3 - 6x^2 + 11x - 6$

Possible rational zeros: $\pm 1, \pm 2, \pm 3$

$$
\begin{array}{r|rrrr}
1 & 1 & -6 & 11 & -6 \\
  &   & 1 & -5 & 6 \\
\hline
  & 1 & -5 & 6 & 0 \\
\end{array}
$$

$x^3 - 6x^2 + 11x - 6 = (x - 1)(x^2 - 5x + 6) = (x - 1)(x - 2)(x - 3)$.

Thus, the real zeros are 1, 2, and 3.

19. $g(x) = x^3 - 4x^2 - x + 4 = x^2(x - 4) - 1(x - 4) = (x - 4)(x^2 - 1)$

$\qquad = (x - 4)(x - 1)(x + 1)$

Thus, the zeros of $g(x)$ are 4 and ± 1.

21. $h(t) = t^3 + 12t^2 + 21t + 10$

Possible rational zeros: $\pm 1, \pm 2, \pm 5, \pm 10$

$$
\begin{array}{r|rrrr}
-1 & 1 & 12 & 21 & 10 \\
   &   & -1 & -11 & -10 \\
\hline
   & 1 & 11 & 10 & 0 \\
\end{array}
$$

$t^3 + 12t^2 + 21t + 10 = (t + 1)(t^2 + 11t + 10)$

$\qquad\qquad\qquad\qquad = (t + 1)(t + 1)(t + 10)$

$\qquad\qquad\qquad\qquad = (t + 1)^2(t + 10)$

Thus, the zeros are -1 and -10.

23. $f(x) = x^3 - 4x^2 + 5x - 2$

Possible rational zeros: $\pm 1, \pm 2$

$$
\begin{array}{r|rrrr}
1 & 1 & -4 & 5 & -2 \\
  &   & 1 & -3 & 2 \\
\hline
  & 1 & -3 & 2 & 0 \\
\end{array}
$$

$x^3 - 4x^2 + 5x - 2 = (x - 1)(x^2 - 3x + 2)$

$\qquad\qquad\qquad\quad = (x - 1)(x - 1)(x - 2)$

$\qquad\qquad\qquad\quad = (x - 1)^2(x - 2)$

Thus, the zeros are 1 and 2.

25. $C(x) = 2x^3 + 3x^2 - 1$

Possible rational zeros: $\pm 1, \pm\frac{1}{2}$

$$
\begin{array}{r|rrrr}
-1 & 2 & 3 & 0 & -1 \\
   &   & -2 & -1 & 1 \\
\hline
   & 2 & 1 & -1 & 0 \\
\end{array}
$$

$2x^3 + 3x^2 - 1 = (x + 1)(2x^2 + x - 1)$

$\qquad\qquad\quad = (x + 1)(x + 1)(2x - 1)$

$\qquad\qquad\quad = (x + 1)^2(2x - 1)$

Thus, the zeros are -1 and $\frac{1}{2}$.

27. $f(x) = 9x^4 - 9x^3 - 58x^2 + 4x + 24$

Possible rational zeros: $\pm 1, \ \pm 2, \ \pm 3, \ \pm 4, \ \pm 6, \ \pm 8, \ \pm 12, \ \pm 24, \ \pm\frac{1}{3}, \ \pm\frac{2}{3},$
$\pm\frac{4}{3}, \ \pm\frac{8}{3}, \ \pm\frac{1}{9}, \ \pm\frac{2}{9}, \ \pm\frac{4}{9}$

$$
\begin{array}{r|rrrrr}
-2 & 9 & -9 & -58 & 4 & 24 \\
   &   & -18 & 54 & 8 & -24 \\
\hline
   & 9 & -27 & -4 & 12 & 0
\end{array}
$$

$$
\begin{array}{r|rrrr}
3 & 9 & -27 & -4 & 12 \\
  &   & 27 & 0 & -12 \\
\hline
  & 9 & 0 & -4 & 0
\end{array}
$$

$$9x^4 - 9x^3 - 58x^2 + 4x - 24 = (x + 2)(x - 3)(9x^2 - 4)$$
$$= (x + 2)(x - 3)(3x - 2)(3x + 2)$$

Thus, the zeros are -2, 3, and $\pm\frac{2}{3}$.

29. $z^4 - z^3 - 2z - 4 = 0$

Possible rational zeros: $\pm 1, \ \pm 2, \ \pm 4$

$$
\begin{array}{r|rrrrr}
-1 & 1 & -1 & 0 & -2 & -4 \\
   &   & -1 & 2 & -2 & 4 \\
\hline
   & 1 & -2 & 2 & -4 & 0
\end{array}
$$

$$
\begin{array}{r|rrrr}
2 & 1 & -2 & 2 & -4 \\
  &   & 2 & 0 & 4 \\
\hline
  & 1 & 0 & 2 & 0
\end{array}
$$

$$z^4 - z^3 - 2z - 4 = (x + 1)(x - 2)(x^2 + 2)$$

The only real zeros are -1 and 2.

31. $2y^4 + 7y^3 - 26y^2 + 23y - 6 = 0$

Possible rational zeros: $\pm 1, \ \pm 2, \ \pm 3, \ \pm 6, \ \pm \frac{1}{2}, \ \pm \frac{3}{2}$

$$
\begin{array}{r|rrrrr}
1 & 2 & 7 & -26 & 23 & -6 \\
  &   & 2 & 9 & -17 & 6 \\
\hline
  & 2 & 9 & -17 & 6 & 0
\end{array}
$$

$$
\begin{array}{r|rrrr}
-6 & 2 & 9 & -17 & 6 \\
   &   & -12 & 18 & -6 \\
\hline
   & 2 & -3 & 1 & 0
\end{array}
$$

$$
\begin{aligned}
2y^4 + 7y^3 - 26y^2 + 23y - 6 &= (y - 1)(y + 6)(2y^2 - 3y + 1) \\
&= (y - 1)(y + 6)(2y - 1)(y - 1) \\
&= (y - 1)^2(y + 6)(2y - 1)
\end{aligned}
$$

The only real zeros are $1, \ -6,$ and $\frac{1}{2}$.

33. $f(x) = x^3 + x^2 - 4x - 4$

(a) Possible rational zeros: $\pm 1, \ \pm 2, \ \pm 4$

(b)

(c) $-2, \ -1, 2$ on graph

35. $f(x) = -4x^3 + 15x^2 - 8x - 3$

(a) Possible rational zeros: $\pm \frac{1}{4}, \ \pm \frac{1}{2}, \ \pm \frac{3}{4}, \ \pm 1, \ \pm \frac{3}{2}, \ \pm 3$

(b)

(c) $-\frac{1}{4}, \ 1, 3$ on graph

37. $f(x) = -2x^4 + 13x^3 - 21x^2 + 2x + 8$

(a) Possible rational zeros: $\pm \frac{1}{2}, \ \pm 1, \ \pm 2, \ \pm 4, \ \pm 8$

(b)

(c) $-\frac{1}{2}, \ 1, \ 2, \ 4$ on graph

39. $f(x) = 32x^3 - 52x^2 + 17x + 3$

(a) Possible rational zeros: ± 1, ± 3, $\pm\frac{1}{2}$, $\pm\frac{3}{2}$, $\pm\frac{1}{4}$, $\pm\frac{3}{4}$, $\pm\frac{1}{8}$, $\pm\frac{3}{8}$,

$\pm\frac{1}{16}$, $\pm\frac{3}{16}$, $\pm\frac{1}{32}$, $\pm\frac{3}{32}$

(b)

(c) $-\frac{1}{8}$, $\frac{3}{4}$, 1 on graph

41. $f(x) = x^4 - 3x^2 + 2$

(a) From the calculator we have

$x = \pm 1$ and $x \approx \pm 1.414$.

(b)

$$
\begin{array}{r|rrrrr}
1 & 1 & 0 & -3 & 0 & 2 \\
  &   & 1 & 1 & -2 & -2 \\
\hline
  & 1 & 1 & -2 & -2 & 0
\end{array}
$$

$$
\begin{array}{r|rrrr}
-1 & 1 & 1 & -2 & -2 \\
   &   & -1 & 0 & 2 \\
\hline
   & 1 & 0 & -2 & 0
\end{array}
$$

$f(x) = (x - 1)(x + 1)(x^2 - 2)$

$\qquad = (x - 1)(x + 1)(x - \sqrt{2})(x + \sqrt{2})$

The exact roots are $x = \pm 1$, $\pm\sqrt{2}$.

43. $h(x) = x^5 - 7x^4 + 10x^3 + 14x^2 - 24x$

(a) $h(x) = x(x^4 - 7x^3 + 10x^2 + 14x - 24)$

From the calculator we have

$x = 0$, 3, 4 and $x \approx \pm 1.414$.

(b)

$$
\begin{array}{r|rrrrr}
3 & 1 & -7 & 10 & 14 & -24 \\
  &   & 3 & -12 & -6 & 24 \\
\hline
  & 1 & -4 & -2 & 8 & 0
\end{array}
$$

$$
\begin{array}{r|rrrr}
4 & 1 & -4 & -2 & 8 \\
  &   & 4 & 0 & -8 \\
\hline
  & 1 & 0 & -2 & 0
\end{array}
$$

$f(x) = x(x - 3)(x - 4)(x^2 - 2)$

$\qquad = x(x - 3)(x - 4)(x - \sqrt{2})(x + \sqrt{2})$

The exact roots are $x = 0$, 3, 4, $\pm\sqrt{2}$.

45. $f(x) = x^4 - 4x^3 + 15$

(a)

$$
\begin{array}{r|rrrrr}
4 & 1 & -4 & 0 & 0 & 15 \\
  &   & 4 & 0 & 0 & 0 \\
\hline
  & 1 & 0 & 0 & 0 & 15
\end{array}
$$

4 is an upper bound.

(b)

$$
\begin{array}{r|rrrrr}
-1 & 1 & -4 & 0 & 0 & 15 \\
   &   & -1 & 5 & -5 & 5 \\
\hline
   & 1 & -5 & 5 & -5 & 20
\end{array}
$$

-1 is a lower bound.

47. $f(x) = x^4 - 4x^3 + 16x - 16$

(a)

$$
\begin{array}{r|rrrrr}
5 & 1 & -4 & 0 & 16 & -16 \\
  &   & 5 & 5 & 25 & 205 \\
\hline
  & 1 & 1 & 5 & 41 & 189
\end{array}
$$

5 is an upper bound.

(b)

$$
\begin{array}{r|rrrrr}
-3 & 1 & -4 & 0 & 16 & -16 \\
   &   & -3 & 21 & -63 & 141 \\
\hline
   & 1 & -7 & 21 & -47 & 125
\end{array}
$$

-3 is a lower bound.

49. $f(x) = 4x^3 - 3x - 1$

Possible rational zeros: $\pm 1, \pm\frac{1}{2}, \pm\frac{1}{4}$

$$
\begin{array}{r|rrrr}
1 & 4 & 0 & -3 & -1 \\
  &   & 4 & 4 & 1 \\
\hline
  & 4 & 4 & 1 & 0
\end{array}
$$

$4x^3 - 3x - 1 = (x - 1)(4x^2 + 4x + 1) = (x - 1)(2x + 1)^2$

Thus, the zeros are 1 and $-\frac{1}{2}$.

51. $f(y) = 4y^3 + 3y^2 + 8y + 6$

Possible rational zeros: $\pm 1, \pm 2, \pm 3, \pm 6, \pm\frac{1}{2}, \pm\frac{3}{2}, \pm\frac{1}{4}, \pm\frac{3}{4}$

$$
\begin{array}{r|rrrr}
-\frac{3}{4} & 4 & 3 & 8 & 6 \\
  &   & -3 & 0 & -6 \\
\hline
  & 4 & 0 & 8 & 0
\end{array}
$$

$4y^3 + 3y^2 + 8y + 6 = \left(y + \frac{3}{4}\right)(4y^2 + 8) = \left(y + \frac{3}{4}\right)4(y^2 + 2) = (4y + 3)(y^2 + 2)$

Thus, the only real zero is $-\frac{3}{4}$.

53. $P(x) = x^4 - \frac{25}{4}x^2 + 9$

$\qquad = \frac{1}{4}(4x^4 - 25x^2 + 36)$

$\qquad = \frac{1}{4}(4x^2 - 9)(x^2 - 4)$

$\qquad = \frac{1}{4}(2x + 3)(2x - 3)(x + 2)(x - 2)$

The zeros are $\pm\frac{3}{2}$ and ± 2.

55. $f(x) = x^3 - \frac{1}{4}x^2 - x + \frac{1}{4}$

$\qquad = \frac{1}{4}(4x^3 - x^2 - 4x + 1)$

$\qquad = \frac{1}{4}[x^2(4x - 1) - 1(4x - 1)]$

$\qquad = \frac{1}{4}(4x - 1)(x^2 - 1)$

$\qquad = \frac{1}{4}(4x - 1)(x + 1)(x - 1)$

The zeros are $\frac{1}{4}$ and ± 1.

57. $f(x) = x^3 - 1 = (x - 1)(x^2 + x + 1)$

Rational zeros: 1 $(x = 1)$

Irrational zeros: 0

Matches (d).

59. $f(x) = x^3 - x = x(x + 1)(x - 1)$

Rational zeros: 3 $(x = 0, \pm 1)$

Irrational zeros: 0

Matches (b).

61. (a)

(b) $V = l \cdot w \cdot h = (15 - 2x)(9 - 2x)x$
$= x(9 - 2x)(15 - 2x)$

Since length, width, and height cannot be negative, we have $0 < x < \frac{9}{2}$ for the domain.

(c)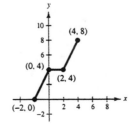

Volume of box

Length of sides of squares removed

The volume is maximum when $x \approx 1.82$.

The dimensions are: length $= 15 - 2(1.82) = 11.36$
width $= 9 - 2(1.82) = 5.36$
height $= x = 1.82$

$1.82 \text{ cm} \times 5.36 \text{ cm} \times 11.36 \text{ cm}$

(d) $56 = x(9 - 2x)(15 - 2x)$
$56 = 135x - 48x^2 + 4x^3$
$0 = 4x^3 - 48x^2 + 135x - 56$

The zeros of this polynomial are $\frac{1}{2}, \frac{7}{2}$, and 8.
x cannot equal 8 since it is not in the domain of V. [The length cannot equal -1 and the width cannot equal -7. The product of $(8)(-1)(-7) = 56$ so it showed up as an extraneous solution.]

63. $g(x) = -f(x)$. This function would have the same zeros as $f(x)$ so r_1, r_2, and r_3 are also zeros of $g(x)$.

65. $g(x) = f(x - 5)$. The graph of $g(x)$ is a horizontal shift of the graph of $f(x)$ five units to the right so the zeros of $g(x)$ are $5 + r_1, 5 + r_2$, and $5 + r_3$.

67. $g(x) = 3 + f(x)$. Since $g(x)$ is a vertical shift of the graph of $f(x)$, the zeros of $g(x)$ cannot be determined.

69.
$$P = -76x^3 + 4830x^2 - 320,000, 0 \le x \le 60$$
$$2,500,000 = -76x^3 + 4830x^2 - 320,000$$
$$76x^3 - 4830x^2 + 2,820,000 = 0$$

The zeros of this equation are $x \approx 46.1$, $x \approx 38.4$, and $x \approx -21.0$. Since $0 \le x \le 60$, we disregard $x \approx -21.0$. The smaller remaining solution is $x \approx 38.4$.

71. $C = 100\left(\dfrac{200}{x^2} + \dfrac{x}{x + 30}\right), 1 \le x$

C is minimum when $3x^3 - 40x^2 - 2400x - 36000 = 0$. The only real zero is $x \approx 40$.

73. $g(x) = f(x - 2)$

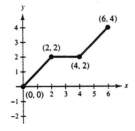

Horizontal shift two units to the right

75. $g(x) = 2f(x)$

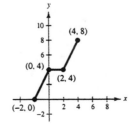

Vertical stretch

77. $g(x) = f(2x)$

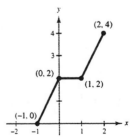

Horizontal shrink

Section 2.5   Complex Numbers

■ $a + bi = c + di$ if and only if $a = c$ and $b = d$

■ Operations on complex numbers

(a) Addition: $(a + bi) + (c + di) = (a + c) + (b + d)i$

(b) Subtraction: $(a + bi) - (c + di) = (a - c) + (b - d)i$

(c) Multiplication: $(a + bi)(c + di) = (ac - bd) + (ad + bc)i$

(d) Division: $\dfrac{a + bi}{c + di} = \dfrac{a + bi}{c + di} \cdot \dfrac{c - di}{c - di} = \dfrac{ac + bd}{c^2 + d^2} + \dfrac{bc - ad}{c^2 + d^2}i$

■ The complex conjugate of $a + bi$ is $a - bi$:

$(a + bi)(a - bi) = a^2 + b^2$

■ $\sqrt{-a} = \sqrt{a}\, i$ for $a > 0$.

Solutions to Odd-Numbered Exercises

1. $a + bi = -10 + 6i$

$a = -10$

$b = 6$

3. $(a - 1) + (b + 3)i = 5 + 8i$

$a - 1 = 5 \quad \Rightarrow \quad a = 6$

$b + 3 = 8 \quad \Rightarrow \quad b = 5$

5. $4 + \sqrt{-9} = 4 + 3i$

7. $2 - \sqrt{-27} = 2 - \sqrt{27}\,i = 2 - 3\sqrt{3}\,i$

9. $\sqrt{-75} = \sqrt{75}\,i = 5\sqrt{3}\,i$

11. $-6i + i^2 = -6i - 1 = -1 - 6i$

13. $8 = 8 + 0i = 8$

15. $\sqrt{-0.09} = \sqrt{0.09}\,i = 0.3i$

17. $(5 + i) + (6 - 2i) = 11 - i$

19. $(8 - i) - (4 - i) = 8 - i - 4 + i = 4$

21. $\left(-2 + \sqrt{-8}\right)\left(5 - \sqrt{50}\right) = -2 + 2\sqrt{2}\,i + 5 - 5\sqrt{2}\,i$

$= 3 - 3\sqrt{2}\,i$

23. $13i - (14 - 7i) = 13i - 14 + 7i = -14 + 20i$

25. $-\left(\frac{3}{2} + \frac{5}{2}i\right) + \left(\frac{5}{3} + \frac{11}{3}i\right) = -\frac{3}{2} - \frac{5}{2}i + \frac{5}{3} + \frac{11}{3}i$

$= -\frac{9}{6} - \frac{15}{6}i + \frac{10}{6} + \frac{22}{6}i$

$= \frac{1}{6} + \frac{7}{6}i$

27. $\sqrt{-6} \cdot \sqrt{-2} = \left(\sqrt{6}\,i\right)\left(\sqrt{2}\,i\right) = \sqrt{12}\,i^2 = \left(2\sqrt{3}\right)(-1) = -2\sqrt{3}\,i$

29. $\left(\sqrt{-10}\right)^2 = \left(\sqrt{10}\,i\right)^2 = 10i^2 = -10$

31. $(1 + i)(3 - 2i) = 3 - 2i + 3i - 2i^2$
$$= 3 + i + 2$$
$$= 5 + i$$

33. $6i(5 - 2i) = 30i - 12i^2 = 30i + 12 = 12 + 30i$

35. $\left(\sqrt{14} + \sqrt{10}\,i\right)\left(\sqrt{14} - \sqrt{10}\,i\right) = 14 - 10i^2 = 14 + 10 = 24$

37. $(4 + 5i)^2 = 16 + 40i + 25i^2 = 16 + 40i - 25$
$$= -9 + 40i$$

39. $(2 + 3i)^2 + (2 - 3i)^2 = 4 + 12i + 9i^2 + 4 - 12i + 9i^2$
$$= 4 + 12i - 9 + 4 - 12i - 9$$
$$= -10$$

41. $\sqrt{-6}\sqrt{-6} = \sqrt{6}\,i\sqrt{6}\,i = 6i^2 = -6$

43. The complex conjugate of $5 + 3i$ is $5 - 3i$.
$(5 + 3i)(5 - 3i) = 25 - 9i^2 = 25 + 9 = 34$

45. The complex conjugate of $-2 - \sqrt{5}\,i$ is $-2 + \sqrt{5}\,i$.
$\left(-2 - \sqrt{5}\,i\right)\left(-2 + \sqrt{5}\,i\right) = 4 - 5i^2 = 4 + 5 = 9$

47. The complex conjugate of $20i$ is $-20i$.
$(20i)(-20i) = -400i^2 = 400$

49. The complex conjugate of $\sqrt{8}$ is $\sqrt{8}$.
$\left(\sqrt{8}\right)\left(\sqrt{8}\right) = 8$

51. $\dfrac{6}{i} = \dfrac{6}{i} \cdot \dfrac{-i}{-i} = \dfrac{-6i}{-i^2} = \dfrac{-6i}{1} = -6i$

53. $\dfrac{4}{4 - 5i} = \dfrac{4}{4 - 5i} \cdot \dfrac{4 + 5i}{4 + 5i} = \dfrac{4(4 + 5i)}{16 + 25} = \dfrac{16 + 20i}{41} = \dfrac{16}{41} + \dfrac{20}{41}i$

55. $\dfrac{2 + i}{2 - i} = \dfrac{2 + i}{2 - i} \cdot \dfrac{2 + i}{2 + i} = \dfrac{4 + 4i + i^2}{4 + 1} = \dfrac{3 + 4i}{5} = \dfrac{3}{5} + \dfrac{4}{5}i$

57. $\dfrac{6 - 7i}{i} = \dfrac{6 - 7i}{i} \cdot \dfrac{-i}{-i} = \dfrac{-6i + 7i^2}{1} = -7 - 6i$

59. $\dfrac{1}{(4 - 5i)^2} = \dfrac{1}{16 - 40i + 25i^2} = \dfrac{1}{-9 - 40i} \cdot \dfrac{-9 + 40i}{-9 + 40i}$
$$= \dfrac{-9 + 40i}{81 + 1600} = \dfrac{-9 + 40i}{1681} = -\dfrac{9}{1681} + \dfrac{40}{1681}i$$

61. $\dfrac{2}{1 + i} - \dfrac{3}{1 - i} = \dfrac{2(1 - i) - 3(1 + i)}{(1 + i)(1 - i)}$
$$= \dfrac{2 - 2i - 3 - 3i}{1 + 1}$$
$$= \dfrac{-1 - 5i}{2}$$
$$= -\dfrac{1}{2} - \dfrac{5}{2}i$$

63. $\dfrac{i}{3-2i} + \dfrac{2i}{3+8i} = \dfrac{i(3+8i) + 2i(3-2i)}{(3-2i)(3+8i)}$

$\qquad = \dfrac{3i + 8i^2 + 6i - 4i^2}{9 + 24i - 6i - 16i^2}$

$\qquad = \dfrac{4i^2 + 9i}{9 + 18i + 16}$

$\qquad = \dfrac{-4+9i}{25+18i} \cdot \dfrac{25-18i}{25-18i}$

$\qquad = \dfrac{-100 + 72i + 225i - 162i^2}{625 + 324}$

$\qquad = \dfrac{-100 + 297i + 162}{949}$

$\qquad = \dfrac{62 + 297i}{949}$

$\qquad = \dfrac{62}{949} + \dfrac{297}{949}i$

65. $x^2 - 2x + 2 = 0$; $\ a = 1, \ \ b = -2, \ \ c = 2$

$\quad x = \dfrac{-(-2) \pm \sqrt{(-2)^2 - 4(1)(2)}}{2(1)} = \dfrac{2 \pm \sqrt{-4}}{2} = \dfrac{2 \pm 2i}{2} = 1 \pm i$

67. $4x^2 + 16x + 17 = 0$; $\ a = 4, \ \ b = 16, \ \ c = 17$

$\quad x = \dfrac{-16 \pm \sqrt{(16)^2 - 4(4)(17)}}{2(4)}$

$\quad\ = \dfrac{-16 \pm \sqrt{-16}}{8} = \dfrac{-16 + 4i}{8}$

$\quad\ = -2 \pm \dfrac{1}{2}i$

69. $4x^2 + 16x + 15 = 0$; $\ a = 4, \ \ b = 16, \ \ c = 15$

$\quad x = \dfrac{-16 \pm \sqrt{(16)^2 - 4(4)(15)}}{2(4)} = \dfrac{-16 \pm \sqrt{16}}{8} = \dfrac{-16 \pm 4}{8}$

$\quad x = -\dfrac{12}{8} = -\dfrac{3}{2} \ \ \text{or} \ \ x = \dfrac{-20}{8} = -\dfrac{5}{2}$

71. $16t^2 - 4t + 3 = 0$; $\ a = 16, \ \ b = -4, \ \ c = 3$

$\quad t = \dfrac{-(-4) \pm \sqrt{(-4)^2 - 4(16)(3)}}{2(16)}$

$\quad\ = \dfrac{4 \pm \sqrt{-176}}{32} = \dfrac{4 \pm 4\sqrt{11}\,i}{32}$

$\quad\ = \dfrac{1}{8} \pm \dfrac{\sqrt{11}}{8}i$

73. $y = \frac{1}{4}(4x^2 - 20x + 25)$ $0 = \frac{1}{4}(4x^2 - 20x + 25)$

$0 = 4x^2 - 20x + 25$

$0 = (2x - 5)^2$

$0 = 2x - 5$

$-2x = -5$

$x = \frac{5}{2}$

x-intercept: $\left(\frac{5}{2}, 0\right)$

75. $y = -(x^2 - 4x + 5)$ $0 = -(x^2 - 4x + 5)$

$0 = x^2 - 4x + 5$

$x = \dfrac{-(-4) \pm \sqrt{(-4)^2 - 4(1)(5)}}{2(1)}$

$= \dfrac{4 \pm 2i}{2} = 2 \pm i$

No x-intercepts   No real solutions

77. The number of x-intercepts of the graph of $y = ax^2 + bx + c$ corresponds to the number of real solutions of the equation $0 = ax^2 + bx + c$. If there are no x-intercepts, the quadratic equation has two complex solutions.

79. $-6i^3 + i^2 = -6i^2i + i^2$
$= -6(-1)i + (-1)$
$= 6i - 1$
$= -1 + 6i$

81. $-5i^5 = -5i^2i^2i$
$= -5(-1)(-1)i$
$= -5i$

83. $\left(\sqrt{-75}\right)^3(5\sqrt{3}\,i)^3 = 5^3\left(\sqrt{3}\right)^3 i^3$
$125\left(3\sqrt{3}\right)(-1)$
$= -375\sqrt{3}\,i$

85. $\dfrac{1}{i^3} = \dfrac{1}{-i} = \dfrac{1}{-i} \cdot \dfrac{i}{i} = \dfrac{i}{-i^2} = \dfrac{i}{1} = i$

87. $(2)^3 = 8$

$(1 + \sqrt{3}i)^3 = (-1)^3 + 3(-1)^2(\sqrt{3}i) + 3(-1)(\sqrt{3}i)^2 + (\sqrt{3}i)^3$
$= -1 + 3\sqrt{3}i - 9i^2 + 3\sqrt{3}i^3$
$= -1 + 3\sqrt{3}\,i + 9 - 3\sqrt{3}i$
$= 8$

$\left(-1 - \sqrt{3}\,i\right)^3 = (-1)^3 + 3(-1)^2\left(-\sqrt{3}\,i\right) + 3(-1)\left(-\sqrt{3}\,i\right)^2 + \left(-\sqrt{3}\,i\right)^3$
$= -1 - 3\sqrt{3}i - 9i^2 - 3\sqrt{3}i^3$
$= -1 - 3\sqrt{3}\,i + 9 + 3\sqrt{3}i$
$= 8$

89. $(a + bi) + (a - bi) = 2a$ which is a real number.

91. $(a + bi)(a - bi) = a^2 - (bi)^2 = a^2 - b^2i^2$
$= a^2 + b^2$ which is a real number.

93. $(a_1 + b_1i) + (a_2 + b_2i) = (a_1 + a_2) + (b_1 + b_2)i$

The complex conjugate of the sum is $(a_1 + a_2) - (b_1 + b_2)i$, and the sum of the conjugates is

$$(a_1 - b_1i) + (a_2 - b_2i) = (a_1 + a_2) + (-b_1 - b_2)i$$

$$= (a_1 + a_2) - (b_1 + b_2)i.$$

Thus, the conjugate of the sum is the sum of the conjugates.

95. $(4 + 3x) + (8 - 6x - x^2) = -x^2 - 3x + 12$

97. $(2x - 5)^2 = (2x)^2 - 2(2x)(5) + (5)^2$

$$= 4x^2 - 20x + 25$$

99.
$$V = \frac{4}{3}\pi a^2 b$$

$$3V = 4\pi a^2 b$$

$$\frac{3V}{4\pi b} = a^2$$

$$\sqrt{\frac{3V}{4\pi b}} = a$$

$$a = \frac{1}{2}\sqrt{\frac{3V}{\pi b}}$$

Section 2.6   The Fundamental Theorem of Algebra

■   You should know that if f is a polynomial of degree $n > 0$, then f has at least one zero in the complex number system.

■   You should know that if $a + bi$ is a complex zero of a polynomial f, with real coefficients, then $a - bi$ is also a complex zero of f.

■   You should know the difference between a factor that is irreducible over the rationals (such as $x^2 - 7$) and a factor that is irreducible over the reals (such as $x^2 + 9$).

Solutions to Odd-Numbered Exercises

1. $f(x) = x(x - 6)^2 = x(x - 6)(x - 6)$

The three zeros are: $x = 0$, $x = 6$, and $x = 6$.

3. $h(t) = (t - 3)(t - 2)(t - 3i)(t + 3i)$

The four zeros are:
$t = 3$, $t = 2$, $t = 3i$, and $t = -3i$.

5. $f(x) = x^3 - 4x^2 + x - 4 = x^2(x - 4) + 1(x - 4)$

$$= (x - 4)(x^2 + 1)$$

The only real zero of $f(x)$ is $x = 4$. This corresponds to the x-intercept of $(4, 0)$ on the graph.

7. $f(x) = x^4 + 4x^2 + 4 = (x^2 + 2)^2$

$f(x)$ has no real zeros and the graph of $f(x)$ has no x-intercepts.

9. $f(x) = x^2 + 25$

$$= (x + 5i)(x - 5i)$$

The zeros of $f(x)$ are $x = \pm 5i$.

11. $h(x) = x^2 - 4x + 1$

h has no rational zeros.

By the Quadratic Formula, the zeros are $x = \dfrac{4 \pm \sqrt{16 - 4}}{2} = 2 \pm \sqrt{3}$.

$h(x) = \left[x - \left(2 + \sqrt{3}\right)\right]\left[x - \left(2 - \sqrt{3}\right)\right] = \left(x - 2 - \sqrt{3}\right)\left(x - 2 + \sqrt{3}\right)$

13. $f(x) = x^4 - 81$

$\qquad = (x^2 - 9)(x^2 + 9)$

$\qquad = (x + 3)(x - 3)(x + 3i)(x - 3i)$

The zeros of $f(x)$ are $x = \pm 3$ and $x = \pm 3i$.

15. $f(z) = z^2 - 2z + 2$

f has no rational zeros.

By the Quadratic Formula, the zeros are $z = \dfrac{2 \pm \sqrt{4 - 8}}{2} = 1 \pm i$.

$f(z) = [z - (1 + i)][z - (1 - i)] = (z - 1 - i)(z - 1 + i)$

17. $g(x) = x^3 - 6x^2 + 13x - 10$

Possible rational zeros: $\pm 1, \ \pm 2, \ \pm 5, \ \pm 10$

$$
\begin{array}{r|rrrr}
2 & 1 & -6 & 13 & -10 \\
  &   & 2 & -8 & 10 \\
\hline
  & 1 & -4 & 5 & 0
\end{array}
$$

By the Quadratic Formula, the zeros of

$x^2 - 4x + 5$ are $x = \dfrac{4 \pm \sqrt{16 - 20}}{2} = 2 \pm i$.

The zeros of $g(x)$ are $x = 2$ and $x = 2 \pm i$.

$g(x) = (x - 2)[x - (2 + i)][x - (2 - i)]$

$\qquad = (x - 2)(x - 2 - i)(x - 2 + i)$

19. $f(t) = t^3 - 3t^2 - 15t + 125$

Possible rational zeros: $\pm 1, \ \pm 5, \ \pm 25, \ \pm 125$

$$
\begin{array}{r|rrrr}
-5 & 1 & -3 & -15 & 125 \\
   &   & -5 & 40 & -125 \\
\hline
   & 1 & -8 & 25 & 0
\end{array}
$$

By the Quadratic Formula, the zeros of

$t^2 - 8t + 25$ are $t = \dfrac{8 \pm \sqrt{64 - 100}}{2} = 4 \pm 3i$.

The zeros of $f(t)$ are $t = -5$ and $t = 4 \pm 3i$.

$f(t) = [t - (-5)][t - (4 + 3i)][t - (4 - 3i)]$

$\qquad = (t + 5)(t - 4 - 3i)(t - 4 + 3i)$

21. $h(x) = x^3 - x + 6$

Possible rational zeros: $\pm 1, \ \pm 2, \ \pm 3, \ \pm 6$

$$
\begin{array}{r|rrrr}
-2 & 1 & 0 & -1 & 6 \\
   &   & -2 & 4 & -6 \\
\hline
   & 1 & -2 & 3 & 0
\end{array}
$$

By the Quadratic Formula, the zeros of $x^2 - 2x + 3$ are

$x = \dfrac{2 \pm \sqrt{4 - 12}}{2} = 1 \pm \sqrt{2}\,i$.

The zeros of $h(x)$ are $x = -2$ and $x = 1 \pm \sqrt{2}\,i$.

$h(x) = [x - (-2)]\left[x - \left(1 + \sqrt{2}\,i\right)\right]\left[x - \left(1 - \sqrt{2}\,i\right)\right]$

$\qquad = (x + 2)\left(x - 1 - \sqrt{2}\,i\right)\left(x - 1 + \sqrt{2}\,i\right)$

23. $f(x) = 5x^3 - 9x^2 + 28x + 6$

Possible rational zeros: $\pm 1, \pm 2, \pm 3, \pm 6, \pm\frac{1}{5}, \pm\frac{2}{5}, \pm\frac{3}{5}, \pm\frac{6}{5}$

$$
\begin{array}{r|rrrr}
-\frac{1}{5} & 5 & -9 & 28 & 6 \\
 & & -1 & 2 & -6 \\
\hline
 & 5 & -10 & 30 & 0
\end{array}
$$

By the Quadratic Formula, the zeros of $5x^2 - 10x + 30 = 5(x^2 - 2x + 6)$ are

$x = \dfrac{2 \pm \sqrt{4 - 24}}{2} = 1 \pm \sqrt{5}\,i.$

The zeros of $f(x)$ are $x = -\frac{1}{5}$ and $x = 1 \pm \sqrt{5}\,i.$

$$f(x) = \left[x - \left(-\tfrac{1}{5}\right)\right](5)\left[x - \left(1 + \sqrt{5}\,i\right)\right]\left[x - \left(1 - \sqrt{5}\,i\right)\right]$$
$$= (5x + 1)\left(x - 1 - \sqrt{5}\,i\right)\left(x - 1 + \sqrt{5}\,i\right)$$

25. $g(x) = x^4 - 4x^3 + 8x^2 - 16x + 16$

Possible rational zeros: $\pm 1, \pm 2, \pm 4, \pm 8, \pm 16$

$$
\begin{array}{r|rrrrr}
2 & 1 & -4 & 8 & -16 & 16 \\
 & & 2 & -4 & 8 & -16 \\
\hline
2 & 1 & -2 & 4 & -8 & \\
 & & 2 & 0 & 8 & \\
\hline
 & 1 & 0 & 4 & 0 &
\end{array}
$$

$g(x) = (x - 2)(x - 2)(x^2 + 4) = (x - 2)^2(x + 2i)(x - 2i)$

The zeros of $g(x)$ are 2 and $\pm 2i$.

27. $f(x) = x^4 + 10x^2 + 9$

$\quad = (x^2 + 1)(x^2 + 9)$

$\quad = (x + i)(x - i)(x + 3i)(x - 3i)$

The zeros of $f(x)$ are $x = \pm i$ and $x = \pm 3i.$

29. $f(x) = x^3 + 24x^2 + 214x + 740$

The graph reveals one zero at $x = -10.$

$$
\begin{array}{r|rrrr}
-10 & 1 & 24 & 214 & 740 \\
 & & -10 & -140 & -740 \\
\hline
 & 1 & 14 & 74 & 0
\end{array}
$$

By the Quadratic Formula, the zeros of $x^2 + 14x + 74$ are

$x = \dfrac{-14 \pm \sqrt{196 - 296}}{2} = -7 \pm 5i.$

The zeros of $f(x)$ are $x = -10$ and $x = -7 \pm 5i.$

31. $f(x) = 16x^3 - 20x^2 - 4x + 15$

The graph reveals one zero at $x = -\frac{3}{4}$.

$$
\begin{array}{r|rrrr}
-\frac{3}{4} & 16 & -20 & -4 & 15 \\
 & & -12 & 24 & -15 \\
\hline
 & 16 & -32 & 20 & 0
\end{array}
$$

By the Quadratic Formula, the zeros of $16x^2 - 32x + 20 = 4(4x^2 - 8x + 5)$ are

$$x = \frac{8 \pm \sqrt{64 - 80}}{8} = 1 \pm \frac{1}{2}i.$$

The zeros of $f(x)$ are $x = -\frac{3}{4}$ and $x = 1 \pm \frac{1}{2}i$.

33. $f(x) = 2x^4 + 5x^3 + 4x^2 + 5x + 2$

The graph reveals zeros at $x = -2$ and $x = -\frac{1}{2}$.

$$
\begin{array}{r|rrrrr}
-2 & 2 & 5 & 4 & 5 & 2 \\
 & & -4 & -2 & -4 & -2 \\
\hline
 & 2 & 1 & 2 & 1 & 0
\end{array}
$$

$$
\begin{array}{r|rrrr}
-\frac{1}{2} & 2 & 1 & 2 & 1 \\
 & & -1 & 0 & -1 \\
\hline
 & 2 & 0 & 2 & 0
\end{array}
$$

The zeros of $2x^2 + 2 = 2(x^2 + 1)$ are $x = \pm i$.

The zeros of $f(x)$ are $x = -2$, $x = -\frac{1}{2}$, and $x = \pm i$.

35. $f(x) = (x - 1)(x - 5i)(x + 5i)$

$\qquad = (x - 1)(x^2 + 25)$

$\qquad = x^3 - x^2 + 25x - 25$

Note: $f(x) = a(x^3 - x^2 + 25x - 25)$,

where a is any nonzero real number, has the zeros 1 and $\pm 5i$.

37. $f(x) = (x - 6)[x - (-5 + 2i)][x - (-5 - 2i)]$

$\qquad = (x - 6)[(x + 5) - 2i][(x + 5) + 2i]$

$\qquad = (x - 6)[(x + 5)^2 - (2i)^2]$

$\qquad = (x - 6)(x^2 + 10x + 25 + 4)$

$\qquad = (x - 6)(x^2 + 10x + 29)$

$\qquad = x^3 + 4x^2 - 31x - 174$

Note: $f(x) = a(x^3 + 4x^2 - 31x - 174)$, where a is any nonzero real number, has the zeros 6, and $-5 \pm 2i$.

39. $f(x) = (x - i)(x + i)(x - 6i)(x + 6i)$

$$= (x^2 + 1)(x^2 + 36)$$

$$= x^4 + 37x^2 + 36$$

Note: $f(x) = a(x^4 + 37x^2 + 36)$, where a is any nonzero real number, has the zeros $\pm i$ and $\pm 6i$.

41. If $3 + \sqrt{2}\,i$ is a zero, so is its conjugate, $3 - \sqrt{2}i$.

$$f(x) = (3x - 2)(x + 1)\left[x - \left(3 + \sqrt{2}\,i\right)\right]\left[x - \left(3 - \sqrt{2}\,i\right)\right]$$

$$= (3x - 2)(x + 1)\left[(x - 3) - \sqrt{2}\,i\right]\left[(x - 3) + \sqrt{2}\,i\right]$$

$$= (3x^2 + x - 2)\left[(x - 3)^2 - \left(\sqrt{2}\,i\right)^2\right]$$

$$= (3x^2 + x - 2)(x^2 - 6x + 9 + 2)$$

$$= (3x^2 + x - 2)(x^2 - 6x + 11)$$

$$= 3x^4 - 17x^3 + 25x^2 + 23x - 22$$

Note: $f(x) = a(3x^4 - 17x^3 + 25x^2 + 23x - 22)$, where a is any nonzero real number, has the zeros $\frac{2}{3}$, -1, and $3 \pm \sqrt{2}\,i$.

43. If $-\frac{1}{2} + i$ is a zero, so is its conjugate, $-\frac{1}{2} - i$.

$$f(x) = 4\left(x - \tfrac{3}{4}\right)(x + 2)\, 2\left[x - \left(-\tfrac{1}{2} + i\right)\right] 2\left[x - \left(-\tfrac{1}{2} - i\right)\right]$$

$$= (4x - 3)(x + 2)[(2x + 1) - 2i][(2x + 1) + 2i]$$

$$= (4x^2 + 5x - 6)[(2x + 1)^2 - (2i)^2]$$

$$= (4x^2 + 5x - 6)(4x^2 + 4x + 1 + 4)$$

$$= (4x^2 + 5x - 6)(4x^2 + 4x + 5)$$

$$= 16x^4 + 36x^3 + 16x^2 + x - 30$$

Note: $f(x) = a(16x^4 + 36x^3 + 16x^2 + x - 30)$, where a is any nonzero real number, has the zeros $x = \frac{3}{4}$, $x = -2$, and $x = -\frac{1}{2} \pm i$. In fact, we used constant multiples of the linear factors in this equation to simplify the fractions. Without these constants, you would have

$$f(x) = \left(x - \tfrac{3}{4}\right)(x + 2)\left(x + \tfrac{1}{2} - i\right)\left(x + \tfrac{1}{2} + i\right)$$

$$= x^4 + \tfrac{9}{4}x^3 + x^2 + \tfrac{1}{16}x - \tfrac{15}{8}.$$

45. $f(x) = x^4 + 6x^2 - 27$

(a) $f(x) = (x^2 + 9)(x^2 - 3)$

(b) $f(x) = (x^2 + 9)\left(x + \sqrt{3}\right)\left(x - \sqrt{3}\right)$

(c) $f(x) = (x + 3i)(x - 3i)\left(x + \sqrt{3}\right)\left(x - \sqrt{3}\right)$

47.

$$
\begin{array}{r}
x^2 - 2x + 3 \\
x^2 - 2x - 2\overline{)x^4 - 4x^3 + 5x^2 - 2x - 6} \\
\underline{x^4 - 2x^3 - 2x^2} \\
-2x^3 + 7x^2 - 2x \\
\underline{-2x^3 + 4x^2 + 4x} \\
3x^2 - 6x - 6 \\
\underline{3x^2 - 6x - 6} \\
0
\end{array}
$$

$$f(x) = (x^2 - 2x - 2)(x^2 - 2x + 3)$$

(a) $f(x) = (x^2 - 2x - 2)(x^2 - 2x + 3)$

(b) $f(x) = \left(x - 1 + \sqrt{3}\right)\left(x - 1 - \sqrt{3}\right)(x^2 - 2x + 3)$

(c) $f(x) = \left(x - 1 + \sqrt{3}\right)\left(x - 1 - \sqrt{3}\right)\left(x - 1 + \sqrt{2}\,i\right)\left(x - 1 - \sqrt{2}\,i\right)$

Note: Use the Quadratic Formula for (b) and (c).

49. $f(x) = 2x^3 + 3x^2 + 50x + 75$

Since $5i$ is a zero, so is $-5i$.

$$
\begin{array}{r|cccc}
5i & 2 & 3 & 50 & 75 \\
 & & 10i & -50 + 15i & -75 \\
\hline
 & 2 & 3 + 10i & 15i & 0
\end{array}
$$

$$
\begin{array}{r|ccc}
-5i & 2 & 3 + 10i & 15i \\
 & & -10i & -15i \\
\hline
 & 2 & 3 & 0
\end{array}
$$

The zero of $2x + 3$ is $x = -\frac{3}{2}$.

The zeros of $f(x)$ are $x = -\frac{3}{2}$ and $x = \pm 5i$.

Alternate Solution

Since $x = \pm 5i$ are zeros of $f(x)$, $(x + 5i)(x - 5i) = x^2 + 25$ is a factor of $f(x)$.
By long division we have:

$$
\begin{array}{r}
2x + 3 \\
x^2 + 0x + 25\overline{)2x^3 + 3x^2 + 50x + 75} \\
\underline{2x^3 + 0x^2 + 50x} \\
3x^2 + 0x + 75 \\
\underline{3x^2 + 0x + 75} \\
0
\end{array}
$$

Thus, $f(x) = (x^2 + 25)(2x + 3)$ and the zeros of f are $x = \pm 5i$ and $x = -\frac{3}{2}$.

51. $f(x) = 2x^4 - x^3 + 7x^2 - 4x - 4$

Since $2i$ is a zero, so is $-2i$.

$$
\begin{array}{r|rrrrr}
2i & 2 & -1 & 7 & -4 & -4 \\
 & & 4i & -8-2i & 4-2i & 4 \\
\hline
 & 2 & -1+4i & -1-2i & -2 & 0
\end{array}
$$

$$
\begin{array}{r|rrrr}
-2i & 2 & -1+4i & -1-2i & -2i \\
 & & -4i & 2i & 2i \\
\hline
 & 2 & -1 & -1 & 0
\end{array}
$$

The zeros of $2x^2 - x - 1 = (2x + 1)(x - 1)$ are $x = -\frac{1}{2}$ and $x = 1$.

The zeros of $f(x)$ are $x = \pm 2i$, $x = -\frac{1}{2}$, and $x = 1$.

<u>Alternate Solution</u>

Since $x = \pm 2i$ are zeros of $f(x)$, $(x + 2i)(x - 2i) = x^2 + 4$ is a factor of $f(x)$.
By long division we have:

$$
\begin{array}{r}
2x^2 - x - 1 \\
x^2 + 0x + 4 \overline{)\,2x^4 - x^3 + 7x^2 - 4x - 4} \\
\underline{2x^4 + 0x^3 + 8x^2} \\
-x^3 - x^2 - 4x \\
\underline{-x^3 + 0x^2 - 4x} \\
-x^2 + 0x - 4 \\
\underline{-x^2 + 0x - 4} \\
0
\end{array}
$$

Thus, $f(x) = (x^2 + 4)(2x^2 - x - 1)$

$\qquad\qquad = (x + 2i)(x - 2i)(2x + 1)(x - 1)$

and the zeros of $f(x)$ are $x = \pm 2i$, $x = -\frac{1}{2}$, and $x = 1$.

53. $g(x) = 4x^3 + 23x^2 + 34x - 10$

Since $-3 + i$ is a zero, so is $-3 - i$.

$-3 + i$	4	23	34	-10
		$-12 + 4i$	$-37 - i$	10
	4	$11 + 4i$	$-3 - i$	0

$-3 - i$	4	$11 + 4i$	$-3 - i$
		$-12 - 4i$	$3 + i$
	4	-1	0

The zero of $4x - 1$ is $x = \frac{1}{4}$. The zeros of $g(x)$ are $x = -3 \pm i$ and $x = \frac{1}{4}$.

Alternate Solution

Since $-3 \pm i$ are zeros of $g(x)$,
$[x - (-3 + i)][x - (-3 - i)] = [(x + 3) - i][(x + 3) + i]$
$$= (x + 3)^2 - i^2$$
$$= x^2 + 6x + 10$$
is a factor of $g(x)$. By long division we have:

$$
\begin{array}{r}
4x - 1 \\
x^2 + 6x + 10\overline{)4x^3 + 23x^2 + 34x - 10} \\
4x^3 + 24x^2 + 40x \\
\hline
-x^2 - 6x - 10 \\
-x^2 - 6x - 10 \\
\hline
0
\end{array}
$$

Thus, $g(x) = (x^2 + 6x + 10)(4x - 1)$ and the zeros of $g(x)$ are $x = -3 \pm i$ and $x = \frac{1}{4}$.

55. Since $-3 + \sqrt{2}\,i$ is a zero, so is $-3 - \sqrt{2}\,i$, and
$\left[x - \left(-3 + \sqrt{2}\,i\right)\right]\left[x - \left(-3 - \sqrt{2}\,i\right)\right]$
$= \left[(x + 3) - \sqrt{2}\,i\right]\left[(x + 3) + \sqrt{2}\,i\right]$
$= (x + 3)^2 - \left(\sqrt{2}\,i\right)^2$
$= x^2 + 6x + 11$

is a factor of $f(x)$. By long division, we have:

$$
\begin{array}{r}
x^2 - 3x + 2 \\
x^2 + 6x + 11\overline{)x^4 + 3x^3 - 5x^2 - 21x + 22} \\
x^4 + 6x^3 + 11x^2 \\
\hline
-3x^3 - 16x^2 - 21x \\
-3x^3 - 18x^2 - 33x \\
\hline
2x^2 + 12x + 22 \\
2x^2 + 12x + 22 \\
\hline
0
\end{array}
$$

Thus, $f(x) = (x^2 + 6x + 11)(x^2 - 3x + 2)$
$= (x^2 + 6x + 11)(x - 1)(x - 2)$
and the zeros of f are $x = -3 \pm \sqrt{2}\,i$, $x = 1$, and $x = 2$.

57. Since $\frac{1}{2}\left(1 - \sqrt{5}\,i\right)$ is a zero, so is $\frac{1}{2}\left(1 + \sqrt{5}\,i\right)$, and
$\left[x - \frac{1}{2}\left(1 - \sqrt{5}\,i\right)\right]\left[x - \frac{1}{2}\left(1 + \sqrt{5}\,i\right)\right]$
$= \left[\left(x - \frac{1}{2}\right) + \frac{1}{2}\sqrt{5}\,i\right]\left[\left(x - \frac{1}{2}\right) - \frac{1}{2}\sqrt{5}\,i\right]$
$= \left(x - \frac{1}{2}\right)^2 - \left(\frac{1}{2}\sqrt{5}\,i\right)^2$
$= x^2 - x + \frac{1}{4} + \frac{5}{4}$
$= x^2 - x + \frac{3}{2}$

is a factor of $h(x)$. By long division, we have:

$$
\begin{array}{r}
8x - 6 \\
x^2 - x + \frac{3}{2}\overline{)8x^3 - 14x^2 + 18x - 9} \\
8x^3 - 8x^2 + 12x \\
\hline
-6x^2 + 6x - 9 \\
-6x^2 + 6x - 9 \\
\hline
0
\end{array}
$$

Thus, $h(x) = \left(x^2 - x + \frac{3}{2}\right)(8x - 6)$ and the zeros of $h(x)$ are

$$x = \frac{3}{4} \text{ and } x = \frac{1}{2} \pm \frac{\sqrt{5}}{2}i.$$

59. $f(x) = x^3 + ix^2 + ix - 1$

(a)

$$
\begin{array}{r|rrrr}
i & 1 & i & i & -1 \\
  &   & i & -2 & -1 - 2i \\
\hline
  & 1 & 2i & -2 + i & -2 - 2i
\end{array}
$$

Since the remainder is not zero, $x = i$ is not a zero of f.

(b) The theorem that states that complex zeros occur in conjugate pairs has the condition that the coefficients of $f(x)$ must be real numbers. This polynomial has complex coefficients for x^2 and x.

61. $f(x) = x^4 - 4x^2 + k$

$$x^2 = \frac{-(-4) \pm \sqrt{(-4)^2 - 4(1)(k)}}{2(1)} = \frac{4 \pm 2\sqrt{4-k}}{2} = 2 \pm \sqrt{4-k}$$

$$x = \pm\sqrt{2 \pm \sqrt{4-k}}$$

(a) For there to be four distinct real roots, both $4 - k$ and $2 \pm \sqrt{4-k}$ must be positive. This occurs when $0 < k < 4$. Thus, some possible k-values are $k = 1$, $k = 2, k = 3, k = \frac{1}{2}, k = \sqrt{2}$, etc.

(b) For there to be two real roots, each of multiplicity 2, $4 - k$ must equal zero. Thus, $k = 4$.

(c) For there to be two real zeros and two complex zeros, $2 + \sqrt{4-k}$ must be positive and $2 - \sqrt{4-k}$ must be negative. This occurs when $k < 0$. Thus, some possible k-values are $k = -1, k = -2, k = -\frac{1}{2}$, etc.

(d) For there to be four complex zeros, $2 \pm \sqrt{4-k}$ must be complex. This occurs when $k > 4$. Some possible k-values are $k = 5, k = 6, k = 7.4$, etc.

63. $h = -16t^2 + 48t, \ 0 \le t \le 3$

$$= -16(t^2 - 3t)$$

$$= -16\left(t^2 - 3t + \tfrac{9}{4} - \tfrac{9}{4}\right)$$

$$= -16\left[\left(t - \tfrac{3}{2}\right)^2 - \tfrac{9}{4}\right]$$

$$= -16\left(t - \tfrac{3}{2}\right)^2 + 36$$

The maximum height that the baseball reaches is 36 feet when $t = 1.5$ seconds. No, it is not possible for the ball to reach a height of 64 feet.

Alternate Solution

Let $h = 64$ and solve for t.

$$64 = -16t^2 + 48t$$

$$16t^2 - 48t + 64 = 0$$

$$16(t^2 - 3t + 4) = 0$$

$$t^2 - 3t + 4 = 0$$

$$t = \frac{3 \pm \sqrt{9-16}}{2} = \frac{3 \pm \sqrt{7}\,i}{2}$$

No, it is not possible since solving this equation yields imaginary roots.

65. (a) $f(x) = (x - \sqrt{b}i)(x + \sqrt{b}i) = x^2 + b$

(b) $f(x) = [x - (a + bi)][x - (a - bi)]$

$\quad = [(x - a) - bi][(x - a) + bi]$

$\quad = (x - a)^2 - (bi)^2$

$\quad = x^2 - 2ax + a^2 + b^2$

67.

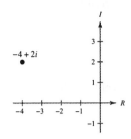

69. $(1.50)(420) = 630$

71. $\dfrac{x}{10} = \dfrac{3}{1.25}$

$1.25x = 30$

$x = 24$ feet

Section 2.7   Rational Functions

■ You should know the following basic facts about rational functions.

(a) A function of the form $f(x) = P(x)/Q(x)$, $Q(x) \neq 0$, where $P(x)$ and $Q(x)$ are polynomials, is called a rational function.

(b) The domain of a rational function is the set of all real numbers except those which make the denominator zero.

(c) If $f(x) = P(x)/Q(x)$ is in reduced form, and a is a value such that $Q(a) = 0$, then the line $x = a$ is a vertical asymptote of the graph of f. $f(x) \to \infty$ or $f(x) \to -\infty$ as $x \to a$.

(d) The line $y = b$ is a horizontal asymptote of the graph of f if $f(x) \to b$ as $x \to \infty$ or $x \to -\infty$.

(e) Let $f(x) = \dfrac{P(x)}{Q(x)} = \dfrac{a_nx^n + a_{n-1}x^{n-1} + \cdots + a_1x + a_0}{b_mx^m + b_{m-1}x^{m-1} + \cdots + b_1x + b_0}$ where $P(x)$ and $Q(x)$ have no common factors.

1. If $n < m$, then the x-axis ($y = 0$) is a horizontal asymptote.

2. If $n = m$, then $y = \dfrac{a_n}{b_m}$ is a horizontal asymptote.

3. If $n > m$, then there are no horizontal asymptotes.

■ You should be able to graph $f(x) = \dfrac{p(x)}{q(x)}$.

(a) Find the x-and y-intercepts.

(b) Find any vertical or horizontal asymptotes.

(c) Plot additional points.

(d) If the degree of the numerator is one more than the degree of the denominator, use long division to find the slant asymptote.

Solutions to Odd-Numbered Exercises

1. $f(x) = \dfrac{1}{x^2}$

Domain: all real numbers except $x = 0$

Vertical asymptote: $x = 0$

Horizontal asymptote: $y = 0$

[Degree of $p(x)$ < degree of $q(x)$]

3. $f(x) = \dfrac{2 + x}{2 - x} = \dfrac{x + 2}{-x + 2}$

Domain: all real numbers except $x = 2$

Vertical asymptote: $x = 2$

Horizontal asymptote: $y = -1$

[Degree of $p(x)$ = degree of $q(x)$]

5. $f(x) = \dfrac{x^3}{x^2 - 1}$

Domain: all real numbers except $x = \pm 1$

Vertical asymptote: $x = \pm 1$

Horizontal asymptotes: None

[Degree of $p(x)$ > degree of $q(x)$]

7. $f(x) = \dfrac{2}{x + 2}$

Vertical asymptote: $x = -2$

Horizontal asymptote: $y = 0$

Matches graph (d).

9. $f(x) = \dfrac{4x + 1}{x}$

Vertical asymptote: $x = 0$

Horizontal asymptote: $y = 4$

Matches graph (f).

11. $f(x) = \dfrac{x - 2}{x - 4}$

Vertical asymptote: $x = 4$

Horizontal asymptote: $y = 1$

Matches graph (e).

13. $f(x) = \dfrac{x^2 - 4}{x + 2}$, $g(x) = x - 2$

(a) Domain of f: all real numbers except $x = -2$
Domain of g: all real numbers

(b) Since $x + 2$ is a common factor of both the numerator and the denominator of $f(x)$, $x = -2$ is not a vertical asymptote of f. f has no vertical asymptotes.

(c)

x	-4	-3	-2.5	-2	-1.5	-1	0
$f(x)$	-6	-5	-4.5	undef.	-3.5	-3	-2
$g(x)$	-6	-5	-4.5	-4	-3.5	-3	-2

(d) f and g differ only where f is undefined.

15. $f(x) = \dfrac{1}{(x + 2)(x - 1)} = \dfrac{1}{x^2 + x - 2}$

17. $f(x) = \dfrac{2x^2}{x^2 + 1}$

19. $f(x) = 4 - \dfrac{1}{x}$

(a) As $x \to \pm\infty$, $f(x) \to 4$

(b) As $x \to \infty$, $f(x) \to 4$ but is less than 4.

(c) As $x \to -\infty$, $f(x) \to 4$ but is greater than 4.

21. $f(x) = \dfrac{2x - 1}{x - 3}$

(a) As $x \to \pm\infty$, $f(x) \to 2$

(b) As $x \to \infty$, $f(x) \to 2$ but is greater than 2.

(c) As $x \to -\infty$, $f(x) \to 2$ but is less than 2.

23. $f(x) = \dfrac{x^2 - 4}{x + 4} = \dfrac{(x + 2)(x - 2)}{x + 1}$

The zeros of f correspond to the zeros of the numerator and are $x = \pm 2$.

25. $f(x) = 1 - \dfrac{2}{x - 3} = \dfrac{x - 5}{x - 3}$

The zero of f corresponds to the zero of the numerator and is $x = 5$.

27. $t = \dfrac{38M + 16{,}965}{10(M + 5000)}$

M	200	400	600	800	1000
t	0.472	0.596	0.710	0.817	0.916

M	1200	1400	1600	1800	2000
t	1.009	1.096	1.178	1.255	1.328

The greater the mass, the more time required per oscillation. Also, the model is a "good fit" to the actual data.

29. $g(x) = \dfrac{2}{x} + 1$

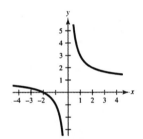

Vertical shift one unit upward

31. $g(x) = -\dfrac{2}{x}$

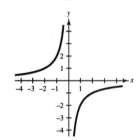

Reflection in the x-axis

33. $f(x) = \dfrac{1}{x + 2}$

y-intercept: $\left(0, \dfrac{1}{2}\right)$

Vertical asymptote: $x = -2$

Horizontal asymptote: $y = 0$

x	-4	-3	-1	0	1
y	$-\frac{1}{2}$	-1	1	$\frac{1}{2}$	$\frac{1}{3}$

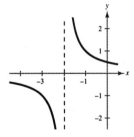

35. $h(x) = -\dfrac{1}{x + 2}$

y-intercept: $\left(0, -\dfrac{1}{2}\right)$

Vertical asymptote: $x = -2$

Horizontal asymptote: $y = 0$

x	-4	-3	-1	0
y	$\frac{1}{2}$	1	-1	$-\frac{1}{2}$

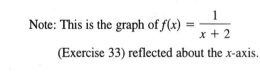

Note: This is the graph of $f(x) = \dfrac{1}{x + 2}$

(Exercise 33) reflected about the x-axis.

37. $C(x) = \dfrac{5 + 2x}{1 + x} = \dfrac{2x + 5}{x + 1}$

x-intercept: $\left(-\dfrac{5}{2}, 0\right)$

y-intercept: $(0, 5)$

Vertical asymptote: $x = -1$

Horizontal asymptote: $y = 2$

x	-4	-3	-1	0	1	2
$C(x)$	1	$\frac{1}{2}$	-1	5	$\frac{7}{2}$	3

39. $g(x) = \dfrac{1}{x + 2} + 2 = \dfrac{2x + 5}{x + 2}$

Intercepts: $\left(-\dfrac{5}{2}, 0\right), \left(0, \dfrac{5}{2}\right)$

Vertical asymptote: $x = -2$

Horizontal asymptote: $y = 2$

x	-4	-3	-1	0	1
y	$\frac{3}{2}$	1	3	$\frac{5}{2}$	$\frac{7}{3}$

Note: This is the graph of $f(x) = \dfrac{1}{x + 2}$ (Exercise 33) shifted upward two units.

41. $f(x) = \dfrac{x^2}{x^2 + 9}$

Intercept: $(0, 0)$

Horizontal asymptote: $y = 1$

y-axis symmetry

x	± 1	± 2	± 3
y	$\frac{1}{10}$	$\frac{4}{13}$	$\frac{1}{2}$

43. $h(x) = \dfrac{x^2}{x^2 - 9}$

Intercept: $(0, 0)$

Vertical asymptotes: $x = \pm 3$

Horizontal asymptote: $y = 1$

y-axis symmetry

x	± 5	± 4	± 2	± 1	0
y	$\frac{25}{16}$	$\frac{16}{7}$	$-\frac{4}{5}$	$-\frac{1}{8}$	0

45. $g(s) = \dfrac{s}{s^2 + 1}$

Intercept: $(0, 0)$

Horizontal asymptote: $y = 0$

Origin symmetry

x	-2	-1	0	1	2
$g(s)$	$-\frac{2}{5}$	$-\frac{1}{2}$	0	$\frac{1}{2}$	$\frac{2}{5}$

47. $g(x) = \dfrac{4(x + 1)}{x(x - 4)}$

Intercept: $(-1, 0)$

Vertical asymptotes: $x = 0$ and $x = 4$

Horizontal asymptote: $y = 0$

x	-2	-1	1	2	3	5	6
y	$-\frac{1}{3}$	0	$-\frac{8}{3}$	-3	$-\frac{16}{3}$	$\frac{24}{5}$	$\frac{7}{3}$

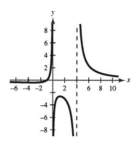

49. $f(x) = \dfrac{3x}{x^2 - x - 2} = \dfrac{3x}{(x + 1)(x - 2)}$

Intercept: $(0, 0)$

Vertical asymptotes: $x = -1, 2$

Horizontal asymptote: $y = 0$

x	-3	0	1	3	4
y	$-\frac{9}{10}$	0	$-\frac{3}{2}$	$\frac{9}{4}$	$\frac{6}{5}$

51. $f(x) = \dfrac{2 + x}{1 - x} = -\dfrac{x + 2}{x - 1}$

x-intercept: $(-2, 0)$

y-intercept: $(0, 2)$

Vertical asymptotes: $x = 1$

Horizontal asymptote: $y = -1$

x	-2	-1	0	2	3
y	0	$\frac{1}{2}$	2	-4	$-\frac{5}{2}$

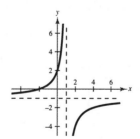

53. $f(t) = \dfrac{3t + 1}{t}$

t-intercept: $\left(-\dfrac{1}{3}, 0\right)$

Vertical asymptotes: $t = 0$

Horizontal asymptote: $y = 3$

t	-2	-1	1	2
$f(t)$	$\frac{5}{2}$	2	4	$\frac{7}{2}$

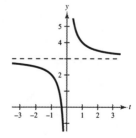

55. $f(x) = \dfrac{x^2 - 1}{x + 1}$, $g(x) = x - 1$

(a) Domain of f: all real numbers except -1

   Domain of g: all real numbers

(b) Since $(x + 1)$ is a factor of both the numerator and the denominator of f, $x = -1$ is not a vertical asymptote. f has no vertical asymptotes.

(c)

x	-3	-2	-1.5	-1	-0.5	0	1
$f(x)$	-4	-3	-2.5	undef.	-1.5	-1	0
$g(x)$	-4	-3	-2.5	-2	-1.5	-1	0

(d)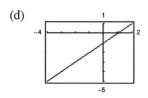

(e) Since there are only a finite number of pixels, the utility may not attempt to evaluate the function where it does not exist.

57. $h(t) = \dfrac{4}{t^2 + 1}$

Domain: all real numbers OR $(-\infty, \infty)$

Horizontal asymptote: $y = 0$

t	± 2	± 1	0
$h(t)$	$\frac{4}{5}$	2	4

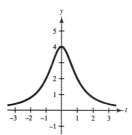

59. $f(t) = \dfrac{2t^2}{t^2 - 4}$

Domain: all real numbers except ± 2,

   OR $(-\infty, -2) \cup (-2, 2) \cup (2, \infty)$

Vertical asymptotes: $x = \pm 2$

Horizontal asymptote: $y = 2$

t	± 4	± 3	± 1	0
$f(t)$	$\frac{8}{3}$	$\frac{18}{5}$	$-\frac{2}{3}$	0

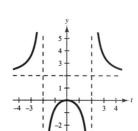

61. $h(x) = \dfrac{6x}{\sqrt{x^2 + 1}}$

Horizontal asymptotes: $y = \pm 6$

63. $f(x) = \dfrac{4(x - 1)^2}{x^2 - 4x + 5}$

Horizontal asymptote: $y = 4$

65. $h(x) = \dfrac{6 - 2x}{3 - x} = \dfrac{2(3 - x)}{3 - x}$

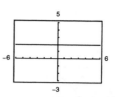

Since $h(x)$ is not reduced and $(3 - x)$ is a factor of both the numerator and the denominator, $x = 3$ is not a horizontal asymptote.

67. False. The graph would have two distinct branches that are separated by the vertical asymptote.

69. $f(x) = \dfrac{2x^2 + 1}{x} = 2x + \dfrac{1}{x}$

Vertical asymptote: $x = 0$

Slant asymptote: $y = 2x$

Origin symmetry

71. $g(x) = \dfrac{x^2 + 1}{x} = x + \dfrac{1}{x}$

Vertical asymptote: $x = 0$

Slant asymptote: $y = x$

Origin symmetry

73. $f(x) = \dfrac{x^3}{x^2 - 1} = x + \dfrac{x}{x^2 - 1}$

Intercept: $(0, 0)$

Vertical asymptotes: $x = \pm 1$

Slant asymptote: $y = x$

Origin symmetry

75. $f(x) = \dfrac{x^2 + 5x + 8}{x + 3} = x + 2 + \dfrac{2}{x + 3}$

Domain: all real numbers except -3

OR $(-\infty, -3) \cup (-3, \infty)$

y-intercept: $\left(0, \dfrac{8}{3}\right)$

Vertical asymptote: $x = -3$

Slant asymptote: $y = x + 2$

77. $y = \dfrac{1}{x + 5} + \dfrac{4}{x}$

(a)

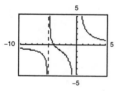

x-intercept: $(-4, 0)$

(b) $\qquad 0 = \dfrac{1}{x + 5} + \dfrac{4}{x}$

$-\dfrac{4}{x} = \dfrac{1}{x + 5}$

$-4(x + 5) = x$

$-4x - 20 = x$

$-5x = 20$

$x = -4$

79. $y = x - \dfrac{6}{x-1}$

(a)

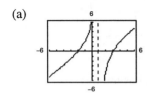

x-intercept: $(-2, 0), (3, 0)$

(b)
$$0 = x - \dfrac{6}{x-1}$$

$$\dfrac{6}{x-1} = x$$

$$6 = x(x-1)$$

$$0 = x^2 - x - 6$$

$$0 = (x+2)(x-3)$$

$$x = -2, \quad x = 3$$

81. (a) $0.25(50) + 0.75(x) = C(50 + x)$

$$C = \dfrac{12.50 + 0.75x}{50 + x} \cdot \dfrac{4}{4}$$

$$C = \dfrac{50 + 3x}{4(50 + x)} = \dfrac{3x + 50}{4(x + 50)}$$

(b) Domain: $x > 0$ and $x \le 1000 - 50$
Thus, $0 \le x \le 950$ OR $[0, 950]$.

(c)

As the tank is filled, the rate at which the concentration is increasing slows down. It approaches the horizontal asymptote of $C = \frac{3}{4} = 0.75$.

Section 2.8   Partial Fractions

■ You should know how to decompose a rational function $\dfrac{N(x)}{D(x)}$ into partial fractions.

(a) If the fraction is improper, divide to obtain

$$\frac{N(x)}{D(x)} = p(x) + \frac{N_1(x)}{D(x)}$$

where $p(x)$ is a polynomial.

(b) Factor the denominator completely into linear and irreducible (over the reals) quadratic factors.

(c) For each factor of the form $(px + q)^m$, the partial fraction decomposition includes the terms

$$\frac{A_1}{(px + q)} + \frac{A_2}{(px + q)^2} + \cdots + \frac{A_m}{(px + q)^m}.$$

(d) For each factor of the form $(ax^2 + bx + c)^n$, the partial fraction decomposition includes the terms

$$\frac{B_1 x + C_1}{ax^2 + bx + c} + \frac{B_2 x + C_2}{(ax^2 + bx + c)^2} + \cdots + \frac{B_n x + C_n}{(ax^2 + bx + c)^n}.$$

■ You should know how to determine the values of the constants in the numerators.

(a) Set $\dfrac{N_1(x)}{D(x)} = $ partial fraction decomposition.

(b) Multiply both sides by $D(x)$. This is called the basic equation.

(c) For distinct linear factors, substitute the roots of the distinct linear factors into the basic equation.

(d) For repeated linear factors, use the coefficients found in part (c) to rewrite the basic equation. Then use other values of x to solve for the remaining coefficients.

(e) For quadratic factors, expand the basic equation, collect like terms, and then equate the coefficients of like terms.

Solutions to Odd-Numbered Exercises

1. $\dfrac{7}{x^2 - 14x} = \dfrac{7}{x(x - 14)} = \dfrac{A}{x} + \dfrac{B}{x - 14}$

3. $\dfrac{12}{x^3 - 10x^2} = \dfrac{12}{x^2(x - 10)} = \dfrac{A}{x} + \dfrac{B}{x^2} + \dfrac{C}{x - 10}$

5. $\dfrac{2x - 3}{x^3 + 10x} = \dfrac{2x - 3}{x(x^2 + 10)} = \dfrac{A}{x} + \dfrac{Bx + C}{x^2 + 10}$

7. $\dfrac{1}{x^2 - 1} = \dfrac{A}{x + 1} + \dfrac{B}{x - 1}$

$1 = A(x - 1) + B(x + 1)$

Let $x = -1$: $1 = -2A \implies A = -\dfrac{1}{2}$

Let $x = 1$: $1 = 2B \implies B = \dfrac{1}{2}$

$\dfrac{1}{x^2 - 1} = \dfrac{1/2}{x - 1} - \dfrac{1/2}{x + 1} = \dfrac{1}{2}\left(\dfrac{1}{x - 1} - \dfrac{1}{x + 1}\right)$

9. $\dfrac{1}{x^2 + x} = \dfrac{A}{x} + \dfrac{B}{x + 1}$

$1 = A(x + 1) + Bx$

Let $x = 0$: $1 = A$

Let $x = -1$: $1 = -B \implies B = -1$

$\dfrac{1}{x^2 + x} = \dfrac{1}{x} - \dfrac{1}{x + 1}$

11. $\dfrac{1}{2x^2 + x} = \dfrac{A}{2x + 1} + \dfrac{B}{x}$

$\qquad 1 = Ax + B(2x + 1)$

Let $x = -\dfrac{1}{2}$: $1 = -\dfrac{1}{2}A \implies A = -2$

Let $x = 0$: $1 = B$

$\dfrac{1}{2x^2 + x} = \dfrac{1}{x} - \dfrac{2}{2x + 1}$

13. $\dfrac{3}{x^2 + x - 2} = \dfrac{A}{x - 1} + \dfrac{B}{x + 2}$

$\qquad 3 = A(x + 2) + B(x - 1)$

Let $x = 1$: $3 = 3A \implies A = 1$

Let $x = -2$: $3 = -3B \implies B = -1$

$\dfrac{3}{x^2 + x - 2} = \dfrac{1}{x - 1} - \dfrac{1}{x + 2}$

15. $\dfrac{x^2 + 12x + 12}{x^3 - 4x} = \dfrac{A}{x} + \dfrac{B}{x + 2} + \dfrac{C}{x - 2}$

$x^2 + 12x + 12 = A(x + 2)(x - 2) + Bx(x - 2) + Cx(x + 2)$

Let $x = 0$: $12 = -4A \implies A = -3$

Let $x = -2$: $-8 = 8B \implies B = -1$

Let $x = 2$: $40 = 8C \implies C = 5$

$\dfrac{x^2 + 12x + 12}{x^3 - 4x} = -\dfrac{3}{x} - \dfrac{1}{x + 2} + \dfrac{5}{x - 2}$

17. $\dfrac{4x^2 + 2x - 1}{x^2(x + 1)} = \dfrac{A}{x} + \dfrac{B}{x^2} + \dfrac{C}{x + 1}$

$4x^2 + 2x - 1 = Ax(x + 1) + B(x + 1) + Cx^2$

Let $x = 0$: $-1 = B$

Let $x = -1$: $1 = C$

Let $x = 1$: $5 = 2A + 2B + C$

$\qquad\qquad\quad 5 = 2A - 2 + 1$

$\qquad\qquad\quad 6 = 2A$

$\qquad\qquad\quad 3 = A$

$\dfrac{4x^2 + 2x - 1}{x^2(x + 1)} = \dfrac{3}{x} - \dfrac{1}{x^2} + \dfrac{1}{x + 1}$

19. $\dfrac{3x}{(x - 3)^2} = \dfrac{A}{x - 3} + \dfrac{B}{(x - 3)^2}$

$\qquad 3x = A(x - 3) + B$

Let $x = 3$: $9 = B$

Let $x = 0$: $0 = -3A + B$

$\qquad\qquad\quad 0 = -3A + 9$

$\qquad\qquad\quad 3 = A$

$\dfrac{3x}{(x - 3)^2} = \dfrac{3}{x - 3} + \dfrac{9}{(x - 3)^2}$

21. $\dfrac{x^2 - 1}{x(x^2 + 1)} = \dfrac{A}{x} + \dfrac{Bx + C}{x^2 + 1}$

$\qquad x^2 - 1 = A(x^2 + 1) + (Bx + C)x$

Let $x = 0$: $-1 = A$

$x^2 - 1 = Ax^2 + A + Bx^2 + Cx$

$\qquad\quad = -x^2 - 1 + Bx^2 + Cx$

$\qquad\quad = x^2(B - 1) + Cx - 1$

Equating coefficients of like powers:

$\qquad 1 = B - 1$

$\qquad 2 = B$ and $\ 0 = C$

$\dfrac{x^2 - 1}{x(x^2 + 1)} = -\dfrac{1}{x} + \dfrac{2x}{x^2 + 1}$

23. $\dfrac{x^2}{x^4 - 2x^2 - 8} = \dfrac{x^2}{(x^2 - 4)(x^2 + 2)} = \dfrac{A}{x + 2} + \dfrac{B}{x - 2} + \dfrac{Cx + D}{x^2 + 2}$

$x^2 = A(x - 2)(x^2 + 2) + B(x + 2)(x^2 + 2) + (Cx + D)(x^2 - 4)$

Let $x = -2$: $4 = -24A \implies A = -\dfrac{1}{6}$

Let $x = 2$: $4 = 24B \implies B = \dfrac{1}{6}$

$x^2 = -\dfrac{1}{6}(x - 2)(x^2 + 2) + \dfrac{1}{6}(x + 2)(x^2 + 2) + (Cx + D)(x^2 - 4)$

$x^2 = -\dfrac{1}{6}x^3 + \dfrac{1}{3}x^2 - \dfrac{1}{3}x + \dfrac{2}{3} + \dfrac{1}{6}x^3 + \dfrac{1}{3}x^2 + \dfrac{1}{3}x + \dfrac{2}{3} + Cx^3 + Dx^2 - 4Cx - 4D$

$x^2 = Cx^3 + \left(\dfrac{2}{3} + D\right)x^2 - 4Cx + \left(\dfrac{4}{3} - 4D\right)$

Equating coefficients of like powers:

$C = 0$

$1 = \dfrac{2}{3} + D \implies D = \dfrac{1}{3}$

$\dfrac{x^2}{x^4 - 2x^2 - 8} = -\dfrac{1}{6(x + 2)} + \dfrac{1}{6(x - 2)} + \dfrac{1}{3(x^2 + 2)}$

25. $\dfrac{x}{16x^4 - 1} = \dfrac{A}{2x + 1} + \dfrac{B}{2x - 1} + \dfrac{Cx + D}{4x^2 + 1}$

$x = A(2x - 1)(4x^2 + 1) + B(2x + 1)(4x^2 + 1) + (Cx + D)(2x + 1)(2x - 1)$

Let $x = -\dfrac{1}{2}$: $-\dfrac{1}{2} = -4A \implies A = \dfrac{1}{8}$

Let $x = \dfrac{1}{2}$: $\dfrac{1}{2} = 4B \implies B = \dfrac{1}{8}$

Let $x = 0$: $0 = -A + B - D$

$0 = -\dfrac{1}{8} + \dfrac{1}{8} - D$

$0 = D$

Let $x = 1$: $1 = 5A + 15B + 3C + 3D$

$1 = \dfrac{5}{8} + \dfrac{15}{8} + 3C + 0$

$-\dfrac{1}{2} = C$

$\dfrac{x}{16x^4 - 1} = \dfrac{1/8}{2x + 1} + \dfrac{1/8}{2x - 1} - \dfrac{x/2}{4x^2 + 1} = \dfrac{1}{8(2x + 1)} + \dfrac{1}{8(2x - 1)} - \dfrac{x}{2(4x^2 + 1)}$

27. $\dfrac{x^2 + 5}{(x + 1)(x^2 - 2x + 3)} = \dfrac{A}{x + 1} + \dfrac{Bx + C}{x^2 - 2x + 3}$

$$x^2 + 5 = A(x^2 - 2x + 3) + (Bx + C)(x + 1)$$

Let $x = -1$: $6 = 6A \implies A = 1$

$x^2 + 5 = x^2 - 2x + 3 + Bx^2 + Bx + Cx + C$

$\qquad = x^2(1 + B) + x(-2 + B + C) + (3 + C)$

Equating coefficients of like powers:

$1 = 1 + B, \quad 0 = -2 + B + C, \quad \text{and} \quad 5 = 3 + C$

$0 = B \qquad\quad\ 0 = -2 + 0 + C \qquad\quad 2 = C$

$\qquad\qquad\qquad\quad 2 = C$

$\dfrac{x^2 + 5}{(x + 1)(x^2 - 2x + 3)} = \dfrac{1}{x + 1} + \dfrac{2}{x^2 - 2x + 3}$

29. $\dfrac{x^4}{(x - 1)^3} = \dfrac{x^4}{x^3 - 3x^2 + 3x - 1} = x + 3 + \dfrac{6x^2 - 8x + 3}{(x - 1)^3}$

$\dfrac{6x^2 - 8x + 3}{(x - 1)^3} = \dfrac{A}{x - 1} + \dfrac{B}{(x - 1)^2} + \dfrac{C}{(x - 1)^3}$

$6x^2 - 8x + 3 = A(x - 1)^2 + B(x - 1) + C$

Let $x = 1$: $1 = C$

$6x^2 - 8x + 3 = Ax^2 - 2Ax + A + Bx - B + 1$

$6x^2 - 8x + 3 = Ax^2 + (-2A + B)x + (A - B + 1)$

Equating coefficients of like powers:

$6 = A, \quad -8 = -2A + B \quad \text{and} \quad 3 = A - B + 1$

$\qquad\qquad -8 = -12 + B \qquad\quad 3 = 6 - B + 1$

$\qquad\qquad\quad 4 = B \qquad\qquad\qquad 4 = B$

$\dfrac{x^4}{(x - 1)^3} = x + 3 + \dfrac{6}{x - 1} + \dfrac{4}{(x - 1)^2} + \dfrac{1}{(x - 1)^3}$

31. $\dfrac{5 - x}{2x^2 + x - 1} = \dfrac{A}{2x - 1} + \dfrac{B}{x + 1}$

$\qquad\quad -x + 5 = A(x + 1) + B(2x - 1)$

Let $x = \dfrac{1}{2}$: $\dfrac{9}{2} = \dfrac{3}{2}A \implies A = 3$

Let $x = -1$: $6 = -3B \implies B = -2$

$\dfrac{5 - x}{2x^2 + x - 1} = \dfrac{3}{2x - 1} - \dfrac{2}{x + 1}$

33. $\dfrac{x-1}{x^3+x^2} = \dfrac{A}{x} + \dfrac{B}{x^2} + \dfrac{C}{x+1}$

$\qquad x - 1 = Ax(x+1) + B(x+1) + Cx^2$

Let $x = -1$: $-2 = C$

Let $x = 0$: $-1 = B$

Let $x = 1$: $0 = 2A + 2B + C$

$\qquad\qquad\quad 0 = 2A - 2 - 2$

$\qquad\qquad\quad 2 = A$

$\dfrac{x-1}{x^3+x^2} = \dfrac{2}{x} - \dfrac{1}{x^2} - \dfrac{2}{x+1}$

35. $\dfrac{x^2+x+2}{(x^2+2)^2} = \dfrac{Ax+B}{x^2+2} + \dfrac{Cx+D}{(x^2+2)^2}$

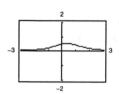

$x^2 + x + 2 = (Ax+B)(x^2+2) + Cx + D$

$x^2 + x + 2 = Ax^3 + Bx^2 + (2A+C)x + (2B+D)$

Equating coefficients of like powers:

$\qquad 0 = A$

$\qquad 1 = B$

$\qquad 1 = 2A + C \implies C = 1$

$\qquad 2 = 2B + D \implies D = 0$

$\dfrac{x^2+x+2}{(x^2+2)^2} = \dfrac{1}{x^2+2} + \dfrac{x}{(x^2+2)^2}$

37. $\dfrac{2x^3 - 4x^2 - 15x + 5}{x^2 - 2x - 8} = 2x + \dfrac{x+5}{(x+2)(x-4)}$

$\dfrac{x+5}{(x+2)(x-4)} = \dfrac{A}{x+2} + \dfrac{B}{x-4}$

$x + 5 = A(x-4) + B(x+2)$

Let $x = -2$: $3 = -6A \implies A = -\dfrac{1}{2}$

Let $x = 4$: $9 = 6B \implies B = \dfrac{3}{2}$

$\dfrac{2x^3 - 4x^2 - 15x + 5}{x^2 - 2x - 8} = 2x + \dfrac{1}{2}\left(\dfrac{3}{x-4} - \dfrac{1}{x+2}\right)$

39. $\dfrac{1}{a^2 - x^2} = \dfrac{A}{a+x} + \dfrac{B}{a-x}$, a is a constant.

$\qquad 1 = A(a-x) + B(a+x)$

Let $x = -a$: $1 = 2aA \implies A = \dfrac{1}{2a}$

Let $x = a$: $1 = 2aB \implies B = \dfrac{1}{2a}$

$\dfrac{1}{a^2 - x^2} = \dfrac{1}{2a}\left(\dfrac{1}{a+x} + \dfrac{1}{a-x}\right)$

41. $\dfrac{1}{y(a-y)} = \dfrac{A}{y} + \dfrac{B}{a-y}$

$$1 = A(a-y) + By$$

Let $y = 0$: $\ 1 = aA \implies A = \dfrac{1}{a}$

Let $y = a$: $\ 1 = aB \implies B = \dfrac{1}{a}$

$$\dfrac{1}{y(a-y)} = \dfrac{1}{a}\left(\dfrac{1}{y} + \dfrac{1}{a-y}\right)$$

43. $\dfrac{x-12}{x(x-4)} = \dfrac{A}{x} + \dfrac{B}{x-4}$

$$x - 12 = A(x-4) + Bx$$

Let $x = 0$: $\ -12 = -4A \implies A = 3$

Let $x = 4$: $\ -8 = 4B \implies B = -2$

$$\dfrac{x-12}{x(x-4)} = \dfrac{3}{x} - \dfrac{2}{x-4}$$

$y = \dfrac{x-12}{x(x-4)}$

Vertical asymptotes: $x = 0$ and $x = 4$

$y = \dfrac{3}{x}$

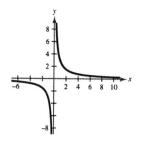

Vertical asymptote: $x = 0$

$y = -\dfrac{2}{x-4}$

Vertical asymptote: $x = 4$

The combination of the vertical asymptotes of the terms of the decompositions are the same as the vertical asymptotes of the rational function.

45. $\dfrac{2(4x - 3)}{x^2 - 9} = \dfrac{A}{x - 3} + \dfrac{B}{x + 3}$

$2(4x - 3) = A(x + 3) + B(x - 3)$

Let $x = 3$: $18 = 6A \implies A = 3$

Let $x = -3$: $-30 = -6B \implies B = 5$

$\dfrac{2(4x - 3)}{x^2 - 9} = \dfrac{3}{x - 3} + \dfrac{5}{x + 3}$

$y = \dfrac{2(4x - 3)}{x^2 - 9}$

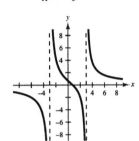

$y = \dfrac{3}{x - 3}$

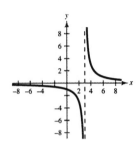

$y = \dfrac{5}{x + 3}$

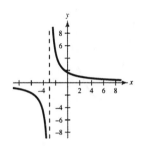

Vertical asymptotes: $x = \pm 3$ Vertical asymptote: $x = 3$ Vertical asymptote: $x = -3$

The combination of the vertical asymptotes of the terms of the decompositions are the same as the vertical asymptotes of the rational function.

47. (a) $\dfrac{2000(4 - 3x)}{(11 - 7x)(7 - 4x)} = \dfrac{A}{11 - 7x} + \dfrac{B}{7 - 4x}$, $0 \le x \le 1$

$2000(4 - 3x) = A(7 - 4x) + B(11 - 7x)$

Let $x = \dfrac{11}{7}$: $-\dfrac{10{,}000}{7} = \dfrac{5}{7}A \implies A = -2000$

Let $x = \dfrac{7}{4}$: $-2500 = -\dfrac{5}{4}B \implies B = 2000$

$\dfrac{2000(4 - 3x)}{(11 - 7x)(7 - 4x)} = \dfrac{-2000}{11 - 7x} + \dfrac{2000}{7 - 4x} = \dfrac{2000}{7 - 4x} - \dfrac{2000}{11 - 7x}$, $0 \le x \le 1$

(b) $y_1 = \dfrac{2000}{7 - 4x}$

$y_2 = \dfrac{2000}{11 - 7x}$

❏ Review Exercises for Chapter 2

Solutions to Odd-Numbered Exercises

1. $f(x) = \left(x + \frac{3}{2}\right)^2 + 1$

Vertex: $\left(-\frac{3}{2}, 1\right)$

y-intercept: $\left(0, \frac{13}{4}\right)$

No x-intercepts

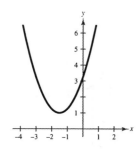

3. $f(x) = \frac{1}{3}(x^2 + 5x - 4)$

$= \frac{1}{3}\left(x^2 + 5x + \frac{25}{4} - \frac{25}{4} - 4\right)$

$= \frac{1}{3}\left[\left(x - \frac{5}{2}\right)^2 - \frac{41}{4}\right]$

$= \frac{1}{3}\left(x - \frac{5}{2}\right)^2 - \frac{41}{12}$

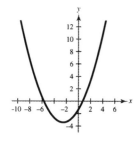

Vertex: $\left(\frac{5}{2}, -\frac{41}{12}\right)$

y-intercept: $\left(0, -\frac{4}{3}\right)$

x-intercept: $0 = \frac{1}{3}(x^2 + 5x - 4)$

$0 = x^2 + 5x - 4$

$x = \frac{-5 \pm \sqrt{41}}{2}$

Use the Quadratic Formula.

$\left(\frac{-5 \pm \sqrt{41}}{2}, 0\right)$

5. Vertex: $(1, -4) \implies f(x) = a(x - 1)^2 - 4$

Point: $(2, -3) \implies -3 = a(2 - 1)^2 - 4$

$1 = a$

Thus, $f(x) = (x - 1)^2 - 4$.

7. $g(x) = x^2 - 2x$

$= x^2 - 2x + 1 - 1$

$= (x - 1)^2 - 1$

The minimum occurs at the vertex $(1, -1)$.

9. $f(x) = 6x - x^2$

$= -(x^2 - 6x + 9 - 9)$

$= -(x - 3)^2 + 9$

The maximum occurs at the vertex $(3, 9)$.

11. $f(t) = -2t^2 + 4t + 1$

$= -2(t^2 - 2t + 1 - 1) + 1$

$= -2[(t - 1)^2 - 1] + 1$

$= -2(t - 1)^2 + 3$

The maximum occurs at the vertex $(1, 3)$.

13. (a)

x	y	Area
1	$4 - \frac{1}{2}(1)$	$(1)[4 - \frac{1}{2}(1)] = \frac{7}{2}$
2	$4 - \frac{1}{2}(2)$	$(2)[4 - \frac{1}{2}(2)] = 6$
3	$4 - \frac{1}{2}(3)$	$(3)[4 - \frac{1}{2}(3)] = \frac{15}{2}$
4	$4 - \frac{1}{2}(4)$	$(4)[4 - \frac{1}{2}(4)] = 8$
5	$4 - \frac{1}{2}(5)$	$(5)[4 - \frac{1}{2}(5)] = \frac{15}{2}$
6	$4 - \frac{1}{2}(6)$	$(6)[4 - \frac{1}{2}(6)] = 6$

(b) The dimensions that will produce a maximum area are $x = 4$ and $y = 2$.

(c) $A = xy = x\left(\dfrac{8 - x}{2}\right)$ since $x + 2y - 8 = 0 \implies y = \dfrac{8 - x}{2}$.

Since the figure is in the first quadrant and x and y must be positive,

the domain of $A = x\left(\dfrac{8 - x}{2}\right)$ is $0 < x < 8$.

(d)

The maximum area of 8 occurs at the vertex when $x = 4$ and $y = \dfrac{8 - 4}{2} = 2$.

(e) $A = x\left(\dfrac{8 - x}{2}\right)$

$\quad = \dfrac{1}{2}(8x - x^2)$

$\quad = -\dfrac{1}{2}(x^2 - 8x)$

$\quad = -\dfrac{1}{2}(x^2 - 8x + 16 - 16)$

$\quad = -\dfrac{1}{2}[(x - 4)^2 - 16]$

$\quad = -\dfrac{1}{2}(x - 4)^2 + 8$

The maximum area of 8 occurs when $x = 4$ and $y = \dfrac{8 - 4}{2} = 2$.

15. $f(x) = -x^2 + 6x + 9$

The degree is even and the leading coefficient is negative. The graph falls to the left and right.

17. $f(x) = \frac{3}{4}(x^4 + 3x^2 + 2)$

The degree is even and the leading coefficient is positive. The graph rises to the left and right.

19. $f(x) = \frac{1}{2}x^3 - 2x + 1$; $g(x) = \frac{1}{2}x^3$

21. $g(x) = x^4 - x^3 - 2x^2$

$$= x^2(x + 1)(x - 2)$$

Intercepts: $(0, 0), (-1, 0), (2, 0)$

The graph rises to the left and to the right.

x	-2	-1	$-\frac{1}{2}$	0	1	2	3
y	16	0	-0.31	0	-2	0	36

23. $f(t) = t^3 - 3t = t(t^2 - 3)$

Intercepts: $(0, 0), \left(\pm\sqrt{3}, 0\right)$

The graph rises to the right and falls to the left.

x	-2	-1	0	1	2
y	-2	2	0	-2	2

25. $f(x) = x(x + 3)^2$

Intercepts: $(0, 0), (-3, 0)$

The graph falls to the left and rises to the right.

x	-4	-3	-2	-1	0	1
y	-4	0	-2	-4	0	16

27. (a) The combined length and girth is

$$y + 4x = 216$$

$$y = 216 - 4x.$$

(b) The volume is $V = x^2y = x^2(216 - 4x)$.

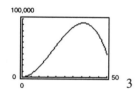

The volume is maximum when $x = 36$ centimeters and $y = 216 - 4(36) = 72$ centimeters.

29. $y_1 = \dfrac{x^2}{x-2}$

$$y_2 = x + 2 + \dfrac{4}{x-2}$$

$$= \dfrac{(x+2)(x-2)}{x-2} + \dfrac{4}{x-2}$$

$$= \dfrac{x^2-4}{x-2} + \dfrac{4}{x-2}$$

$$= \dfrac{x^2}{x-2}$$

$$= y_1$$

31.

$$
\begin{array}{r}
8x + 5 \\
3x-2\overline{\smash{)}24x^2 - x - 8} \\
\underline{24x^2 - 16x} \\
15x - 8 \\
\underline{15x - 10} \\
2
\end{array}
$$

Thus, $\dfrac{24x^2 - x - 8}{3x-2} = 8x + 5 + \dfrac{2}{3x-2}.$

33.

$$
\begin{array}{r}
x^2 \qquad\quad - 2 \\
x^2 + 0x - 1\overline{\smash{)}x^4 + 0x^3 - 3x^2 + 0x + 2} \\
\underline{x^4 + 0x^3 - \ x^2} \\
-2x^2 + 0x + 2 \\
\underline{-2x^2 + 0x + 2} \\
0
\end{array}
$$

Thus, $\dfrac{x^4 - 3x^2 + 2}{x^2 - 1} = x^2 - 2.$

35.

$$
\begin{array}{r}
x^2 - \ x + 1 \\
x^2 + 2x\overline{\smash{)}x^4 + \ x^3 - \ x^2 + 2x + 0} \\
\underline{x^4 + 2x^3} \\
-x^3 - \ x^2 \\
\underline{-x^3 - 2x^2} \\
x^2 + 2x \\
\underline{x^2 + 2x} \\
0
\end{array}
$$

Thus, $\dfrac{x^4 + x^3 - x^2 + 2x}{x^2 + 2x} = x^2 - x + 1.$

37.

$$
\begin{array}{r|rrrrr}
2 & 0.25 & -4 & 0 & 0 & 0 \\
 & & 0.50 & -7 & -14 & -28 \\
\hline
 & 0.25 & -3.50 & -7 & -14 & -28
\end{array}
$$

Thus, $\dfrac{0.25x^4 - 4x^3}{x-2} = 0.25x^3 - 3.50x^2 - 7x - 14 - \dfrac{28}{x-2}.$

39.

$$
\begin{array}{r|rrrrr}
\frac{2}{3} & 6 & -4 & -27 & 18 & 0 \\
 & & 4 & 0 & -18 & 0 \\
\hline
 & 6 & 0 & -27 & 0 & 0
\end{array}
$$

Thus, $\dfrac{6x^4 - 4x^3 - 27x^2 + 18x}{x - (2/3)} = 6x^3 - 27x.$

41. $f(x) = 2x^3 + 3x^2 - 20x - 21$

(a) 4 |
$$\begin{array}{r|rrrr} 4 & 2 & 3 & -20 & -21 \\ & & 8 & 44 & 96 \\ \hline & 2 & 11 & 24 & 75 \end{array}$$

No, $x = 4$ is not a zero of f.

(b) -1
$$\begin{array}{r|rrrr} -1 & 2 & 3 & -20 & -21 \\ & & -2 & -1 & 21 \\ \hline & 2 & 1 & -21 & 0 \end{array}$$

Yes, $x = -1$ is a zero of f.

(c) $-\frac{7}{2}$
$$\begin{array}{r|rrrr} -\frac{7}{2} & 2 & 3 & -20 & -21 \\ & & -7 & 14 & 21 \\ \hline & 2 & -4 & -6 & 0 \end{array}$$

Yes, $x = -\frac{7}{2}$ is a zero of f.

(d) 0
$$\begin{array}{r|rrrr} 0 & 2 & 3 & -20 & -21 \\ & & 0 & 0 & 0 \\ \hline & 2 & 3 & -20 & -21 \end{array}$$

No, $x = 0$ is not a zero of f.

43. $(7 + 5i) + (-4 + 2i) = (7 - 4) + (5i + 2i) = 3 + 7i$

45. $5i(13 - 8i) = 65i - 40i^2 = 40 + 65i$

47. $\dfrac{6 + i}{i} = \dfrac{6 + i}{i} \cdot \dfrac{-i}{-i} = \dfrac{-6i - i^2}{-i^2} = \dfrac{-6i + 1}{1} = 1 - 6i$

49. $f(x) = 6(x + 1)^2 \left(x - \frac{1}{3}\right)\left(x + \frac{1}{2}\right)$ Multiply by 6 to clear the fractions.

$= (x + 1)^2\, 3\left(x - \frac{1}{3}\right) 2\left(x + \frac{1}{2}\right)$

$= (x^2 + 2x + 1)(3x - 1)(2x + 1)$

$= (x^2 + 2x + 1)(6x^2 + x - 1)$

$= 6x^4 + 13x^3 + 7x^2 - x - 1$

Note: $f(x) = a(6x^4 + 13x^3 + 7x^2 - x - 1)$, where a is any real nonzero number, has zeros $-1, -1, \frac{1}{3}$, and $-\frac{1}{2}$.

51. $f(x) = 4x^3 - 11x^2 + 10x - 3$

Possible rational zeros: $\pm 1, \pm 3, \pm\frac{1}{2}, \pm\frac{3}{2}, \pm\frac{1}{4}, \pm\frac{3}{4}$

$$\begin{array}{r|rrrr} 1 & 4 & -11 & 10 & -3 \\ & & 4 & -7 & 3 \\ \hline & 4 & -7 & 3 & 0 \end{array}$$

$4x^3 - 11x^2 + 10x - 3 = (x - 1)(4x^2 - 7x + 3) = (x - 1)^2(4x - 3)$

Thus, the zeros of $f(x)$ are $x = 1$ and $x = \frac{3}{4}$.

53. $f(x) = 6x^3 - 5x^2 + 24x - 20$

$= x^2(6x - 5) + 4(6x - 5)$

$= (6x - 5)(x^2 + 4)$

$= (6x - 5)(x + 2i)(x - 2i)$

Thus, the zeros of f are $x = \frac{5}{6}$ and $x = \pm 2i$.

55. $f(x) = 6x^4 - 25x^3 + 14x^2 + 27x - 18$

Possible rational zeros: $\pm 1, \pm 2, \pm 3, \pm 6, \pm 9, \pm 18, \pm \frac{1}{2}, \pm \frac{3}{2}, \pm \frac{9}{2}, \pm \frac{1}{3}, \pm \frac{2}{3}, \pm \frac{1}{6}$

$$
\begin{array}{r|rrrrr}
-1 & 6 & -25 & 14 & 27 & -18 \\
   &   & -6 & 31 & -45 & 18 \\
\hline
   & 6 & -31 & 45 & -18 & 0
\end{array}
$$

$$
\begin{array}{r|rrrr}
3 & 6 & -31 & 45 & -18 \\
  &   & 18 & -39 & 18 \\
\hline
  & 6 & -13 & 6 & 0
\end{array}
$$

$$6x^4 - 25x^3 + 14x^2 + 27x - 18 = (x + 1)(x - 3)(6x^2 - 13x + 6)$$

$$= (x + 1)(x - 3)(3x - 2)(2x - 3)$$

Thus, the zeros of $f(x)$ are $x = -1$, $x = 3$, $x = \frac{2}{3}$, and $x = \frac{3}{2}$.

57. $f(x) = x^4 + 2x + 1$

(a)

(b) The graph has two x-intercepts, so there are two real zeros.

(c) The zeros are $x = -1$ and $x \approx -0.54$.

59. $h(x) = x^3 - 6x^2 + 12x - 10$

(a)

(b) The graph has one x-intercept, so there is one real zero.

(c) $x \approx 3.26$

61. (a) $S = 1.209 + 0.290t + 0.176t^2 - 0.031t^3 + 0.0013t^4$

The model is a fairly "good fit."

(b) One explanation may be a recession. The model also shows a downturn in sales.

(c) $S(9) - S(11) \approx 0.54$
The actual decrease of 0.90 was more than this.

(d) $S(15) \approx 6.35$

63. $f(x) = \dfrac{-5}{x^2}$

y-axis symmetry

Vertical asymptote: $x = 0$

Horizontal asymptote: $y = 0$

x	± 3	± 2	± 1
y	$-\frac{5}{9}$	$-\frac{5}{4}$	-5

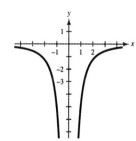

65. $p(x) = \dfrac{x^2}{x^2 + 1}$

Intercept: $(0, 0)$

y-axis symmetry

Horizontal asymptote: $y = 1$

x	± 3	± 2	± 1	0
y	$\frac{9}{10}$	$\frac{4}{5}$	$\frac{1}{2}$	0

67. $f(x) = \dfrac{x}{x^2 + 1}$

Intercept: $(0, 0)$

Origin symmetry

Horizontal asymptote: $y = 0$

x	-2	-1	0	1	2
y	$-\frac{2}{5}$	$-\frac{1}{2}$	0	$\frac{1}{2}$	$\frac{2}{5}$

69. $f(x) = \dfrac{2x^3}{x^2 + 1} = 2x - \dfrac{2x}{x^2 + 1}$

Intercept: $(0, 0)$

Origin symmetry

Slant asymptote: $y = 2x$

x	-2	-1	0	1	2
y	$-\frac{16}{5}$	-1	0	1	$\frac{16}{5}$

71. $s(x) = \dfrac{8x^2}{x^2 + 4}$

Intercept: $(0, 0)$

Horizontal asymptote: $y = 8$

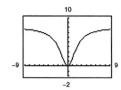

73. $g(x) = \dfrac{x^2 + 1}{x + 1} = x - 1 + \dfrac{2}{x + 1}$

Intercept: $(0, 1)$

Slant asymptote: $y = x - 1$

Vertical asymptote: $x = -1$

75. $\dfrac{4 - x}{x^2 + 6x + 8} = \dfrac{A}{x + 2} + \dfrac{B}{x + 4}$

$\qquad 4 - x = A(x + 4) + B(x + 2)$

$\qquad$ Let $x = -2$: $6 = 2A \implies A = 3$

$\qquad$ Let $x = -4$: $8 = -2B \implies B = -4$

$\qquad \dfrac{4 - x}{x^2 + 6x + 8} = \dfrac{3}{x + 2} - \dfrac{4}{x + 4}$

77. $\dfrac{x^2}{x^2 + 2x - 15} = 1 - \dfrac{2x - 15}{x^2 + 2x - 15}$

$\qquad \dfrac{-2x + 15}{(x + 5)(x - 3)} = \dfrac{A}{x + 5} + \dfrac{B}{x - 3}$

$\qquad -2x + 15 = A(x - 3) + B(x + 5)$

$\qquad$ Let $x = -5$: $25 = -8A \implies A = -\dfrac{25}{8}$

$\qquad$ Let $x = 3$: $9 = 8B \implies B = \dfrac{9}{8}$

$\qquad \dfrac{x^2}{x^2 + 2x - 15} = 1 + \dfrac{9}{8(x - 3)} - \dfrac{25}{8(x + 5)}$

79. $\dfrac{x^2 + 2x}{x^3 - x^2 + x - 1} = \dfrac{A}{x - 1} + \dfrac{Bx + C}{x^2 + 1}$

$\qquad x^2 + 2x = A\,(x^2 + 1) + (Bx + C)(x - 1)$

$\qquad$ Let $x = 1$: $3 = 2A \implies A = \dfrac{3}{2}$

$\qquad$ Let $x = 0$: $0 = A - C \implies C = \dfrac{3}{2}$

$\qquad$ Let $x = 2$: $8 = 5A + 2B + C$

$\qquad\qquad 8 = \left(\dfrac{15}{2}\right) + 2B + \left(\dfrac{3}{2}\right) \implies B = -\dfrac{1}{2}$

$\qquad \dfrac{x^2 + 2x}{x^3 - x^2 + x - 1} = \dfrac{3/2}{x - 1} + \dfrac{-(1/2)x + 3/2}{x^2 + 1}$

$\qquad\qquad = \dfrac{1}{2}\left(\dfrac{3}{x - 1} - \dfrac{x - 3}{x^2 + 1}\right)$

❏ Practice Test for Chapter 2

1. Sketch the graph of $f(x) = x^2 - 6x + 5$ and identify the vertex and the intercepts.

2. Find the number of units x that produce a minimum cost C if
   $C = 0.01x^2 - 90x + 15,000$.

3. Find the quadratic function that has a maximum at $(1, 7)$ and passes through the point $(2, 5)$.

4. Find two quadratic functions that have x-intercepts $(2, 0)$ and $\left(\frac{4}{3}, 0\right)$.

5. Use the leading coefficient test to determine the right and left end behavior of the graph of the polynomial function $f(x) = -3x^5 + 2x^3 - 17$.

6. Find all the real zeros of $f(x) = x^5 - 5x^3 + 4x$.

7. Find a polynomial function with 0, 3, and -2 as zeros.

8. Sketch $f(x) = x^3 - 12x$.

9. Divide $3x^4 - 7x^2 + 2x - 10$ by $x - 3$ using long division.

10. Divide $x^3 - 11$ by $x^2 + 2x - 1$.

11. Use synthetic division to divide $3x^5 + 13x^4 + 12x - 1$ by $x + 5$.

12. Use synthetic division to find $f(-6)$ given $f(x) = 7x^3 + 40x^2 - 12x + 15$.

13. Find the real zeros of $f(x) = x^3 - 19x - 30$.

14. Find the real zeros of $f(x) = x^4 + x^3 - 8x^2 - 9x - 9$.

15. List all possible rational zeros of the function $f(x) = 6x^3 - 5x^2 + 4x - 15$.

16. Find the rational zeros of the polynomial $f(x) = x^3 - \frac{20}{3}x^2 + 9x - \frac{10}{3}$.

17. Write $f(x) = x^4 + x^3 + 5x - 10$ as a product of linear factors.

18. Find a polynomial with real coefficients that has 2, $3 + i$, and $3 - 2i$ as zeros.

19. Use synthetic division to show that $3i$ is a zero of $f(x) = x^3 + 4x^2 + 9x + 36$.

20. Sketch the graph of $f(x) = \dfrac{x - 1}{2x}$ and label all intercepts and asymptotes.

21. Find all the asymptotes of $f(x) = \dfrac{8x^2 - 9}{x^2 + 1}$.

22. Find all the asymptotes of $f(x) = \dfrac{4x^2 - 2x + 7}{x - 1}$.

23. Given $z_1 = 4 - 3i$ and $z_2 = -2 + i$, find the following:

    (a) $z_1 - z_2$

    (b) $z_1 z_2$

    (c) z_1/z_2

For Exercises 24–25, write the partial fraction decomposition for the rational expression.

24. $\dfrac{1 - 2x}{x^2 + x}$

25. $\dfrac{6x - 17}{(x - 3)^2}$

C H A P T E R 3
Exponential and Logarithmic Functions

CHAPTER 3
Exponential and Logarithmic Functions

Section 3.1 Exponential Functions and Their Graphs

- You should know that a function of the form $y = a^x$, where $a > 0$, $a \neq 1$, is called an exponential function with base a.
- You should be able to graph exponential functions.
- You should know formulas for compound interest.

  (a) For n compoundings per year: $A = P\left(1 + \dfrac{r}{n}\right)^{nt}$.

  (b) For continuous compoundings: $A = Pe^{rt}$.

Solutions to Odd-Numbered Exercises

1. $(3.4)^{5.6} \approx 946.852$

3. $(1.005)^{400} \approx 7.352$

5. $5^{-\pi} \approx 0.006$

7. $100^{\sqrt{2}} \approx 673.639$

9. $e^{-3/4} \approx 0.472$

11. $f(x) = 3^{x-2}$
$$= 3^x 3^{-2}$$
$$= 3^x\left(\frac{1}{3^2}\right)$$
$$= \frac{1}{9}(3^x)$$
$$= h(x)$$

Thus, $f(x) \neq g(x)$, but $f(x) = h(x)$.

13. $f(x) = 16(4^{-x})$ and $f(x) = 16(4^{-x})$
$$\qquad = 4^2(4^{-x}) \qquad\qquad = 16(2^2)^{-x}$$
$$\qquad = 4^{2-x} \qquad\qquad\quad = 16(2^{-2x})$$
$$\qquad = \left(\frac{1}{4}\right)^{-(2-x)} \qquad\quad = h(x)$$
$$\qquad = \left(\frac{1}{4}\right)^{x-2}$$
$$\qquad = g(x)$$

Thus, $f(x) = g(x) = h(x)$.

15. $f(x) = 2^x$ rises to the right.

Asymptote: $y = 0$
Intercept: $(0, 1)$
Matches graph (d).

17. $f(x) = 2^{-x}$ falls to the right.

Asymptote: $y = 0$
Intercept: $(0, 1)$
Matches graph (a).

19. $g(x) = 5^x$

x	-2	-1	0	1	2
$g(x)$	$\frac{1}{25}$	$\frac{1}{5}$	1	5	25

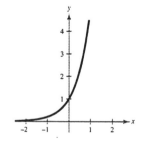

21. $f(x) = \left(\dfrac{1}{5}\right)^x = 5^{-x}$

x	-2	-1	0	1	2
y	25	5	1	$\frac{1}{5}$	$\frac{1}{25}$

23. $h(x) = 5^{x-2}$

x	-1	0	1	2	3
y	$\frac{1}{125}$	$\frac{1}{25}$	$\frac{1}{5}$	1	5

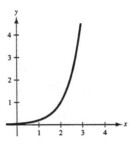

25. $g(x) = 5^{-x} - 3$

x	-1	0	1	2
y	2	-2	$-2\frac{4}{5}$	$-2\frac{24}{25}$

Asymptote: $y = -3$

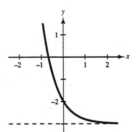

27. $y = 2^{-x^2}$

x	± 2	± 1	0
y	$\frac{1}{16}$	$\frac{1}{2}$	1

29. $f(x) = 3^{x-2} + 1$

x	-1	0	1	2	3	4
y	$1\frac{1}{27}$	$1\frac{1}{9}$	$1\frac{1}{3}$	2	4	10

Asymptote: $y = 1$

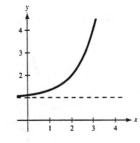

31. $y = 1.08^{-5x}$

x	-1	0	1	2
y	1.47	1	0.68	0.46

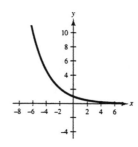

33. $s(t) = 2e^{0.12t}$

t	-4	0	4	8
$s(t)$	1.24	2	3.23	5.22

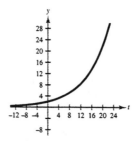

35. $g(x) = 1 + e^{-x}$

x	-2	-1	0	1	2
y	8.39	3.72	2	1.37	1.14

Asymptote: $y = 1$

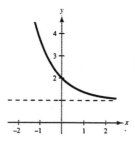

37. $y = 3^x$ and $y = 4^x$

x	-2	-1	0	1	2
3^x	$\frac{1}{9}$	$\frac{1}{3}$	1	3	9
4^x	$\frac{1}{16}$	$\frac{1}{4}$	1	4	16

(a) $4^x < 3^x$ when $x < 0$.

(b) $4^x > 3^x$ when $x > 0$.

39. $f(x) = 3^x$

(a) $g(x) = f(x - 2) = 3^{x-2}$

(b) $h(x) = -\frac{1}{2}f(x) = -\frac{1}{2}(3^x)$

(c) $q(x) = f(-x) + 3 = 3^{-x} + 3$

Horizontal shift 2 units to the right

Vertical shrink and a reflection about the x-axis

Reflection about the y-axis and a vertical translation 3 units upward

41. (a) $f(x) = x^2 e^{-x}$

Decreasing: $(-\infty, 0)$, $(2, \infty)$
Increasing: $(0, 2)$
Relative maximum: $(2, 4e^{-2})$
Relative minimum: $(0, 0)$

(b) $g(x) = x2^{3-x}$

Decreasing: $(1.44, \infty)$
Increasing: $(-\infty, 1.44)$
Relative maximum: $(1.44, 4.25)$

43. The exponential function, $y = e^x$, increases at a faster rate than the polynomial function, $y = x^n$.

45. $f(x) = \left(1 + \dfrac{0.5}{x}\right)^x$ and $g(x) = e^{0.5}$ (Horizontal line)

As $x \to \infty$, $f(x) \to g(x)$.

47. $P = \$2500$, $r = 12\%$, $t = 10$ years

Compounded n times per year: $A = 2500\left(1 + \dfrac{0.12}{n}\right)^{10n}$

Compounded continuously: $A = 2500e^{0.12(10)}$

n	1	2	4	12	365	Continuous Compounding
A	\$7,764.62	\$8,017.84	\$8,155.09	\$8250.97	\$8298.66	\$8,300.29

49. $P = \$2500$, $r = 12\%$, $t = 20$ years

Compounded n times per year: $A = 2500\left(1 + \dfrac{0.12}{n}\right)^{20n}$

Compounded continuously: $A = 2500e^{0.12(20)}$

n	1	2	4	12	365	Continuous Compounding
A	\$24,115.73	\$25,714.29	\$26,602.23	\$27,231.38	\$27,547.07	\$27,557.94

51. $A = Pe^{rt}$

$100,000 = Pe^{0.09t}$

$\dfrac{100,000}{e^{0.09t}} = P$

$P = 100,000e^{-0.09t}$

t	1	10	20	30	40	50
P	\$91,393.12	\$40,656.97	\$16,529.89	\$6,720.55	\$2,732.37	\$1,110.90

53. $A = 25,000e^{(0.0875)(25)} \approx \$222,822.57$

55. (a) The graph that is increasing faster represents 7% compounded annually. When interest is compounded, you earn interest on that interest. With simple interest there is no compounding so the growth is linear.

Compounded Interest

Simple Interest

(b) Compound interest formula: $A = 500\left(1 + \dfrac{0.07}{1}\right)^{(1)t}$

$$= 500(1.07)^t$$

Simple interest formula: $A = Prt + P$

$$= 500(0.07)t + 500$$

57. $C(10) = 23.95(1.04)^{10} \approx \$35.45$

59. $P(t) = 100e^{0.2197t}$

    (a) $P(0) = 100$

    (b) $P(5) \approx 300$

    (c) $P(10) \approx 900$

61. $Q = 25\left(\frac{1}{2}\right)^{t/1620}$

    (a) When $t = 0$, $Q = 25\left(\frac{1}{2}\right)^{0/1620} = 25(1) = 25$ units.

    (b) When $t = 1000$, $Q = 25\left(\frac{1}{2}\right)^{1000/1620} \approx 16.30$ units.

    (c)

63. $P = 10{,}958e^{-0.15h}$

    (a)

    (b)

h	0	5	10	15	20
P	10,958	5176	2445	1155	546

    The model is a "good fit."

    (c) $P(8) \approx 3300 \text{ kg/m}^2$

    (d) $2000 = 10{,}958e^{-0.15h}$ when $x \approx 11.3$ km.

65. False, $e \neq \dfrac{271{,}801}{99{,}990}$.

Since e is an irrational number it cannot equal a rational number.

67. Since $\sqrt{2} \approx 1.414$ we know that $1 < \sqrt{2} < 2$.

Thus, $2^1 < 2^{\sqrt{2}} < 2^2$

$2 < 2^{\sqrt{2}} < 4$.

69. $y_4 = 1 + \dfrac{x}{1!} + \dfrac{x^2}{2!} + \dfrac{x^3}{3!} + \dfrac{x^4}{4!}$

$e^x = 1 + \dfrac{x}{1!} + \dfrac{x^2}{2!} + \dfrac{x^3}{3!} + \dfrac{x^4}{4!} + \dfrac{x^5}{5!} + \cdots$

71. $2x - 7y + 14 = 0$

$2x + 14 = 7y$

$\frac{1}{7}(2x + 14) = y$

73. $x^2 + y^2 = 25$

$y^2 = 25 - x^2$

$y = \pm\sqrt{25 - x^2}$

Section 3.2   Logarithmic Functions and Their Graphs

- You should know that a function of the form $y = \log_a x$, where $a > 0$, $a \neq 1$, and $x > 0$, is called a logarithm of x to base a.
- You should be able to convert from logarithmic form to exponential form and vice versa.

  $$y = \log_a x \iff a^y = x$$
- You should know the following properties of logarithms.
  - (a) $\log_a 1 = 0$ since $a^0 = 1$.
  - (b) $\log_a a = 1$ since $a^1 = a$.
  - (c) $\log_a a^x = x$ since $a^x = a^x$.
  - (d) If $\log_a x = \log_a y$, then $x = y$.
- You should know the definition of the natural logarithmic function.

  $$\log_e x = \ln x, x > 0$$
- You should know the properties of the natural logarithmic function.
  - (a) $\ln 1 = 0$ since $e^0 = 1$.
  - (b) $\ln e = 1$ since $e^1 = e$.
  - (c) $\ln e^x = x$ since $e^x = e^x$.
  - (d) If $\ln x = \ln y$, then $x = y$.
- You should be able to graph logarithmic functions.

Solutions to Odd-Numbered Exercises

1. $\log_4 64 = 3 \implies 4^3 = 64$

3. $\log_7 \frac{1}{49} = -2 \implies 7^{-2} = \frac{1}{49}$

5. $\log_{32} 4 = \frac{2}{5} \implies 32^{2/5} = 4$

7. $\ln 1 = 0 \implies e^0 = 1$

9. $5^3 = 125 \implies \log_5 125 = 3$

11. $81^{1/4} = 3 \implies \log_{81} 3 = \frac{1}{4}$

13. $6^{-2} = \frac{1}{36} \implies \log_6 \frac{1}{36} = -2$

15. $e^3 = 20.0855\ldots \implies \ln 20.0855\ldots = 3$

17. $e^x = 4 \implies \ln 4 = x$

19. $\log_2 16 = \log_2 2^4 = 4$

21. $\log_{16} 4 = \log_{16} 16^{1/2} = \frac{1}{2}$

23. $\log_7 1 = \log_7 7^0 = 0$

25. $\log_{10} 0.01 = \log_{10} 10^{-2} = -2$

27. $\log_8 32 = \log_8 8^{5/3} = \frac{5}{3}$

29. $\ln e^3 = 3$

31. $\log_{10} 345 \approx 2.538$

33. $\log_{10} 145 \approx 2.161$

35. $\ln 18.42 \approx 2.913$

37. $\ln(1 + \sqrt{3}) \approx 1.005$

39. $\ln 0.32 \approx -1.139$

41. $f(x) = 3^x$, $g(x) = \log_3 x$

f and *g* are inverses. Their graphs are reflected about the line $y = x$.

43. $f(x) = e^x$, $g(x) = \ln x$

f and *g* are inverses. Their graphs are reflected about the line $y = x$.

45. $f(x) = \log_3 x + 2$
Asymptote: $x = 0$
Point on graph: $(1, 2)$
Matches graph (c).

47. $f(x) = -\log_3(x + 2)$
Asymptote: $x = -2$
Point on graph: $(-1, 0)$
Matches graph (d).

49. $f(x) = \log_3(1 - x)$
Asymptote: $x = 1$
Point on graph: $(0, 0)$
Matches graph (b).

51. $f(x) = \log_4 x$

Domain: $x > 0 \implies$ The domain is $(0, \infty)$.

Vertical asymptote: $x = 0$

x-intercept: $(1, 0)$

$y = \log_4 x \implies 4^y = x$

x	$\frac{1}{4}$	1	4	2
y	-1	0	1	$\frac{1}{2}$

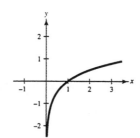

53. $y = -\log_3 x + 2$

Domain: $(0, \infty)$

Vertical asymptote: $x = 0$

x-intercept: $-\log_3 x + 2 = 0$

$$2 = \log_3 x$$
$$3^2 = x$$
$$9 = x$$

The *x*-intercept is $(9, 0)$.

$y = -\log_2 x + 2$

$\log_3 x = 2 - y \implies 3^{2-y} = x$

x	27	9	3	1	$\frac{1}{3}$
y	-1	0	1	2	3

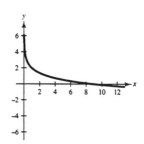

55. $f(x) = -\log_6(x + 2)$

Domain: $x + 2 > 0 \implies x > -2$
The domain is $(-2, \infty)$.
Vertical asymptote: $x + 2 = 0 \implies x = -2$
x-intercept: $0 = -\log_6(x + 2)$
$$0 = \log_6(x + 2)$$
$$6^0 = x + 2$$
$$1 = x + 2$$
$$-1 = x$$

The x-intercept is $(-1, 0)$.
$$y = -\log_6(x + 2)$$
$$-y = \log_6(x + 2)$$
$$6^{-y} - 2 = x$$

x	4	-1	$-1\frac{5}{6}$	$-1\frac{35}{36}$
y	-1	0	1	2

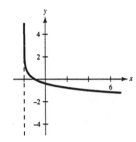

57. $y = \log_{10}\left(\dfrac{x}{5}\right)$

Domain: $\dfrac{x}{5} > 0 \implies x > 0$

The domain is $(0, \infty)$.

Vertical asymptote: $\dfrac{x}{5} = 0 \implies x = 0$

The vertical asymptote is the y-axis.

x-intercept: $\log_{10}\left(\dfrac{x}{5}\right) = 0$

$$\frac{x}{5} = 10^0$$

$$\frac{x}{5} = 1 \implies x = 5$$

The x-intercept is $(5, 0)$.

x	1	2	3	4	5	6	7
y	-0.70	-0.40	-0.22	-0.10	0	0.08	0.15

59. $f(x) = \ln(x - 2)$

Domain: $x - 2 > 0 \implies x > 2$
The domain is $(2, \infty)$.
Vertical asymptote: $x - 2 = 0 \implies x = 2$
x-intercept: $0 = \ln(x - 2)$
$$e^0 = x - 2$$
$$3 = x$$
The x-intercept is $(3, 0)$.

x	2.5	3	4	5
y	-0.69	0	0.69	1.10

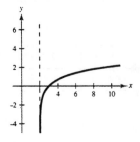

61. $g(x) = \ln(-x)$

Domain: $-x > 0 \implies x < 0$

The domain is $(-\infty, 0)$.

Vertical asymptote: $-x = 0 \implies x = 0$

x-intercept: $0 = \ln(-x)$

$e^0 = -x$

$-1 = x$

The x-intercept is $(-1, 0)$.

x	-0.5	-1	-2	-3
y	-0.69	0	0.69	1.10

63. $f(x) = |\ln x|$

Increasing on $(1, \infty)$

Decreasing on $(0, 1)$

Relative minimum: $(1, 0)$

65. $f(x) = \dfrac{x}{2} - \ln \dfrac{x}{4}$

Increasing on $(2, \infty)$

Decreasing on $(0, 2)$

Relative minimum:

$\left(2, 1 - \ln \tfrac{1}{2}\right)$

67. (a) $f(x) = \ln x$

$g(x) = \sqrt{x}$

The natural log function grows at a slower rate than the square root function.

(b) $f(x) = \ln x$

$g(x) = \sqrt[4]{x}$

The natural log function grows at a slower rate than the fourth root function.

69. $y_1 = \ln x$

$y_2 = x - 1$

$y_3 = (x - 1) - \frac{1}{2}(x - 1)^2$

$y_4 = (x - 1) - \frac{1}{2}(x - 1)^2 + \frac{1}{3}(x - 1)^3$

71. $f(t) = 80 - 17 \log_{10}(t + 1), \, 0 \le t \le 12$

(a) $f(0) = 80 - 17 \log_{10} 1 = 80.0$

(b) $f(4) = 80 - 17 \log_{10} 5 \approx 68.1$

(c) $f(10) = 80 - 17 \log_{10} 11 \approx 62.3$

73. $t = \dfrac{\ln 2}{r}$

r	0.005	0.01	0.015	0.02	0.025	0.03
t	138.6 yr	69.3 yr	46.2 yr	34.7 yr	27.7 yr	23.1 yr

75. $y = 80.4 - 11 \ln x$

$y(300) = 80.4 - 11 \ln 300 \approx 17.66 \text{ ft}^3/\text{min}$

77. $W = 19,440(\ln 9 - \ln 3) \approx 21,357$ ft-lb

79. $t = 10.042 \ln\left(\dfrac{1316.35}{1316.35 - 1250}\right) \approx 30$ years

81. Total amount $= (1316.35)(30)(12) = \$473,886$

Interest $= 473,886 - 150,000 = \$323,886$

83. $f(x) = \dfrac{\ln x}{x}$

(a)

x	1	5	10	10^2	10^4	10^6
$f(x)$	0	0.322	0.230	0.046	0.00092	0.0000138

(b) As $x \to \infty$, $f(x) \to 0$.

(c)

85. $8n - 3$

87. $83.95 + 37.50t$ Parts and labor

Section 3.3   Properties of Logarithms

■ You should know the following properties of logarithms.

    (a) $\log_a x = \dfrac{\log_b x}{\log_b a}$

    (b) $\log_a(uv) = \log_a u + \log_a v$ $\ln(uv) = \ln u + \ln v$

    (c) $\log_a(u/v) = \log_a u - \log_a v$ $\ln(u/v) = \ln u - \ln v$

    (d) $\log_a u^n = n \log_a u$ $\ln u^n = n \ln u$

■ You should be able to rewrite logarithmic expressions using these properties.

Solutions to Odd-Numbered Exercises

1. $f(x) = \log_{10} x$

$g(x) = \dfrac{\ln x}{\ln 10}$

$f(x) = g(x)$

3. $\log_3 5 = \dfrac{\log_{10} 5}{\log_{10} 3}$

5. $\log_2 x = \dfrac{\log_{10} x}{\log_{10} 2}$

7. $\log_3 5 = \dfrac{\ln 5}{\ln 3}$

9. $\log_2 x = \dfrac{\ln x}{\ln 2}$

11. $\log_3 7 = \dfrac{\log_{10} 7}{\log_{10} 3} = \dfrac{\ln 7}{\ln 3} \approx 1.771$

13. $\log_{1/2} 4 = \dfrac{\log_{10} 4}{\log_{10}(1/2)} = \dfrac{\ln 4}{\ln(1/2)} = -2.000$

15. $\log_9 (0.4) = \dfrac{\log_{10} 0.4}{\log_{10} 9} = \dfrac{\ln 0.4}{\ln 9} \approx -0.417$

17. $\log_{15} 1250 = \dfrac{\log_{10} 1250}{\log_{10} 15} = \dfrac{\ln 1250}{\ln 15} \approx 2.633$

19. $\log_{10} 5x = \log_{10} 5 + \log_{10} x$

21. $\log_{10} \dfrac{5}{x} = \log_{10} 5 - \log_{10} x$

23. $\log_8 x^4 = 4 \log_8 x$

25. $\ln \sqrt{z} = \ln z^{1/2} = \frac{1}{2} \ln z$

27. $\ln xyz = \ln x + \ln y + \ln z$

29. $\ln \sqrt{a-1} = \frac{1}{2} \ln(a-1)$

31. $\ln z(z-1)^2 = \ln z + \ln(z-1)^2$

$\qquad\qquad\qquad = \ln z + 2 \ln(z-1)$

33. $\ln \sqrt[3]{\dfrac{x}{y}} = \dfrac{1}{3} \ln \dfrac{x}{y}$

$\qquad\qquad = \dfrac{1}{3} [\ln x - \ln y]$

$\qquad\qquad = \dfrac{1}{3} \ln x - \dfrac{1}{3} \ln y$

35. $\ln \left(\dfrac{x^4 \sqrt{y}}{z^5} \right) = \ln x^4 \sqrt{y} - \ln z^5$

$\qquad\qquad\quad = \ln x^4 + \ln \sqrt{y} - \ln z^5$

$\qquad\qquad\quad = 4 \ln x + \dfrac{1}{2} \ln y - 5 \ln z$

37. $\log_b \left(\dfrac{x^2}{y^2 z^3} \right) = \log_b x^2 - \log_b y^2 z^3$

$\qquad\qquad\quad = \log_b x^2 - [\log_b y^2 + \log_b z^3]$

$\qquad\qquad\quad = 2 \log_b x - 2 \log_b y - 3 \log_b z$

39. $y_1 = \ln[x^3(x+4)]$

$y_2 = 3 \ln x + \ln(x+4)$

$y_1 = y_2$

41. $\ln x + \ln 2 = \ln 2x$

43. $\log_4 z - \log_4 y = \log_4 \dfrac{z}{y}$

45. $2 \log_2(x+4) = \log_2(x+4)^2$

47. $\frac{1}{3} \log_3 5x = \log_3 (5x)^{1/3} = \log_3 \sqrt[3]{5x}$

49. $\ln x - 3 \ln(x+1) = \ln x - \ln(x+1)^3$

$\qquad\qquad\qquad\quad = \ln \dfrac{x}{(x+1)^3}$

51. $\ln(x-2) - \ln(x+2) = \ln \left(\dfrac{x-2}{x+2} \right)$

53. $\ln x - 2[\ln(x + 2) + \ln(x - 2)] = \ln x - 2\ln(x + 2)(x - 2)$

$$= \ln x - 2\ln(x^2 - 4)$$

$$= \ln x - \ln(x^2 - 4)^2$$

$$= \ln \frac{x}{(x^2 - 4)^2}$$

55. $\frac{1}{3}[2\ln(x + 3) + \ln x - \ln(x^2 - 1)] = \frac{1}{3}[\ln(x + 3)^2 + \ln x - \ln(x^2 - 1)]$

$$= \frac{1}{3}[\ln x(x + 3)^2 - \ln(x^2 - 1)]$$

$$= \frac{1}{3}\ln \frac{x(x + 3)^2}{x^2 - 1}$$

$$= \ln \sqrt[3]{\frac{x(x + 3)^2}{x^2 - 1}}$$

57. $\frac{1}{3}[\ln y + 2\ln(y + 4)] - \ln(y - 1) = \frac{1}{3}[\ln y + \ln(y + 4)^2] - \ln(y - 1)$

$$= \frac{1}{3}\ln y(y + 4)^2 - \ln(y - 1)$$

$$= \ln \sqrt[3]{y(y + 4)^2} - \ln(y - 1)$$

$$= \ln \frac{\sqrt[3]{y(y + 4)^2}}{y - 1}$$

59. $2\ln 3 - \frac{1}{2}\ln(x^2 + 1) = \ln 3^2 - \ln \sqrt{x^2 + 1}$

$$= \ln \frac{9}{\sqrt{x^2 + 1}}$$

61. $y_1 = 2[\ln 8 - \ln(x^2 + 1)]$

$y_2 = \ln\left[\dfrac{64}{(x^2 + 1)^2}\right]$

$y_1 = y_2$

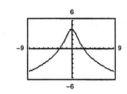

63. $y_1 = \ln x^2$

$y_2 = 2\ln x$

$y_1 = y_2$ for $x > 0$

They are not equivalent. The domain of $f(x)$ is all real numbers except 0. The domain of $g(x)$ is $x > 0$.

65. $\log_2\left(\frac{32}{4}\right) = \log_2 32 - \log_2 4$ by Property 2.

67. $f(x) = \ln \dfrac{x}{2}, \ g(x) = \dfrac{\ln x}{\ln 2}, \ h(x) = \ln x - \ln 2$

$f(x) = h(x)$ by Property 2.

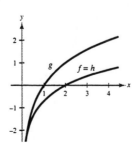

69. $\log_3 9 = 2 \log_3 3 = 2$

71. $\log_4 16^{1.2} = 1.2(\log_4 16) = 1.2(2) = 2.4$

73. $\log_3(-9)$ is undefined. -9 is not in the domain of $\log_3 x$.

75. $\log_5 75 - \log_5 3 = \log_5 \frac{75}{3} = \log_5 25 = \log_5 5^2 = 2 \log_5 5 = 2$

77. $\ln e^2 - \ln e^5 = 2 - 5 = -3$

79. $\log_{10} 0$ is undefined. 0 is not in the domain of $\log_{10} x$.

81. $\ln e^{4.5} = 4.5$

83. $\log_4 8 = \log_4 2^3 = 3 \log_4 2 = 3 \log_4 \sqrt{4} = 3 \log_4 4^{1/2} = 3\left(\frac{1}{2}\right) \log_4 4 = \frac{3}{2}$

85. $\log_5 \frac{1}{250} = \log_5 1 - \log_5 250 = 0 - \log_5(125 \cdot 2)$

$\qquad = -\log_5(5^3 \cdot 2) = -[\log_5 5^3 + \log_5 2]$

$\qquad = -[3 \log_5 5 + \log_5 2] = -3 - \log_5 2$

87. $\ln(5e^6) = \ln 5 + \ln e^6 = \ln 5 + 6 = 6 + \ln 5$

89. $f(t) = 90 - 15 \log_{10}(t + 1), \ 0 \le t \le 12$

(a) $f(0) = 90$

(b) $f(6) \approx 77$

(c) $f(12) \approx 73$

(d) $\quad 75 = 90 - 15 \log_{10}(t + 1)$

$\quad -15 = -15 \log_{10}(t + 1)$

$\qquad 1 = \log_{10}(t + 1)$

$\quad 10^1 = t + 1$

$\qquad t = 9$ months

(e) $f(t) = 90 - \log_{10}(t + 1)^{15}$

(f)

91. $f(x) = \ln x$

False, $f(0) \ne 0$ since 0 is not in the domain of $f(x)$. $f(1) = \ln 1 = 0$

93. False. $f(x) - f(2) = \ln x - \ln 2 = \ln \frac{x}{2} \ne \ln(x - 2)$

95. False. $f(u) = 2f(v) \implies \ln u = 2 \ln v \implies \ln u = \ln v^2 \implies u = v^2$

97. Let $x = \log_b u$ and $y = \log_b v$, then $b^x = u$ and $b^y = v$.

$$\frac{u}{v} = \frac{b^x}{b^y} = b^{x-y}$$

$$\log_b\left(\frac{u}{v}\right) = \log_b(b^{x-y}) = x - y = \log_b u - \log_b v$$

99. $\dfrac{24xy^{-2}}{16x^{-3}y} = \dfrac{24xx^3}{16yy^2} = \dfrac{3x^4}{2y^3}, \ x \ne 0$

101. $(18x^3y^4)^{-3}(18x^3y^4)^3 = \dfrac{(18x^3y^4)^3}{(18x^3y^4)^3} = 1$ if $x \ne 0, \ y \ne 0$.

Section 3.4   Exponential and Logarithmic Equations

■ To solve an exponential equation, isolate the exponential expression, then take the logarithm of both sides. Then solve for the variable.
  1. $\log_a a^x = x$
  2. $\ln e^x = x$

■ To solve a logarithmic equation, rewrite it in exponential form. Then solve for the variable.
  1. $a^{\log_a x} = x$
  2. $e^{\ln x} = x$

■ If $a > 0$ and $a \neq 1$ we have the following:
  1. $\log_a x = \log_a y \implies x = y$
  2. $a^x = a^y \implies x = y$

Solutions to Odd-Numbered Exercises

1. $4^{2x-7} = 64$

(a) $x = 5$

$4^{2(5)-7} = 4^3 = 64$

Yes, $x = 5$ is a solution.

(b) $\qquad x = 2$

$4^{2(2)-7} = 4^{-3} = \frac{1}{64} \neq 64$

No, $x = 2$ is not a solution.

3. $3e^{x+2} = 75$

(a) $x = -2 + e^{25}$

$3e^{(-2+e^{25})+2} = 3e^{e^{25}} \neq 75$

No, $x = -2 + e^{25}$ is not a solution.

(b) $x = -2 + \ln 25$

$3e^{(-2+\ln 25)+2} = 3e^{\ln 25} = 3(25) = 75$

Yes, $x = -2 + \ln 25$ is a solution.

(c) $x \approx 1.2189$

$3e^{1.2189+2} = 3e^{3.2189} \approx 75$

Yes, $x \approx 1.2189$ is a solution.

5. $\log_4(3x) = 3 \implies 3x = 4^3 \implies 3x = 64$

(a) $x \approx 20.3560$

$3(20.3560) = 61.0680 \neq 64$

No, $x \approx 20.3560$ is not a solution.

(b) $x = -4$

$3(-4) = -12 \neq 64$

No, $x = -4$ is not a solution.

(c) $x = \frac{64}{3}$

$3\left(\frac{64}{3}\right) = 64$

Yes, $x = \frac{64}{3}$ is a solution.

7. $f(x) = g(x)$

$2^x = 8$

$2^x = 2^3$

$x = 3$

Point of intersection: $(3, 8)$

9. $f(x) = g(x)$

$\log_3 x = 2$

$x = 3^2$

$x = 9$

Point of intersection: $(9, 2)$

11. $4^x = 16$

$4^x = 4^2$

$x = 2$

13. $7^x = \frac{1}{49}$

$7^x = 7^{-2}$

$x = -2$

15. $\left(\frac{3}{4}\right)^x = \frac{27}{64}$

$\left(\frac{3}{4}\right)^x = \left(\frac{3}{4}\right)^3$

$x = 3$

17. $\log_4 x = 3$

$x = 4^3$

$x = 64$

19. $\log_{10} x = -1$

$\quad\quad x = 10^{-1}$

$\quad\quad x = \frac{1}{10}$

21. $\log_{10} 10^{x^2} = x^2$

23. $e^{\ln(5x+2)} = 5x + 2$

25. $e^{\ln x^2} = x^2$

27. $e^x = 10$

$\quad\quad x = \ln 10 \approx 2.303$

29. $7 - 2e^x = 5$

$\quad\quad -2e^x = -2$

$\quad\quad\quad e^x = 1$

$\quad\quad\quad x = \ln 1 = 0$

31. $e^{3x} = 12$

$\quad\quad 3x = \ln 12$

$\quad\quad x = \dfrac{\ln 12}{3} \approx 0.828$

33. $500e^{-x} = 300$

$\quad\quad e^{-x} = \dfrac{3}{5}$

$\quad\quad -x = \ln \dfrac{3}{5}$

$\quad\quad x = -\ln \dfrac{3}{5} = \ln \dfrac{5}{3} \approx 0.511$

35. $\quad e^{2x} - 4e^x - 5 = 0$

$\quad\quad (e^x - 5)(e^x + 1) = 0$

$\quad\quad e^x = 5 \text{ or } e^x = -1 \quad \text{(No solution)}$

$\quad\quad x = \ln 5 \approx 1.609$

37. $20(100 - e^{x/2}) = 500$

$\quad\quad 100 - e^{x/2} = 25$

$\quad\quad -e^{x/2} = -75$

$\quad\quad e^{x/2} = 75$

$\quad\quad \dfrac{x}{2} = \ln 75$

$\quad\quad x = 2 \ln 75 \approx 8.635$

39. $10^x = 42$

$\quad\quad x = \log_{10} 42 \approx 1.623$

41. $\quad 3^{2x} = 80$

$\quad\quad \ln 3^{2x} = \ln 80$

$\quad\quad 2x \ln 3 = \ln 80$

$\quad\quad x = \dfrac{\ln 80}{2 \ln 3} \approx 1.994$

43. $5^{-t/2} = 0.20$

$\quad\quad 5^{-t/2} = \dfrac{1}{5}$

$\quad\quad 5^{-t/2} = 5^{-1}$

$\quad\quad -\dfrac{t}{2} = -1$

$\quad\quad t = 2$

45. $\quad\quad 2^{3-x} = 565$

$\quad\quad \ln 2^{3-x} = \ln 565$

$\quad\quad (3 - x) \ln 2 = \ln 565$

$\quad\quad 3 \ln 2 - x \ln 2 = \ln 565$

$\quad\quad -x \ln 2 = \ln 565 - \ln 2^3$

$\quad\quad x \ln 2 = \ln 8 - \ln 565$

$\quad\quad x = \dfrac{\ln 8 - \ln 565}{\ln 2} \approx -6.142$

47. $g(x) = 6e^{1-x} - 25$

The zero is $x \approx -0.427$.

49. $g(t) = e^{0.09t} - 3$

The zero is $x \approx 12.207$.

51. $8(10^{3x}) = 12$

$$10^{3x} = \frac{12}{8}$$

$$3x = \log_{10}\left(\frac{3}{2}\right)$$

$$x = \tfrac{1}{3}\log_{10}\left(\frac{3}{2}\right) \approx 0.059$$

53. $\left(1 + \dfrac{0.065}{365}\right)^{365t} = 4$

$$\ln\left(1 + \frac{0.065}{365}\right)^{365t} = \ln 4$$

$$365t\ln\left(1 + \frac{0.065}{365}\right) = \ln 4$$

$$t = \frac{\ln 4}{365\ln\left(1 + \frac{0.065}{365}\right)} \approx 21.330$$

55. $\ln x = -3$

$$x = e^{-3} \approx 0.050$$

57. $\ln 2x = 2.4$

$$2x = e^{2.4}$$

$$x = \frac{e^{2.4}}{2} \approx 5.512$$

59. $\ln\sqrt{x + 2} = 1$

$$\sqrt{x + 2} = e^1$$

$$x + 2 = e^2$$

$$x = e^2 - 2 \approx 5.389$$

61. $\log_{10}(z - 3) = 2$

$$z - 3 = 10^2$$

$$z = 10^2 + 3 = 103$$

63. $\ln x + \ln(x - 2) = 1$

$$\ln[x(x - 2)] = 1$$

$$x(x - 2) = e^1$$

$$x^2 - 2x - e = 0$$

$$x = \frac{2 \pm \sqrt{4 + 4e}}{2}$$

$$= \frac{2 \pm 2\sqrt{1 + e}}{2}$$

$$= 1 \pm \sqrt{1 + e}$$

Using the positive value for x, we have
$x = 1 + \sqrt{1 + e} \approx 2.928$.

65. $\log_{10}(x + 4) - \log_{10} x = \log_{10}(x + 2)$

$$\log_{10}\left(\frac{x + 4}{x}\right) = \log_{10}(x + 2)$$

$$\frac{x + 4}{x} = x + 2$$

$$x + 4 = x^2 + 2x \quad \text{Quadratic}$$

$$0 = x^2 + x - 4 \quad \text{Formula}$$

$$x = \frac{-1 \pm \sqrt{17}}{2}$$

Choosing the positive value of x (the negative value is extraneous), we have

$$x = \frac{-1 + \sqrt{17}}{2} \approx 1.562.$$

67. $\log_3 x + \log_3(x^2 - 8) = \log_3 8x$

$$\log_3 x(x^2 - 8) = \log_3 8x$$

$$x(x^2 - 8) = 8x$$

$$x^3 - 8x = 8x$$

$$x^3 - 16x = 0$$

$$x(x + 4)(x - 4) = 0$$

$$x = 0, \ x = -4, \ \text{or} \ x = 4$$

The only solution that is in the domain is $x = 4$.
Both $x = 0$ and $x = -4$ are extraneous.

69. $\ln(x + 5) = \ln(x - 1) - \ln(x + 1)$

$$\ln(x + 5) = \ln\left(\frac{x - 1}{x + 1}\right)$$

$$x + 5 = \frac{x - 1}{x + 1}$$

$$(x + 5)(x + 1) = x - 1$$

$$x^2 + 6x + 5 = x - 1$$

$$x^2 + 5x + 6 = 0$$

$$(x + 2)(x + 3) = 0$$

$$x = -2 \ \text{or} \ x = -3$$

Both of these solutions are extraneous, so the equation has no solution.

71. $6 \log_3(0.5x) = 11$

$\log_3(0.5x) = \frac{11}{6}$

$0.5x = 3^{11/6}$

$x = 2(3^{11/6}) \approx 14.988$

73. $2 \ln x = 7$

$\ln x = \frac{7}{2}$

$x = e^{7/2} \approx 33.115$

75. $\ln x + \ln(x^2 + 1) = 8$

$\ln x(x^2 + 1) = 8$

$x(x^2 + 1) = e^8$

$x^3 + x - e^8 = 0$

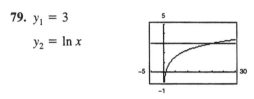

From the graph we have $x \approx 14.369$.

77. $y_1 = 7$

$y_2 = 2^x$

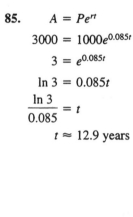

From the graph we have $x \approx 2.807$ when $y = 7$.

79. $y_1 = 3$

$y_2 = \ln x$

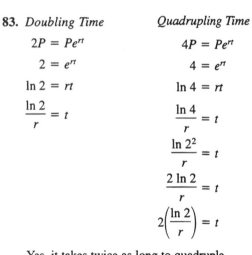

From the graph we have $x \approx 20.806$ when $y = 3$.

81. $A = Pe^{rt}$

$2000 = 1000e^{0.085t}$

$2 = e^{0.085t}$

$\ln 2 = 0.085t$

$\dfrac{\ln 2}{0.085} = t$

$t \approx 8.2$ years

83. *Doubling Time*

$2P = Pe^{rt}$

$2 = e^{rt}$

$\ln 2 = rt$

$\dfrac{\ln 2}{r} = t$

Quadrupling Time

$4P = Pe^{rt}$

$4 = e^{rt}$

$\ln 4 = rt$

$\dfrac{\ln 4}{r} = t$

$\dfrac{\ln 2^2}{r} = t$

$\dfrac{2 \ln 2}{r} = t$

$2\left(\dfrac{\ln 2}{r}\right) = t$

Yes, it takes twice as long to quadruple.

85. $A = Pe^{rt}$

$3000 = 1000e^{0.085t}$

$3 = e^{0.085t}$

$\ln 3 = 0.085t$

$\dfrac{\ln 3}{0.085} = t$

$t \approx 12.9$ years

87. $p = 500 - 0.5(e^{0.004x})$

(a) $p = 350$

$350 = 500 - 0.5(e^{0.004x})$

$300 = e^{0.004x}$

$0.004x = \ln 300$

$x \approx 1426$ units

(b) $p = 300$

$300 = 500 - 0.5(e^{0.004x})$

$400 = e^{0.004x}$

$0.004x = \ln 400$

$x \approx 1498$ units

89. $V = 6.7e^{-48.1/t}$, $t \geq 0$

(a)

(b) As $x \to \infty$, $V \to 6.7$.

Horizontal asymptote: $y = 6.7$

The yield will approach
6.7 million cubic feet per acre.

(c) $1.3 = 6.7e^{-48.1/t}$

$$\frac{1.3}{6.7} = e^{-48.1/t}$$

$$\ln\left(\frac{13}{67}\right) = \frac{-48.1}{t}$$

$$t = \frac{-48.1}{\ln(13/67)} \approx 29.3 \text{ years}$$

91. (a) From the graph shown in the textbook, we see horizontal asymptotes at
$y = 0$ and $y = 100$. These represent the lower and upper percent bounds.

(b)   Males

$$50 = \frac{100}{1 + e^{-0.6114(x - 69.71)}}$$

$$1 + e^{-0.6114(x - 69.71)} = 2$$

$$e^{-0.6114(x - 69.71)} = 1$$

$$-0.6114(x - 69.71) = \ln 1$$

$$-0.6114(x - 69.71) = 0$$

$$x = 69.71 \text{ inches}$$

Females

$$50 = \frac{100}{1 + e^{-0.66607(x - 64.51)}}$$

$$1 + e^{-0.66607(x - 64.51)} = 2$$

$$e^{-0.66607(x - 64.51)} = 1$$

$$-0.66607(x - 64.51) = \ln 1$$

$$-0.66607(x - 64.51) = 0$$

$$x = 64.51 \text{ inches}$$

93. $T = 20[1 + 7(2^{-h})]$

(a) From the graph in the textbook we see a horizontal asymptote at $y = 20$. This
represents the room temperature.

(b) $100 = 20[1 + 7(2^{-h})]$

$$5 = 1 + 7(2^{-h})$$

$$4 = 7(2^{-h})$$

$$\frac{4}{7} = 2^{-h}$$

$$\ln\left(\frac{4}{7}\right) = \ln 2^{-h}$$

$$\ln\left(\frac{4}{7}\right) = -h \ln 2$$

$$\frac{\ln\left(\frac{4}{7}\right)}{-\ln 2} = h$$

$$h \approx 0.81 \text{ hour}$$

95. $\sqrt{48x^2y^5} = \sqrt{16x^2y^4 3y} = 4|x|y^2\sqrt{3y}$

97. $\sqrt[3]{25}\sqrt[3]{15} = \sqrt[3]{375} = \sqrt[3]{125 \cdot 3} = 5\sqrt[3]{3}$

Section 3.5   Exponential and Logarithmic Models

- You should be able to solve compound interest problems.

  (a) Compound interest formulas:

    1. $A = P\left(1 + \dfrac{r}{n}\right)^{nt}$

    2. $A = Pe^{rt}$

  (b) Doubling time:

    1. $t = \dfrac{\ln 2}{n \ln[1 + (r/n)]}$, n compoundings per year

    2. $t = \dfrac{\ln 2}{r}$, continuous compounding

- You should be able to solve growth and decay problems.

  (a) Exponential growth if $b > 0$ and $y = ae^{bx}$.

  (b) Exponential decay if $b > 0$ and $y = ae^{-bx}$.

- You should be able to use the Gaussian model

  $y = ae^{-(x-b)^2/c}$.

- You should be able to use the logistics growth model

  $y = \dfrac{a}{1 + be^{-(x-c)/d}}$.

- You should be able to use the logarithmic models

  $y = \ln(ax + b)$ and $y = \log_{10}(ax + b)$.

Solutions to Odd-Numbered Exercises

1. $y = 2e^{x/4}$

This is an exponential growth model. Matches graph (c)

3. $y = \frac{1}{16}(x^2 + 8x + 32)$

This is a quadratic function. Its graph is a parabola. Matches graph (a)

5. $y = \ln(x + 1)$

This is a logarithmic model. Matches graph (d)

7. Since $A = 1000e^{0.12t}$, the time to double is given by $2000 = 1000e^{0.12t}$ and we have

$t = \dfrac{\ln 2}{0.12} \approx 5.78$ years.

Amount after 10 years: $A = 1000e^{1.2} \approx \$3320.12$

9. Since $A = 750e^{rt}$ and $A = 1500$ when $t = 7.75$, we have the following.

$1500 = 750e^{7.75r}$

$r = \dfrac{\ln 2}{7.75} \approx 0.0894 = 8.94\%$

Amount after 10 years: $A = 750e^{0.0894(10)} \approx \$1833.67$

11. Since $A = 500e^{rt}$ and $A = 1292.85$ when $t = 10$, we have the following.

$$1292.85 = 500e^{10r}$$

$$r = \frac{\ln(1292.85/500)}{10} \approx 0.9095 = 9.5\%$$

The time to double is given by

$$1000 = 500e^{0.095t}$$

$$t = \frac{\ln 2}{0.095} \approx 7.30 \text{ years.}$$

13. Since $A = Pe^{0.045t}$ and $A = 10,000.00$ when $t = 10$, we have the following.

$$10,000.00 = Pe^{0.045(10)}$$

$$\frac{10,000.00}{e^{0.045(10)}} = P \approx \$6376.28$$

The time to double is given by

$$t = \frac{\ln 2}{0.045} \approx 15.40 \text{ years.}$$

15. $$500,000 = P\left(1 + \frac{0.075}{12}\right)12(20)$$

$$P = \frac{500,000}{\left(1 + \frac{0.075}{12}\right)}12(20) = \$112,087.09$$

17. $P = 1000, r = 11\%$

(a) $n = 1$

$$t = \frac{\ln 2}{\ln(1 + 0.11)} \approx 6.642 \text{ years}$$

(b) $n = 12$

$$t = \frac{\ln 2}{12 \ln\left(1 + \frac{0.11}{12}\right)} \approx 6.330 \text{ years}$$

(c) $n = 365$

$$t = \frac{\ln 2}{365 \ln\left(1 + \frac{0.11}{365}\right)} \approx 6.302 \text{ years}$$

(d) Continuously

$$t = \frac{\ln 2}{0.11} \approx 6.301 \text{ years}$$

19. $3P = Pe^{rt}$

$3 = e^{rt}$

$\ln 3 = rt$

$\dfrac{\ln 3}{r} = t$

r	2%	4%	6%	8%	10%	12%
$t = \dfrac{\ln 3}{r}$	54.93	27.47	18.31	13.73	10.99	9.16

21. $3P = P(1 + r)^t$

$3 = (1 + r)^t$

$\ln 3 = \ln(1 + r)^t$

$\ln 3 = t \ln(1 + r)$

$\dfrac{\ln 3}{\ln(1 + r)} = t$

r	2%	4%	6%	8%	10%	12%
$t = \dfrac{\ln 3}{\ln(1 + r)}$	55.48	28.01	18.85	14.27	11.53	9.69

23. Continuous compounding results in faster growth.

$A = 1 + 0.075[\![t]\!]$ and $A = e^{0.07t}$

25. $\frac{1}{2}C = Ce^{k(1620)}$

$k = \dfrac{\ln 0.5}{1620}$

Given $C = 10$ grams, after 1000 years we have

$y = 10e^{[(\ln 0.5)/1620](1000)}$

≈ 6.52 grams.

27. $\frac{1}{2}C = Ce^{k(5730)}$

$k = \dfrac{\ln 0.5}{5730}$

Given $y = 2$ grams after 1000 years, we have

$2 = Ce^{[(\ln 0.5)/5730](1000)}$

$C \approx 2.26$ grams.

29. $\frac{1}{2}C = Ce^{k(24,360)}$

$k = \dfrac{\ln 0.5}{24,360}$

Given $y = 2.1$ grams after 1000 years, we have

$2.1 = Ce^{[(\ln 0.5)/24,360](1000)}$

$C \approx 2.16$ grams.

31. $\quad y = ae^{bx}$

$1 = ae^{b(0)} \implies 1 = a$

$10 = e^{b(3)}$

$\ln 10 = 3b$

$\dfrac{\ln 10}{3} = b \qquad \implies \quad b \approx 0.7675$

Thus, $y = e^{0.7675x}$.

33. $\quad y = ae^{bx}$

$1 = ae^{b(0)} \implies 1 = a$

$\dfrac{1}{4} = e^{b(3)}$

$\ln\left(\dfrac{1}{4}\right) = 3b$

$\dfrac{\ln\left(\frac{1}{4}\right)}{3} = b \qquad \implies \quad b \approx -0.4621$

Thus, $y = e^{-0.4621x}$.

35. $\quad P = 105,300e^{0.015t}$

$150,000 = 105,300e^{0.015t}$

$\ln\frac{1500}{1053} = 0.015t$

$t \approx 23.59$

The population will reach 150,000 during 2013.
[Note: $1990 + 23.59$]

37. For 1945, use $t = -45$.

$1350 = 2500d^{k(-45)}$

$\ln\left(\frac{1350}{2500}\right) = -45k \implies k \approx 0.0137$

For 2010, use $t = 20$.

$P = 2500e^{0.0137(20)} \approx 3288$ people

39. $\quad y = ae^{bt}$

$4.22 = ae^{b(0)} \implies a = 4.22$

$6.49 = 4.22e^{b(10)}$

$\dfrac{6.49}{4.22} = e^{10b}$

$\ln\left(\dfrac{6.49}{4.22}\right) = 10b \quad \implies \quad b \approx 0.0430$

$y = 4.22e^{0.0430t}$

When $t = 20$,
$y = 4.22e^{0.0430(20)} \approx 9.97$ million.

41. $\quad y = ae^{bt}$

$3.00 = ae^{b(0)} \implies a = 3$

$2.74 = 3e^{b(10)}$

$\dfrac{2.74}{3} = e^{10b}$

$\ln\left(\dfrac{2.74}{3}\right) = 10b \quad \implies \quad b \approx -0.0091$

$y = 3e^{-0.0091t}$

When $t = 20$,
$y = 3e^{-0.0091(20)} \approx 2.50$ million.

43. b is determined by the growth rate. The greater the rate of growth, the greater the value of b.

45. $N = 100e^{kt}$

$300 = 100e^{5k}$

$k = \dfrac{\ln 3}{5} \approx 0.2197$

$N = 100e^{0.2197t}$

$200 = 100e^{0.2197t}$

$t = \dfrac{\ln 2}{0.2197} \approx 3.15$ hours

47. $y = Ce^{kt}$

$$\frac{1}{2}C = Ce^{(1620)k}$$

$$\ln\frac{1}{2} = 1620k$$

$$k = \frac{\ln(1/2)}{1620}$$

When $t = 100$, we have

$y = Ce^{[\ln(1/2)/1620](100)} \approx 0.958C = 95.8\%C.$

After 100 years, approximately 95.8% of the radioactive radium will remain.

49. $(0, \ 22{,}000), \ (2, \ 13{,}000)$

(a) $m = \dfrac{13{,}000 - 22{,}000}{2 - 0} = -4500$

    $b = 22{,}000$

    Thus, $V = -4500t + 22{,}000.$

(b) $a = 22{,}000$

    $13{,}000 = 22{,}000e^{k(2)}$

    $\dfrac{13}{22} = e^{2k}$

    $\ln\left(\dfrac{13}{22}\right) = 2k \Rightarrow k \approx -0.263$

    Thus, $V = 22{,}000e^{-0.263t}.$

(c) The exponential model depreciates faster in the first two years.

(d)

t	1	3
$V = -4500t + 22{,}000$	\$17,500	\$8500
$V = 22{,}000e^{-0.263t}$	\$16,912	\$9995

(e) The slope of the linear model means that the car depreciates \$4500 per year.

51. $S(t) = 100(1 - e^{kt})$

(a) $15 = 100(1 - e^{k(1)})$

     $-85 = -100e^{k}$

     $k = \ln 0.85$

     $k \approx -0.1625$

     $S(t) = 100(1 - e^{-0.1625t})$

(b)

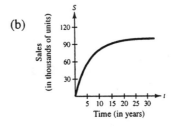

(c) $S(5) = 100(1 - e^{-0.1625(5)})$

     $\approx 55.625 = 55{,}625$ units

53. $S = 10(1 - e^{kx})$

$x = 5$ (in hundreds), $S = 2.5$ (in thousands)

(a) $2.5 = 10(1 - e^{k(5)})$

$0.25 = 1 - e^{5k}$

$e^{5k} = 0.75$

$5k = \ln 0.75$

$k \approx -0.0575$

$S = 10(1 - e^{-0.0575x})$

(b) When $x = 7$,
$S = 10(1 - e^{-0.0575(7)}) \approx 3.314$
which corresponds to 3314 units.

55. $N = 30(1 - e^{kt})$

(a) $N = 19$, $t = 20$

$19 = 30(1 - e^{20k})$

$20k = \ln \frac{11}{30}$

$k \approx -0.050$

$N = 30(1 - e^{-0.050t})$

(b) $N = 25$

$25 = 30(1 - e^{-0.05t})$

$\frac{5}{30} = e^{-0.05t}$

$t = -\frac{1}{0.05} \ln \frac{5}{30} \approx 36$ days

(c) No, this is not a linear function.

57. $R = \log_{10} \frac{I}{I_0} = \log_{10} I$ since $I_0 = 1$.

(a) $R = \log_{10} 80,500,000 \approx 7.91$

(b) $R = \log_{10} 48,275,000 \approx 7.68$

59. $\beta(I) = 10 \log_{10} \frac{I}{I_0}$ where $I_0 = 10^{-16}$ watt/cm^2.

(a) $\beta(10^{-14}) = 10 \log_{10} \frac{10^{-14}}{10^{-16}} = 10 \log_{10} 10^2 = 20$ decibels

(b) $\beta(10^{-9}) = 10 \log_{10} \frac{10^{-9}}{10^{-16}} = 10 \log_{10} 10^7 = 70$ decibels

(c) $\beta(10^{-6.5}) = 10 \log_{10} \frac{10^{-6.5}}{10^{-16}} = 10 \log_{10} 10^{9.5} = 95$ decibels

(d) $\beta(10^{-4}) = 10 \log_{10} \frac{10^{-4}}{10^{-16}} = 10 \log_{10} 10^{12} = 120$ decibels

61. $\beta = 10 \log_{10} \frac{I}{I_0}$

$10^{\beta/10} = \frac{I}{I_0}$

$I = I_0 10^{\beta/10}$

% decrease $= \frac{I_0 10^{9.3} - I_0 10^{8.0}}{I_0 10^{9.3}} \times 100 \approx 95\%$

63. pH $= -\log_{10}[\text{H}^+] = -\log_{10}[2.3 \times 10^{-5}] \approx 4.64$

65. $5.8 = -\log_{10}[\text{H}^+]$

$10^{-5.8} = \text{H}^+$

$\text{H}^+ \approx 1.58 \times 10^{-6}$ moles per liter

67. $2.5 = -\log_{10}[\text{H}^+]$

$10^{-2.5} = \text{H}^+$ for the fruit.

$9.5 = -\log_{10}[\text{H}^+]$

$10^{-9.5} = \text{H}^+$ for the antacid tablet.

$\frac{10^{-2.5}}{10^{-9.5}} = 10^7$

69. Interest: $u = M - \left(M - \dfrac{Pr}{12}\right)\left(1 + \dfrac{r}{12}\right)^{12t}$

Principle: $v = \left(M - \dfrac{Pr}{12}\right)\left(1 + \dfrac{r}{12}\right)^{12t}$

(a) $P = 120{,}000$, $t = 35$, $r = 0.095$, $M = 985.93$

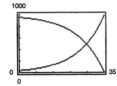

(b) In the early years of the mortgage, the majority of the monthly payment goes toward interest. The principle and interest are nearly equal when $t \approx 27.676 \approx 28$ years.

(c) $P = 120{,}000$, $t = 20$, $r = 0.095$, $M = 1118.56$

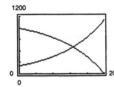

The interest is still the majority of the monthly payment in the early years. Now the principle and interest are nearly equal when $t \approx 12.675 \approx 12.7$ years.

71. $t_1 = 40.757 + 0.556s - 15.817 \ln s$

$t_2 = 1.2259 + 0.0023s^2$

(a) Linear model: $t_3 \approx 0.2729s - 6.0143$

Exponential model: $t_4 \approx 1.5385e^{1.0291s}$

(b)

(c)

s	30	40	50	60	70	80	90
t_1	3.6	4.6	6.7	9.4	12.5	15.9	19.6
t_2	3.3	4.9	7.0	9.5	12.5	15.9	19.9
t_3	2.2	4.9	7.6	10.4	13.1	15.8	18.5
t_4	3.7	4.9	6.6	8.8	11.8	15.8	21.2

(d) Model t_1: $S_1 = |3.4 - 3.6| + |5 - 4.6| + |7 - 6.7| + |9.3 - 9.4| + |12 - 12.5| + |15.8 - 15.9| + |20 - 19.6| \doteq 2.0$

Model t_2: $S_2 = |3.4 - 3.3| + |5 - 4.9| + |7 - 7| + |9.3 - 9.5| + |12 - 12.5| + |15.8 - 15.9| + |20 - 19.9| = 1.1$

Model t_3: $S_3 = |3.4 - 2.2| + |5 - 4.9| + |7 - 7.6| + |9.3 - 10.4| + |12 - 13.1| + |15.8 - 15.8| + |20 - 18.5| = 5.6$

Model t_4: $S_4 = |3.4 - 3.7| + |5 - 4.9| + |7 - 6.6| + |9.3 - 8.8| + |12 - 11.8| + |15.8 - 15.8| + |20 - 21.2| = 2.7$

t_2, the Quadratic model, is the best fit with the data.

73. Answers will vary.

75.

$$\begin{array}{r|rrrr} -4 & 4 & 4 & -39 & 36 \\ & & -16 & 48 & -36 \\ \hline & 4 & -12 & 9 & 0 \end{array}$$

Thus, $\dfrac{4x^3 + 4x^2 - 39x + 36}{x + 4} = 4x^2 - 12x + 9.$

77.

$$\begin{array}{r|rrrr} 4 & 2 & -8 & 3 & -9 \\ & & 8 & 0 & 12 \\ \hline & 2 & 0 & 3 & 3 \end{array}$$

Thus, $\dfrac{2x^3 - 8x^2 + 3x - 9}{x - 4} = 2x^2 + 3 + \dfrac{3}{x - 4}.$

❏ Review Exercises for Chapter 3

Solutions to Odd-Numbered Exercises

1. $f(x) = 4^x$

Intercept: $(0, 1)$

Horizontal asymptote: x-axis

Increasing on: $(-\infty, \infty)$

Matches graph (e)

3. $f(x) = -4^x$

Intercept: $(0, -1)$

Horizontal asymptote: x-axis

Decreasing on: $(-\infty, \infty)$

Matches graph (a)

5. $f(x) = \log_4 x$

Intercept: $(1, 0)$

Vertical asymptote: y-axis

Increasing on: $(0, \infty)$

Matches graph (d)

7. $f(x) = 0.3^x$

x	-2	-1	0	1	2
y	11.11	3.33	1	0.3	0.09

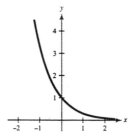

9. $h(x) = e^{-x/2}$

x	-2	-1	0	1	2
y	2.72	1.65	1	0.61	0.37

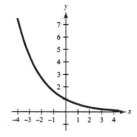

11. $f(x) = e^{x+2}$

x	-3	-2	-1	0	1
y	0.37	1	2.72	7.39	20.09

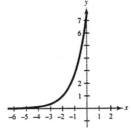

13. $g(x) = 200e^{4/x}$

As $x \to \infty$, $g(x) \to 200$ so we have a horizontal asymptote at $y = 200$.

15. $A = 3500\left(1 + \dfrac{0.105}{n}\right)^{10n}$ or $A = 3500e^{(0.105)(10)}$

n	1	2	4	12	365	Continuous Compounding
A	\$9,499.28	\$9,738.91	\$9,867.22	\$9,956.20	\$10,000.27	\$10,001.78

17. $200,000 = Pe^{0.08t}$

$$P = \frac{200,000}{e^{0.08t}}$$

t	1	10	20	30	40	50
P	\$184,623.27	\$89,865.79	\$40,379.30	\$18,143.59	\$8,152.44	\$3,663.13

19. $F(t) = 1 - e^{-t/3}$

(a) $F\left(\frac{1}{2}\right) \approx 0.154$

(b) $F(2) \approx 0.487$

(c) $F(5) \approx 0.811$

21. (a) $A = 50,000e^{(0.0875)(35)} \approx \$1,069,047.14$

(b) The doubling time is

$$\frac{\ln 2}{0.0875} \approx 7.9 \text{ years.}$$

23. $g(x) = \log_2 x \implies 2^y = x$

Domain: $(0, \infty)$

Vertical asymptote: $x = 0$

x	$\frac{1}{4}$	$\frac{1}{2}$	1	2	4
y	-2	-1	0	1	2

25. $f(x) = \ln x + 3$

Domain: $(0, \infty)$.

Vertical asymptote: $x = 0$

x	1	2	3	$\frac{1}{2}$	$\frac{1}{4}$
$f(x)$	3	3.69	4.10	2.31	1.61

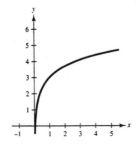

27. $h(x) = \ln(e^{x-1})$

$\quad = (x - 1) \ln e$

$\quad = x - 1$

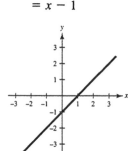

29. $y = \log_{10}(x^2 + 1)$

31. $4^3 = 64$

$\quad\quad \log_4 64 = 3$

33. $\log_{10} 1000 = \log_{10} 10^3 = 3$

35. $\ln e^7 = 7$

37. $\log_4 9 = \dfrac{\log_{10} 9}{\log_{10} 4} \approx 1.585$

$\quad\ \log_4 9 = \dfrac{\ln 9}{\ln 4} \approx 1.585$

39. $\log_{12} 200 = \dfrac{\log_{10} 200}{\log_{10} 12} \approx 2.132$

$\quad\ \log_{12} 200 = \dfrac{\ln 200}{\ln 12} \approx 2.132$

41. $\log_5 5x^2 = \log_5 5 + \log_5 x^2$

$\quad\quad\quad\quad\ = 1 + 2 \log_5 |x|$

43. $\log_{10} \dfrac{5\sqrt{y}}{x^2} = \log_{10} 5\sqrt{y} - \log_{10} x^2$

$\quad\quad\quad\quad\ = \log_{10} 5 + \log_{10} \sqrt{y} - \log_{10} x^2$

$\quad\quad\quad\quad\ = \log_{10} 5 + \dfrac{1}{2} \log_{10} y - 2 \log_{10} |x|$

45. $\log_2 5 + \log_2 x = \log_2 5x$

47. $\dfrac{1}{2} \ln|2x - 1| - 2 \ln|x + 1| = \ln \sqrt{|2x - 1|} - \ln|x + 1|^2$

$\quad\quad\quad\quad\quad\quad\quad\quad\quad\quad = \ln \dfrac{\sqrt{|2x - 1|}}{(x + 1)^2}$

49. True; by the inverse properties, $\log_b b^{2x} = 2x$.

51. False; $\ln x + \ln y = \ln(xy) \ne \ln(x + y)$

53. True, $\log\left(\dfrac{10}{x}\right) = \log 10 - \log x = 1 - \log x$.

55. $S = 25 - \dfrac{13 \ln(10/12)}{\ln 3} \approx 27.16$ miles

57. $e^x = 12$

$\quad x = \ln 12 \approx 2.485$

59. $3e^{-5x} = 132$

$\quad\ e^{-5x} = 44$

$\quad\ -5x = \ln 44$

$\quad\quad\ x = \dfrac{\ln 44}{-5} \approx -0.757$

61. $e^{2x} - 7e^x + 10 = 0$

$\quad (e^x - 2)(e^x - 5) = 0$

$\quad e^x = 2 \quad$ or $\quad e^x = 5$

$\quad x = \ln 2 \quad\quad x = \ln 5$

$\quad x \approx 0.693 \quad\ x \approx 1.609$

63. $\ln 3x = 8.2$

$\quad 3x = e^{8.2}$

$\quad\ x = \dfrac{e^{8.2}}{3} \approx 1213.650$

65. $\ln x - \ln 3 = 2$

$\quad\quad \ln \dfrac{x}{3} = 2$

$\quad\quad\ \dfrac{x}{3} = e^2$

$\quad\quad\ x = 3e^2 \approx 22.167$

67. $\log(x - 1) = \log(x - 2) - \log(x + 2)$

$$\log(x - 1) = \log\left(\frac{x - 2}{x + 2}\right)$$

$$x - 1 = \frac{x - 2}{x + 2}$$

$$(x - 1)(x + 2) = x - 2$$

$$x^2 + x - 2 = x - 2$$

$$x^2 = 0$$

$$x = 0$$

Since $x = 0$ is not in the domain of $\ln(x - 1)$ or of $\ln(x - 2)$, it is an extraneous solution. The equation has no solution.

71. $2\ln(x + 3) + 3x = 8$

Graph $y_1 = 2\ln(x + 3) + 3x - 8$

The x-intercept is at $x \approx 1.64$.

75. $p = 500 - 0.5e^{0.004x}$

(a) $p = 450$

$$450 = 500 - 0.5e^{0.004x}$$

$$0.5e^{0.004x} = 50$$

$$e^{0.004x} = 100$$

$$0.004x = \ln 100$$

$$x \approx 1151 \text{ units}$$

77. (a) $\dfrac{\ln 2}{r} = 5$

$$\ln 2 = 5r$$

$$r = \frac{\ln 2}{5} \approx 0.1386 = 13.86\%$$

(b) $A = 10,000e^{0.1386(1)} \approx \$11,486.65$

69. $2^{0.6x} - 3x = 0$

Graph $y_1 = 2^{0.6x} - 3x$

The x-intercepts are at $x \approx 0.39$ and at $x \approx 7.48$.

73.

$$y = ae^{bx}$$

$$2 = ae^{b(0)} \implies a = 2$$

$$3 = 2e^{b(4)}$$

$$1.5 = e^{4b}$$

$$\ln 1.5 = 4b \implies b \approx 0.1014$$

Thus, $y \approx 2e^{0.1014x}$

(b) $p = 400$

$$400 = 500 - 0.5e^{0.004x}$$

$$0.5e^{0.004x} = 100$$

$$e^{0.004x} = 200$$

$$0.004x = \ln 200$$

$$x \approx 1325 \text{ units}$$

79. $R = \log_{10} I$ since $I_0 = 1$.

(a) $\log_{10} I = 8.4$

$$I = 10^{8.4}$$

(b) $\log_{10} I = 6.85$

$$I = 10^{6.85}$$

(c) $\log_{10} I = 9.1$

$$I = 10^{9.1}$$

❑ **Practice Test for Chapter 3**

1. Solve for x: $x^{3/5} = 8$.

2. Solve for x: $3^{x-1} = \frac{1}{81}$.

3. Graph $f(x) = 2^{-x}$.

4. Graph $g(x) = e^x + 1$.

5. If \$5000 is invested at 9% interest, find the amount after three years if the interest is compounded

   (a) monthly   (b) quarterly   (c) continuously.

6. Write the equation in logarithmic form: $7^{-2} = \frac{1}{49}$.

7. Solve for x: $x - 4 = \log_2 \frac{1}{64}$.

8. Given $\log_b 2 = 0.3562$ and $\log_b 5 = 0.8271$, evaluate $\log_b \sqrt[4]{8/25}$.

9. Write $5 \ln x - \frac{1}{2} \ln y + 6 \ln z$ as a single logarithm.

10. Using your calculator and the change of base formula, evaluate $\log_9 28$.

11. Use your calculator to solve for N: $\log_{10} N = 0.6646$

12. Graph $y = \log_4 x$.

13. Determine the domain of $f(x) = \log_3(x^2 - 9)$.

14. Graph $y = \ln(x - 2)$.

15. True or false: $\dfrac{\ln x}{\ln y} = \ln(x - y)$

16. Solve for x: $5^x = 41$

17. Solve for x: $x - x^2 = \log_5 \frac{1}{25}$

18. Solve for x: $\log_2 x + \log_2(x - 3) = 2$

19. Solve for x: $\dfrac{e^x + e^{-x}}{3} = 4$

20. Six thousand dollars is deposited into a fund at an annual interest rate of 13%. Find the time required for the investment to double if the interest is compounded continuously.

CHAPTER 4
Trigonometry

CHAPTER 4
Trigonometry

Section 4.1   Radian and Degree Measure

You should know the following basic facts about angles, their measurement, and their applications.

- Types of Angles:
  - (a) Acute: Measure between 0° and 90°.
  - (b) Right: Measure 90°.
  - (c) Obtuse: Measure between 90° and 180°.
  - (d) Straight: Measure 180°.
- α and β are complementary if $\alpha + \beta = 90°$. They are supplementary if $\alpha + \beta = 180°$.
- Two angles in standard position that have the same terminal side are called coterminal angles.
- To convert degrees to radians, use $1° = \pi/180$ radians.
- To convert radians to degrees, use 1 radian $= (180/\pi)°$.
- $1' =$ one minute $= 1/60$ of $1°$.
- $1'' =$ one second $= 1/60$ of $1' = 1/3600$ of $1°$.
- The length of a circular arc is $s = r\theta$ where θ is measured in radians.
- Speed = distance/time
- Angular speed $= \theta/t = s/rt$

Solutions to Odd-Numbered Exercises

1.

The angle shown is approximately 2 radians.

3.

The angle shown is approximately -3 radians.

5. (a) Since $0 < \dfrac{\pi}{5} < \dfrac{\pi}{2}$; $\dfrac{\pi}{5}$ lies in Quadrant I.

   (b) Since $\pi < \dfrac{7\pi}{5} < \dfrac{3\pi}{2}$; $\dfrac{7\pi}{5}$ lies in Quadrant III.

7. (a) Since $-\dfrac{\pi}{2} < -\dfrac{\pi}{12} < 0$; $-\dfrac{\pi}{12}$ lies in Quadrant IV.

   (b) Since $-\dfrac{3\pi}{2} < -\dfrac{11\pi}{9} < -\pi$; $-\dfrac{11\pi}{9}$ lies in Quadrant II.

9. (a) Since $\pi < 3.5 < \dfrac{3\pi}{2}$; 3.5 lies in Quadrant III.

   (b) Since $\dfrac{\pi}{2} < 2.25 < \pi$; 2.25 lies in Quadrant II.

11. (a)   (b)

13. (a)   (b)

15. (a) Coterminal angles for $\dfrac{\pi}{12}$

$$\dfrac{\pi}{12} + 2\pi = \dfrac{25\pi}{12}$$

$$\dfrac{\pi}{12} - 2\pi = -\dfrac{23\pi}{12}$$

(b) Coterminal angles for $\dfrac{2\pi}{3}$

$$\dfrac{2\pi}{3} + 2\pi = \dfrac{8\pi}{3}$$

$$\dfrac{2\pi}{3} - 2\pi = -\dfrac{4\pi}{3}$$

17. (a) Coterminal angles for $-\dfrac{9\pi}{4}$

$$-\dfrac{9\pi}{4} + 4\pi = \dfrac{7\pi}{4}$$

$$\dfrac{7\pi}{4} - 2\pi = -\dfrac{\pi}{4}$$

(b) Coterminal angles for $-\dfrac{2\pi}{15}$

$$-\dfrac{2\pi}{15} + 2\pi = \dfrac{28\pi}{15}$$

$$-\dfrac{2\pi}{15} - 2\pi = -\dfrac{32\pi}{15}$$

19. (a) Complement: $\dfrac{\pi}{2} - \dfrac{\pi}{3} = \dfrac{\pi}{6}$

Supplement: $\pi - \dfrac{\pi}{3} = \dfrac{2\pi}{3}$

(b) Complement: Not possible; $\dfrac{3\pi}{4}$ is greater than $\dfrac{\pi}{2}$.

Supplement: $\pi - \dfrac{3\pi}{4} = \dfrac{\pi}{4}$

21.

The angle shown is approximately 210°.

23.

The angle shown is approximately −45°.

25. (a) Since 90° < 130° < 180°; 130° lies in Quadrant II.

(b) Since 270° < 285° < 360°; 285° lies in Quadrant IV.

27. (a) Since −180° < −132°50′ < −90°; −132° 50′ lies in Quadrant III.

(b) Since −360° < −336° < −270°; −336° lies in Quadrant I.

29. (a)

(b)

31. (a)

(b)

33. (a) Coterminal angles for 45°

$45° + 360° = 405°$

$45° - 360° = -315°$

(b) Coterminal angles for −36°

$-36° + 360° = 324°$

$-36° - 360° = -396°$

35. (a) Coterminal angles for 300°

$300° + 360° = 660°$

$300° - 360° = -60°$

(b) Coterminal angles for 740°

$740° - 2(360°) = 20°$

$20° - 360° = -340°$

37. (a) Complement: $90° - 18° = 72°$

Supplement: $180° - 18° = 162°$

(b) Complement: Not possible; 115° is greater than 90°.

Supplement: $180° - 115° = 65°$

39. (a) $30° = 30\left(\dfrac{\pi}{180}\right) = \dfrac{\pi}{6}$

(b) $150° = 150\left(\dfrac{\pi}{180}\right) = \dfrac{5\pi}{6}$

41. (a) $-20° = -20\left(\dfrac{\pi}{180}\right) = -\dfrac{\pi}{9}$

(b) $-240° = -240\left(\dfrac{\pi}{180}\right) = -\dfrac{4\pi}{3}$

43. (a) $\dfrac{3\pi}{2} = \dfrac{3\pi}{2}\left(\dfrac{180}{\pi}\right)^° = 270°$

(b) $\dfrac{7\pi}{6} = \dfrac{7\pi}{6}\left(\dfrac{180}{\pi}\right)^° = 210°$

45. (a) $\dfrac{7\pi}{3} = \dfrac{7\pi}{3}\left(\dfrac{180}{\pi}\right)^° = 420°$

(b) $-\dfrac{11\pi}{30} = -\dfrac{11\pi}{30}\left(\dfrac{180}{\pi}\right)^° = -66°$

47. $115° = 115\left(\dfrac{\pi}{180}\right) \approx 2.007$ radians

49. $-216.35° = -216.35\left(\dfrac{\pi}{180}\right) \approx -3.776$ radians

51. $532° = 532\left(\dfrac{\pi}{180}\right) \approx 9.285$ radians

53. $-0.83° = -0.83\left(\dfrac{\pi}{180}\right) \approx -0.014$ radian

55. $\dfrac{\pi}{7} = \dfrac{\pi}{7}\left(\dfrac{180}{\pi}\right) \approx 25.714°$

57. $\dfrac{15\pi}{8} = \dfrac{15\pi}{8}\left(\dfrac{180}{\pi}\right) = 337.5°$

59. $-4.2\pi = -4.2\pi\left(\dfrac{180}{\pi}\right) = -756°$

61. $-2 = -2\left(\dfrac{180}{\pi}\right) \approx -114.592°$

63. (a) $54° \ 45' = 54° + \left(\frac{45}{60}\right)° = 54.75°$

(b) $-128° \ 30' = -128° - \left(\frac{30}{60}\right)° = -128.5°$

65. (a) $85° \ 18' \ 30'' = \left(85 + \frac{18}{60} + \frac{30}{3600}\right)° \approx 85.308°$

(b) $330° \ 25'' = \left(330 + \frac{25}{3600}\right)° \approx 330.007°$

67. (a) $240.6° = 240° + 0.6(60)' = 240° \ 36'$

(b) $-145.8° = -[145° + 0.8(60')] = -145° \ 48'$

69. (a) $2.5 = 2.5\left(\frac{180}{\pi}\right)° \approx 143.23945° \approx 143° \ 14' \ 22''$

(b) $-3.58 = -3.58\left(\frac{180}{\pi}\right)° \approx -205.11889° \approx -205° \ 7' \ 8''$

71. $s = r\theta$

$6 = 5\theta$

$\theta = \frac{6}{5}$ radians

73. $s = r\theta$

$32 = 7\theta$

$\theta = \frac{32}{7} = 4\frac{4}{7}$ radians

75. $s = r\theta$

$4 = 15\theta$

$\theta = \frac{4}{15}$ radian

77. $s = r\theta$

$25 = 14.5\theta$

$\theta = \frac{25}{14.5} \approx 1.724$ radians

79. $s = r\theta$, θ in radians

$s = 15(180)\left(\frac{\pi}{180}\right) = 15\pi$ inches

≈ 47.12 inches

81. $s = r\theta$, θ in radians

$s = 6(2) = 12$ meters

83. $\theta = 41° \ 15' \ 42'' - 32° \ 47' \ 9'' = 8° \ 28' \ 33'' \approx 8.47583° \approx 0.14793$ radian

$s = r\theta = 4000(0.14793) \approx 591.72$ miles

85. $\theta = 42° \ 7' \ 15'' - 25° \ 46' \ 37'' = 16° \ 20' \ 38'' \approx 0.285255$ radian

$s = r\theta = 4000(0.285255) \approx 1141.02$ miles

87. $\theta = \frac{s}{r} = \frac{600}{6378} \approx 0.094$ radian $\approx 5.39°$

89. $\theta = \frac{s}{r} = \frac{2.5}{6} = \frac{25}{60} = \frac{5}{12}$ radian

91. (a) 50 miles per hour $= 50(5280)/60 = 4400$ feet per minute

The circumference of the tire is $C = 2.5\pi$ feet.

The number of revolutions per minute is $r = 4400/2.5\pi \approx 560.2$ rev/min.

(b) The angular speed is θ/t.

$\theta = \frac{4400}{2.5\pi}(2\pi) = 3520$ radians

Angular speed $= \frac{3520 \text{ radians}}{1 \text{ minute}} = 3520$ rad/min

93. 1 Radian $= \left(\frac{180}{\pi}\right)° \approx 57.3°$, so one radian is much larger than one degree.

95. Circumference: $C = 2\pi(1.68) = 3.36\pi$ inches

360 rev/min $= 6$ rev/sec

Linear speed: $(3.36\pi)(6) = 20.16$ inches/sec

97. The area of a circle is $A = \pi r^2 \Rightarrow \pi = \dfrac{A}{r^2}$.

The circumference of a circle is $C = 2\pi r$.

$$C = 2\left(\frac{A}{r^2}\right)r$$

$$C = \frac{2A}{r}$$

$$\frac{Cr}{2} = A$$

For a sector, $C = s = r\theta$

Thus, $A = \dfrac{(r\theta)r}{2} = \dfrac{1}{2}\theta r^2$ for a sector.

99. $s = r\theta = (4000 \text{ miles})(0.031)\left(\dfrac{\pi}{180}\right) \approx 2.164$ miles

Section 4.2   Trigonometric Functions: The Unit Circle

- You should know the definition of the trigonometric functions in terms of the unit circle. Let t be a real number and (x, y) the point on the unit circle corresponding to t.

$$\sin t = y \qquad\qquad\qquad \csc t = \frac{1}{y}, \quad y \neq 0$$

$$\cos t = x \qquad\qquad\qquad \sec t = \frac{1}{x}, \quad x \neq 0$$

$$\tan t = \frac{y}{x}, \quad x \neq 0 \qquad\qquad \cot t = \frac{x}{y}, \quad y \neq 0$$

- The cosine and secant functions are even.

$$\cos(-t) = \cos t \qquad\qquad \sec(-t) = \sec t$$

- The other four trigonometric functions are odd.

$$\sin(-t) = -\sin t \qquad\qquad \csc(-t) = -\csc t$$

$$\tan(-t) = -\tan t \qquad\qquad \cot(-t) = -\cot t$$

- Be able to evaluate the trigonometric functions with a calculator.

Solutions to Odd-Numbered Exercises

1. $x = -\dfrac{3}{5}, \quad y = \dfrac{4}{5}$

$$\sin t = y = \frac{4}{5} \qquad\qquad \csc t = \frac{1}{y} = \frac{5}{4}$$

$$\cos t = x = -\frac{3}{5} \qquad\qquad \sec t = \frac{1}{x} = -\frac{5}{3}$$

$$\tan t = \frac{y}{x} = -\frac{4}{3} \qquad\qquad \cot t = \frac{x}{y} = -\frac{3}{4}$$

3. $x = \dfrac{8}{17}, \quad y = -\dfrac{15}{17}$

$$\sin t = y = -\frac{15}{17} \qquad\qquad \csc t = \frac{1}{y} = -\frac{17}{15}$$

$$\cos t = x = \frac{8}{17} \qquad\qquad \sec t = \frac{1}{x} = \frac{17}{8}$$

$$\tan t = \frac{y}{x} = -\frac{15}{8} \qquad\qquad \cot t = \frac{x}{y} = -\frac{8}{15}$$

5. $t = \dfrac{\pi}{4}$ corresponds to $\left(\dfrac{\sqrt{2}}{2}, \dfrac{\sqrt{2}}{2}\right)$.

7. $t = \dfrac{5\pi}{6}$ corresponds to $\left(-\dfrac{\sqrt{3}}{2}, \dfrac{1}{2}\right)$.

9. $t = \dfrac{4\pi}{3}$ corresponds to $\left(-\dfrac{1}{2}, -\dfrac{\sqrt{3}}{2}\right)$.

11. $t = \dfrac{3\pi}{2}$ corresponds to $(0, -1)$.

13. $t = \dfrac{\pi}{4}$ corresponds to $\left(\dfrac{\sqrt{2}}{2}, \dfrac{\sqrt{2}}{2}\right)$.

$\sin t = y = \dfrac{\sqrt{2}}{2}$

$\cos t = x = \dfrac{\sqrt{2}}{2}$

$\tan t = \dfrac{y}{x} = 1$

15. $t = -\dfrac{\pi}{6}$ corresponds to $\left(\dfrac{\sqrt{3}}{2}, -\dfrac{1}{2}\right)$.

$\sin t = y = -\dfrac{1}{2}$

$\cos t = x = \dfrac{\sqrt{3}}{2}$

$\tan t = \dfrac{y}{x} = -\dfrac{1}{\sqrt{3}}$

17. $t = -\dfrac{5\pi}{4}$ corresponds to $\left(-\dfrac{\sqrt{2}}{2}, \dfrac{\sqrt{2}}{2}\right)$.

$\sin t = y = \dfrac{\sqrt{2}}{2}$

$\cos t = x = -\dfrac{\sqrt{2}}{2}$

$\tan t = \dfrac{y}{x} = -1$

19. $t = \dfrac{11\pi}{6}$ corresponds to $\left(\dfrac{\sqrt{3}}{2}, -\dfrac{1}{2}\right)$.

$\sin t = y = -\dfrac{1}{2}$

$\cos t = x = \dfrac{\sqrt{3}}{2}$

$\tan t = \dfrac{y}{x} = -\dfrac{1}{\sqrt{3}}$

21. $t = \dfrac{4\pi}{3}$ corresponds to $\left(-\dfrac{1}{2}, -\dfrac{\sqrt{3}}{2}\right)$.

$\sin t = y = -\dfrac{\sqrt{3}}{2}$

$\cos t = x = -\dfrac{1}{2}$

$\tan t = \dfrac{y}{x} = \sqrt{3}$

23. $t = -\dfrac{3\pi}{2}$ corresponds to $(0, 1)$.

$\sin t = y = 1$
$\cos t = x = 0$
$\tan t = \dfrac{y}{x}$ is undefined.

25. $t = \dfrac{3\pi}{4}$ corresponds to $\left(-\dfrac{\sqrt{2}}{2}, \dfrac{\sqrt{2}}{2}\right)$.

$\sin t = y = \dfrac{\sqrt{2}}{2}$ $\csc t = \dfrac{1}{y} = \sqrt{2}$

$\cos t = x = -\dfrac{\sqrt{2}}{2}$ $\sec t = \dfrac{1}{x} = -\sqrt{2}$

$\tan t = \dfrac{y}{x} = -1$ $\cot t = \dfrac{x}{y} = -1$

27. $t = \dfrac{\pi}{2}$ corresponds to $(0, 1)$.

$\sin t = y = 1$ $\csc t = \dfrac{1}{y} = 1$

$\cos t = x = 0$ $\sec t = \dfrac{1}{x}$ is undefined.

$\tan t = \dfrac{y}{x}$ is undefined. $\cot t = \dfrac{x}{y} = 0$

29. $t = -\dfrac{4\pi}{3}$ corresponds to $\left(-\dfrac{1}{2}, \dfrac{\sqrt{3}}{2}\right)$.

$\sin t = y = \dfrac{\sqrt{3}}{2}$ $\csc t = \dfrac{1}{y} = \dfrac{2\sqrt{3}}{3}$

$\cos t = x = -\dfrac{1}{2}$ $\sec t = \dfrac{1}{x} = -2$

$\tan t = \dfrac{y}{x} = -\sqrt{3}$ $\cot t = \dfrac{x}{y} = -\dfrac{\sqrt{3}}{3}$

31. $\sin 3\pi = \sin \pi = 0$

33. $\cos \dfrac{8\pi}{3} = \cos \dfrac{2\pi}{3} = -\dfrac{1}{2}$

35. $\cos \dfrac{19\pi}{6} = \cos \dfrac{7\pi}{6} = -\dfrac{\sqrt{3}}{2}$

37. $\sin\left(-\dfrac{9\pi}{4}\right) = \sin\left(-\dfrac{\pi}{4}\right) = -\dfrac{\sqrt{2}}{2}$

39. $\sin t = \dfrac{1}{3}$

    (a) $\sin(-t) = -\sin t = -\dfrac{1}{3}$

    (b) $\csc(-t) = -\csc t = -3$

41. $\cos(-t) = -\dfrac{7}{8}$

    (a) $\cos t = \cos(-t) = -\dfrac{7}{8}$

    (b) $\sec(-t) = \dfrac{1}{\cos(-t)} = -\dfrac{8}{7}$

43. $\sin y = \dfrac{4}{5}$

    (a) $\sin(\pi - t) = \sin t = \dfrac{4}{5}$

    (b) $\sin(t + \pi) = -\sin t = -\dfrac{4}{5}$

45. $\sin \dfrac{\pi}{4} \approx 0.7071$

47. $\cos(-3) \approx -0.9900$

49. $\cos(-1.7) \approx -0.1288$

51. $\csc 0.8 = \dfrac{1}{\sin 0.8} \approx 1.3940$

53. $\sec 22.8 = \dfrac{1}{\cos 22.8} \approx -1.4486$

55. (a) $\sin 5 \approx -1$

    (b) $\cos 2 \approx -0.4$

57. (a) $\sin t = 0.25$

        $t \approx 0.25$ or 2.89

    (b) $\cos t = -0.25$

        $t \approx 1.82$ or 4.46

59. $\cos 1.5 \approx 0.0707$

    $2 \cos 0.75 \approx 1.4634$

    $\cos 2t \neq 2 \cos t$

61. (a) The points have y-axis symmetry.

    (b) $\sin t_1 = \sin(\pi - t_1)$ since they have the same y-value.

    (c) $-\cos t_1 = \cos(\pi - t_1)$ since the x-values have the opposite signs.

63. $y(t) = \dfrac{1}{4} \cos 6t$

    (a) $y(0) = \dfrac{1}{4} \cos 0 = 0.2500$ feet

    (b) $y\left(\dfrac{1}{4}\right) = \dfrac{1}{4} \cos \dfrac{3}{2} \approx 0.0177$ feet

    (c) $y\left(\dfrac{1}{2}\right) = \dfrac{1}{4} \cos 3 \approx -0.2475$ feet

65. $I = 5e^{-2(0.7)} \sin(0.7) \approx 0.794$

67. Let $h(t) = f(t)g(t)$

           $= \sin t \cos t.$

    Then, $h(-t) = \sin(-t) \cos(-t)$

                $= -\sin t \cos t$

                $= -h(t).$

    Thus, $h(t)$ is odd.

69. $f(x) = \dfrac{1}{2}(3x - 2)$

         $y = \dfrac{1}{2}(3x - 2)$

         $x = \dfrac{1}{2}(3y - 2)$

       $2x = 3y - 2$

    $2x + 2 = 3y$

    $\dfrac{2}{3}(x + 1) = y$

     $f^{-1}(x) = \dfrac{2}{3}(x + 1)$

71. $f(x) = \sqrt{x^2 - 4}, \quad x \geq 2, \quad y \geq 0$

$y = \sqrt{x^2 - 4}$

$x = \sqrt{y^2 - 4}$

$x^2 = y^2 - 4$

$x^2 + 4 = y^2$

$\sqrt{x^2 + 4} = y, \quad x \geq 0$

$f^{-1}(x) = \sqrt{x^2 + 4}, \quad x \geq 0$

Note: The domain of $f^{-1}(x)$ equals the range of $f(x)$.

Section 4.3   **Right Triangle Trigonometry**

- You should know the right triangle definition of trigonometric functions.

  (a) $\sin \theta = \dfrac{\text{opp}}{\text{hyp}}$

  (b) $\cos \theta = \dfrac{\text{adj}}{\text{hyp}}$

  (c) $\tan \theta = \dfrac{\text{opp}}{\text{adj}}$

  (d) $\csc \theta = \dfrac{\text{hyp}}{\text{opp}}$

  (e) $\sec \theta = \dfrac{\text{hyp}}{\text{adj}}$

  (f) $\cot \theta = \dfrac{\text{adj}}{\text{opp}}$

- You should know the following identities.

  (a) $\sin \theta = \dfrac{1}{\csc \theta}$

  (b) $\csc \theta = \dfrac{1}{\sin \theta}$

  (c) $\cos \theta = \dfrac{1}{\sec \theta}$

  (d) $\sec \theta = \dfrac{1}{\cos \theta}$

  (e) $\tan \theta = \dfrac{1}{\cot \theta}$

  (f) $\cot \theta = \dfrac{1}{\tan \theta}$

  (g) $\tan \theta = \dfrac{\sin \theta}{\cos \theta}$

  (h) $\cot \theta = \dfrac{\cos \theta}{\sin \theta}$

  (i) $\sin^2 \theta + \cos^2 \theta = 1$

  (j) $1 + \tan^2 \theta = \sec^2 \theta$ (k) $1 + \cot^2 \theta = \csc^2 \theta$

- You should know that two acute angles α and β are complementary if $\alpha + \beta = 90°$, and that cofunctions of complementary angles are equal.

- You should know the trigonometric function values of 30°, 45°, and 60°, or be able to construct triangles from which you can determine them.

Solutions to Odd-Numbered Exercises

1.

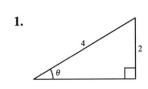

$\text{adj} = \sqrt{4^2 - 2^2} = \sqrt{12} = 2\sqrt{3}$

$\sin \theta = \dfrac{\text{opp}}{\text{hyp}} = \dfrac{2}{4} = \dfrac{1}{2}$ $\csc \theta = \dfrac{\text{hyp}}{\text{opp}} = \dfrac{4}{2} = 2$

$\cos \theta = \dfrac{\text{adj}}{\text{hyp}} = \dfrac{2\sqrt{3}}{4} = \dfrac{\sqrt{3}}{2}$ $\sec \theta = \dfrac{\text{hyp}}{\text{adj}} = \dfrac{4}{2\sqrt{3}} = \dfrac{2\sqrt{3}}{3}$

$\tan \theta = \dfrac{\text{opp}}{\text{adj}} = \dfrac{2}{2\sqrt{3}} = \dfrac{\sqrt{3}}{3}$ $\cot \theta = \dfrac{\text{adj}}{\text{opp}} = \dfrac{2\sqrt{3}}{2} = \sqrt{3}$

3.

$\text{hyp} = \sqrt{8^2 + 15^2} = 17$

$\sin \theta = \dfrac{\text{opp}}{\text{hyp}} = \dfrac{8}{17}$ $\csc \theta = \dfrac{\text{hyp}}{\text{opp}} = \dfrac{17}{8}$

$\cos \theta = \dfrac{\text{adj}}{\text{hyp}} = \dfrac{15}{17}$ $\sec \theta = \dfrac{\text{hyp}}{\text{adj}} = \dfrac{17}{15}$

$\tan \theta = \dfrac{\text{opp}}{\text{adj}} = \dfrac{8}{15}$ $\cot \theta = \dfrac{\text{adj}}{\text{opp}} = \dfrac{15}{8}$

5.

$\text{adj} = \sqrt{3^2 - 1^2} = \sqrt{8} = 2\sqrt{2}$

$\sin \theta = \dfrac{\text{opp}}{\text{hyp}} = \dfrac{1}{3}$ $\csc \theta = \dfrac{\text{hyp}}{\text{opp}} = 3$

$\cos \theta = \dfrac{\text{adj}}{\text{hyp}} = \dfrac{2\sqrt{2}}{3}$ $\sec \theta = \dfrac{\text{hyp}}{\text{adj}} = \dfrac{3}{2\sqrt{2}} = \dfrac{3\sqrt{2}}{4}$

$\tan \theta = \dfrac{\text{opp}}{\text{adj}} = \dfrac{1}{2\sqrt{2}} = \dfrac{\sqrt{2}}{4}$ $\cot \theta = \dfrac{\text{adj}}{\text{opp}} = 2\sqrt{2}$

$\text{adj} = \sqrt{6^2 - 2^2} = \sqrt{32} = 4\sqrt{2}$

$\sin \theta = \dfrac{\text{opp}}{\text{hyp}} = \dfrac{2}{6} = \dfrac{1}{3}$ $\csc \theta = \dfrac{\text{hyp}}{\text{opp}} = \dfrac{6}{2} = 3$

$\cos \theta = \dfrac{\text{adj}}{\text{hyp}} = \dfrac{4\sqrt{2}}{6} = \dfrac{2\sqrt{2}}{3}$ $\sec \theta = \dfrac{\text{hyp}}{\text{adj}} = \dfrac{6}{4\sqrt{2}} = \dfrac{3}{2\sqrt{2}} = \dfrac{3\sqrt{2}}{4}$

$\tan \theta = \dfrac{\text{opp}}{\text{adj}} = \dfrac{2}{4\sqrt{2}} = \dfrac{1}{2\sqrt{2}} = \dfrac{\sqrt{2}}{4}$ $\cot \theta = \dfrac{\text{adj}}{\text{opp}} = \dfrac{4\sqrt{2}}{2} = 2\sqrt{2}$

The function values are the same since the triangles are similar and the corresponding sides are proportional.

7.

$\text{opp} = \sqrt{10^2 - 8^2} = 6$

$\sin \theta = \dfrac{\text{opp}}{\text{hyp}} = \dfrac{6}{10} = \dfrac{3}{5}$ $\csc \theta = \dfrac{\text{hyp}}{\text{opp}} = \dfrac{10}{6} = \dfrac{5}{3}$

$\cos \theta = \dfrac{\text{adj}}{\text{hyp}} = \dfrac{8}{10} = \dfrac{4}{5}$ $\sec \theta = \dfrac{\text{hyp}}{\text{adj}} = \dfrac{10}{8} = \dfrac{5}{4}$

$\tan \theta = \dfrac{\text{opp}}{\text{adj}} = \dfrac{6}{8} = \dfrac{3}{4}$ $\cot \theta = \dfrac{\text{adj}}{\text{opp}} = \dfrac{8}{6} = \dfrac{4}{3}$

$\text{opp} = \sqrt{2.5^2 - 2^2} = 1.5$

$\sin \theta = \dfrac{\text{opp}}{\text{hyp}} = \dfrac{1.5}{2.5} = \dfrac{3}{5}$ $\csc \theta = \dfrac{\text{hyp}}{\text{opp}} = \dfrac{2.5}{1.5} = \dfrac{5}{3}$

$\cos \theta = \dfrac{\text{adj}}{\text{hyp}} = \dfrac{2}{2.5} = \dfrac{4}{5}$ $\sec \theta = \dfrac{\text{hyp}}{\text{adj}} = \dfrac{2.5}{2} = \dfrac{5}{4}$

$\tan \theta = \dfrac{\text{opp}}{\text{adj}} = \dfrac{1.5}{2} = \dfrac{3}{4}$ $\cot \theta = \dfrac{\text{adj}}{\text{opp}} = \dfrac{2}{1.5} = \dfrac{4}{3}$

The function values are the same since the triangles are similar and the corresponding sides are proportional.

9. Given: $\sin \theta = \dfrac{2}{3} = \dfrac{\text{opp}}{\text{hyp}}$

$2^2 + (\text{adj})^2 = 3^2$

$\text{adj} = \sqrt{5}$

$\cos \theta = \dfrac{\sqrt{5}}{3}$

$\tan \theta = \dfrac{2\sqrt{5}}{5}$

$\cot \theta = \dfrac{\sqrt{5}}{2}$

$\sec \theta = \dfrac{3\sqrt{5}}{5}$

$\csc \theta = \dfrac{3}{2}$

13. Given: $\tan \theta = 3 = \dfrac{3}{1} = \dfrac{\text{opp}}{\text{adj}}$

$3^2 + 1^2 = (\text{hyp})^2$

$\text{hyp} = \sqrt{10}$

$\sin \theta = \dfrac{3\sqrt{10}}{10}$

$\cos \theta = \dfrac{\sqrt{10}}{10}$

$\cot \theta = \dfrac{1}{3}$

$\sec \theta = \sqrt{10}$

$\csc \theta = \dfrac{\sqrt{10}}{3}$

17. $\sin 60° = \dfrac{\sqrt{3}}{2}$, $\cos 60° = \dfrac{1}{2}$

(a) $\tan 60° = \dfrac{\sin 60°}{\cos 60°} = \sqrt{3}$

(b) $\sin 30° = \cos 60° = \dfrac{1}{2}$

(c) $\cos 30° = \sin 60° = \dfrac{\sqrt{3}}{2}$

(d) $\cot 60° = \dfrac{\cos 60°}{\sin 60°} = \dfrac{1}{\sqrt{3}} = \dfrac{\sqrt{3}}{3}$

11. Given: $\sec \theta = 2 = \dfrac{2}{1} = \dfrac{\text{hyp}}{\text{adj}}$

$(\text{opp})^2 + 1^2 = 2^2$

$\text{opp} = \sqrt{3}$

$\sin \theta = \dfrac{\sqrt{3}}{2}$

$\cos \theta = \dfrac{1}{2}$

$\tan \theta = \sqrt{3}$

$\cot \theta = \dfrac{\sqrt{3}}{3}$

$\csc \theta = \dfrac{2\sqrt{3}}{3}$

15. Given: $\cot \theta = \dfrac{3}{2} = \dfrac{\text{adj}}{\text{opp}}$

$2^2 + 3^2 = (\text{hyp})^2$

$\text{hyp} = \sqrt{13}$

$\sin \theta = \dfrac{2}{\sqrt{13}} = \dfrac{2\sqrt{13}}{13}$

$\cos \theta = \dfrac{3}{\sqrt{13}} = \dfrac{3\sqrt{13}}{13}$

$\tan \theta = \dfrac{2}{3}$

$\csc \theta = \dfrac{\sqrt{13}}{2}$

$\sec \theta = \dfrac{\sqrt{13}}{3}$

19. $\csc \theta = 3$, $\sec \theta = \dfrac{3\sqrt{2}}{4}$

(a) $\sin \theta = \dfrac{1}{\csc \theta} = \dfrac{1}{3}$

(b) $\cos \theta = \dfrac{1}{\sec \theta} = \dfrac{2\sqrt{2}}{3}$

(c) $\tan \theta = \dfrac{\sin \theta}{\cos \theta} = \dfrac{1/3}{(2\sqrt{2})/3} = \dfrac{\sqrt{2}}{4}$

(d) $\sec(90° - \theta) = \csc \theta = 3$

21. $\cos \alpha = \dfrac{1}{4}$

(a) $\sec \alpha = \dfrac{1}{\cos \alpha} = 4$

(b) $\sin^2 \alpha + \cos^2 \alpha = 1$

$$\sin^2 \alpha + \left(\dfrac{1}{4}\right)^2 = 1$$

$$\sin^2 \alpha = \dfrac{15}{16}$$

$$\sin \alpha = \dfrac{\sqrt{15}}{4}$$

(c) $\cot \alpha = \dfrac{\cos \alpha}{\sin \alpha} = \dfrac{1/4}{\sqrt{15}/4} = \dfrac{1}{\sqrt{15}} = \dfrac{\sqrt{15}}{15}$

(d) $\sin(90° - \alpha) = \cos \alpha = \dfrac{1}{4}$

23. $\tan \theta \cot \theta = \tan \theta \left(\dfrac{1}{\tan \theta}\right) = 1$

25. $\tan \alpha \cos \alpha = \left(\dfrac{\sin \alpha}{\cos \alpha}\right) \cos \alpha = \sin \alpha$

27. $(1 + \cos \theta)(1 - \cos \theta) = 1 - \cos^2 \theta$
$$= (\sin^2 \theta + \cos^2 \theta) - \cos^2 \theta$$
$$= \sin^2 \theta$$

29. $(\sec \theta + \tan \theta)(\sec \theta - \tan \theta) = \sec^2 \theta - \tan^2 \theta$
$$= (1 + \tan^2 \theta) - \tan^2 \theta$$
$$= 1$$

31. $\dfrac{\sin \theta}{\cos \theta} + \dfrac{\cos \theta}{\sin \theta} = \dfrac{\sin^2 \theta + \cos^2 \theta}{\sin \theta \cos \theta}$

$$= \dfrac{1}{\sin \theta \cos \theta}$$

$$= \dfrac{1}{\sin \theta} \cdot \dfrac{1}{\cos \theta}$$

$$= \csc \theta \sec \theta$$

33. (a) $\cos 60° = \dfrac{1}{2}$

(b) $\tan \dfrac{\pi}{6} = \dfrac{1}{\sqrt{3}} = \dfrac{\sqrt{3}}{3}$

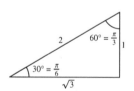

35. (a) $\cot 45° = 1$

(b) $\cos 45° = \dfrac{1}{\sqrt{2}} = \dfrac{\sqrt{2}}{2}$

37. (a) $\sin 10° \approx 0.1736$

(b) $\cos 80° \approx 0.1736$

Note: $\cos 80° = \sin(90° - 80°) = \sin 10°$

39. (a) $\sin 16.35° \approx 0.2815$

(b) $\csc 16.35° = \dfrac{1}{\sin 16.35°} \approx 3.5523$

41. (a) $\sec 42° 12' = \sec 42.2° = \dfrac{1}{\cos 42.2°} \approx 1.3499$

(b) $\csc 48° 7' = \dfrac{1}{\sin \left(48 + \frac{7}{60}\right)°} \approx 1.3432$

43. Make sure that your calculator is in radian mode.

(a) $\cot \dfrac{\pi}{16} = \dfrac{1}{\tan (\pi/16)} \approx 5.0273$

(b) $\tan \dfrac{\pi}{16} \approx 0.1989$

45. Make sure that your calculator is in radian mode.

(a) $\csc 1 = \dfrac{1}{\sin 1} \approx 1.1884$

(b) $\tan \dfrac{1}{2} \approx 0.5463$

47. (a) $\sin \theta = \dfrac{1}{2} \implies \theta = 30° = \dfrac{\pi}{6}$

(b) $\csc \theta = 2 \implies \theta = 30° = \dfrac{\pi}{6}$

49. (a) $\sec \theta = 2 \implies \theta = 60° = \dfrac{\pi}{3}$

(b) $\cot \theta = 1 \implies \theta = 45° = \dfrac{\pi}{4}$

51. (a) $\csc \theta = \dfrac{2\sqrt{3}}{3} \implies \theta = 60° = \dfrac{\pi}{3}$

(b) $\sin \theta = \dfrac{\sqrt{2}}{2} \implies \theta = 45° = \dfrac{\pi}{4}$

53. (a) $\sin \theta = 0.8191 \implies \theta \approx 55° \approx 0.960$ radian

(b) $\cos \theta = 0.0175 \implies \theta \approx 89° \approx 1.553$ radians

55. (a) $\tan \theta = 1.1920 \implies \theta \approx 50° \approx 0.873$ radian

(b) $\tan \theta = 0.4663 \implies \theta \approx 25° \approx 0.436$ radian

57. $\tan 30° = \dfrac{y}{75}$

$\dfrac{\sqrt{3}}{3} = \dfrac{y}{75}$

$75\left(\dfrac{\sqrt{3}}{3}\right) = y$

$25\sqrt{3} = y$

59. $\cot 60° = \dfrac{x}{32}$

$\dfrac{\sqrt{3}}{3} = \dfrac{x}{32}$

$\dfrac{32\sqrt{3}}{3} = x$

61. $\sin 40° = \dfrac{15}{r}$

$r = \dfrac{15}{\sin 40°} \approx 23.3$

63. $\sin 50° = \dfrac{y}{8}$

$y = 8 \sin 50° \approx 6.1$

65. $\dfrac{h}{23} = \dfrac{6}{8}$

$h = \dfrac{138}{8} = \dfrac{69}{4} = 17\frac{1}{4}$ ft

67. (a)

(b) $\sin 75° = \dfrac{x}{30}$

(c) $x = 30 \sin 75° \approx 29$ meters

69. Let $x =$ distance from the boat to the shoreline

$\tan 3° = \dfrac{60}{x}$

$x = \dfrac{60}{\tan 3°} \approx 1144.9$ feet

71.

$$\sin 30° = \frac{y_1}{56}$$

$$y_1 = (\sin 30°)(56) = \left(\frac{1}{2}\right)(56) = 28$$

$$\cos 30° = \frac{x_1}{56}$$

$$x_1 = \cos 30°(56) = \frac{\sqrt{3}}{2}(56) = 28\sqrt{3}$$

$$(x_1, y_1) = (28\sqrt{3}, 28)$$

$$\sin 60° = \frac{y_2}{56}$$

$$y_2 = \sin 60°(56) = \left(\frac{\sqrt{3}}{2}\right)(56) = 28\sqrt{3}$$

$$\cos 60° = \frac{x_2}{56}$$

$$x_2 = (\cos 60°)(56) = \left(\frac{1}{2}\right)(56) = 28$$

$$(x_2, y_2) = (28, 28\sqrt{3})$$

73. $x \approx 9.397, \ y \approx 3.420$

$$\sin\theta = \frac{y}{10} \approx 0.34$$

$$\cos\theta = \frac{x}{10} \approx 0.94$$

$$\tan\theta = \frac{y}{x} \approx 0.36$$

$$\cot\theta = \frac{x}{y} \approx 2.75$$

$$\sec\theta = \frac{10}{x} \approx 1.06$$

$$\csc\theta = \frac{10}{y} \approx 2.92$$

75. (a)

θ	0	0.1	0.2	0.3	0.4	0.5
$\sin\theta$	0	0.0998	0.1987	0.2955	0.3894	0.4794

(b) In the interval $(0, 0.5]$, $\theta > \sin\theta$

(c) As $\theta \to 0$, $\sin\theta \to 0$

77. True, $\csc x = \dfrac{1}{\sin x} \ \Rightarrow \ \sin 60° \csc 60° = \sin 60°\left(\dfrac{1}{\sin 60°}\right) = 1$

79. False, $\dfrac{\sqrt{2}}{2} + \dfrac{\sqrt{2}}{2} = \sqrt{2} \neq 1$

81. False, $\dfrac{\sin 60°}{\sin 30°} = \dfrac{\cos 30°}{\sin 30°} = \cot 30° \approx 1.7321$; $\sin 2° \approx 0.0349$

83. $\dfrac{x^2 - 6x}{x^2 + 4x - 12} \cdot \dfrac{x^2 + 12x + 36}{x^2 - 36} = \dfrac{x\cancel{(x-6)}}{\cancel{(x+6)}(x-2)} \cdot \dfrac{\cancel{(x+6)}(x+6)}{\cancel{(x+6)}\cancel{(x-6)}}$

$$= \dfrac{x}{x - 2}$$

85. $\dfrac{3}{x+2} - \dfrac{2}{x-2} + \dfrac{x}{x^2 + 4x + 4} = \dfrac{3(x+2)(x-2) - 2(x+2)^2 + x(x-2)}{(x-2)(x+2)^2}$

$$= \dfrac{3(x^2 - 4) - 2(x^2 + 4x + 4) + x^2 - 2x}{(x-2)(x+2)^2}$$

$$= \dfrac{2x^2 - 10x - 20}{(x-2)(x+2)^2} = \dfrac{2(x^2 - 5x - 10)}{(x-2)(x+2)^2}$$

Section 4.4   Trigonometric Functions of Any Angle

■ Know the Definitions of Trigonometric Functions of Any Angle.

If θ is in standard position, (x, y) a point on the terminal side and $r = \sqrt{x^2 + y^2} \neq 0$, then

$$\sin \theta = \frac{y}{r} \qquad\qquad \csc \theta = \frac{r}{y},\ y \neq 0$$

$$\cos \theta = \frac{x}{r} \qquad\qquad \sec \theta = \frac{r}{x},\ x \neq 0$$

$$\tan \theta = \frac{y}{x},\ x \neq 0 \qquad\qquad \cot \theta = \frac{x}{y},\ y \neq 0$$

■ You should know the signs of the trigonometric functions in each quadrant.

■ You should know the trigonometric function values of the quadrant angles 0, $\dfrac{\pi}{2}$, π, and $\dfrac{3\pi}{2}$.

■ You should be able to find reference angles.

■ You should be able to evaluate trigonometric functions of any angle. (Use reference angles.)

■ You should know that the period of sine and cosine is 2π.

Solutions to Odd-Numbered Exercises

1. (a) $(x, y) = (4, 3)$

$r = \sqrt{16 + 9} = 5$

$\sin \theta = \dfrac{y}{r} = \dfrac{3}{5} \qquad \csc \theta = \dfrac{r}{y} = \dfrac{5}{3}$

$\cos \theta = \dfrac{x}{r} = \dfrac{4}{5} \qquad \sec \theta = \dfrac{r}{x} = \dfrac{5}{4}$

$\tan \theta = \dfrac{y}{x} = \dfrac{3}{4} \qquad \cot \theta = \dfrac{x}{y} = \dfrac{4}{3}$

(b) $(x, y) = (-8, -15)$

$r = \sqrt{64 + 225} = 17$

$\sin \theta = \dfrac{y}{r} = -\dfrac{15}{17} \qquad \csc \theta = \dfrac{r}{y} = -\dfrac{17}{15}$

$\cos \theta = \dfrac{x}{r} = -\dfrac{8}{17} \qquad \sec \theta = \dfrac{r}{x} = -\dfrac{17}{8}$

$\tan \theta = \dfrac{y}{x} = \dfrac{15}{8} \qquad \cot \theta = \dfrac{x}{y} = \dfrac{8}{15}$

3. (a) $(x, y) = \left(-\sqrt{3}, -1\right)$

$r = \sqrt{3 + 1} = 2$

$\sin \theta = \dfrac{y}{r} = -\dfrac{1}{2}$ $\qquad \csc \theta = \dfrac{r}{y} = -2$

$\cos \theta = \dfrac{x}{r} = -\dfrac{\sqrt{3}}{2}$ $\qquad \sec \theta = \dfrac{r}{x} = -\dfrac{2\sqrt{3}}{3}$

$\tan \theta = \dfrac{y}{x} = \dfrac{\sqrt{3}}{3}$ $\qquad \cot \theta = \dfrac{x}{y} = \sqrt{3}$

(b) $(x, y) = (-2, 2)$

$r = \sqrt{4 + 4} = 2\sqrt{2}$

$\sin \theta = \dfrac{y}{r} = \dfrac{\sqrt{2}}{2}$ $\qquad \csc \theta = \dfrac{r}{y} = \sqrt{2}$

$\cos \theta = \dfrac{x}{r} = -\dfrac{\sqrt{2}}{2}$ $\qquad \sec \theta = \dfrac{r}{x} = -\sqrt{2}$

$\tan \theta = \dfrac{y}{x} = -1$ $\qquad \cot \theta = \dfrac{x}{y} = -1$

5. (a) $(x, y) = (7, 24)$

$r = \sqrt{49 + 576} = 25$

$\sin \theta = \dfrac{y}{r} = \dfrac{24}{25}$ $\qquad \csc \theta = \dfrac{r}{y} = \dfrac{25}{24}$

$\cos \theta = \dfrac{x}{r} = \dfrac{7}{25}$ $\qquad \sec \theta = \dfrac{r}{x} = \dfrac{25}{7}$

$\tan \theta = \dfrac{y}{x} = \dfrac{24}{7}$ $\qquad \cot \theta = \dfrac{x}{y} = \dfrac{7}{24}$

(b) $(x, y) = (7, -24)$

$r = \sqrt{49 + 576} = 25$

$\sin \theta = \dfrac{y}{r} = -\dfrac{24}{25}$ $\qquad \csc \theta = \dfrac{r}{y} = -\dfrac{25}{24}$

$\cos \theta = \dfrac{x}{r} = \dfrac{7}{25}$ $\qquad \sec \theta = \dfrac{r}{x} = \dfrac{25}{7}$

$\tan \theta = \dfrac{y}{x} = -\dfrac{24}{7}$ $\qquad \cot \theta = \dfrac{x}{y} = -\dfrac{7}{24}$

7. (a) $(x, y) = (-4, 10)$

$r = \sqrt{16 + 100} = 2\sqrt{29}$

$\sin \theta = \dfrac{y}{r} = \dfrac{5\sqrt{29}}{29}$ $\qquad \csc \theta = \dfrac{r}{y} = \dfrac{\sqrt{29}}{5}$

$\cos \theta = \dfrac{x}{r} = -\dfrac{2\sqrt{29}}{29}$ $\qquad \sec \theta = \dfrac{r}{x} = -\dfrac{\sqrt{29}}{2}$

$\tan \theta = \dfrac{y}{x} = -\dfrac{5}{2}$ $\qquad \cot \theta = \dfrac{x}{y} = -\dfrac{2}{5}$

(b) $(x, y) = (3, -5)$

$r = \sqrt{9 + 25} = \sqrt{34}$

$\sin \theta = \dfrac{y}{r} = -\dfrac{5\sqrt{34}}{34}$ $\qquad \csc \theta = \dfrac{r}{y} = -\dfrac{\sqrt{34}}{5}$

$\cos \theta = \dfrac{x}{r} = \dfrac{3\sqrt{34}}{34}$ $\qquad \sec \theta = \dfrac{r}{x} = \dfrac{\sqrt{34}}{3}$

$\tan \theta = \dfrac{y}{x} = -\dfrac{5}{3}$ $\qquad \cot \theta = \dfrac{x}{y} = -\dfrac{3}{5}$

9. (a) $\sin \theta < 0 \implies \theta$ lies in Quadrant III or in Quadrant IV.

$\cos \theta < 0 \implies \theta$ lies in Quadrant II or in Quadrant III.

$\sin \theta < 0$ *and* $\cos \theta < 0 \implies \theta$ lies in Quadrant III.

(b) $\sin \theta > 0 \implies \theta$ lies in Quadrant I or in Quadrant II.

$\cos \theta < \theta \implies \theta$ lies in Quadrant II or in Quadrant III.

$\sin \theta > 0$ *and* $\cos \theta < 0 \implies \theta$ lies in Quadrant II.

11. (a) $\sin \theta > 0 \implies \theta$ lies in Quadrant I or in Quadrant II.

$\tan \theta < 0 \implies \theta$ lies in Quadrant II or in Quadrant IV.

$\sin \theta > 0$ *and* $\tan \theta < 0 \implies \theta$ lies in Quadrant II.

(b) $\cos \theta > 0 \implies \theta$ lies in Quadrant I or in Quadrant IV.

$\tan \theta < 0 \implies \theta$ lies in Quadrant II or in Quadrant IV.

$\cos \theta > 0$ *and* $\tan \theta < 0 \implies \theta$ lies in Quadrant IV.

13. $\sin \theta = \dfrac{y}{r} = \dfrac{3}{5} \implies x^2 = 25 - 9 = 16$

θ in Quadrant II $\implies x = -4$

$\sin \theta = \dfrac{y}{r} = \dfrac{3}{5}$ $\csc \theta = \dfrac{r}{y} = \dfrac{5}{3}$

$\cos \theta = \dfrac{x}{r} = -\dfrac{4}{5}$ $\sec \theta = \dfrac{r}{x} = -\dfrac{5}{4}$

$\tan \theta = \dfrac{y}{x} = -\dfrac{3}{4}$ $\cot \theta = \dfrac{x}{y} = -\dfrac{4}{3}$

15. $\sin \theta < 0 \implies y < 0$

$\tan \theta = \dfrac{y}{x} = \dfrac{-15}{8} \implies r = 17$

$\sin \theta = \dfrac{y}{r} = -\dfrac{15}{17}$ $\csc \theta = \dfrac{r}{y} = -\dfrac{17}{15}$

$\cos \theta = \dfrac{x}{r} = \dfrac{8}{17}$ $\sec \theta = \dfrac{r}{x} = \dfrac{17}{8}$

$\tan \theta = \dfrac{y}{x} = -\dfrac{15}{8}$ $\cot \theta = \dfrac{x}{y} = -\dfrac{8}{15}$

17. $\cot \theta = \dfrac{x}{y} = -\dfrac{3}{1} = \dfrac{3}{-1}$

$\cos \theta > 0 \implies x$ is positive; $x = 3, y = -1, r = \sqrt{10}$

$\sin \theta = \dfrac{y}{r} = -\dfrac{\sqrt{10}}{10}$ $\csc \theta = \dfrac{r}{y} = -\sqrt{10}$

$\cos \theta = \dfrac{x}{r} = \dfrac{3\sqrt{10}}{10}$ $\sec \theta = \dfrac{r}{x} = \dfrac{\sqrt{10}}{3}$

$\tan \theta = \dfrac{y}{x} = -\dfrac{1}{3}$ $\cot \theta = \dfrac{x}{y} = -3$

19. $\sec \theta = \dfrac{r}{x} = \dfrac{2}{-1} \implies y^2 = 4 - 1 = 3$

$\sin \theta > 0 \implies y = \sqrt{3}$

$\sin \theta = \dfrac{y}{r} = \dfrac{\sqrt{3}}{2}$ $\csc \theta = \dfrac{r}{y} = \dfrac{2\sqrt{3}}{3}$

$\cos \theta = \dfrac{x}{r} = -\dfrac{1}{2}$ $\sec \theta = \dfrac{r}{x} = -2$

$\tan \theta = \dfrac{y}{x} = -\sqrt{3}$ $\cot \theta = \dfrac{x}{y} = -\dfrac{\sqrt{3}}{3}$

21. $\sin \theta = 0 \implies \theta = n\pi$

$\sec \theta = -1 \implies \theta = \pi$

$\sin \theta = \dfrac{y}{r} = \dfrac{0}{r} = 0$ $\csc \theta = \dfrac{r}{y}$ is undefined.

$\cos \theta = \dfrac{x}{r} = \dfrac{-r}{r} = -1$ $\sec \theta = \dfrac{r}{x} = -1$

$\tan \theta = \dfrac{y}{x} = \dfrac{0}{x} = 0$ $\cot \theta = \dfrac{x}{y}$ is undefined.

23. To find a point on the terminal side of θ, use any point on the line $y = -x$ that lies in Quadrant II. $(-1, 1)$ is one such point.

$x = -1, y = 1, r = \sqrt{2}$

$\sin \theta = \dfrac{1}{\sqrt{2}} = \dfrac{\sqrt{2}}{2}$ $\csc \theta = \sqrt{2}$

$\cos \theta = -\dfrac{1}{\sqrt{2}} = -\dfrac{\sqrt{2}}{2}$ $\sec \theta = -\sqrt{2}$

$\tan \theta = -1$ $\cot \theta = -1$

25. To find a point on the terminal side of θ, use any point on the line $y = 2x$ that lies in Quadrant III. $(-1, -2)$ is one such point.

$x = -1, y = -2, r = \sqrt{5}$

$\sin \theta = -\dfrac{2}{\sqrt{5}} = -\dfrac{2\sqrt{5}}{5}$ $\csc \theta = \dfrac{\sqrt{5}}{-2} = -\dfrac{\sqrt{5}}{2}$

$\cos \theta = -\dfrac{1}{\sqrt{5}} = -\dfrac{\sqrt{5}}{5}$ $\sec \theta = \dfrac{\sqrt{5}}{-1} = -\sqrt{5}$

$\tan \theta = \dfrac{-2}{-1} = 2$ $\cot \theta = \dfrac{-1}{-2} = \dfrac{1}{2}$

27. $(x, y) = (-1, 0)$

$\cos \pi = \dfrac{x}{r} = \dfrac{-1}{1} = -1$

29. $(x, y) = (-1, 0)$

$\sec \pi = \dfrac{r}{x} = \dfrac{1}{-1} = -1$

31. $(x, y) = (0, 1)$

$\tan \dfrac{\pi}{2} = \dfrac{y}{x} = \dfrac{1}{0}$ undefined

33. $(x, y) = (0, 1)$

$\cot \dfrac{\pi}{2} = \dfrac{x}{y} = \dfrac{0}{1} = 0$

35. (a) $\theta = 203°$

$\theta' = 203° - 180° = 23°$

(b) $\theta = 127°$

$\theta' = 180° - 127° = 53°$

37. (a) $\theta = -245°$

$360° - 245° = 115°$ (coterminal angle)

$\theta' = 180° - 115° = 65°$

(b) $\theta = -72°$

$\theta' = 72°$

39. (a) $\theta = \dfrac{2\pi}{3}$

$\theta' = \pi - \dfrac{2\pi}{3} = \dfrac{\pi}{3}$

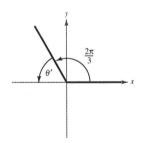

(b) $\theta = \dfrac{7\pi}{6}$

$\theta' = \dfrac{7\pi}{6} - \pi = \dfrac{\pi}{6}$

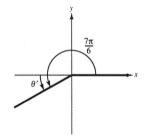

41. (a) $\theta = 3.5$

$\theta' = 3.5 - \pi$

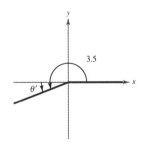

(b) $\theta = 5.8$

$\theta' = 2\pi - 5.8$

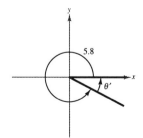

43. (a) $\theta' = 45°$, Quadrant III

$\sin 225° = -\sin 45° = -\dfrac{\sqrt{2}}{2}$

$\cos 225° = -\cos 45° = -\dfrac{\sqrt{2}}{2}$

$\tan 225° = \tan 45° = 1$

(b) $\theta' = 45°$, Quadrant II

$\sin(-225°) = \sin 45° = \dfrac{\sqrt{2}}{2}$

$\cos(-225°) = -\cos 45° = -\dfrac{\sqrt{2}}{2}$

$\tan(-225°) = -\tan 45° = -1$

45. (a) $\theta' = 30°$, Quadrant I

$\sin 750° = \sin 30° = \dfrac{1}{2}$

$\cos 750° = \cos 30° = \dfrac{\sqrt{3}}{2}$

$\tan 750° = \tan 30° = \dfrac{\sqrt{3}}{3}$

(b) $\theta' = 30°$, Quadrant II

$\sin 510° = \sin 30° = \dfrac{1}{2}$

$\cos 510° = -\cos 30° = -\dfrac{\sqrt{3}}{2}$

$\tan 510° = -\tan 30° = -\dfrac{\sqrt{3}}{3}$

47. (a) $\theta' = \dfrac{\pi}{3}$, Quadrant III

$\sin \dfrac{4\pi}{3} = -\sin \dfrac{\pi}{3} = -\dfrac{\sqrt{3}}{2}$

$\cos \dfrac{4\pi}{3} = -\cos \dfrac{\pi}{3} = -\dfrac{1}{2}$

$\tan \dfrac{4\pi}{3} = \tan \dfrac{\pi}{3} = \sqrt{3}$

(b) $\theta' = \dfrac{\pi}{3}$, Quadrant II

$\sin \dfrac{2\pi}{3} = \sin \dfrac{\pi}{3} = \dfrac{\sqrt{3}}{2}$

$\cos \dfrac{2\pi}{3} = -\cos \dfrac{\pi}{3} = -\dfrac{1}{2}$

$\tan \dfrac{2\pi}{3} = -\tan \dfrac{\pi}{3} = -\sqrt{3}$

49. (a) $\theta' = \dfrac{\pi}{6}$, Quadrant IV

$\sin\left(-\dfrac{\pi}{6}\right) = -\sin \dfrac{\pi}{6} = -\dfrac{1}{2}$

$\cos\left(-\dfrac{\pi}{6}\right) = \cos \dfrac{\pi}{6} = \dfrac{\sqrt{3}}{2}$

$\tan\left(-\dfrac{\pi}{6}\right) = -\tan \dfrac{\pi}{6} = -\dfrac{\sqrt{3}}{3}$

(b) $\theta' = \dfrac{\pi}{6}$, Quadrant II

$\sin \dfrac{5\pi}{6} = \sin \dfrac{\pi}{6} = \dfrac{1}{2}$

$\cos \dfrac{5\pi}{6} = -\cos \dfrac{\pi}{6} = -\dfrac{\sqrt{3}}{2}$

$\tan \dfrac{5\pi}{6} = -\tan \dfrac{\pi}{6} = -\dfrac{\sqrt{3}}{3}$

51. (a) $\theta' = \dfrac{\pi}{4}$, Quadrant II

$\sin \dfrac{11\pi}{4} = \sin \dfrac{\pi}{4} = \dfrac{\sqrt{2}}{2}$

$\cos \dfrac{11\pi}{4} = -\cos \dfrac{\pi}{4} = -\dfrac{\sqrt{2}}{2}$

$\tan \dfrac{11\pi}{4} = -\tan \dfrac{\pi}{4} = -1$

(b) $\theta' = \dfrac{\pi}{6}$, Quadrant IV

$\sin\left(-\dfrac{13\pi}{6}\right) = -\sin \dfrac{\pi}{6} = -\dfrac{1}{2}$

$\cos\left(-\dfrac{13\pi}{6}\right) = \cos \dfrac{\pi}{6} = \dfrac{\sqrt{3}}{2}$

$\tan\left(-\dfrac{13\pi}{6}\right) = -\tan \dfrac{\pi}{6} = -\dfrac{\sqrt{3}}{3}$

53. (a) $\sin 10° \approx 0.1736$

(b) $\csc 10° = \dfrac{1}{\sin 10°} \approx 5.7588$

55. (a) $\cos(-110°) \approx -0.3420$

(b) $\cos 250° \approx -0.3420$

57. (a) $\tan 240° \approx 1.7321$ (b) $\cot 210° = \dfrac{1}{\tan 210°} \approx 1.7321$

59. (a) $\tan \dfrac{\pi}{9} \approx 0.3640$ (b) $\tan \dfrac{10\pi}{9} \approx 0.3640$

61. (a) $\sin 0.65 \approx 0.6052$ (b) $\sin(-5.63) \approx 0.6077$

63. (a) $\sin \theta = \dfrac{1}{2} \Rightarrow$ reference angle is $30°$ or $\dfrac{\pi}{6}$ and θ is in Quadrant I or Quadrant II.

Values in degrees: $30°, 150°$

Values in radian: $\dfrac{\pi}{6}, \dfrac{5\pi}{6}$

(b) $\sin \theta = -\dfrac{1}{2} \Rightarrow$ reference angle is $30°$ or $\dfrac{\pi}{6}$ and θ is in Quadrant III or Quadrant IV.

Values in degrees: $210°, 330°$

Values in radians: $\dfrac{7\pi}{6}, \dfrac{11\pi}{6}$

65. (a) $\csc \theta = \dfrac{2\sqrt{3}}{3} \Rightarrow$ reference angle is $60°$ or $\dfrac{\pi}{3}$ and θ is in Quadrant I or Quadrant II.

Values in degrees: $60°, 120°$

Values in radians: $\dfrac{\pi}{3}, \dfrac{2\pi}{3}$

(b) $\cot \theta = -1 \Rightarrow$ reference angle is $45°$ or $\dfrac{\pi}{4}$ and θ is in Quadrant II or Quadrant IV.

Values in degrees: $135°, 315°$

Values in radians: $\dfrac{3\pi}{4}, \dfrac{7\pi}{4}$

67. (a) $\tan \theta = 1 \Rightarrow$ reference angle is $45°$ or $\dfrac{\pi}{4}$ and θ is in Quadrant I or Quadrant III.

Values in degrees: $45°, 225°$

Values in radians: $\dfrac{\pi}{4}, \dfrac{5\pi}{4}$

(b) $\cot \theta = -\sqrt{3} \Rightarrow$ reference angle is $30°$ or $\dfrac{\pi}{6}$ and θ is in Quadrant II or Quadrant IV.

Values in degrees: $150°, 330°$

Values in radians: $\dfrac{5\pi}{6}, \dfrac{11\pi}{6}$

69. (a) $\sin \theta = 0.8191 \Rightarrow \theta' \approx 54.99°$

Quadrant I: $\theta = \sin^{-1} 0.8191 \approx 54.99°$

Quadrant II: $\theta = 180° - \sin^{-1} 0.8191 \approx 125.01°$

(b) $\theta' = \sin^{-1} 0.2589 \approx 15.00°$

Quadrant III: $\theta = 180° + 15° = 195°$

Quadrant IV: $\theta = 360° - 15° = 345°$

71. (a) $\cos \theta = 0.9848 \implies \theta' \approx 0.175$

Quadrant I: $\theta = \cos^{-1}(0.9848) \approx 0.175$

Quadrant IV: $\theta = 2\pi - \theta' \approx 6.109$

(b) $\theta' = \cos^{-1} 0.5890 \approx 0.941$

Quadrant II: $\theta = \pi - 0.941 \approx 2.201$

Quadrant III: $\theta = \pi + 0.941 \approx 4.083$

73. (a) $\tan \theta = 1.192 \implies \theta' \approx 0.873$

Quadrant I: $\theta = \tan^{-1} 1.192 \approx 0.873$

Quadrant III: $\theta = \pi + \theta' \approx 4.014$

(b) $\theta' = \tan^{-1} 8.144 \approx 1.4486$

Quadrant II: $\theta = \pi - 1.4486 \approx 1.693$

Quadrant IV: $\theta = 2\pi - 1.4486 \approx 4.835$

75. $\sin \theta = -\frac{3}{5}$

$\sin^2 \theta + \cos^2 \theta = 1$

$\cos^2 \theta = 1 - \sin^2 \theta$

$\cos^2 \theta = 1 - \left(-\frac{3}{5}\right)^2$

$\cos^2 \theta = 1 - \frac{9}{25}$

$\cos^2 \theta = \frac{16}{25}$

$\cos \theta > 0$ in Quadrant IV.

$\cos \theta = \frac{4}{5}$

77. $\tan \theta = \frac{3}{2}$

$\sec^2 \theta = 1 + \tan^2 \theta$

$\sec^2 \theta = 1 + \left(\frac{3}{2}\right)^2$

$\sec^2 \theta = 1 + \frac{9}{4}$

$\sec^2 \theta = \frac{13}{4}$

$\sec \theta < 0$ in Quadrant III.

$\sec \theta = -\frac{\sqrt{13}}{2}$

79. $\cos \theta = \frac{5}{8}$

$\cos \theta = \frac{1}{\sec \theta} \implies \sec \theta = \frac{1}{\cos \theta}$

$\sec \theta = \frac{1}{5/8} = \frac{8}{5}$

81. (a) $t = 1$

$T = 45 - 23 \cos \left[\frac{2\pi}{365}(1 - 32)\right] \approx 25.2° \text{ F}$

(b) $t = 185$

$T = 45 - 23 \cos \left[\frac{2\pi}{365}(185 - 32)\right] \approx 65.1° \text{ F}$

(c) $t = 291$

$T = 45 - 23 \cos \left[\frac{2\pi}{365}(291 - 32)\right] \approx 50.8° \text{ F}$

83. $\sin \theta = \frac{6}{d} \implies d = \frac{6}{\sin \theta}$

(a) $d = \frac{6}{\sin 30°} = 12$ miles

(b) $d = \frac{6}{\sin 90°} = 6$ miles

(c) $d = \frac{6}{\sin 120°} \approx 6.9$ miles

85. $y = 2^{x-1}$

x	-1	0	1	2	3
y	$\frac{1}{4}$	$\frac{1}{2}$	1	2	4

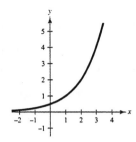

87. $y = \ln(x - 1)$

Domain: $x - 1 > 0 \implies x > 1$

x	1.1	1.5	2	3	4
y	-2.30	-0.69	0	0.69	1.10

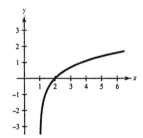

Section 4.5 Graphs of Sine and Cosine Functions

- ■ You should be able to graph $y = a \sin(bx - c)$ and $y = a \cos(bx - c)$.
- ■ Amplitude: $|a|$
- ■ Period: $\dfrac{2\pi}{|b|}$
- ■ Shift: Solve $bx - c = 0$ and $bx - c = 2\pi$.
- ■ Key Increments: $\dfrac{1}{4}$ (period)

Solutions to Odd-Numbered Exercises

1. $y = 3 \sin 2x$

Period: $\dfrac{2\pi}{2} = \pi$

Amplitude: $|3| = 3$

3. $y = \dfrac{5}{2}\cos\dfrac{x}{2}$

Period: $\dfrac{2\pi}{1/2} = 4\pi$

Amplitude: $\left|\dfrac{5}{2}\right| = \dfrac{5}{2}$

5. $y = \dfrac{2}{3}\sin \pi x$

Period: $\dfrac{2\pi}{\pi} = 2$

Amplitude: $\left|\dfrac{2}{3}\right| = \dfrac{2}{3}$

7. $y = -2 \sin x$

Period: $\dfrac{2\pi}{1} = 2\pi$

Amplitude: $|-2| = 2$

9. $y = 3 \sin 10x$

Period: $\dfrac{2\pi}{10} = \dfrac{\pi}{5}$

Amplitude: $|3| = 3$

11. $y = \dfrac{1}{2}\cos\dfrac{2\pi}{3}$

Period: $\dfrac{2\pi}{2/3} = 3\pi$

Amplitude: $\left|\dfrac{1}{2}\right| = \dfrac{1}{2}$

13. $y = 3 \sin 4\pi x$

Period: $\dfrac{2\pi}{4\pi} = \dfrac{1}{2}$

Amplitude: $|3| = 3$

15. $f(x) = \sin x$

$g(x) = \sin(x - \pi)$

The graph of g is a horizontal shift to the right π units of the graph of f (a phase shift).

17. $f(x) = \cos 2x$

$g(x) = -\cos 2x$

The graph of g is a reflection in the x-axis of the graph of f.

19. $f(x) = \cos x$

$g(x) = \cos 2x$

The period of f is twice that of g.

21. $f(x) = \sin x$

$f(x) = 2 + \sin x$

The graph of g is a vertical shift 2 units upward of the graph of f.

23. The graph of g has twice the amplitude as the graph of f. The period is the same.

25. The graph of g is a horizontal shift π units to the right of the graph of f.

27. $y_1 = \dfrac{1}{2}\sin x$; $y_2 = \dfrac{3}{2}\sin x$; $y_3 = -3\sin x$

Changing the value of a changes the amplitude.

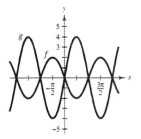

29. $y_1 = \sin\left(\dfrac{1}{2}x\right)$; $y_2 = \sin\left(\dfrac{3}{2}x\right)$; $y_3 = \sin(4x)$

Changing the value of b changes the period.

31. $f(x) = -2 \sin x$

Period: 2π

Amplitude: 2

$g(x) = 4 \sin x$

Period: 2π

Amplitude: 4

33. $f(x) = \cos x$

Period: 2π

Amplitude: 1

$g(x) = 1 + \cos x$

is a vertical shift of the graph of $f(x)$ one unit upward.

35. $f(x) = -\dfrac{1}{2}\sin\dfrac{x}{2}$

Period: 4π

Amplitude: $\dfrac{1}{2}$

$g(x) = 3 - \dfrac{1}{2}\sin\dfrac{x}{2}$ is the graph of $f(x)$ shifted vertically three units upward.

37. $f(x) = 2\cos x$

Period: 2π

Amplitude: 2

$g(x) = 2\cos(x + \pi)$ is the graph of $f(x)$ shifted π units to the left.

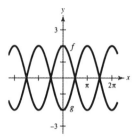

39. Since sine and cosine are cofunctions and x and $x - (\pi/2)$ are complementary, we have

$$\sin x = \cos\left(x - \dfrac{\pi}{2}\right).$$

Period: 2π

Amplitude: 1

41. $f(x) = \cos x$

$g(x) = -\sin\left(x - \dfrac{\pi}{2}\right) = \sin\left(\dfrac{\pi}{2} - x\right) = \cos x$

Thus, $f(x) = g(x)$.

43. $y = -2\sin 6x$; $a = -2$, $b = 6$, $c = 0$

Period: $\dfrac{2\pi}{6} = \dfrac{\pi}{3}$

Amplitude: $|-2| = 2$

Key points: $(0, 0), \left(\dfrac{\pi}{12}, -2\right), \left(\dfrac{\pi}{6}, 0\right), \left(\dfrac{\pi}{4}, 2\right), \left(\dfrac{\pi}{3}, 0\right)$

45. $y = \cos 2\pi x$

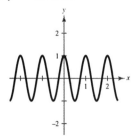

Period: $\dfrac{2\pi}{2\pi} = 1$

Amplitude: 1

Key points: $(1, 0), \left(0, \dfrac{1}{4}\right), \left(-1, \dfrac{1}{2}\right), \left(0, \dfrac{3}{4}\right), (1, 1)$

47. $y = -\sin\dfrac{2\pi x}{3}$; $a = -1, b = \dfrac{2\pi}{3}, c = 0$

Period: $\dfrac{2\pi}{2\pi/3} = 3$

Amplitude: 1

Key points: $(0, 0)$, $\left(\dfrac{3}{4}, -1\right)$, $\left(\dfrac{3}{2}, 0\right)$, $\left(\dfrac{9}{4}, 1\right)$, $(3, 0)$

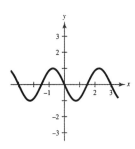

49. $y = \sin\left(x - \dfrac{\pi}{4}\right)$; $a = 1$, $b = 1$, $c = \dfrac{\pi}{4}$

Period: 2π

Amplitude: 1

Shift: Set $x - \dfrac{\pi}{4} = 0$ and $x - \dfrac{\pi}{4} = 2\pi$

$\qquad x = \dfrac{\pi}{4} \qquad\qquad x = \dfrac{9\pi}{4}$

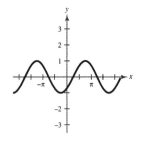

Key points: $\left(\dfrac{\pi}{4}, 0\right)$, $\left(\dfrac{3\pi}{4}, 1\right)$, $\left(\dfrac{5\pi}{4}, 0\right)$, $\left(\dfrac{7\pi}{4}, -1\right)$. $\left(\dfrac{9\pi}{4}, 0\right)$

51. $y = 3\cos(x + \pi)$

Period: 2π

Amplitude: 3

Shift: Set $x + \pi = \;\;0$ and $x + \pi = 2\pi$

$\qquad x = -\pi \qquad\quad x = \pi$

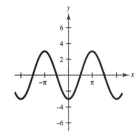

Key points: $(-\pi, 3)$, $\left(-\dfrac{\pi}{2}, 0\right)$, $(0, -3)$, $\left(\dfrac{\pi}{2}, 0\right)$, $(\pi, 3)$

53. $y = \dfrac{1}{10}\cos(60\pi x)$; $a = \dfrac{1}{10}$, $b = 60\pi$, $c = 0$

Period: $\dfrac{2\pi}{60\pi} = \dfrac{1}{30}$

Amplitude: $\dfrac{1}{10}$

Key points: $\left(0, \dfrac{1}{10}\right)$, $\left(\dfrac{1}{120}, 0\right)$, $\left(\dfrac{1}{60}, -\dfrac{1}{10}\right)$, $\left(\dfrac{1}{40}, 0\right)$, $\left(\dfrac{1}{30}, \dfrac{1}{10}\right)$

55. $y = 2 - \sin \dfrac{2\pi x}{3}$

Vertical shift 2 units upward of the graph in Exercise 47.

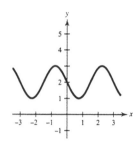

57. $y = 3\cos(x + \pi) - 3$

Vertical shift 3 units downward of the graph in Exercise 51.

59. $y = \dfrac{2}{3}\cos\left(\dfrac{x}{2} - \dfrac{\pi}{4}\right)$; $a = \dfrac{2}{3}$, $b = \dfrac{1}{2}$, $c = \dfrac{\pi}{4}$

Period: 4π

Amplitude: $\dfrac{2}{3}$

$\dfrac{x}{2} - \dfrac{\pi}{4} = 0$ and $\dfrac{x}{2} - \dfrac{\pi}{4} = 2\pi$

$x = \dfrac{\pi}{2}$ $\qquad x = \dfrac{9\pi}{2}$

Key points: $\left(\dfrac{\pi}{2}, \dfrac{2}{3}\right)$, $\left(\dfrac{3\pi}{2}, 0\right)$, $\left(\dfrac{5\pi}{2}, \dfrac{-2}{3}\right)$, $\left(\dfrac{7\pi}{2}, 0\right)$, $\left(\dfrac{9\pi}{2}, \dfrac{2}{3}\right)$

61. $y = -2\sin(4x + \pi)$

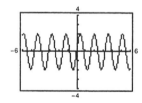

63. $y = \cos\left(2\pi x - \dfrac{\pi}{2}\right) + 1$

65. $y = -0.1\sin\left(\dfrac{\pi x}{10} + \pi\right)$

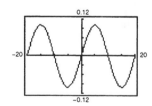

67. $y = 5\cos(\pi - 2x) + 2$

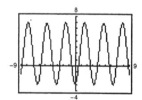

69. $f(x) = a\cos x + d$

Amplitude: $\frac{1}{2}[5 - (-1)] = 3 \implies a = 3$

Vertical shift 2 units upward of
$g(x) = 3\cos x \implies d = 2$.
Thus, $f(x) = 3\cos x + 2 = 2 + 3\cos x$.

71. $f(x) = a\cos x + d$

Amplitude: $\frac{1}{2}[8 - 0] = 4$

Since $f(x)$ is the graph of $g(x) = 4\cos x$ reflected about the x-axis and shifted vertically 4 units upward, we have $a = -4$ and $d = 4$.

Thus, $f(x) = -4\cos x + 4$.

73. $y = a \sin(bx - c)$

Amplitude: $|a| = |3|$ Since the graph is reflected about the x-axis, we have $a = -3$.

Period: $\dfrac{2\pi}{b} = \pi \implies b = 2$

Phase shift: $c = 0$

Thus, $y = -3 \sin 2x$.

75. $y = a \sin(bx + c)$

Amplitude: $a = 1$

Period: $2\pi \implies b = 1$

Phase shift: $bx + c = 0$ when $x = \dfrac{\pi}{4}$

$$(1)\left(\frac{\pi}{4}\right) + c = 0 \implies c = -\frac{\pi}{4}$$

Thus, $y = \sin\left(x - \dfrac{\pi}{4}\right)$.

77. $y_1 = \sin x$

$y_2 = -\dfrac{1}{2}$

In the interval $[-2\pi, 2\pi]$, $\sin x = -\dfrac{1}{2}$ when

$x = -\dfrac{5\pi}{6}, -\dfrac{\pi}{6}, \dfrac{7\pi}{6}, \dfrac{11\pi}{6}$.

79. $y_1 = \cos x$

$y_2 = \dfrac{\sqrt{2}}{2}$

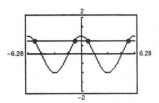

In the interval $[-2\pi, 2\pi]$, $\cos x = \dfrac{\sqrt{2}}{2}$ when

$x = \pm\dfrac{\pi}{4}, \pm\dfrac{7\pi}{4}$.

81. (a) $h(x) = \cos^2 x$ is even.

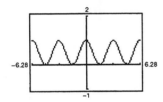

(b) $g(x) = \sin^2 x$ is even.

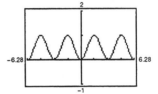

83. $y = 0.85 \sin \dfrac{\pi t}{3}$

(a) Time for one cycle = one period $= \dfrac{2\pi}{\pi/3} = 6$ sec

(b) Cycles per min $= \dfrac{60}{6} = 10$ cycles per min

(c) Amplitude: 0.85

Period: 6

Key points: $(0, 0)$, $\left(\dfrac{3}{2}, 0.85\right)$, $(3, 0)$, $\left(\dfrac{9}{2}, -0.85\right)$, $(6, 0)$

85. $y = 0.001 \sin 880\pi t$

(a) Period: $\dfrac{2\pi}{880\pi} = \dfrac{1}{440}$ seconds

(b) $f = \dfrac{1}{p} = 440$ cycles per second

87. $S = 22.3 - 3.4 \cos \dfrac{\pi t}{6}$, $1 \le t \le 12$

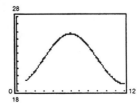

89. (a) $C(t) = 56.35 + 27.35 \sin\left(\dfrac{\pi t}{6} + 4.19\right)$

(b)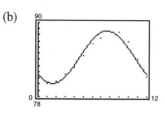

The model is a good fit for most months.

(c)

The model is a good fit.

(d) Use the constant term of each model to estimate the average annual temperature.

Honolulu: 84.40°

Chicago: 58.50°

(e) Each model has a period of 12. This corresponds to the 12 months in a year.

(f) Chicago has a greater variability in temperatures during the year. The amplitude of each model indicates this variability.

91. (a) $\sin x \approx x - \dfrac{x^3}{3!} + \dfrac{x^5}{5!}$

Near $x = 0$ the graphs are approximately the same. They appear to coincide from $-\pi/2$ to $\pi/2$.

(b) $\cos x \approx 1 - \dfrac{x^2}{2!} + \dfrac{x^4}{4!}$

Near $x = 0$ the graphs are approximately the same. They appear to coincide from $-\pi/2$ to $\pi/2$.

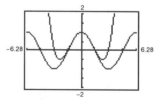

(c) $\sin x \approx x - \dfrac{x^3}{3!} + \dfrac{x^5}{5!} - \dfrac{x^7}{7!}$

$\cos x \approx 1 - \dfrac{x^2}{2!} + \dfrac{x^4}{4!} - \dfrac{x^6}{6!}$

The accuracy is increased.

93. (a)

Day (300 ↔ October 21)

(b) $y = \dfrac{1}{2} + \dfrac{1}{2} \sin\left[\dfrac{\pi}{15}(t - 303)\right]$

(c)

Day (300 ↔ October 21)

The model is a good fit.

(d) $y(356) \approx 0.003 \approx 0$

95. $\log_2\left[x^2(x - 3)\right] = \log_2 x^2 + \log_2(x - 3)$

$\qquad\qquad\qquad\quad = 2\log_2 x + \log_2(x - 3)$

97. $\ln\sqrt{\dfrac{z}{z^2 + 1}} = \dfrac{1}{2}\ln\left(\dfrac{z}{z^2 + 1}\right) = \dfrac{1}{2}\left[\ln z - \ln(z^2 + 1)\right]$

$\qquad\qquad\qquad\qquad\qquad\qquad = \dfrac{1}{2}\ln z - \dfrac{1}{2}\ln(z^2 + 1)$

Section 4.6   Graphs of Other Trigonometric Functions

- ■ You should be able to graph

  $\qquad y = a\tan(bx - c) \qquad\qquad y = a\cot(bx - c)$

  $\qquad y = a\sec(bx - c) \qquad\qquad y = a\csc(bx - c)$

- ■ When graphing $y = a\sec(bx - c)$ or $y = a\csc(bx - c)$ you should first graph $y = a\cos(bx - c)$ or $y = a\sin(bx - c)$ because

  (a) The x-intercepts of sine and cosine are the vertical asymptotes of cosecant and secant.

  (b) The maximums of sine and cosine are the local minimums of cosecant and secant.

  (c) The minimums of sine and cosine are the local maximums of cosecant and secant.

- ■ You should be able to graph using a damping factor.

Solutions to Odd-Numbered Exercises

1. $y = \sec \dfrac{x}{2}$

Period: $\dfrac{2\pi}{1/2} = 4\pi$

Matches graph (g).

3. $y = \tan 2x$

Period: $\dfrac{\pi}{2}$

Matches graph (f).

5. $y = \cot \dfrac{\pi x}{2}$

Period: $\dfrac{\pi}{\pi/2} = 2$

Matches graph (b).

7. $y = -\csc x$

Period: 2π

Matches graph (e).

9. $y = \dfrac{1}{3}\tan x$

Period: π

Two consecutive asymptotes:

$$x = -\dfrac{\pi}{2} \text{ and } x = \dfrac{\pi}{2}$$

x	$-\dfrac{\pi}{4}$	0	$\dfrac{\pi}{4}$
y	$-\dfrac{1}{3}$	0	$\dfrac{1}{3}$

11. $y = \tan 2x$

Period: $\dfrac{\pi}{2}$

Two consecutive asymptotes: $2x = -\dfrac{\pi}{2} \Rightarrow x = -\dfrac{\pi}{4}$

$\qquad\qquad\qquad\qquad\qquad 2x = \dfrac{\pi}{2} \Rightarrow x = \dfrac{\pi}{4}$

x	$-\dfrac{\pi}{8}$	0	$\dfrac{\pi}{8}$
y	-1	0	1

13. $y = -\dfrac{1}{2}\sec x$

Graph $y = -\dfrac{1}{2}\cos x$ first.

Period: 2π

One cycle: 0 to 2π

15. $y = \sec \pi x$

Graph $y = \cos \pi x$ first.

Period: $\dfrac{2\pi}{\pi} = 2$

One cycle: 0 to 2

17. $y = \sec \pi x - 1$

Reflect the graph in Exercise 15 about the x-axis and then shift it vertically down one unit.

19. $y = \csc \dfrac{x}{2}$

Graph $y = \sin \dfrac{x}{2}$ first.

Period: $\dfrac{2\pi}{1/2} = 4\pi$

One cycle: 0 to 4π

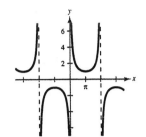

21. $y = \cot \dfrac{x}{2}$

Period: $\dfrac{\pi}{1/2} = 2\pi$

Two consecutive asymptotes: $\dfrac{x}{2} = 0 \implies x = 0$

$\dfrac{x}{2} = \pi \implies x = 2\pi$

x	$\dfrac{\pi}{2}$	π	$\dfrac{3\pi}{2}$
y	1	0	-1

23. $y = \dfrac{1}{2} \sec 2x$

Graph $y = \dfrac{1}{2} \cos 2x$ first.

Period: $\dfrac{2\pi}{2} = \pi$

One cycle: 0 to π

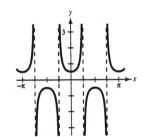

25. $y = \tan \dfrac{\pi x}{4}$

Period: $\dfrac{\pi}{\pi/4} = 4$

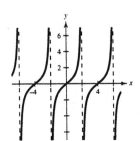

Two consecutive asymptotes: $\dfrac{\pi x}{4} = -\dfrac{\pi}{2} \implies x = -2$

$\dfrac{\pi x}{4} = \dfrac{\pi}{2} \implies x = 2$

x	-1	0	1
y	-1	0	1

27. $y = \csc(\pi - x)$

   Graph $y = \sin(\pi - x)$ first.

   Period: 2π

   Shift: Set $\pi - x = 0$ and $\pi - x = 2\pi$

   $\qquad x = \pi \qquad\qquad x = -\pi$

29. $y = \dfrac{1}{4}\csc\left(x + \dfrac{\pi}{4}\right)$

   Graph $y = \dfrac{1}{4}\sin\left(x + \dfrac{\pi}{4}\right)$ first.

   Period: 2π

   Shift: Set $x + \dfrac{\pi}{4} = 0$ and $x + \dfrac{\pi}{4} = 2\pi$

   $\qquad x = -\dfrac{\pi}{4}$ to $\qquad x = \dfrac{7\pi}{4}$

31. $y = \tan\dfrac{x}{3}$

33. $y = -2\sec 4x$

   $= \dfrac{-2}{\cos 4x}$

35. $y = \tan\left(x - \dfrac{\pi}{4}\right)$

37. $y = \dfrac{1}{4}\cot\left(x - \dfrac{\pi}{2}\right)$

   $= \dfrac{1}{4\tan(x - \pi/2)}$

39. $y = 2\sec(2x - \pi)$

   $y = \dfrac{2}{\cos(2x - \pi)}$

41. $\tan x = 1$

$$x = -\frac{7\pi}{4}, \ -\frac{3\pi}{4}, \frac{\pi}{4}, \frac{5\pi}{4}$$

43. $\sec x = -2$

$$x = \pm\frac{2\pi}{3}, \ \pm\frac{4\pi}{3}$$

45. Thus graph of $f(x) = \sec x$ has y-axis symmetry. Thus, the function is even.

47. As $x \rightarrow \dfrac{\pi}{2}$ from the left, $f(x) = \tan x \rightarrow \infty$.

As $x \rightarrow \dfrac{\pi}{2}$ from the right, $f(x) = \tan x \rightarrow -\infty$.

49. $f(x) = 2 \sin x$

$g(x) = \dfrac{1}{2} \csc x$

(a)

(b) $f > g$ on the interval, $\dfrac{\pi}{6} < x < \dfrac{5\pi}{6}$

(c) As $x \rightarrow \pi, f(x) = 2 \sin x \rightarrow 0$ and

$g(x) = \dfrac{1}{2} \csc x \rightarrow \pm\infty$ since $g(x)$ is the reciprocal of $f(x)$.

51. $y_1 = \sin x \csc x$ and $y_2 = 1$

$$\sin x \csc x = \sin x \left(\frac{1}{\sin x}\right) = 1, \sin x \neq 0$$

53. $y_1 = \dfrac{\cos x}{\sin x}$ and $y_2 = \cot x = \dfrac{1}{\tan x}$

$$\cot x = \frac{\cos x}{\sin x}$$

55. $f(x) = x \cos x$

As $x \rightarrow 0, f(x) \rightarrow 0$.

Matches graph (d).

57. $g(x) = |x| \sin x$

As $x \rightarrow 0, g(x) \rightarrow 0$.

Matches graph (b).

59. $f(x) = \sin x + \cos\left(x + \dfrac{\pi}{2}\right), g(x) = 0$

$f(x) = g(x)$ The graph is the line $y = 0$.

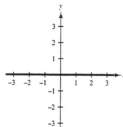

61. $f(x) = \sin^2 x, g(x) = \dfrac{1}{2}(1 - \cos 2x)$

$f(x) = g(x)$

63. $f(x) = 2^{-x/4} \cos \pi x$

$-2^{-x/4} \leq f(x) \leq 2^{-2x/4}$

The damping factor is $y = 2^{-x/4}$.

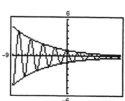

65. $g(x) = e^{-x^2/2} \sin x$

$-e^{-x^2/2} \leq g(x) \leq e^{-x^2/2}$

The damping factor is

$y = e^{-x^2/2}$.

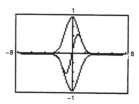

67. $\tan x = \dfrac{5}{d}$

$d = \dfrac{5}{\tan x} = 5 \cot x$

69. As the predator population increases, the number of prey decrease. When the number of prey is small, the number of predators decreases.

71. (a)

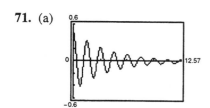

(b) The displacement function is a damped sine wave. It approaches 0 as t increases.

73. $\tan x \approx x + \dfrac{2x^3}{3!} + \dfrac{16x^5}{5!}$

The graphs are approximately the same when x is near zero. As x gets larger, the graphs are further apart.

75. (a) $y_1 = \dfrac{4}{\pi}\left(\sin \pi x + \dfrac{1}{3}\sin 3\pi x\right)$

$y_2 = \dfrac{4}{\pi}\left(\sin \pi x + \dfrac{1}{3}\sin 3\pi x + \dfrac{1}{5}\sin 5\pi x\right)$

(b) $y_3 = \dfrac{4}{\pi}\left(\sin \pi x + \dfrac{1}{3}\sin 3\pi x + \dfrac{1}{5}\sin 5\pi x + \dfrac{1}{7}\sin 7\pi x\right)$

(c) $y_4 = \dfrac{4}{\pi}\left(\sin \pi x + \dfrac{1}{3}\sin 3\pi x + \dfrac{1}{5}\sin 5\pi x + \dfrac{1}{7}\sin 7\pi x + \dfrac{1}{9}\sin 9\pi x\right)$

77. $y = \dfrac{6}{x} + \cos x, \ x > 0$

As $x \to 0, \ y \to \infty$.

79. $g(x) = \dfrac{\sin x}{x}$

As $x \to 0, \ g(x) \to 1$.

81. $f(x) = \sin \dfrac{1}{x}$

As $x \to 0, f(x)$ oscillates between -1 and 1.

83. $e^{2x} = 54$

$2x = \ln 54$

$x = \dfrac{\ln 54}{2} \approx 1.994$

85. $\ln(x^2 + 1) = 3.2$

$x^2 + 1 = e^{3.2}$

$x^2 = e^{3.2} - 1$

$x = \pm\sqrt{e^{3.2} - 1} \approx \pm 4.851$

Section 4.7 Inverse Trigonometric Functions

■ You should know the definitions, domains, and ranges of $y = \arcsin x$, $y = \arccos x$, and $y = \arctan x$.

Function	Domain	Range
$y = \arcsin x \implies x = \sin y$	$-1 \le x \le 1$	$-\dfrac{\pi}{2} \le y \le \dfrac{\pi}{2}$
$y = \arccos x \implies x = \cos y$	$-1 \le x \le 1$	$0 \le y \le \pi$
$y = \arctan x \implies x = \tan y$	$-\infty < x < \infty$	$-\dfrac{\pi}{2} < x < \dfrac{\pi}{2}$

■ You should know the inverse properties of the inverse trigonometric functions.

$$\sin(\arcsin x) = x \quad \text{and} \quad \arcsin(\sin y) = y, \; -\frac{\pi}{2} \le y \le \frac{\pi}{2}$$

$$\cos(\arccos x) = x \quad \text{and} \quad \arccos(\cos y) = y, \; 0 \le y \le \pi$$

$$\tan(\arctan x) = x \quad \text{and} \quad \arctan(\tan y) = y, \; -\frac{\pi}{2} < y < \frac{\pi}{2}$$

■ You should be able to use the triangle technique to convert trigonometric functions of inverse trigonometric functions into algebraic expressions.

Solutions to Odd-Numbered Exercises

1. False, $\dfrac{5\pi}{6}$ is not in the range of the arcsine function.

3. $y = \arcsin \dfrac{1}{2} \implies \sin y = \dfrac{1}{2}$ for $-\dfrac{\pi}{2} \le y \le \dfrac{\pi}{2} \implies y = \dfrac{\pi}{6}$

5. $y = \arccos \dfrac{1}{2} \implies \cos y = \dfrac{1}{2}$ for $0 \le y \le \pi \implies y = \dfrac{\pi}{3}$

7. $y = \arctan \dfrac{\sqrt{3}}{3} \implies \tan y = \dfrac{\sqrt{3}}{3}$ for $-\dfrac{\pi}{2} < y < \dfrac{\pi}{2} \implies y = \dfrac{\pi}{6}$

9. $y = \arccos\left(-\dfrac{\sqrt{3}}{2}\right) \implies \cos y = -\dfrac{\sqrt{3}}{2}$ for $0 \le y \le \pi \implies y = \dfrac{5\pi}{6}$

11. $y = \arctan\left(-\sqrt{3}\right) \implies \tan y = -\sqrt{3}$ for $-\dfrac{\pi}{2} < y < \dfrac{\pi}{2} \implies y = -\dfrac{\pi}{3}$

13. $y = \arccos\left(-\dfrac{1}{2}\right) \implies \cos y = -\dfrac{1}{2}$ for $0 \le y \le \pi \implies y = \dfrac{2\pi}{3}$

15. $y = \arcsin \dfrac{\sqrt{3}}{2} \implies \sin y = \dfrac{\sqrt{3}}{2}$ for $-\dfrac{\pi}{2} \le y \le \dfrac{\pi}{2} \implies y = \dfrac{\pi}{3}$

17. $y = \arctan 0 \implies \tan y = 0$ for $-\dfrac{\pi}{2} < y < \dfrac{\pi}{2} \implies y = 0$

19. $\arccos 0.28 = \cos^{-1} 0.28 \approx 1.29$

21. $\arcsin(-0.75) = \sin^{-1}(-0.75) \approx -0.85$

23. $\arctan(-3) = \tan^{-1}(-3) \approx -1.25$

25. $\arcsin 0.31 = \sin^{-1} 0.31 \approx 0.32$

27. $\arccos(-0.41) = \cos^{-1}(-0.41) \approx 1.99$

29. $\arctan 0.92 = \tan^{-1} 0.92 \approx 0.74$

31. This is the graph of $y = \arctan x$. The coordinates are $\left(-\sqrt{3}, -\dfrac{\pi}{3}\right)$, $\left(-\dfrac{1}{\sqrt{3}}, -\dfrac{\pi}{6}\right)$, and $\left(1, \dfrac{\pi}{4}\right)$.

33. $f(x) = \tan x$ and $g(x) = \arctan x$

   Graph $y_1 = \tan x$

   $y_2 = \tan^{-1} x$

   $y_3 = x$

35. $\tan\theta = \dfrac{x}{4}$

   $\theta = \arctan \dfrac{x}{4}$

37. $\sin\theta = \dfrac{x + 2}{5}$

   $\theta = \arcsin\left(\dfrac{x + 2}{5}\right)$

39. $\sin(\arcsin 0.3) = 0.3$

41. $\cos[\arccos(-0.1)] = -0.1$

43. $\arcsin(\sin 3\pi) = \arcsin(0) = 0$

Note: 3π is not in the range of the arcsine function.

45. Let $y = \arctan \dfrac{3}{4}$. Then,

   $\tan y = \dfrac{3}{4},\ 0 < y < \dfrac{\pi}{2}$

   and $\sin y = \dfrac{3}{5}$.

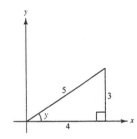

47. Let $y = \arctan 2$. Then,

   $\tan y = 2 = \dfrac{2}{1},\ 0 < y < \dfrac{\pi}{2}$

   and $\cos y = \dfrac{1}{\sqrt{5}} = \dfrac{\sqrt{5}}{5}$.

49. Let $y = \arcsin \dfrac{5}{13}$. Then,

$$\sin y = \frac{5}{13}, \quad 0 < y < \frac{\pi}{2}$$

and $\cos y = \dfrac{12}{13}$.

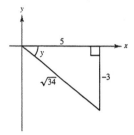

51. Let $y = \arctan\left(-\dfrac{3}{5}\right)$. Then,

$$\tan y = -\frac{3}{5}, \quad -\frac{\pi}{2} < y < 0$$

and $\sec y = \dfrac{\sqrt{34}}{5}$.

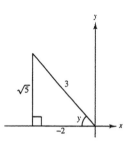

53. Let $y = \arccos\left(-\dfrac{2}{3}\right)$. Then,

$$\cos y = -\frac{2}{3}, \quad \frac{\pi}{2} < y < \pi$$

and $\sin y = \dfrac{\sqrt{5}}{3}$.

55. Let $y = \arctan x$. Then,

$$\tan y = x = \frac{x}{1}$$

and $\cot y = \dfrac{1}{x}$.

57. Let $y = \arcsin(2x)$. Then,

$$\sin y = 2x = \frac{2x}{1}$$

and $\cos y = \sqrt{1 - 4x^2}$.

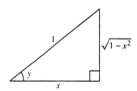

59. Let $y = \arccos x$. Then,

$$\cos y = x = \frac{x}{1}$$

and $\sin y = \sqrt{1 - x^2}$.

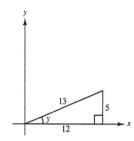

61. Let $y = \arccos\left(\dfrac{x}{3}\right)$. Then,

$$\cos y = \frac{x}{3}$$

and $\tan y = \dfrac{\sqrt{9-x^2}}{x}$.

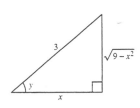

63. Let $y = \arctan \dfrac{x}{\sqrt{2}}$. Then,

$$\tan y = \frac{x}{\sqrt{2}}$$

and $\csc y = \dfrac{\sqrt{x^2+2}}{x}$.

65. $f(x) = \sin(\arctan 2x)$, $g(x) = \dfrac{2x}{\sqrt{1-4x^2}}$

Let $y = \arctan 2x$. Then,

$$\tan y = 2x = \frac{2x}{1}$$

and $\sin y = \dfrac{2x}{\sqrt{1+4x^2}}$.

$$g(x) = \frac{2x}{\sqrt{1+4x^2}} = f(x)$$

The graph has horizontal asymptotes at $y = \pm 1$.

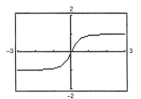

67. Let $y = \arctan \dfrac{9}{x}$. Then,

$$\tan y = \frac{9}{x} \text{ and } \sin y = \frac{9}{\sqrt{x^2+81}}.$$

Thus, $\arcsin y = \dfrac{9}{\sqrt{x^2+81}}$.

69. Let $y = \arccos \dfrac{3}{\sqrt{x^2-2x+10}}$. Then,

$$\cos y = \frac{3}{\sqrt{x^2-2x+10}} = \frac{3}{\sqrt{(x-1)^2+9}}$$

and $\sin y = \dfrac{|x-1|}{\sqrt{(x-1)^2+9}}$.

Thus, $\arcsin y = \dfrac{|x-1|}{\sqrt{(x-1)^2+9}} = \arcsin \dfrac{|x-1|}{\sqrt{x^2-2x+10}}$.

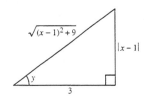

71. $y = 2 \arccos x$

Domain: $-1 \le x \le 1$

Range: $0 \le y \le 2\pi$

Vertical stretch of $f(x) = \arccos x$

73. The graph of $f(x) = \arcsin(x - 1)$ is a horizontal translation of the graph of $y = \arcsin x$ by one unit.

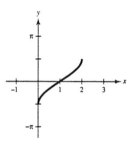

75. $f(x) = \arctan 2x$

Domain: all real numbers

Range: $-\dfrac{\pi}{2} < y < \dfrac{\pi}{2}$

77. $h(v) = \tan(\arccos v) = \dfrac{\sqrt{1 - v^2}}{v}$

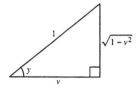

Domain: $-1 \le v \le 1,\ v \ne 0$

Range: all real numbers

79. $f(t) = 3\cos 2t + 3\sin 2t = \sqrt{3^2 + 3^2}\,\sin\!\left(3t + \arctan\dfrac{3}{3}\right)$

$$= 3\sqrt{2}\,\sin(3t + \arctan 1)$$

$$= 3\sqrt{2}\,\sin\!\left(3t + \dfrac{\pi}{4}\right)$$

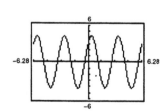

The graphs are the same.

81. $f(x) = \sin x,\ f^{-1}(x) = \arcsin x$

(a) $f \circ f^{-1} = f(f^{-1}(x)) = f(\arcsin x) = \sin(\arcsin x)$

$f^{-1} \circ f = f^{-1}(f(x)) = f^{-1}(\sin x) = \arcsin(\sin x)$

 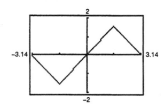

(b) Both the domain and range of $f \circ f^{-1} = \sin(\arcsin x)$ are the intervals of $[-1, 1]$.

The domain of $f^{-1} \circ f$ is all real numbers. The range is the interval $\left[-\dfrac{\pi}{2}, \dfrac{\pi}{2}\right]$.

Neither graph is the line $y = x$ because of these domain/range restrictions.

83. (a) $\sin\theta = \dfrac{10}{s}$

$\theta = \arcsin \dfrac{10}{s}$

(b) $s = 48$: $\theta = \arcsin \dfrac{10}{48} \approx 0.21$

$s = 24$: $\theta = \arcsin \dfrac{10}{24} \approx 0.43$

85. $\beta = \arctan \dfrac{3x}{x^2 + 4}$

(a)

(b) β is maximum when $x = 2$.

(c) The graph has a horizontal asymptote at $\beta = 0$. As x increases, β decreases.

87. (a) $\tan\theta = \dfrac{5}{x}$

$\theta = \arctan \dfrac{5}{x}$

(b) $x = 10$: $\theta = \arctan \dfrac{5}{10} \approx 26.6°$

$x = 3$: $\theta = \arctan \dfrac{5}{3} \approx 59.0°$

89. $y = \text{arccot } x$ if and only if $\cot y = x$.

Domain: $-\infty < x < \infty$

Range: $0 < x < \pi$

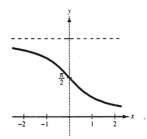

91. $y = \text{arccsc } x$ if and only if $\csc y = x$.

Domain: $(-\infty, -1] \cup [1, \infty)$

Range: $\left[-\dfrac{\pi}{2}, 0\right) \cup \left(0, \dfrac{\pi}{2}\right]$

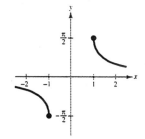

93. Let $y = \arcsin(-x)$. Then,

$$\sin y = -x$$
$$-\sin y = x$$
$$\sin(-y) = x$$
$$-y = \arcsin x$$
$$y = -\arcsin x.$$

Therefore, $\arcsin(-x) = -\arcsin x$.

95.
$$y = \pi - \arccos x$$
$$\cos y = \cos(\pi - \arccos x)$$
$$\cos y = \cos \pi \cos(\arccos x) + \sin \pi \sin(\arccos x)$$
$$\cos y = -x$$
$$y = \arccos(-x)$$

97. Let $\alpha = \arcsin x$ and $\beta = \arccos x$, then $\sin \alpha = x$ and $\cos \beta = x$. Thus, $\sin \alpha = \cos \beta$ which implies that α and β are complementary angles and we have

$$\alpha + \beta = \frac{\pi}{2}$$
$$\arcsin x + \arccos x = \frac{\pi}{2}.$$

99. Now: Cost $= 23{,}500 + 725 = \$24{,}225$

Wait a month: Cost $= 23{,}500\,(1.04) = \$24{,}440$

The customer should buy now and save $\$215$.

101. Let $x =$ the number of people presently in the group. Each person's share is now $\dfrac{250{,}000}{x}$.

If two more join the group, each person's share would then be $\dfrac{250{,}000}{x+2}$.

$$\begin{array}{l}\text{Share per person with} \\ \text{two more people}\end{array} = \begin{array}{l}\text{Original share} \\ \text{per person}\end{array} - 6250$$

$$\frac{250{,}000}{x+2} = \frac{250{,}000}{x} - 6250$$
$$250{,}000x = 250{,}000(x+2) - 6250x(x+2)$$
$$250{,}000x = 250{,}000x + 500{,}000 - 6250x^2 - 12500x$$

$$6250x^2 + 12500x - 500{,}000 = 0$$
$$6250(x^2 + 2x - 80) = 0$$
$$6250(x+10)(x-8) = 0$$
$$x = -10 \quad \text{or} \quad x = 8$$

Not possible

There were 8 people in the original group.

Section 4.8   Applications and Models

Solutions to Odd-Numbered Exercises

- ■ You should be able to solve right triangles.
- ■ You should be able to solve right triangle applications.
- ■ You should be able to solve applications of simple harmonic motion.

---

1. Given: $A = 20°$, $b = 10$

$\tan A = \dfrac{a}{b} \implies a = b \tan A = 10 \tan 20° \approx 3.64$

$\cos A = \dfrac{a}{c} \implies c = \dfrac{a}{\cos A} = \dfrac{10}{\cos 20°} \approx 10.64$

$B = 90° - 20° = 70°$

3. Given: $B = 71°$, $b = 24$

$\tan B = \dfrac{b}{a} \implies a = \dfrac{b}{\tan B} = \dfrac{24}{\tan 71°} \approx 8.26$

$\sin B = \dfrac{b}{c} \implies c = \dfrac{b}{\sin B} = \dfrac{24}{\sin 71°} \approx 25.38$

$A = 90° - 71° = 19°$

5. Given: $a = 6$, $b = 10$

$c^2 = a^2 + b^2 \implies c = \sqrt{36 + 100}$
$\qquad\qquad\qquad\quad = 2\sqrt{34} \approx 11.66$

$\tan A = \dfrac{a}{b} = \dfrac{6}{10} \implies A = \arctan \dfrac{3}{5} \approx 30.96°$

$B = 90° - 30.96° = 59.04°$

7. $b = 16$, $c = 52$

$a = \sqrt{52^2 - 16^2}$
$\quad = \sqrt{2448} = 12\sqrt{17} \approx 49.48$

$\cos A = \dfrac{16}{52}$

$\quad A = \arccos \dfrac{16}{52} \approx 72.08°$

$\quad B = 90° - 72.08° \approx 17.92°$

9. $A = 12°15'$, $c = 430.5$

$B = 90° - 12°15' = 77°45'$

$\sin 12°15' = \dfrac{a}{430.5}$

$\qquad a = 430.5 \sin 12°15' \approx 91.34$

$\cos 12°15' = \dfrac{b}{430.5}$

$\qquad b = 430.5 \cos 12°15' \approx 420.70$

11. $\tan \theta = \dfrac{h}{1/2\,b} \implies h = \dfrac{1}{2} b \tan \theta$

$\qquad h = \dfrac{1}{2}(4) \tan 52° \approx 2.56$ in.

13. $\tan 30° = \dfrac{60}{x}$

$\dfrac{1}{\sqrt{3}} = \dfrac{60}{x}$

$x = 60\sqrt{3}$

≈ 103.9 feet

15. $\sin 74° = \dfrac{h}{16}$

$16 \sin 74° = h$

$h \approx 15.4$ feet

17. (a)

(b) Let the height of the church $= x$ and the height of the church and steeple $= y$. Then,

$$\tan 35° = \dfrac{x}{50} \quad \text{and} \quad \tan 47°40' = \dfrac{y}{50}$$

$x = 50 \tan 35°$ and $y = 50 \tan 47°40'$

$h = y - x = 50 \left(\tan 47°40' - \tan 35°\right).$

(c) $h \approx 19.9$ feet

19. $\sin 34° = \dfrac{x}{4000}$

$x = 4000 \sin 34°$

≈ 2236.8 feet

21. $\tan \theta = \dfrac{75}{50}$

$\theta = \arctan \dfrac{3}{2} \approx 56.3°$

23. $\sin \theta = \dfrac{4000}{4150}$

$\theta = \arcsin \left(\dfrac{4000}{4150}\right)$

$\theta \approx 74.5°$

$\alpha = 90° - 74.5° = 15.5°$

25. Since the airplane speed is

$$\left(275\dfrac{\text{ft}}{\text{sec}}\right)\left(60\dfrac{\text{sec}}{\text{min}}\right) = 16,500\dfrac{\text{ft}}{\text{min}},$$

after one minute its distance travelled in 16,500 feet.

$\sin 18° = \dfrac{a}{16,500}$

$a = 16,500 \sin 18°$

≈ 5099 ft

27. $\sin 10.5° = \dfrac{x}{4}$

$x = 4 \sin 10.5°$

≈ 0.73 mile

29. The plane has traveled 1.5 (550)= 825 miles.

$$\sin 38° = \frac{a}{825} \implies a \approx 508 \text{ miles north}$$

$$\cos 38° = \frac{b}{825} \implies b \approx 650 \text{ miles east}$$

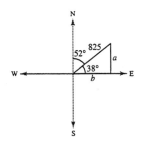

31. $\theta = 32°, \quad \phi = 68°$

(a) $\alpha = 90° - 32° = 58°$

Bearing from A to C: N 58° E

(b) $\quad \beta = \theta = 32°$

$\quad \gamma = 90° - \phi = 22°$

$\quad C = \beta + \gamma = 54°$

$\quad \tan C = \dfrac{d}{50} \implies \tan 54° = \dfrac{d}{50} \implies d \approx 68.82 \text{ meters}$

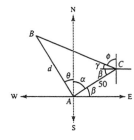

33. $\tan \theta = \frac{45}{30} \implies \theta \approx 56.3°$

Bearing: N 56.3° W

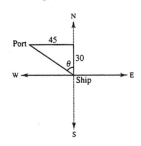

35. $\tan 6.5° = \dfrac{350}{d} \implies d \approx 3071.91 \text{ ft}$

$\tan 4° = \dfrac{350}{D} \implies D \approx 5005.23 \text{ ft}$

Distance between ships: $D - d \approx 1933.32 \text{ ft}$

37.
$$\tan 57° = \frac{a}{x} \implies x = a \cot 57°$$

$$\tan 16° = \frac{a}{x + (55/6)}$$

$$\tan 16° = \frac{a}{a \cot 57° + (55/6)}$$

$$\cot 16° = \frac{a \cot 57° + (55/6)}{a}$$

$$a \cot 16° - a \cot 57° = \frac{55}{6} \implies a \approx 3.23 \text{ miles}$$

$$\approx 17,054 \text{ ft}$$

39. L_1: $3x - 2y = 5 \implies y = \frac{3}{2}x - \frac{5}{2} \implies m_1 = \frac{3}{2}$

L_2: $x - y = 1 \implies y = -x + 1 \implies m_2 = -1$

$\tan\alpha = \left| \dfrac{-1 - \frac{3}{2}}{1 + (-1)\left(\frac{3}{2}\right)} \right| = \left| \dfrac{-\frac{5}{2}}{-\frac{1}{2}} \right| = 5$

$\alpha = \arctan 5 \approx 78.7°$

41. The diagonal of the base has a length of $\sqrt{a^2 + a^2} = \sqrt{2}a$.

Now, we have $\tan\theta = \dfrac{a}{\sqrt{2}a} = \dfrac{1}{\sqrt{2}}$

$\theta = \arctan\dfrac{1}{\sqrt{2}}$

$\theta \approx 35.3°$.

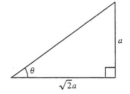

43. $\cos 30° = \dfrac{b}{r}$

$b = \cos 30° r$

$b = \dfrac{\sqrt{3}r}{2}$

$y = 2b = 2\left(\dfrac{\sqrt{3}r}{2}\right) = \sqrt{3}r$

45. $\sin 36° = \dfrac{d}{25} \implies d \approx 14.69$

Length of side: $2d \approx 29.38$ inches

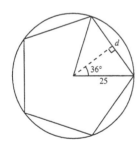

47. $\tan 35° = \dfrac{a}{10}$

$a = 10 \tan 35° \approx 7$

$\cos 33° = \dfrac{10}{c}$

$c = \dfrac{10}{\cos 35°} \approx 12.2$

49. $d = 4 \cos 8\pi t$

(a) Maximum displacement = amplitude = 4

(b) Frequency $= \dfrac{\omega}{2\pi} = \dfrac{8\pi}{2\pi}$

$\qquad = 4$ cycles per unit of time

(c) $8\pi t = \dfrac{\pi}{2} \implies t = \dfrac{1}{16}$

51. $d = \dfrac{1}{16} \sin 120\pi t$

(a) Maximum displacement = amplitude $= \dfrac{1}{16}$

(b) Frequency $= \dfrac{\omega}{2\pi} = \dfrac{120\pi}{2\pi}$

$\qquad = 60$ cycles per unit of time

(c) $120\pi t = \pi \implies t = \dfrac{1}{120}$

53. $d = 0$ when $t = 0$, $a = 4$, Period $= 2$

Use $d = a \sin \omega t$ since $d = 0$ when $t = 0$.

$$\frac{2\pi}{\omega} = 2 \implies \omega = \pi$$

Thus, $d = 4 \sin \pi t$.

55. $d = 3$ when $t = 0$, $a = 3$, Period $= 1.5$

Use $d = a \cos \omega t$ since $d = 3$ when $t = 0$.

$$\frac{2\pi}{\omega} = 1.5 \implies \omega = \frac{4\pi}{3}$$

Thus, $d = 3 \cos\left(\frac{4\pi}{3}t\right) = 3 \cos\left(\frac{4\pi t}{3}\right)$.

57. $d = a \sin \omega t$

$$\text{Period} = \frac{2\pi}{\omega} = \frac{1}{\text{frequency}}$$

$$\frac{2\pi}{\omega} = \frac{1}{264}$$

$$\omega = 2\pi(264) = 528\pi$$

59. $y = \frac{1}{4} \cos 16t$, $t > 0$

(a)

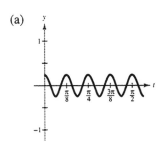

(b) Period: $\dfrac{2\pi}{16} = \dfrac{\pi}{8}$

(c) $\dfrac{1}{4} \cos 16t = 0$ when $16t = \dfrac{\pi}{2} \implies t = \dfrac{\pi}{32}$

61. (a) & (b)

Base 1	Base 2	Altitude	Area
8	$8 + 16 \cos 10°$	$8 \sin 10°$	22.1
8	$8 + 16 \cos 20°$	$8 \sin 20°$	42.5
8	$8 + 16 \cos 30°$	$8 \sin 30°$	59.7
8	$8 + 16 \cos 40°$	$8 \sin 40°$	72.7
8	$8 + 16 \cos 50°$	$8 \sin 50°$	80.5
8	$8 + 16 \cos 60°$	$8 \sin 60°$	83.1
8	$8 + 16 \cos 70°$	$8 \sin 70°$	80.7

The maximum occurs when $\theta = 60°$ and is approximately 83.1 square feet.

(c) $A(\theta) = [8 + (8 + 16 \cos \theta)]\left[\dfrac{8 \sin \theta}{2}\right]$

$ = (16 + 16 \cos \theta)(4 \sin \theta)$

$ = 64 (1 + \cos \theta)(\sin \theta)$

(d)

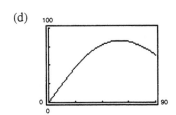

The maximum occurs when $\theta = \dfrac{\pi}{3} = 60°$.

63. (a)

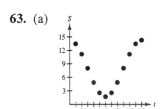

(b) $a = \dfrac{1}{2}(14.3 - 1.7) = 6.3$

$$\dfrac{2\pi}{b} = 12 \implies b = \dfrac{\pi}{6}$$

Shift: $d = 14.3 - 6.3 = 8$

$S = d + a \cos bt$

$$S = 8 + 6.3 \cos\left(\dfrac{\pi t}{6}\right)$$

The model is a good fit.

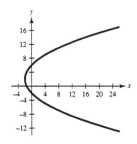

(c) Period: $\dfrac{2\pi}{\pi/6} = 12$

This corresponds to the 12 months in a year. Since the sales of outerwear is seasonal this is reasonable.

(d) The amplitude represents the maximum displacement from average sales of 8 million dollars. Sales are greatest in December (cold weather + Christmas) and least in June.

65. $(y - 2)^2 = 8(x + 2)$

Parabola

Vertex: $(-2, 2)$

$p = 2 > 0,$ opens to the right

67. $\dfrac{x^2}{4} - y^2 = 1$

Hyperbola

Horizontal major axis

Center: $(0, 0)$

Vertices: $(\pm 2, 0)$

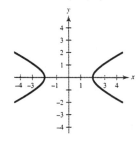

❏ **Review Exercises for Chapter 4**

Solutions to Odd-Numbered Exercises

1. $\theta = \dfrac{11\pi}{4}$

Coterminal angles: $\dfrac{11\pi}{4} - 2\pi = \dfrac{3\pi}{4}$

$\dfrac{3\pi}{4} - 2\pi = -\dfrac{5\pi}{4}$

3. $\theta = -110°$

Coterminal angles: $-110° + 360° = 250°$

$-110° - 360° = -470°$

5. $135° \, 16' \, 45'' = \left(135 + \frac{16}{60} + \frac{45}{3600}\right)° \approx 135.28°$

7. $5° \, 22' \, 53'' = \left(5 + \frac{22}{60} + \frac{53}{3600}\right)° \approx 5.38°$

9. $135.27° = 135° + (0.27)(60)'$
$= 135° + 16' + 0.2(60)''$
$= 135° \, 16' \, 12''$

11. $-85.15° = -[85° + (0.15)(60)'] = -85° \, 9'$

13. $\dfrac{5\pi \text{ rad}}{7} = \dfrac{5\pi \text{ rad}}{7} \cdot \dfrac{180°}{\pi \text{ rad}} \approx 128.57°$

15. $-3.5 \text{ rad} = -3.5 \text{ rad} \cdot \dfrac{180°}{\pi \text{ rad}} \approx -200.54°$

17. $480° = 480° \cdot \dfrac{\pi \text{ rad}}{180°} = \dfrac{8\pi}{3} \text{ rad} \approx 8.3776 \text{ rad}$

19. $-33° \, 45' = -33.75° = -33.75° \cdot \dfrac{\pi \text{ rad}}{180°} = -\dfrac{3\pi}{16} \text{ rad} \approx -0.5890 \text{ rad}$

21. $252°$ is in Quadrant III.

Reference angle $= 252° - 180° = 72°$

23. $-\dfrac{6\pi}{5}$ is in Quadrant II and is coterminal to $\dfrac{4\pi}{5}$.

Reference angle $= \pi - \dfrac{4\pi}{5} = \dfrac{\pi}{5}$

25. $t = \dfrac{7\pi}{6}$ corresponds to the point $\left(-\dfrac{\sqrt{3}}{2}, -\dfrac{1}{2}\right)$.

$\sin \dfrac{7\pi}{6} = -\dfrac{1}{2}$

$\cos \dfrac{7\pi}{6} = -\dfrac{\sqrt{3}}{2}$

$\tan \dfrac{7\pi}{6} = \dfrac{1}{\sqrt{3}}$

27. $t = -\dfrac{\pi}{3}$ corresponds to the point $\left(\dfrac{1}{2}, -\dfrac{\sqrt{3}}{2}\right)$.

$\sin\left(-\dfrac{\pi}{3}\right) = -\dfrac{\sqrt{3}}{2}$

$\cos\left(-\dfrac{\pi}{3}\right) = \dfrac{1}{2}$

$\tan\left(-\dfrac{\pi}{3}\right) = -\sqrt{3}$

29. $x = 12, y = 16, r = \sqrt{144 + 256} = \sqrt{400} = 20$

$$\sin \theta = \frac{y}{r} = \frac{4}{5} \qquad \csc \theta = \frac{r}{y} = \frac{5}{4}$$

$$\cos \theta = \frac{x}{r} = \frac{3}{5} \qquad \sec \theta = \frac{r}{x} = \frac{5}{3}$$

$$\tan \theta = \frac{y}{x} = \frac{4}{3} \qquad \cot \theta = \frac{x}{y} = \frac{3}{4}$$

31. $\sec \theta = \frac{6}{5}$, $\tan \theta < 0 \implies \theta$ is in Quadrant IV.

$$r = 6, x = 5, y = -\sqrt{36 - 25} = -\sqrt{11}$$

$$\sin \theta = \frac{y}{r} = -\frac{\sqrt{11}}{6} \qquad \csc \theta = -\frac{6\sqrt{11}}{11}$$

$$\cos \theta = \frac{x}{r} = \frac{5}{6} \qquad \sec \theta = \frac{6}{5}$$

$$\tan \theta = \frac{y}{x} = -\frac{\sqrt{11}}{5} \qquad \cot \theta = -\frac{5\sqrt{11}}{11}$$

33. $\tan \frac{\pi}{3} = \sqrt{3}$

35. $\cos 495° = -\cos 45° = -\frac{\sqrt{2}}{2}$

37. $\tan 33° \approx 0.65$

39. $\sec \frac{12\pi}{5} = \frac{1}{\cos\left(\frac{12\pi}{5}\right)} \approx 3.24$

41. $\cos \theta = -\frac{\sqrt{2}}{2} \implies \theta$ is in Quadrant II or III.

Reference angle: $\frac{\pi}{4}$

$\theta = \frac{3\pi}{4}, \frac{5\pi}{4}$ or $\theta = 135°, 225°$

43. $\sin \theta = 0.8387 \implies \theta$ is in Quadrant I or II.

Reference angle: $\arcsin 0.8387 \approx 0.9949$

$\theta \approx 0.9949$ rad or $0.9949 \cdot \frac{180}{\pi} \approx 57.0°$

$\theta \approx \pi - 0.9949 \approx 2.1467$ rad or

$$2.1467 \cdot \frac{180}{\pi} \approx 123.0°$$

45. $\theta = 120°$
$m = \tan 120° = -\sqrt{3}$

47. $x + y - 10 = 0$
$y = -x + 1 \implies m = -1$
$\tan \theta = -1$
$\theta = 135°$

49. $y = 3 \cos 2\pi x$

Amplitude: 3

Period: $\frac{2\pi}{2\pi} = 1$

51. $f(x) = 5 \sin \frac{2x}{5}$.

Amplitude: 5

Period: $\frac{2\pi}{2/5} = 5\pi$

53. $f(x) = -\dfrac{1}{4} \cos \dfrac{\pi x}{4}$

Amplitude: $\left| -\dfrac{1}{4} \right| = \dfrac{1}{4}$

Period: $\dfrac{2\pi}{\pi/4} = 8$

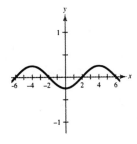

55. $g(t) = \dfrac{5}{2} \sin(t - \pi)$

Amplitude: $\dfrac{5}{2}$

Period: 2π

Shift: $t - \pi = 0$ to $t - \pi = 2\pi$

$\qquad\qquad t = \pi \qquad\qquad t = 3\pi$

57. $h(t) = \tan\left(t - \dfrac{\pi}{4} \right)$

Period: π

Two consecutive asymptotes: $t - \dfrac{\pi}{4} = -\dfrac{\pi}{2}$ and $t - \dfrac{\pi}{4} = \dfrac{\pi}{2}$

$\qquad\qquad\qquad\qquad\qquad t = -\dfrac{\pi}{4} \qquad\qquad t = \dfrac{3\pi}{4}$

t	0	$\dfrac{\pi}{4}$	$\dfrac{\pi}{2}$
$h(t)$	-1	0	1

59. $y = \arcsin \dfrac{x}{2}$

Domain: $-2 \le x \le 2$

Range: $-\dfrac{\pi}{2} \le y \le \dfrac{\pi}{2}$

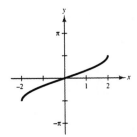

61. $f(x) = \dfrac{x}{4} - \sin x$

Not periodic.

63. $f(x) = \dfrac{\pi}{2} + \arctan x$

Not periodic.

67. $f(t) = 2.5e^{-t/4}\sin 2\pi t$
$-2.5e^{-t/4} \le f(t) \le 2.5e^{-t/4}$

Not periodic.

65. $h(\theta) = \theta \sin \pi\theta$

Not periodic.

69. $f(x) = e^{\sin x}$

The graph is periodic. The period is 2π.

Maximum: $\left(\dfrac{\pi}{2}, e\right)$

Minimum: $\left(\dfrac{3\pi}{2}, e^{-1}\right)$

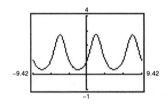

71. $g(x) = 2\sin x \cos^2 x$

The graph is periodic. The period is 2π.

Relative Minimum: $\left(\dfrac{\pi}{2}, 0\right)$, $(3.76, -0.77)$, $(5.67, -0.77)$

Relative Maximum: $(0.61, 0.77)$, $(2.53, 0.77)$, $\left(\dfrac{3\pi}{2}, 0\right)$

73. Let $y = \arcsin(x - 1)$. Then, $\sin y = (x - 1) = \dfrac{x - 1}{1}$, and

$$\sec y = \dfrac{1}{\sqrt{1 - (x - 1)^2}} = \dfrac{1}{\sqrt{-x^2 + 2x}} = \dfrac{\sqrt{-x^2 + 2x}}{-x^2 + 2x}.$$

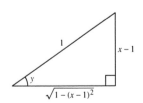

75. Let $y = \arccos \dfrac{x^2}{4 - x^2}$. Then $\cos y = \dfrac{x}{4 - x^2}$, and

$$\sin y = \frac{\sqrt{(4 - x^2)^2 - (x^2)^2}}{4 - x^2}$$

$$= \frac{\sqrt{16 - 8x^2}}{4 - x^2}$$

$$= \frac{2\sqrt{4 - 2x^2}}{4 - x^2}.$$

77. $\sin 50° = \dfrac{h}{12}$

$\quad\quad h = 12 \sin 50°$

$\quad\quad\quad \approx 9.2$ m

79. $\tan 25° = \dfrac{h}{2.5}$

$\quad\quad h = 2.5 \tan 25°$

$\quad\quad\quad \approx 1.2$ miles

81. $\tan 1° \ 10' = \dfrac{a}{3.5}$

$\quad a = 3.5 \tan 1° \ 10'$

$\quad\quad \approx 0.07$ km

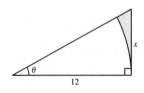

83. (a) $\tan \theta = \dfrac{x}{12}$

$\quad\quad x = 12 \tan \theta$

Area = Area of triangle − Area of sector

$$= \left(\tfrac{1}{2}bh\right) - \left(\tfrac{1}{2}r^2\theta\right)$$

$$= \tfrac{1}{2}(12)(12 \tan \theta) - \tfrac{1}{2}(12^2)(\theta)$$

$$= 72 \tan \theta - 72\theta$$

$$= 72(\tan \theta - \theta)$$

(b)

As $\theta \rightarrow \dfrac{\pi}{2}$, $A \rightarrow \infty$. The area increases without

bound as θ approaches $\dfrac{\pi}{2}$.

❑ Practice Test for Chapter 4

1. Express 350° in radian measure.

2. Express $(5\pi)/9$ in degree measure.

3. Convert 135° 14′ 12″ to decimal form.

4. Convert −22.569° to D° M′ S″ form.

5. If $\cos\theta = \frac{2}{3}$, use the trigonometric identities to find $\tan\theta$.

6. Find θ given $\sin\theta = 0.9063$, $0 \le \theta < 2\pi$.

7. Solve for x in the figure below.

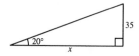

8. Find the magnitude of the reference angle for $\theta = (6\pi)/5$.

9. Evaluate csc 3.92.

10. Find $\sec\theta$ given that θ lies in Quadrant III and $\tan\theta = 6$.

11. Graph $y = 3\sin\dfrac{x}{2}$.

12. Graph $y = -2\cos(x - \pi)$.

13. Graph $y = \tan 2x$.

14. Graph $y = -\csc\left(x + \dfrac{\pi}{4}\right)$.

15. Graph $y = 2x + \sin x$, using a graphing calculator.

16. Graph $y = 3x\cos x$, using a graphing calculator.

17. Evaluate arcsin 1.

18. Evaluate arctan(−3).

19. Evaluate $\sin\left(\arccos\dfrac{4}{\sqrt{35}}\right)$.

20. Write an algebraic expression for $\cos\left(\arcsin\dfrac{x}{4}\right)$.

For Exercises 21–23, solve the right triangle.

21. $A = 40°$, $c = 12$

22. $B = 6.84°$, $a = 21.3$

23. $a = 5$, $b = 9$

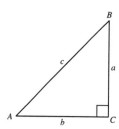

24. A 20-foot ladder leans against the side of a barn. Find the height of the top of the ladder if the angle of elevation of the ladder is 67°.

25. An observer in a lighthouse 250 feet above sea level spots a ship off the shore. If the angle of depression to the ship is 5°, how far out is the ship?

C H A P T E R 5
Analytic Trigonometry

C H A P T E R 5
Analytic Trigonometry

Section 5.1 Using Fundamental Identities

■ You should know the fundamental trigonometric identities.

(a) Reciprocal Identities

$$\sin u = \frac{1}{\csc u} \qquad\qquad \csc u = \frac{1}{\sin u}$$

$$\cos u = \frac{1}{\sec u} \qquad\qquad \sec u = \frac{1}{\cos u}$$

$$\tan u = \frac{1}{\cot u} = \frac{\sin u}{\cos u} \qquad \cot u = \frac{1}{\tan u} = \frac{\cos u}{\sin u}$$

(b) Pythagorean Identities

$$\sin^2 u + \cos^2 u = 1$$
$$1 + \tan^2 u = \sec^2 u$$
$$1 + \cot^2 u = \csc^2 u$$

(c) Cofunction Identities

$$\sin\left(\frac{\pi}{2} - u\right) = \cos u \qquad\qquad \cos\left(\frac{\pi}{2} - u\right) = \sin u$$

$$\tan\left(\frac{\pi}{2} - u\right) = \cot u \qquad\qquad \cot\left(\frac{\pi}{2} - u\right) = \tan u$$

$$\sec\left(\frac{\pi}{2} - u\right) = \csc u \qquad\qquad \csc\left(\frac{\pi}{2} - u\right) = \sec u$$

(d) Negative Angle Identities

$$\sin(-x) = -\sin x \qquad\qquad \csc(-x) = -\csc x$$
$$\cos(-x) = \cos x \qquad\qquad \sec(-x) = \sec x$$
$$\tan(-x) = -\tan x \qquad\qquad \cot(-x) = -\cot x$$

■ You should be able to use these fundamental identities to find function values.

■ You should be able to convert trigonometric expressions to equivalent forms by using the fundamental identities.

Solutions to Odd-Numbered Exercises

1. $\sin x = \dfrac{1}{2}$, $\cos x = \dfrac{\sqrt{3}}{2} \implies x$ is in
Quadrant I.

$\tan x = \dfrac{\sin x}{\cos x} = \dfrac{1/2}{\sqrt{3}/2} = \dfrac{1}{\sqrt{3}} = \dfrac{\sqrt{3}}{3}$

$\cot x = \dfrac{1}{\tan x} = \sqrt{3}$

$\sec x = \dfrac{1}{\cos x} = \dfrac{2}{\sqrt{3}} = \dfrac{2\sqrt{3}}{3}$

$\csc x = \dfrac{1}{\sin x} = 2$

3. $\sec \theta = \sqrt{2}$, $\sin \theta = -\dfrac{\sqrt{2}}{2} \implies \theta$ is in
Quadrant IV.

$\cos \theta = \dfrac{1}{\sec \theta} = \dfrac{1}{\sqrt{2}} = \dfrac{\sqrt{2}}{2}$

$\tan \theta = \dfrac{\sin \theta}{\cos \theta} = \dfrac{-\sqrt{2}/2}{\sqrt{2}/2} = -1$

$\cot \theta = \dfrac{1}{\tan \theta} = -1$

$\csc \theta = \dfrac{1}{\sin \theta} = -\sqrt{2}$

5. $\tan x = \dfrac{5}{12}$, $\sec x = -\dfrac{13}{12} \implies x$ is in
Quadrant III.

$\cos x = \dfrac{1}{\sec x} = -\dfrac{12}{13}$

$\sin x = -\sqrt{1 - \cos^2 x} = -\sqrt{1 - \dfrac{144}{169}} = -\dfrac{5}{13}$

$\cot x = \dfrac{1}{\tan x} = \dfrac{12}{5}$

$\csc x = \dfrac{1}{\sin x} = -\dfrac{13}{5}$

7. $\sec \phi = -1$, $\sin \phi = 0 \implies \phi = \pi$

$\cos \phi = -1$

$\tan \phi = 0$

$\cot \phi$ is undefined.

$\csc \phi$ is undefined.

9. $\sin(-x) = -\sin x = -\dfrac{2}{3} \implies \sin x = \dfrac{2}{3}$

$\sin x = \dfrac{2}{3}$, $\tan x = -\dfrac{2\sqrt{5}}{5} \implies x$ is in
Quadrant II.

$\cos x = -\sqrt{1 - \sin^2 x} = -\sqrt{1 - \dfrac{4}{9}} = -\dfrac{\sqrt{5}}{3}$

$\cot x = \dfrac{1}{\tan x} = -\dfrac{\sqrt{5}}{2}$

$\sec x = \dfrac{1}{\cos x} = -\dfrac{3\sqrt{5}}{5}$

$\csc x = \dfrac{1}{\sin x} = \dfrac{3}{2}$

11. $\tan \theta = 2$, $\sin \theta < 0 \implies \theta$ is in Quadrant III.

$\sec \theta = -\sqrt{\tan^2 \theta + 1} = -\sqrt{4 + 1} = -\sqrt{5}$

$\cos \theta = \dfrac{1}{\sec \theta} = -\dfrac{1}{\sqrt{5}} = -\dfrac{\sqrt{5}}{5}$

$\sin \theta = -\sqrt{1 - \cos^2 \theta}$

$\quad = -\sqrt{1 - \dfrac{1}{5}} = -\dfrac{2}{\sqrt{5}} = -\dfrac{2\sqrt{5}}{5}$

$\csc \theta = \dfrac{1}{\sin \theta} = -\dfrac{\sqrt{5}}{2}$

$\cot \theta = \dfrac{1}{\tan \theta} = \dfrac{1}{2}$

13. $\sin \theta = -1$, $\cot \theta = 0 \implies \theta = \dfrac{3\pi}{2}$

$\cos \theta = \sqrt{1 - \sin^2 \theta} = 0$

$\sec \theta$ is undefined.

$\tan \theta$ is undefined.

$\csc \theta = -1$

15. By looking at the basic graphs of $\sin x$ and $\csc x$, we see that as $x \to \dfrac{\pi-}{2}$, $\sin x \to 1$ and $\csc x \to 1$.

17. By looking at the basic graphs of $\tan x$ and $\cot x$, we see that as
$x \rightarrow \dfrac{\pi-}{2}$, $\tan x \rightarrow \infty$ and $\cot x \rightarrow 0$.

19. $\sec x \cos x = \sec x \cdot \dfrac{1}{\sec x} = 1$

The expression is matched with (d).

21. $\tan^2 x - \sec^2 x = \tan^2 x - (\tan^2 x + 1) = -1$

The expression is matched with (a).

23. $\dfrac{\sin(-x)}{\cos(-x)} = \dfrac{-\sin x}{\cos x} = -\tan x$

The expression is matched with (e).

25. $\sin x \sec x = \sin x \cdot \dfrac{1}{\cos x} = \tan x$

The expression is matched with (b).

27. $\sec^4 x - \tan^4 x = (\sec^2 x + \tan^2 x)(\sec^2 x - \tan^2 x)$

$\qquad\qquad = (\sec^2 x + \tan^2 x)(1) = \sec^2 x + \tan^2 x$

The expression is matched with (f).

29. $\dfrac{\sec^2 x - 1}{\sin^2 x} = \dfrac{\tan^2 x}{\sin^2 x} = \dfrac{\sin^2 x}{\cos^2 x} \cdot \dfrac{1}{\sin^2 x} = \sec^2 x$

The expression is matched with (e).

31. $\tan \phi \csc \phi = \dfrac{\sin \phi}{\cos \phi} \cdot \dfrac{1}{\sin \phi} = \dfrac{1}{\cos \phi} = \sec \phi$

33. $\cos \beta \tan \beta = \cos \beta \left(\dfrac{\sin \beta}{\cos \beta} \right)$

$\qquad\qquad = \sin \beta$

35. $\dfrac{\cot x}{\csc x} = \dfrac{\cos x/\sin x}{1/\sin x}$

$\qquad = \dfrac{\cos x}{\sin x} \cdot \dfrac{\sin x}{1} = \cos x$

37. $\sec \alpha \dfrac{\sin \alpha}{\tan \alpha} = \dfrac{1}{\cos \alpha} (\sin \alpha) \cot \alpha$

$\qquad = \dfrac{1}{\cos \alpha} (\sin \alpha) \left(\dfrac{\cos \alpha}{\sin \alpha} \right) = 1$

39. $\dfrac{\sin(-x)}{\cos x} = -\dfrac{\sin x}{\cos x} = -\tan x$

41. $\cos\left(\dfrac{\pi}{2} - x \right)\sec x = (\sin x)(\sec x)$

$\qquad\qquad = (\sin x)\left(\dfrac{1}{\cos x} \right)$

$\qquad\qquad = \dfrac{\sin x}{\cos x}$

$\qquad\qquad = \tan x$

43. $\dfrac{\cos^2 y}{1 - \sin y} = \dfrac{1 - \sin^2 y}{1 - \sin y}$

$\qquad = \dfrac{(1 + \sin y)(1 - \sin y)}{1 - \sin y}$

$\qquad = 1 + \sin y$

45. $\tan^2 x - \tan^2 x \sin^2 x = \tan^2 x(1 - \sin^2 x)$

$\qquad\qquad = \tan^2 x \cos^2 x$

$\qquad\qquad = \dfrac{\sin^2 x}{\cos^2 x} \cdot \cos^2 x$

$\qquad\qquad = \sin^2 x$

47. $\sin^2 x \sec^2 x - \sin^2 x = \sin^2 x(\sec^2 x - 1)$
$$= \sin^2 x \tan^2 x$$

49. $\tan^4 x + 2 \tan^2 x + 1 = (\tan^2 x + 1)^2$
$$= (\sec^2 x)^2$$
$$= \sec^4 x$$

51. $\sin^4 x - \cos^4 x = (\sin^2 x + \cos^2 x)(\sin^2 x - \cos^2 x)$
$$= (1)(\sin^2 x - \cos^2 x)$$
$$= \sin^2 x - \cos^2 x$$

53. $(\sin x + \cos x)^2 = \sin^2 x + 2\sin x \cos x + \cos^2 x$
$$= (\sin^2 x + \cos^2 x) + 2 \sin x \cos x$$
$$= 1 + 2 \sin x \cos x$$

55. $(\sec x + 1)(\sec x - 1) = \sec^2 x - 1 = \tan^2 x$

57. $\dfrac{1}{1 + \cos x} + \dfrac{1}{1 - \cos x} = \dfrac{1 - \cos x + 1 + \cos x}{(1 + \cos x)(1 - \cos x)}$
$$= \dfrac{2}{1 - \cos^2 x}$$
$$= \dfrac{2}{\sin^2 x}$$
$$= 2 \csc^2 x$$

59. $\dfrac{\cos x}{1 + \sin x} + \dfrac{1 + \sin x}{\cos x} = \dfrac{\cos^2 x + (1 + \sin x)^2}{\cos x(1 + \sin x)} = \dfrac{\cos^2 x + 1 + 2 \sin x + \sin^2 x}{\cos x(1 + \sin x)}$
$$= \dfrac{2 + 2 \sin x}{\cos x(1 + \sin x)}$$
$$= \dfrac{2(1 + \sin x)}{\cos x(1 + \sin x)}$$
$$= \dfrac{2}{\cos x}$$
$$= 2 \sec x$$

61. $\dfrac{\sin^2 y}{1 - \cos y} = \dfrac{1 - \cos^2 y}{1 - \cos y}$
$$= \dfrac{(1 + \cos y)(1 - \cos y)}{1 - \cos y}$$
$$= 1 + \cos y$$

63. $\dfrac{3}{\sec x - \tan x} \cdot \dfrac{\sec x + \tan x}{\sec x + \tan x} = \dfrac{3(\sec x + \tan x)}{\sec^2 x - \tan^2 x}$
$$= \dfrac{3(\sec x + \tan x)}{1}$$
$$= 3(\sec x + \tan x)$$

65. $y_1 = \cos\left(\dfrac{\pi}{2} - x\right)$, $y_2 = \sin x$

x	0.2	0.4	0.6	0.8	1.0	1.2	1.4
y_1	0.1987	0.3894	0.5646	0.7174	0.8415	0.9320	0.9854
y_2	0.1987	0.3894	0.5646	0.7174	0.8415	0.9320	0.9854

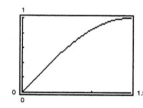

Conclusion: $y_1 = y_2$

67. $y_1 = \dfrac{\cos x}{1 - \sin x}$, $y_2 = \dfrac{1 + \sin x}{\cos x}$

x	0.2	0.4	0.6	0.8	1.0	1.2	1.4
y_1	1.2230	1.5085	1.8958	2.4650	3.4082	5.3319	11.6814
y_2	1.2230	1.5085	1.8958	2.4650	3.4082	5.3319	11.6814

Conclusion: $y_1 = y_2$

69. $y_1 = \cos x \cot x + \sin x = \csc x$

71. $\sqrt{25 - x^2} = \sqrt{25 - (5\sin\theta)^2}$, $x = 5\sin\theta$
$$= \sqrt{25 - 25\sin^2\theta}$$
$$= \sqrt{25(1 - \sin^2\theta)}$$
$$= \sqrt{25\cos^2\theta}$$
$$= 5\cos\theta$$

73. $\sqrt{x^2 - 9} = \sqrt{(3\sec\theta)^2 - 9}$, $x = 3\sec\theta$
$$= \sqrt{9\sec^2\theta - 9}$$
$$= \sqrt{9(\sec^2\theta - 1)}$$
$$= \sqrt{9\tan^2\theta}$$
$$= 3\tan\theta$$

75. $\sqrt{x^2 + 25} = \sqrt{(5\tan\theta)^2 + 25}$, $x = 5\tan\theta$
$$= \sqrt{25\tan^2\theta + 25}$$
$$= \sqrt{25(\tan^2\theta + 1)}$$
$$= \sqrt{25\sec^2\theta}$$
$$= 5\sec\theta$$

77. $\sin\theta = \sqrt{1 - \cos^2\theta}$

Let $y_1 = \sin x$ and $y_2 = \sqrt{1 - \cos^2 x}$, $0 \le x \le 2\pi$.

$y_1 = y_2$ for $0 \le x \le \pi$, so we have

$\sin\theta = \sqrt{1 - \cos^2\theta}$ for $0 \le \theta \le \pi$.

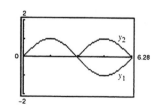

79. $\sec\theta = \sqrt{1 + \tan^2\theta}$

Let $y_1 = \dfrac{1}{\cos x}$ and $y_2 = \sqrt{1 + \tan^2 x}$, $0 \le x \le 2\pi$.

$y_1 = y_2$ for $0 \le x < \dfrac{\pi}{2}$ and $\dfrac{3\pi}{2} < x \le 2\pi$, so we have

$\sec\theta = \sqrt{1 + \tan^2\theta}$ for $0 \le \theta < \dfrac{\pi}{2}$ and $\dfrac{3\pi}{2} < \theta \le 2\pi$.

81. $\ln|\cos\theta| - \ln|\sin\theta| = \ln\dfrac{|\cos\theta|}{|\sin\theta|} = \ln|\cot\theta|$

83. False; $\dfrac{\sin k\theta}{\cos k\theta} = \tan k\theta$

85. True; $\sin\theta \csc\theta = \sin\theta\left(\dfrac{1}{\sin\theta}\right) = 1$,

provided $\sin\theta \ne 0$.

87. (a) $\csc^2 132° - \cot^2 132° \approx 1.8107 - 0.8107 = 1$

(b) $\csc^2\dfrac{2\pi}{7} - \cot^2\dfrac{2\pi}{7} \approx 1.6360 - 0.6360 = 1$

89. $\cos\left(\dfrac{\pi}{2} - \theta\right) = \sin\theta$

(a) $\theta = 80°$

$\cos(90° - 80°) = \sin 80°$

$0.9848 = 0.9848$

(b) $\theta = 0.8$

$\cos\left(\dfrac{\pi}{2} - 0.8\right) = \sin 0.8$

$0.7174 = 0.7174$

91. Since $\sin^2\theta + \cos^2\theta = 1$ and $\cos^2\theta = 1 - \sin^2\theta$:

$\cos\theta = \pm\sqrt{1 - \sin^2\theta}$

$\tan\theta = \dfrac{\sin\theta}{\cos\theta} = \pm\dfrac{\sin\theta}{\sqrt{1 - \sin^2\theta}}$

$\cot\theta = \dfrac{1}{\tan\theta} = \pm\dfrac{\sqrt{1 - \sin^2\theta}}{\sin\theta}$

$\sec\theta = \dfrac{1}{\cos\theta} = \pm\dfrac{1}{\sqrt{1 - \sin^2\theta}}$

$\csc\theta = \dfrac{1}{\sin\theta}$

93. $\left(\sqrt{x} + 5\right)\left(\sqrt{x} - 5\right) = \left(\sqrt{x}\right)^2 - (5)^2 = x - 25$

95. $\left(2\sqrt{z} + 3\right)^2 = \left(2\sqrt{z}\right)^2 + 2\left(2\sqrt{z}\right)(3) + (3)^2$

$= 4z + 12\sqrt{z} + 9$

Section 5.2   Verifying Trigonometric Identities

- You should know the difference between an expression, a conditional equation, and an identity.
- You should be able to solve trigonometric identities, using the following techniques.
  (a) Work with *one* side at a time. Do not "cross" the equal sign.
  (b) Use algebraic techniques such as combining fractions, factoring expressions, rationalizing denominators, and squaring binomials.
  (c) Use the fundamental identities.
  (d) Convert all the terms into sines and cosines.

Solutions to Odd-Numbered Exercises

1. $\sin t \csc t = \sin t\left(\dfrac{1}{\sin t}\right) = 1$

3. $(1 + \sin\alpha)(1 - \sin\alpha) = (1 - \sin^2\alpha) = \cos^2\alpha$

5. $\cos^2 \beta - \sin^2 \beta = (1 - \sin^2 \beta) - \sin^2 \beta$

$= 1 - 2 \sin^2 \beta$

7. $\tan^2 \theta + 4 = (\sec^2 \theta - 1) + 4$

$= \sec^2 \theta + 3$

9. $\sin^2 \alpha - \sin^4 \alpha = \sin^2 \alpha (1 - \sin^2 \alpha)$

$= (1 - \cos^2 \alpha)(\cos^2 \alpha)$

$= \cos^2 \alpha - \cos^4 \alpha$

11. $\dfrac{\sec^2 x}{\tan x} = \sec^2 x \cdot \dfrac{1}{\tan x} = \dfrac{1}{\cos^2 x} \cdot \dfrac{\cos x}{\sin x}$

$= \dfrac{1}{\cos x} \cdot \dfrac{1}{\sin x}$

$= \sec x \csc x$

13. $\dfrac{\cot^2 t}{\csc t} = \dfrac{\cos^2 t}{\sin^2 t} \cdot \sin t$

$= \dfrac{\cos^2 t}{\sin t}$

$= \dfrac{1 - \sin^2 t}{\sin t} = \dfrac{1}{\sin t} - \dfrac{\sin^2 t}{\sin t}$

$= \csc t - \sin t$

15. $\sin^{1/2} x \cos x - \sin^{5/2} x \cos x = \sin^{1/2} x \cos x (1 - \sin^2 x) = \sin^{1/2} x \cos x \cdot \cos^2 x = \cos^3 x \sqrt{\sin x}$

17. $\dfrac{1}{\sec x \tan x} = \cos x \cot x = \cos x \cdot \dfrac{\cos x}{\sin x}$

$= \dfrac{\cos^2 x}{\sin x}$

$= \dfrac{1 - \sin^2 x}{\sin x}$

$= \dfrac{1}{\sin x} - \sin x$

$= \csc x - \sin x$

19. $\csc x - \sin x = \dfrac{1}{\sin x} - \sin x$

$= \dfrac{1 - \sin^2 x}{\sin x}$

$= \dfrac{\cos^2 x}{\sin x}$

$= \cos x \cdot \dfrac{\cos x}{\sin x}$

$= \cos x \cot x$

21. $\cos x + \sin x \tan x = \cos x + \sin x \cdot \dfrac{\sin x}{\cos x}$

$= \dfrac{\cos^2 x + \sin^2 x}{\cos x}$

$= \dfrac{1}{\cos x}$

$= \sec x$

23. $\dfrac{1}{\tan x} + \dfrac{1}{\cot x} = \dfrac{\cot x + \tan x}{\tan x \cot x}$

$= \dfrac{\cot x + \tan x}{1}$

$= \tan x + \cot x$

25. $\dfrac{\cos \theta \cot \theta}{1 - \sin \theta} - 1 = \dfrac{\cos \theta \cot \theta - (1 - \sin \theta)}{1 - \sin \theta}$

$= \dfrac{\cos \theta (\cos \theta / \sin \theta) - 1 + \sin \theta}{1 - \sin \theta} \cdot \dfrac{\sin \theta}{\sin \theta}$

$= \dfrac{\cos^2 \theta - \sin \theta + \sin^2 \theta}{\sin \theta (1 - \sin \theta)}$

$= \dfrac{1 - \sin \theta}{\sin \theta (1 - \sin \theta)}$

$= \dfrac{1}{\sin \theta}$

$= \csc \theta$

27. $\dfrac{1}{\cot x + 1} + \dfrac{1}{\tan x + 1} = \dfrac{\tan x + 1 + \cot x + 1}{(\cot x + 1)(\tan x + 1)}$

$\qquad\qquad\qquad\qquad = \dfrac{\tan x + \cot x + 2}{\cot x \tan x + \cot x + \tan x + 1}$

$\qquad\qquad\qquad\qquad = \dfrac{\tan x + \cot x + 2}{\tan x + \cot x + 2}$

$\qquad\qquad\qquad\qquad = 1$

29. $\cos\left(\dfrac{\pi}{2} - x\right)\csc x = \sin x \left(\dfrac{1}{\sin x}\right) = 1$

31. $\dfrac{\csc(-x)}{\sec(-x)} = \dfrac{1/\sin(-x)}{1/\cos(-x)}$

$\qquad\quad = \dfrac{\cos(-x)}{\sin(-x)}$

$\qquad\quad = \dfrac{\cos x}{-\sin x}$

$\qquad\quad = -\cot x$

33. $\dfrac{\cos(-\theta)}{1 + \sin(-\theta)} = \dfrac{\cos\theta}{1 - \sin\theta} \cdot \dfrac{1 + \sin\theta}{1 + \sin\theta}$

$\qquad\qquad\quad = \dfrac{\cos\theta(1 + \sin\theta)}{1 - \sin^2\theta}$

$\qquad\qquad\quad = \dfrac{\cos\theta(1 + \sin\theta)}{\cos^2\theta}$

$\qquad\qquad\quad = \dfrac{1 + \sin\theta}{\cos\theta}$

$\qquad\qquad\quad = \dfrac{1}{\cos\theta} + \dfrac{\sin\theta}{\cos\theta}$

$\qquad\qquad\quad = \sec\theta + \tan\theta$

35. $\dfrac{\sin x \cos y + \cos x \sin y}{\cos x \cos y - \sin x \sin y} = \dfrac{\dfrac{\sin x \cos y}{\cos x \cos y} + \dfrac{\cos x \sin y}{\cos x \cos y}}{\dfrac{\cos x \cos y}{\cos x \cos y} - \dfrac{\sin x \sin y}{\cos x \cos y}} = \dfrac{\tan x + \tan y}{1 - \tan x \tan y}$

37. $\dfrac{\tan x + \cot y}{\tan x \cot y} = \dfrac{\dfrac{1}{\cot x} + \dfrac{1}{\tan y}}{\dfrac{1}{\cot x} \cdot \dfrac{1}{\tan y}} \cdot \dfrac{\cot x \tan y}{\cot x \tan y} = \tan y + \cot x$

39. $\sqrt{\dfrac{1 + \sin\theta}{1 - \sin\theta}} = \sqrt{\dfrac{1 + \sin\theta}{1 - \sin\theta} \cdot \dfrac{1 + \sin\theta}{1 + \sin\theta}}$

$\qquad\qquad\quad = \sqrt{\dfrac{(1 + \sin\theta)^2}{1 - \sin^2\theta}}$

$\qquad\qquad\quad = \sqrt{\dfrac{(1 + \sin\theta)^2}{\cos^2\theta}}$

$\qquad\qquad\quad = \dfrac{1 + \sin\theta}{|\cos\theta|}$

41. $\sin^2 x + \sin^2\left(\dfrac{\pi}{2} - x\right) = \sin^2 x + \cos^2 x = 1$

43. $\csc x \cos\left(\dfrac{\pi}{2} - x\right) = \dfrac{1}{\sin x} \cdot \sin x = 1$

45. $2 \sec^2 x - 2 \sec^2 x \sin^2 x - \sin^2 x - \cos^2 x = 2 \sec^2 x(1 - \sin^2 x) - (\sin^2 x + \cos^2 x)$

$$= 2 \sec^2 x(\cos^2 x) - 1$$

$$= 2 \cdot \frac{1}{\cos^2 x} \cdot \cos^2 x - 1$$

$$= 2 - 1$$

$$= 1$$

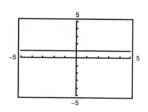

47. $2 + \cos^2 x - 3 \cos^4 x = (1 - \cos^2 x)(2 + 3 \cos^2 x)$

$$= \sin^2 x(2 + 3 \cos^2 x)$$

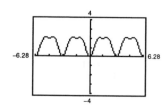

49. $\csc^4 x - 2 \csc^2 x + 1 = (\csc^2 x - 1)^2$

$$= (\cot^2 x)^2 = \cot^4 x$$

51. $\sec^4 \theta - \tan^4 \theta = (\sec^2 \theta + \tan^2 \theta)(\sec^2 \theta - \tan^2 \theta)$

$$= (1 + \tan^2 \theta + \tan^2 \theta)(1)$$

$$= 1 + 2 \tan^2 \theta$$

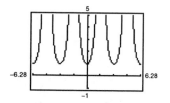

53. $\dfrac{\sin \beta}{1 - \cos \beta} \cdot \dfrac{1 + \cos \beta}{1 + \cos \beta} = \dfrac{\sin \beta(1 + \cos \beta)}{1 - \cos^2 \beta}$

$$= \frac{1 + \cos \beta}{\sin \beta}$$

55. $\dfrac{\tan^3 \alpha - 1}{\tan \alpha - 1} = \dfrac{(\tan \alpha - 1)(\tan^2 \alpha + \tan \alpha + 1)}{\tan \alpha - 1} = \tan^2 \alpha + \tan \alpha + 1$

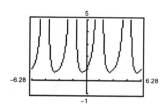

57. $\ln|\tan \theta| = \ln \left| \dfrac{\sin \theta}{\cos \theta} \right|$

$$= \ln \frac{|\sin \theta|}{|\cos \theta|}$$

$$= \ln|\sin \theta| - \ln|\cos \theta|$$

59. $-\ln(1 + \cos \theta) = \ln(1 + \cos \theta)^{-1}$

$$= \ln \frac{1}{1 + \cos \theta} \cdot \frac{1 - \cos \theta}{1 - \cos \theta}$$

$$= \ln \frac{1 - \cos \theta}{1 - \cos^2 \theta}$$

$$= \ln \frac{1 - \cos \theta}{\sin^2 \theta}$$

$$= \ln(1 - \cos \theta) - \ln \sin^2 \theta$$

$$= \ln(1 - \cos \theta) - 2 \ln|\sin \theta|$$

61. Since $\sin^2 \theta = 1 - \cos^2 \theta$, then
$\sin \theta = \pm\sqrt{1 - \cos^2 \theta}$; $\sin \theta \neq \sqrt{1 - \cos \theta}$
if θ lies in Quadrant III or IV.

One such angle is $\theta = \dfrac{7\pi}{4}$.

63. $\sqrt{\tan^2 \theta} = |\tan \theta|$

$\sqrt{\tan^2 \theta} \neq \tan \theta$ if θ lies in Quadrant II or IV.

One such angle is $\theta = \dfrac{3\pi}{4}$.

65. $\sin^2 25° + \cos^2 25° = 1$

67. $\cos^2 20° + \cos^2 52° + \cos^2 38° + \cos^2 70° = \cos^2 20° + \cos^2 52^2 + \sin^2(90° - 38°) + \sin^2(90° - 70°)$
$$= \cos^2 20° + \cos^2 52^2 + \sin^2 52° + \sin^2 20°$$
$$= (\cos^2 20° + \sin^2 20°) + (\cos^2 52° + \sin^2 52°)$$
$$= 1 + 1$$
$$= 2$$

69. When n is even,
$$\cos\left[\frac{(2n + 1)\pi}{2}\right] = \cos\frac{\pi}{2} = 0.$$
When n is odd,
$$\cos\left[\frac{(2n + 1)\pi}{2}\right] = \cos\frac{3\pi}{2} = 0.$$
Thus, $\cos\left[\dfrac{(2n + 1)\pi}{2}\right] = 0$ for all integers n.

71. $\cos x - \csc x \cot x = \cos x - \dfrac{1}{\sin x}\dfrac{\cos x}{\sin x}$

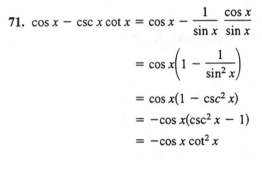

$$= \cos x\left(1 - \frac{1}{\sin^2 x}\right)$$
$$= \cos x(1 - \csc^2 x)$$
$$= -\cos x(\csc^2 x - 1)$$
$$= -\cos x \cot^2 x$$

73.

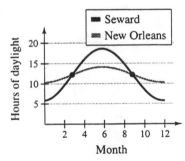

From the graph, you can see that Seward has the greater variation in the number of daylight hours.

Constant in Seward model: 6.4

Constant in New Orleans model: 1.9

75. $(2 + 3i) - \sqrt{-26} = 2 + 3i - \sqrt{26}i = 2 + (3 - \sqrt{26})i$

77. $\sqrt{-16}(1 + \sqrt{-4}) = 4i(1 + 2i) = 4i + 8i^2 = 4i - 8$

Section 5.3   Solving Trigonometric Equations

> ■ You should be able to identify and solve trigonometric equations.
>
> ■ A trigonometric equation is a conditional equation. It is true for a specific set of values.
>
> ■ To solve trigonometric equations, use algebraic techniques such as collecting like terms, taking square roots, factoring, squaring, converting to quadratic form, using formulas, and using inverse functions. Study the examples in this section.

Solutions to Odd-Numbered Exercises

1. $y = \sin \dfrac{\pi x}{2} + 1$

From the graph in the textbook we see that the curve has x-intercepts at $x = -1$ and at $x = 3$.

3. $y = \tan^2\left(\dfrac{\pi x}{6}\right) - 3$

From the graph in the textbook we see that the curve has x-intercepts at $x = \pm 2$.

5. $2\cos x - 1 = 0$

(a) $2\cos \dfrac{\pi}{3} - 1 = 2\left(\dfrac{1}{2}\right) - 1 = 0$

(b) $2\cos \dfrac{5\pi}{3} - 1 = 2\left(\dfrac{1}{2}\right) - 1 = 0$

7. $3\tan^2 2x - 1 = 0$

(a) $3\left[\tan 2\left(\dfrac{\pi}{12}\right)\right]^2 - 1 = 3\tan^2 \dfrac{\pi}{6} - 1$

$= 3\left(\dfrac{1}{\sqrt{3}}\right)^2 - 1$

$= 0$

(b) $3\left[\tan 2\left(\dfrac{5\pi}{12}\right)\right]^2 - 1 = 3\tan^2 \dfrac{5\pi}{6} - 1$

$= 3\left(-\dfrac{1}{\sqrt{3}}\right)^2 - 1$

$= 0$

9. $2\sin^2 x - \sin x - 1 = 0$

(a) $2\sin^2 \dfrac{\pi}{2} - \sin \dfrac{\pi}{2} - 1 = 2(1)^2 - 1 - 1$

$= 0$

(b) $2\sin^2 \dfrac{7\pi}{6} - \sin \dfrac{7\pi}{6} - 1 = 2\left(-\dfrac{1}{2}\right)^2 - \left(-\dfrac{1}{2}\right) - 1$

$= \dfrac{1}{2} + \dfrac{1}{2} - 1$

$= 0$

11. $2 \cos x + 1 = 0$

$$2 \cos x = -1$$

$$\cos x = -\frac{1}{2}$$

$$x = \frac{2\pi}{3} + 2n\pi$$

$$\text{or } x = \frac{4\pi}{3} + 2n\pi$$

13. $\sqrt{3} \csc x - 2 = 0$

$$\sqrt{3} \csc x = 2$$

$$\csc x = \frac{2}{\sqrt{3}}$$

$$x = \frac{\pi}{3} + 2n\pi$$

$$\text{or } x = \frac{2\pi}{3} + 2n\pi$$

15. $3 \sec^2 x - 4 = 0$

$$\sec x = \pm \frac{2}{\sqrt{3}}$$

$$x = \frac{\pi}{6} + n\pi$$

$$\text{or } x = \frac{5\pi}{6} + n\pi$$

17. $2 \sin^2 2x = 1$

$$\sin 2x = \pm \frac{1}{\sqrt{2}} = \pm \frac{\sqrt{2}}{2}$$

$$2x = \frac{\pi}{4} + 2n\pi, \ 2x = \frac{3\pi}{4} + 2n\pi, \ 2x = \frac{5\pi}{4} + 2n\pi, \ 2x = \frac{7\pi}{4} + 2n\pi,$$

$$2x = \frac{9\pi}{4} + 2n\pi, \ 2x = \frac{11\pi}{4} + 2n\pi, \ 2x = \frac{13\pi}{4} + 2n\pi, \ 2x = \frac{15\pi}{4} + 2n\pi,$$

$$\text{Thus, } x = \frac{\pi}{8} + n\pi, \ \frac{3\pi}{8} + n\pi, \ \frac{5\pi}{8} + n\pi, \ \frac{7\pi}{8} + n\pi, \ \frac{9\pi}{8} + n\pi, \ \frac{11\pi}{8} + n\pi,$$

$$\frac{13\pi}{8} + n\pi, \ \frac{15\pi}{8} + n\pi.$$

19. $4 \sin^2 x - 3 = 0$

$$\sin x = \pm \frac{\sqrt{3}}{2}$$

$$x = \frac{\pi}{3} + n\pi$$

$$\text{or } x = \frac{2\pi}{3} + n\pi$$

21.

$$\sin^2 x = 3 \cos^2 x$$

$$\sin^2 x - 3(1 - \sin^2 x) = 0$$

$$4 \sin^2 x = 3$$

$$\sin x = \pm \frac{\sqrt{3}}{2}$$

$$x = \frac{\pi}{3} + n\pi$$

$$\text{or } x = \frac{2\pi}{3} + n\pi$$

23. $(3 \tan^2 x - 1)(\tan^2 x - 3) = 0$

$$3 \tan^2 x - 1 = 0 \qquad \text{or} \qquad \tan^2 x - 3 = 0$$

$$\tan x = \pm \frac{1}{\sqrt{3}} \qquad\qquad\qquad \tan x = \pm \sqrt{3}$$

$$x = \frac{\pi}{6} + n\pi \qquad\qquad\qquad x = \frac{\pi}{3} + n\pi$$

$$\text{or } x = \frac{5\pi}{6} + n\pi \qquad\qquad \text{or } x = \frac{2\pi}{3} + n\pi$$

25.
$$\cos^3 x = \cos x$$
$$\cos^3 x - \cos x = 0$$
$$\cos x(\cos^2 x - 1) = 0$$

$\cos x = 0$ or $\cos^2 x - 1 = 0$

$x = \dfrac{\pi}{2}, \dfrac{3\pi}{2}$ $\cos x = \pm 1$

$x = 0, \pi$

27. $3 \tan^3 x - \tan x = 0$

$\tan x(3 \tan^2 x - 1) = 0$

$\tan x = 0$ or $3 \tan^2 x - 1 = 0$

$x = 0, \pi$ $\tan x = \pm \dfrac{\sqrt{3}}{3}$

$x = \dfrac{\pi}{6}, \dfrac{5\pi}{6}, \dfrac{7\pi}{6}, \dfrac{11\pi}{6}$

29. $\sec^2 x - \sec x - 2 = 0$

$(\sec x - 2)(\sec x + 1) = 0$

$\sec x - 2 = 0$ or $\sec x + 1 = 0$

$\sec x = 2$ $\sec x = -1$

$x = \dfrac{\pi}{3}, \dfrac{5\pi}{3}$ $x = \pi$

31. $2 \sin x + \csc x = 0$

$2 \sin x + \dfrac{1}{\sin x} = 0$

$2 \sin^2 x + 1 = 0$

$\sin^2 x = -\dfrac{1}{2} \Longrightarrow$ No solution

33.
$$\csc x + \cot x = 1$$
$$\dfrac{1}{\sin x} + \dfrac{\cos x}{\sin x} = 1$$
$$1 + \cos x = \sin x$$
$$(1 + \cos x)^2 = \sin^2 x$$
$$1 + 2\cos x + \cos^2 x = 1 - \cos^2 x$$
$$2\cos^2 x + 2\cos x = 0$$
$$2\cos x(\cos x + 1) = 0$$

$\cos x = 0$ or $\cos x = -1$

$x = \dfrac{\pi}{2}, \dfrac{3\pi}{2}$ $x = \pi$

($3\pi/2$ is extraneous.)   (π is extraneous.)

$x = \pi/2$ is the only solution.

35. $\cos\left(\dfrac{x}{2}\right) = \dfrac{\sqrt{2}}{2}$

$\dfrac{x}{2} = \dfrac{\pi}{4}$ or $\dfrac{x}{2} = \dfrac{7\pi}{4}$

$x = \dfrac{\pi}{2}$ $x = \dfrac{7\pi}{2}$

(Disregard since it is
outside the interval $[0, 2\pi)$.)

37. $\dfrac{1 + \cos x}{1 - \cos x} = 0$

$1 + \cos x = 0$

$\cos x = -1$

$x = \pi$

39. $2 \sec^2 x + \tan^2 x - 3 = 0$

$2(\tan^2 x + 1) + \tan^2 x - 3 = 0$

$3 \tan^2 x - 1 = 0$

$\tan x = \pm \dfrac{\sqrt{3}}{3}$

$x = \dfrac{\pi}{6}, \dfrac{5\pi}{6}, \dfrac{7\pi}{6}, \dfrac{11\pi}{6}$

41. $6y^2 - 13y + 6 = 0$

$(3y - 2)(2y - 3) = 0$

$3y - 2 = 0$ or $2y - 3 = 0$

$y = \frac{2}{3}$ $y = \frac{3}{2}$

$6\cos^2 x - 13\cos x + 6 = 0$

$(3\cos x - 2)(2\cos x - 3) = 0$

$3\cos x - 2 = 0$ or $2\cos x - 3 = 0$

$\cos x = \frac{2}{3}$ $\cos x = \frac{3}{2}$

$x \approx 0.8411, 5.4421$ (No solution)

43. $2\cos x - \sin x = 0$

$$2 = \frac{\sin x}{\cos x}$$

$$2 = \tan x$$

$$x = \arctan 2 \approx 1.1071$$

or $x = \arctan 2 + \pi \approx 4.2487$

Graph $y_1 = 2\cos x - \sin x$.

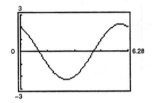

The x-intercepts occur at $x \approx 1.1071$ and $x \approx 4.2387$.

45. $$\frac{1 + \sin x}{\cos x} + \frac{\cos x}{1 + \sin x} = 4$$

$$\frac{(1 + \sin x)^2 + \cos^2 x}{\cos x(1 + \sin x)} = 4$$

$$\frac{1 + 2\sin x + \sin^2 x + \cos^2 x}{\cos x(1 + \sin x)} = 4$$

$$\frac{2 + 2\sin x}{\cos x(1 + \sin x)} = 4$$

$$\frac{2}{\cos x} = 4$$

$$\cos x = \frac{1}{2}$$

$$x = \frac{\pi}{3}, \frac{5\pi}{3}$$

Graph $y_1 = \dfrac{1 + \sin x}{\cos x} + \dfrac{\cos x}{1 + \sin x} - 4$.

The x-intercepts occur at $x = \dfrac{\pi}{3} \approx 1.0472$ and

$x = \dfrac{5\pi}{3} \approx 5.2360$.

47. $2\sin x - x = 0$

Graph $y_1 = 2\sin x - x$.

The x-intercepts occur at $x = 0$ and $x \approx 1.8955$.

49. $\sec^2 x + 0.5\tan x - 1 = 0$

Graph $y_1 = \dfrac{1}{(\cos x)^2} + 0.5\tan x - 1$.

The x-intercepts occur at $x = 0$, $x \approx 2.6779$, $x = \pi \approx 3.1416$, and $x \approx 5.8195$.

51. $2 \tan^2 x + 7 \tan x - 15 = 0$

$(2 \tan x - 3)(\tan x + 5) = 0$

$2 \tan x - 3 = 0$ or $\tan x + 5 = 0$

$\tan x = 1.5$ $\tan x = -5$

$x \approx 0.9828, 4.1244$ $x \approx 1.7682, \ 4.9098$

Graph $y_1 = 2 \tan^2 x + 7 \tan x - 15$.

The x-intercepts occur at $x \approx 0.9828$, $x \approx 1.7682$, $x \approx 4.1244$, and $x \approx 4.9098$.

53. $12 \sin^2 x - 13 \sin x + 3 = 0$

$(3 \sin x - 1)(4 \sin x - 3) = 0$

$3 \sin x - 1 = 0$ or $4 \sin x - 3 = 0$

$\sin x = \frac{1}{3}$ $\sin x = \frac{3}{4}$

$x \approx 0.3398, \ 2.8018$ $x \approx 0.8481, \ 2.2935$

Graph $y_1 = 12 \sin^2 x - 13 \sin x + 3$.

The x-intercepts occur at $x \approx 0.3398$, $x \approx 0.8481$, $x \approx 2.2935$, and $x \approx 2.8018$.

55. $\sin^2 x + 2 \sin x - 1 = 0$

$\sin x = \dfrac{-2 \pm \sqrt{4 + 4}}{2} \approx 0.4142, \ -2.4142$

$\sin x \approx 0.4142$ or $\sin x \approx -2.4142$

$x \approx 0.4271, \ 2.7145$ (No solution)

Graph $y_1 = \sin^2 x + 2 \sin x - 1$.

The x-intercepts occur at $x \approx 0.4271$ and $x \approx 2.7145$.

57. (a) $f(x) = \sin x + \cos x$

Maximum: $\left(\dfrac{\pi}{4},\ \sqrt{2}\right)$

Minimum: $\left(\dfrac{5\pi}{4},\ -\sqrt{2}\right)$

(b) $\cos x - \sin x = 0$

$$\cos x = \sin x$$

$$1 = \frac{\sin x}{\cos x}$$

$$\tan x = 1$$

$$x = \frac{\pi}{4},\ \frac{5\pi}{4}$$

$$f\left(\frac{\pi}{4}\right) = \sin\frac{\pi}{4} + \cos\frac{\pi}{4} = \frac{\sqrt{2}}{2} + \frac{\sqrt{2}}{2} = \sqrt{2}$$

$$f\left(\frac{5\pi}{4}\right) = \sin\frac{5\pi}{4} + \cos\frac{5\pi}{4} = -\sin\frac{\pi}{4} + \left(-\cos\frac{\pi}{4}\right) = -\frac{\sqrt{2}}{2} - \frac{\sqrt{2}}{2} = -\sqrt{2}$$

Therefore, the maximum point in the interval $[0, 2\pi)$ is $\left(\pi/4,\ \sqrt{2}\right)$ and the minimum point is $\left(5\pi/4,\ -\sqrt{2}\right)$.

59. $f(x) = \tan\dfrac{\pi x}{4}$

Since $\tan 0 = 0$, $x = 1$ is the smallest nonnegative fixed point.

61. $f(x) = \cos\dfrac{1}{x}$

(a) The domain of $f(x)$ is all real numbers except 0.

(b) The graph has y-axis symmetry and a horizontal asymptote at $y = 1$.

(c) As $x \to 0$, $f(x)$ oscillates between -1 and 1.

(d) There are infinitely many solutions in the interval $[-1, 1]$.

(e) The greatest solution appears to occur at $x \approx 0.6366$.

63.
$$y = \frac{1}{12}(\cos 8t - 3\sin 8t)$$

$$\frac{1}{12}(\cos 8t - 3\sin 8t) = 0$$

$$\cos 8t = 3\sin 8t$$

$$\frac{1}{3} = \tan 8t$$

$$8t \approx 0.32175 + n\pi$$

$$t \approx 0.04 + \frac{n\pi}{8}$$

In the interval $0 \le t \le 1$, $t \approx 0.04$, 0.43, and 0.83.

65. $r = \frac{1}{32}v_0^2 \sin 2\theta$, $r = 300$, $v_0 = 100$

$$300 = \frac{1}{32}(100)^2 \sin 2\theta$$

$$\sin 2\theta = 0.96$$

$2\theta \approx 1.2870$ or $2\theta \approx \pi - 1.287 \approx 1.855$

$\quad \theta \approx 0.6435 \approx 37°$ $\theta \approx 0.9275 \approx 53°$

67. $A = 2x\cos x$, $0 < x < \dfrac{\pi}{2}$

(a)

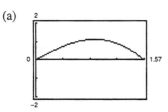

The maximum area of $A \approx 1.12$ occurs when $x \approx 0.86$.

(b) $A \ge 1$ for $0.6 < x < 1.1$

69. (a)

(b) By checking the graphs we see that
$(iii)\ r = 1.05\sin(0.95)(t + 6.32) + 6.20$
best fits the data.

(c) The constant term gives the rate of 6.20%.

(d) Period: $\dfrac{2\pi}{0.95} \approx 7$ years.

(e) $r \approx 6.00$ when $t \approx 10$ which corresponds to 2000.

Section 5.4   Sum and Difference Formulas

■ You should memorize the sum and difference formulas.

$\sin(u \pm v) = \sin u \cos v \pm \cos u \sin v$

$\cos(u \pm v) = \cos u \cos v \mp \sin u \sin v$

$\tan(u \pm v) = \dfrac{\tan u \pm \tan v}{1 \mp \tan u \tan v}$

■ You should be able to use these formulas to find the values of the trigonometric functions of angles whose sums or differences are special angles.

■ You should be able to use these formulas to solve trigonometric equations.

Solutions to Odd-Numbered Exercises

1. (a) $\cos\left(\dfrac{\pi}{4} + \dfrac{\pi}{3}\right) = \cos\dfrac{\pi}{4}\cos\dfrac{\pi}{3} - \sin\dfrac{\pi}{4}\sin\dfrac{\pi}{3}$

$= \dfrac{\sqrt{2}}{2} \cdot \dfrac{1}{2} - \dfrac{\sqrt{2}}{2} \cdot \dfrac{\sqrt{3}}{2}$

$= \dfrac{\sqrt{2} - \sqrt{6}}{4}$

(b) $\cos\dfrac{\pi}{4} + \cos\dfrac{\pi}{3} = \dfrac{\sqrt{2}}{2} + \dfrac{1}{2} = \dfrac{\sqrt{2} + 1}{2}$

3. (a) $\sin\left(\dfrac{7\pi}{6} - \dfrac{\pi}{3}\right) = \sin\dfrac{5\pi}{6} = \sin\dfrac{\pi}{6} = \dfrac{1}{2}$

(b) $\sin\dfrac{7\pi}{6} - \sin\dfrac{\pi}{3} = -\dfrac{1}{2} - \dfrac{\sqrt{3}}{2} = \dfrac{-1 - \sqrt{3}}{2}$

5. Both statements are false. Parts (a) and (b) are unequal in Exercises 1–4.

7. $\sin 75° = \sin(30° + 45°)$

$\qquad = \sin 30° \cos 45° + \sin 45° \cos 30°$

$\qquad = \dfrac{1}{2} \cdot \dfrac{\sqrt{2}}{2} + \dfrac{\sqrt{2}}{2} \cdot \dfrac{\sqrt{3}}{2}$

$\qquad = \dfrac{\sqrt{2}}{4}\left(1 + \sqrt{3}\right)$

$\cos 75° = \cos(30° + 45°)$

$\qquad = \cos 30° \cos 45° - \sin 30° \sin 45°$

$\qquad = \dfrac{\sqrt{3}}{2} \cdot \dfrac{\sqrt{2}}{2} - \dfrac{1}{2} \cdot \dfrac{\sqrt{2}}{2}$

$\qquad = \dfrac{\sqrt{2}}{4}\left(\sqrt{3} - 1\right)$

$\tan 75° = \tan(30° + 45°)$

$\qquad = \dfrac{\tan 30° + \tan 45°}{1 - \tan 30° \tan 45°}$

$\qquad = \dfrac{(\sqrt{3}/3) + 1}{1 - (\sqrt{3}/3)} = \dfrac{\sqrt{3} + 3}{3 - \sqrt{3}} \cdot \dfrac{3 + \sqrt{3}}{3 + \sqrt{3}}$

$\qquad = \dfrac{6\sqrt{3} + 12}{6} = \sqrt{3} + 2$

9. $\sin 105° = \sin(60° + 45°)$

$\qquad = \sin 60° \cos 45° + \sin 45° \cos 60°$

$\qquad = \dfrac{\sqrt{3}}{2} \cdot \dfrac{\sqrt{2}}{2} + \dfrac{\sqrt{2}}{2} \cdot \dfrac{1}{2}$

$\qquad = \dfrac{\sqrt{2}}{4}\left(\sqrt{3} + 1\right)$

$\cos 105° = \cos(60° + 45°)$

$\qquad = \cos 60° \cos 45° - \sin 60° \sin 45°$

$\qquad = \dfrac{1}{2} \cdot \dfrac{\sqrt{2}}{2} - \dfrac{\sqrt{3}}{2} \cdot \dfrac{\sqrt{2}}{2}$

$\qquad = \dfrac{\sqrt{2}}{4}\left(1 - \sqrt{3}\right)$

$\tan 105° = \tan(60° + 45°)$

$\qquad = \dfrac{\tan 60° + \tan 45°}{1 - \tan 60° \tan 45°}$

$\qquad = \dfrac{\sqrt{3} + 1}{1 - \sqrt{3}} = \dfrac{\sqrt{3} + 1}{1 - \sqrt{3}} \cdot \dfrac{1 + \sqrt{3}}{1 + \sqrt{3}}$

$\qquad = \dfrac{4 + 2\sqrt{3}}{-2} = -2 - \sqrt{3}$

11. $\sin 195° = \sin(225° - 30°)$

$\qquad = \sin 225° \cos 30° - \sin 30° \cos 225°$

$\qquad = -\sin 45° \cos 30° + \sin 30° \cos 45°$

$\qquad = -\dfrac{\sqrt{2}}{2} \cdot \dfrac{\sqrt{3}}{2} + \dfrac{1}{2} \cdot \dfrac{\sqrt{2}}{2}$

$\qquad = \dfrac{\sqrt{2}}{4}\left(\sqrt{3} - 1\right)$

$\cos 195° = \cos(225° - 30°)$

$\qquad = \cos 225° \cos 30° + \sin 225° \sin 30°$

$\qquad = -\cos 45° \cos 30° - \sin 45° \sin 30°$

$\qquad = -\dfrac{\sqrt{2}}{2} \cdot \dfrac{\sqrt{3}}{2} - \dfrac{\sqrt{2}}{2} \cdot \dfrac{1}{2}$

$\qquad = -\dfrac{\sqrt{2}}{4}\left(\sqrt{3} + 1\right)$

$\tan 195° = \tan(225° - 30°)$

$\qquad = \dfrac{\tan 225° - \tan 30°}{1 + \tan 225° \tan 30°}$

$\qquad = \dfrac{\tan 45° - \tan 30°}{1 + \tan 45° \tan 30°}$

$\qquad = \dfrac{1 - (\sqrt{3}/3)}{1 + (\sqrt{3}/3)} = \dfrac{3 - \sqrt{3}}{3 + \sqrt{3}} \cdot \dfrac{3 - \sqrt{3}}{3 - \sqrt{3}}$

$\qquad = \dfrac{12 - 6\sqrt{3}}{6} = 2 - \sqrt{3}$

13. $\sin \dfrac{11\pi}{12} = \sin\left(\dfrac{3\pi}{4} + \dfrac{\pi}{6}\right)$

$\qquad = \sin \dfrac{3\pi}{4} \cos \dfrac{\pi}{6} + \sin \dfrac{\pi}{6} \cos \dfrac{3\pi}{4}$

$\qquad = \dfrac{\sqrt{2}}{2} \cdot \dfrac{\sqrt{3}}{2} + \dfrac{1}{2}\left(-\dfrac{\sqrt{2}}{2}\right)$

$\qquad = \dfrac{\sqrt{2}}{4}\left(\sqrt{3} - 1\right)$

$\cos \dfrac{11\pi}{12} = \cos\left(\dfrac{3\pi}{4} + \dfrac{\pi}{6}\right)$

$\qquad = \cos \dfrac{3\pi}{4} \cos \dfrac{\pi}{6} - \sin \dfrac{3\pi}{4} \sin \dfrac{\pi}{6}$

$\qquad = -\dfrac{\sqrt{2}}{2} \cdot \dfrac{\sqrt{3}}{2} - \dfrac{\sqrt{2}}{2} \cdot \dfrac{1}{2}$

$\qquad = -\dfrac{\sqrt{2}}{4}\left(\sqrt{3} + 1\right)$

$\tan \dfrac{11\pi}{4} = \tan\left(\dfrac{3\pi}{4} + \dfrac{\pi}{6}\right)$

$\qquad = \dfrac{\tan(3\pi/4) + \tan(\pi/6)}{1 - \tan(3\pi/4)\tan(\pi/6)}$

$\qquad = \dfrac{-1 + (\sqrt{3}/3)}{1 - (-1)(\sqrt{3}/3)}$

$\qquad = \dfrac{-3 + \sqrt{3}}{3 + \sqrt{3}} \cdot \dfrac{3 - \sqrt{3}}{3 - \sqrt{3}}$

$\qquad = \dfrac{-12 + 6\sqrt{3}}{6} = -2 + \sqrt{3}$

15. $\sin \dfrac{17\pi}{12} = \sin\left(\dfrac{9\pi}{4} - \dfrac{5\pi}{6}\right)$

$\qquad = \sin \dfrac{9\pi}{4} \cos \dfrac{5\pi}{6} - \sin \dfrac{5\pi}{6} \cos \dfrac{9\pi}{4}$

$\qquad = \dfrac{\sqrt{2}}{2}\left(-\dfrac{\sqrt{3}}{2}\right) - \left(\dfrac{1}{2}\right)\left(\dfrac{\sqrt{2}}{2}\right)$

$\qquad = -\dfrac{\sqrt{2}}{4}\left(\sqrt{3} + 1\right)$

$\cos \dfrac{17\pi}{12} = \cos\left(\dfrac{9\pi}{4} - \dfrac{5\pi}{6}\right)$

$\qquad = \cos \dfrac{9\pi}{4} \cos \dfrac{5\pi}{6} + \sin \dfrac{9\pi}{4} \sin \dfrac{5\pi}{6}$

$\qquad = \dfrac{\sqrt{2}}{2}\left(-\dfrac{\sqrt{3}}{2}\right) + \dfrac{\sqrt{2}}{2}\left(\dfrac{1}{2}\right)$

$\qquad = \dfrac{\sqrt{2}}{4}\left(1 - \sqrt{3}\right)$

$\tan \dfrac{17\pi}{12} = \tan\left(\dfrac{9\pi}{4} - \dfrac{5\pi}{6}\right)$

$\qquad = \dfrac{\tan(9\pi/4) - \tan(5\pi/6)}{1 + \tan(9\pi/4)\tan(5\pi/6)}$

$\qquad = \dfrac{1 - (-\sqrt{3}/3)}{1 + (-\sqrt{3}/3)}$

$\qquad = \dfrac{3 + \sqrt{3}}{3 - \sqrt{3}} \cdot \dfrac{3 + \sqrt{3}}{3 + \sqrt{3}}$

$\qquad = \dfrac{12 + 6\sqrt{3}}{6} = 2 + \sqrt{3}$

17. $\qquad 285° = 225° + 60°$

$\sin 285° = \sin(225° + 60°)$

$\qquad = \sin 225° \cos 60° + \cos 225° \sin 60°$

$\qquad = -\dfrac{\sqrt{2}}{2}\left(\dfrac{1}{2}\right) - \dfrac{\sqrt{2}}{2}\left(\dfrac{\sqrt{3}}{2}\right) = -\dfrac{\sqrt{2}}{4}\left(1 + \sqrt{3}\right)$

$\cos 285° = \cos(225° + 60°)$

$\qquad = \cos 225° \cos 60° - \sin 225° \sin 60°$

$\qquad = -\dfrac{\sqrt{2}}{2}\left(\dfrac{1}{2}\right) - \left(-\dfrac{\sqrt{2}}{2}\right)\left(\dfrac{\sqrt{3}}{2}\right) = \dfrac{\sqrt{2}}{4}\left(-1 + \sqrt{3}\right)$

$\qquad = \dfrac{\sqrt{2}}{4}\left(\sqrt{3} - 1\right)$

$\tan 285° = \tan(225° + 60°)$

$\qquad = \dfrac{\tan 225° + \tan 60°}{1 - \tan 225° \tan 60°} = \dfrac{1 + \sqrt{3}}{1 - \sqrt{3}} \cdot \dfrac{1 + \sqrt{3}}{1 + \sqrt{3}}$

$\qquad = \dfrac{4 + 2\sqrt{3}}{-2} = -2 - \sqrt{3} = -\left(2 + \sqrt{3}\right)$

19.
$$-\frac{13\pi}{12} = -\left(\frac{3\pi}{4} + \frac{\pi}{3}\right)$$

$$\sin\left[-\left(\frac{3\pi}{4} + \frac{\pi}{3}\right)\right] = -\sin\left(\frac{3\pi}{4} + \frac{\pi}{3}\right)$$

$$= -\left[\sin\frac{3\pi}{4}\cos\frac{\pi}{3} + \cos\frac{3\pi}{4}\sin\frac{\pi}{3}\right]$$

$$= -\left[\frac{\sqrt{2}}{2}\left(\frac{1}{2}\right) + \left(-\frac{\sqrt{2}}{2}\right)\left(\frac{\sqrt{3}}{2}\right)\right]$$

$$= -\frac{\sqrt{2}}{4}\left(1 - \sqrt{3}\right) = \frac{\sqrt{2}}{4}\left(\sqrt{3} - 1\right)$$

$$\cos\left[-\left(\frac{3\pi}{4} + \frac{\pi}{3}\right)\right] = \cos\left(\frac{3\pi}{4} + \frac{\pi}{3}\right)$$

$$= \cos\frac{3\pi}{4}\cos\frac{\pi}{3} - \sin\frac{3\pi}{4}\sin\frac{\pi}{3}$$

$$= -\frac{\sqrt{2}}{2}\left(\frac{1}{2}\right) - \frac{\sqrt{2}}{2}\left(\frac{\sqrt{3}}{2}\right) = -\frac{\sqrt{2}}{4}\left(1 + \sqrt{3}\right)$$

$$\tan\left[-\left(\frac{3\pi}{4} + \frac{\pi}{3}\right)\right] = -\tan\left(\frac{3\pi}{4} + \frac{\pi}{3}\right)$$

$$= -\frac{\tan(3\pi/4) + \tan(\pi/3)}{1 - \tan(3\pi/4)\tan(\pi/3)} = -\frac{-1 + \sqrt{3}}{1 - (-\sqrt{3})}$$

$$= \frac{1 - \sqrt{3}}{1 + \sqrt{3}} \cdot \frac{1 - \sqrt{3}}{1 - \sqrt{3}} = \frac{4 - 2\sqrt{3}}{-2} = -2 + \sqrt{3}$$

21. $\cos 25° \cos 15° - \sin 25° \sin 15° = \cos(25° + 15°) = \cos 40°$

23. $\sin 230° \cos 30° - \cos 230° \sin 30° = \sin(230° - 30°) = \sin 200°$

25. $\dfrac{\tan 325° - \tan 86°}{1 + \tan 325° \tan 86°} = \tan(325° - 86°) = \tan 239°$

27. $\sin 3 \cos 1.2 - \cos 3 \sin 1.2 = \sin(3 - 1.2) = \sin 1.8$

29. $\dfrac{\tan 2x + \tan x}{1 - \tan 2x \tan x} = \tan(2x + x) = \tan 3x$

For Exercises 31 – 37, we have:

$\sin u = \frac{5}{13},\ u$ **in Quadrant II** $\implies \cos u = -\frac{12}{13}$

$\cos v = -\frac{3}{5},\ v$ **in Quadrant II** $\implies \sin v = \frac{4}{5}$

31. $\sin(u + v) = \sin u \cos v + \cos u \sin v$

$$= \left(\tfrac{5}{13}\right)\left(-\tfrac{3}{5}\right) + \left(-\tfrac{12}{13}\right)\left(\tfrac{4}{5}\right)$$

$$= -\tfrac{63}{65}$$

33. $\cos(u + v) = \cos u \cos v - \sin u \sin v$

$$= \left(-\tfrac{12}{13}\right)\left(-\tfrac{3}{5}\right) - \left(\tfrac{5}{13}\right)\left(\tfrac{4}{5}\right)$$

$$= \tfrac{16}{65}$$

35. $\sec(u + v) = \dfrac{1}{\cos(u + v)} = \dfrac{1}{16/65} = \dfrac{65}{16}$

Use Exercise 33 for $\cos(u + v)$.

37. $\tan(u - v) = \dfrac{\tan u - \tan v}{1 + \tan u \tan v} = \dfrac{-5/12 - (-4/3)}{1 + (-5/12)(-4/3)}$

$\qquad = \dfrac{11/12}{14/9} = \dfrac{33}{56}$

For Exercises 39–43, we have:

$\sin u = -\dfrac{7}{25}, u$ **in Quadrant III** $\implies \cos u = -\dfrac{24}{25}$

$\cos v = -\dfrac{4}{5}, v$ **in Quadrant III** $\implies \sin v = -\dfrac{3}{5}$

39. $\cos(u + v) = \cos u \cos v - \sin u \sin v$

$\qquad = \left(-\dfrac{24}{25}\right)\left(-\dfrac{4}{5}\right) - \left(-\dfrac{7}{25}\right)\left(-\dfrac{3}{5}\right)$

$\qquad = \dfrac{3}{5}$

41. $\sin(v - u) = \sin v \cos u - \cos v \sin u$

$\qquad = \left(-\dfrac{3}{5}\right)\left(-\dfrac{24}{25}\right) - \left(-\dfrac{4}{5}\right)\left(-\dfrac{7}{25}\right)$

$\qquad = \dfrac{44}{125}$

43. $\csc(u + v) = \dfrac{1}{\sin(u + v)} = \dfrac{1}{\sin u \cos v + \cos u \sin v}$

$\qquad = \dfrac{1}{\left(-\dfrac{7}{25}\right)\left(-\dfrac{4}{5}\right) + \left(-\dfrac{24}{25}\right)\left(-\dfrac{3}{5}\right)} = \dfrac{1}{\frac{4}{5}} = \dfrac{5}{4}$

45. $\sin(3\pi - x) = \sin 3\pi \cos x - \sin x \cos 3\pi = (0)(\cos x) - (\sin x)(-1) = \sin x$

47. $\sin\left(\dfrac{\pi}{6} + x\right) = \sin \dfrac{\pi}{6} \cos x + \sin x \cos \dfrac{\pi}{6} = \dfrac{1}{2}\left(\cos x + \sqrt{3} \sin x\right)$

49. $\cos(\pi - \theta) + \sin\left(\dfrac{\pi}{2} + \theta\right) = \cos \pi \cos \theta + \sin \pi \sin \theta + \sin \dfrac{\pi}{2} \cos \theta + \sin \theta \cos \dfrac{\pi}{2}$

$\qquad = (-1)(\cos \theta) + (0)(\sin \theta) + (1)(\cos \theta) + (\sin \theta)(0)$

$\qquad = -\cos \theta + \cos \theta$

$\qquad = 0$

51. $\cos(x + y) \cos(x - y) = (\cos x \cos y - \sin x \sin y)(\cos x \cos y + \sin x \sin y)$

$\qquad = \cos^2 x \cos^2 y - \sin^2 x \sin^2 y$

$\qquad = \cos^2 x (1 - \sin^2 y) - \sin^2 x \sin^2 y$

$\qquad = \cos^2 x - \cos^2 x \sin^2 y - \sin^2 x \sin^2 y$

$\qquad = \cos^2 x - \sin^2 y(\cos^2 x + \sin^2 x)$

$\qquad = \cos^2 x - \sin^2 y$

53. $\sin(x + y) + \sin(x - y) = \sin x \cos y + \sin y \cos x + \sin x \cos y - \sin y \cos x$

$$= 2 \sin x \cos y$$

55. $\cos(n\pi + \theta) = \cos n\pi \cos \theta - \sin n\pi \sin \theta$

$$= (-1)^n (\cos \theta) - (0)(\sin \theta)$$

$$= (-1)^n (\cos \theta), \text{ where } n \text{ is an integer.}$$

57. $C = \arctan \dfrac{b}{a} \implies \sin C = \dfrac{b}{\sqrt{a^2 + b^2}}, \cos C = \dfrac{a}{\sqrt{a^2 + b^2}}$

$$\sqrt{a^2 + b^2} \sin(B\theta + C) = \sqrt{a^2 + b^2}\left(\sin B\theta \cdot \dfrac{a}{\sqrt{a^2 + b^2}} + \dfrac{b}{\sqrt{a^2 + b^2}} \cdot \cos \beta\theta \right) = a \sin B\theta + b \cos B\theta$$

59. $\cos\left(\dfrac{3\pi}{2} - x\right) = \cos \dfrac{3\pi}{2} \cos x + \sin \dfrac{3\pi}{2} \sin x$

$$= (0)(\cos x) + (-1)(\sin x)$$

$$= -\sin x$$

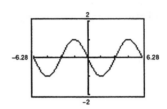

61. $\sin\left(\dfrac{3\pi}{2} + \theta\right) + \sin(\pi - \theta)$

$$= \sin \dfrac{3\pi}{2} \cos \theta + \cos \dfrac{3\pi}{2} \sin \theta + \sin \pi \cos \theta - \cos \pi \sin \theta$$

$$= (-1)(\cos \theta) + (0)(\sin \theta) + (0)(\cos \theta) - (-1)(\sin \theta)$$

$$= -\cos \theta + \sin \theta$$

$$= \sin \theta - \cos \theta$$

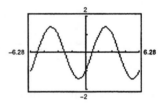

63. $\sin \theta + \cos \theta$

$a = 1, \ b = 1, \ B = 1$

(a) $C = \arctan \dfrac{b}{a} = \arctan 1 = \dfrac{\pi}{4}$

$\quad \sin \theta + \cos \theta = \sqrt{a^2 + b^2} \sin(B\theta + C)$

$$= \sqrt{2} \sin\left(\theta + \dfrac{\pi}{4}\right)$$

(b) $C = \arctan \dfrac{a}{b} = \arctan 1 = \dfrac{\pi}{4}$

$\quad \sin \theta + \cos \theta = \sqrt{a^2 + b^2} \cos(B\theta - C)$

$$= \sqrt{2} \cos\left(\theta - \dfrac{\pi}{4}\right)$$

65. $12 \sin 3\theta + 5 \cos 3\theta$

$a = 12, \ b = 5, \ B = 3$

(a) $C = \arctan \dfrac{b}{a} = \arctan \dfrac{5}{12} \approx 0.3948$

$12 \sin 3\theta + 5 \cos 3\theta = \sqrt{a^2 + b^2} \sin(B\theta + C)$

$\approx 13 \sin(3\theta + 0.3948)$

(b) $C = \arctan \dfrac{a}{b} = \arctan \dfrac{12}{5} \approx 1.1760$

$12 \sin 3\theta + 5 \cos 3\theta = \sqrt{a^2 + b^2} \cos(B\theta - C)$

$\approx 13 \cos(3\theta - 1.1760)$

67. $C = \arctan \dfrac{b}{a} = \dfrac{\pi}{2} \implies a = 0$

$\sqrt{a^2 + b^2} = 2 \implies b = 2$

$B = 1$

$2 \sin\left(\theta + \dfrac{\pi}{2}\right) = (0)(\sin\theta) + (2)(\cos\theta) = 2 \cos \theta$

69. $\sin(\arcsin x + \arccos x) = \sin(\arcsin x) \cos(\arccos x) + \sin(\arccos x) \cos(\arcsin x)$

$= x \cdot x + \sqrt{1 - x^2} \cdot \sqrt{1 - x^2}$

$= x^2 + 1 - x^2$

$= 1$

$\theta = \arcsin x$

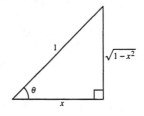

$\theta = \arccos x$

71.
$$\sin\left(x + \dfrac{\pi}{3}\right) + \sin\left(x - \dfrac{\pi}{3}\right) = 1$$

$$\sin x \cos \dfrac{\pi}{3} + \cos x \sin \dfrac{\pi}{3} + \sin x \cos \dfrac{\pi}{3} - \cos x \sin \dfrac{\pi}{3} = 1$$

$$2 \sin x (0.5) = 1$$

$$\sin x = 1$$

$$x = \dfrac{\pi}{2}$$

73. $\cos\left(x + \dfrac{\pi}{4}\right) - \cos\left(x - \dfrac{\pi}{4}\right) = 1$

$$\cos x \cos \dfrac{\pi}{4} - \sin x \sin \dfrac{\pi}{4} - \left(\cos x \cos \dfrac{\pi}{4} + \sin x \sin \dfrac{\pi}{4}\right) = 1$$

$$-2\sin x \left(\dfrac{\sqrt{2}}{2}\right) = 1$$

$$-\sqrt{2}\sin x = 1$$

$$\sin x = -\dfrac{1}{\sqrt{2}}$$

$$\sin x = -\dfrac{\sqrt{2}}{2}$$

$$x = \dfrac{5\pi}{4}, \ \dfrac{7\pi}{4}$$

75.   Analytically: $\cos\left(x + \dfrac{\pi}{4}\right) + \cos\left(x - \dfrac{\pi}{4}\right) = 1$

$$\cos x \cos \dfrac{\pi}{4} - \sin x \sin \dfrac{\pi}{4} + \cos x \cos \dfrac{\pi}{4} + \sin x \sin \dfrac{\pi}{4} = 1$$

$$2\cos x \left(\dfrac{\sqrt{2}}{2}\right) = 1$$

$$\sqrt{2}\cos x = 1$$

$$\cos x = \dfrac{1}{\sqrt{2}}$$

$$\cos x = \dfrac{\sqrt{2}}{2}$$

$$x = \dfrac{\pi}{4}, \ \dfrac{7\pi}{4}$$

Graphically: Graph $y_1 = \cos\left(x + \dfrac{\pi}{4}\right) + \cos\left(x - \dfrac{\pi}{4}\right)$ and $y_2 = 1$.

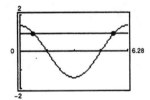

The points of intersection occur at $x = \dfrac{\pi}{4}$ and $x = \dfrac{7\pi}{4}$.

77. $\sin^2\left(\theta + \dfrac{\pi}{4}\right) + \sin^2\left(\theta - \dfrac{\pi}{4}\right) = \left[\sin\theta\cos\dfrac{\pi}{4} + \cos\theta\sin\dfrac{\pi}{4}\right]^2 + \left[\sin\theta\cos\dfrac{\pi}{4} - \cos\theta\sin\dfrac{\pi}{4}\right]^2$

$ = \left[\dfrac{\sin\theta}{\sqrt{2}} + \dfrac{\cos\theta}{\sqrt{2}}\right]^2 + \left[\dfrac{\sin\theta}{\sqrt{2}} - \dfrac{\cos\theta}{\sqrt{2}}\right]^2$

$ = \dfrac{\sin^2\theta}{2} + \sin\theta\cos\theta + \dfrac{\cos^2\theta}{2} + \dfrac{\sin^2\theta}{2} - \sin\theta\cos\theta + \dfrac{\cos^2\theta}{2}$

$ = \sin^2\theta + \cos^2\theta$

$ = 1$

79. $y = \dfrac{1}{3}\sin 2t + \dfrac{1}{4}\cos 2t$

(a) $a = \dfrac{1}{3}$, $b = \dfrac{1}{4}$, $B = 2$

$ C = \arctan\dfrac{b}{a} = \arctan\dfrac{3}{4} \approx 0.6435$

$ y \approx \sqrt{\left(\tfrac{1}{3}\right)^2 + \left(\tfrac{1}{4}\right)^2}\,\sin(2t + 0.6435)$

$ = \dfrac{5}{12}\sin(2t + 0.6435)$

(b) Amplitude: $\dfrac{5}{12}$ feet

(c) Frequency: $\dfrac{1}{\text{period}} = \dfrac{b}{2\pi} = \dfrac{2}{2\pi} = \dfrac{1}{\pi}$ cycles per second

Section 5.5   Multiple-Angle and Product-to-Sum Formulas

■ You should know the following double-angle formulas.

(a) $\sin 2u = 2 \sin u \cos u$

(b) $\cos 2u = \cos^2 u - \sin^2 u$

$\qquad = 2 \cos^2 u - 1$

$\qquad = 1 - 2 \sin^2 u$

(c) $\tan 2u = \dfrac{2 \tan u}{1 - \tan^2 u}$

■ You should be able to reduce the power of a trigonometric function.

(a) $\sin^2 u = \dfrac{1 - \cos 2u}{2}$

(b) $\cos^2 u = \dfrac{1 + \cos 2u}{2}$

(c) $\tan^2 u = \dfrac{1 - \cos 2u}{1 + \cos 2u}$

■ You should be able to use the half-angle formulas.

(a) $\sin \dfrac{u}{2} = \pm \sqrt{\dfrac{1 - \cos u}{2}}$

(b) $\cos \dfrac{u}{2} = \pm \sqrt{\dfrac{1 + \cos u}{2}}$

(c) $\tan \dfrac{u}{2} = \dfrac{1 - \cos u}{\sin u} = \dfrac{\sin u}{1 + \cos u}$

■ You should be able to use the product-sum formulas.

(a) $\sin u \sin v = \dfrac{1}{2} [\cos(u - v) - \cos(u + v)]$

(b) $\cos u \cos v = \dfrac{1}{2} [\cos(u - v) + \cos(u + v)]$

(c) $\sin u \cos v = \dfrac{1}{2} [\sin(u + v) + \sin(u - v)]$

(d) $\cos u \sin v = \dfrac{1}{2} [\sin(u + v) - \sin(u - v)]$

■ You should be able to use the sum-product formulas.

(a) $\sin x + \sin y = 2 \sin\left(\dfrac{x + y}{2}\right) \cos\left(\dfrac{x - y}{2}\right)$

(b) $\sin x - \sin y = 2 \cos\left(\dfrac{x + y}{2}\right) \sin\left(\dfrac{x - y}{2}\right)$

(c) $\cos x + \cos y = 2 \cos\left(\dfrac{x + y}{2}\right) \cos\left(\dfrac{x - y}{2}\right)$

(d) $\cos x - \cos y = -2 \sin\left(\dfrac{x + y}{2}\right) \sin\left(\dfrac{x - y}{2}\right)$

Solutions to Odd-Numbered Exercises

Figure for Exercises 1–7

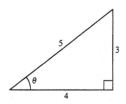

$$\sin \theta = \tfrac{3}{5}$$
$$\cos \theta = \tfrac{4}{5}$$
$$\tan \theta = \tfrac{3}{4}$$

1. $\sin \theta = \tfrac{3}{5}$

3. $\cos 2\theta = 2\cos^2\theta - 1$
$$= 2\left(\tfrac{4}{5}\right)^2 - 1$$
$$= \tfrac{32}{25} - \tfrac{25}{25}$$
$$= \tfrac{7}{25}$$

5. $\tan 2\theta = \dfrac{2\tan\theta}{1-\tan^2\theta}$
$$= \dfrac{2(3/4)}{1-(3/4)^2}$$
$$= \dfrac{3/2}{1-9/16}$$
$$= \dfrac{3}{2}\cdot\dfrac{16}{7}$$
$$= \dfrac{24}{7}$$

7. $\csc 2\theta = \dfrac{1}{\sin 2\theta}$
$$= \dfrac{1}{2\sin\theta\cos\theta}$$
$$= \dfrac{1}{2(3/5)(4/5)}$$
$$= \dfrac{25}{24}$$

9.
$$\sin 2x - \sin x = 0$$
$$2\sin x\cos x - \sin x = 0$$
$$\sin x(2\cos x - 1) = 0$$
$$\sin x = 0 \quad \text{or} \quad 2\cos x - 1 = 0$$
$$x = 0,\ \pi \qquad\qquad \cos x = \tfrac{1}{2}$$
$$x = \tfrac{\pi}{3},\ \tfrac{5\pi}{3}$$
$$x = 0,\ \tfrac{\pi}{3},\ \pi,\ \tfrac{5\pi}{3}$$

11. $4\sin x\cos x = 1$
$$2\sin 2x = 1$$
$$\sin 2x = \tfrac{1}{2}$$
$$2x = \tfrac{\pi}{6} + 2n\pi \quad \text{or} \quad 2x = \tfrac{5\pi}{6} + 2n\pi$$
$$x = \tfrac{\pi}{12} + n\pi \qquad\qquad x = \tfrac{5\pi}{12} + n\pi$$
$$x = \tfrac{\pi}{12},\ \tfrac{13\pi}{12} \qquad\qquad x = \tfrac{5\pi}{12},\ \tfrac{17\pi}{12}$$

13.
$$\cos 2x = \cos x$$
$$\cos^2 x - \sin^2 x = \cos x$$
$$\cos^2 x - (1 - \cos^2 x) - \cos x = 0$$
$$2 \cos^2 x - \cos x - 1 = 0$$
$$(2 \cos x + 1)(\cos x - 1) = 0$$

$2 \cos x + 1 = 0 \qquad$ or $\quad \cos x - 1 = 0$

$$\cos x = -\frac{1}{2} \qquad\qquad \cos x = 1$$

$$x = \frac{2\pi}{3}, \frac{4\pi}{3} \qquad\qquad x = 0$$

15. $\qquad \tan 2x - \cot x = 0$

$$\frac{2 \tan x}{1 - \tan^2 x} = \cot x$$

$$2 \tan x = \cot x(1 - \tan^2 x)$$
$$2 \tan x = \cot x - \cot x \tan^2 x$$
$$2 \tan x = \cot x - \tan x$$
$$3 \tan x = \cot x$$
$$3 \tan x - \cot x = 0$$
$$3 \tan x - \frac{1}{\tan x} = 0$$
$$\frac{3 \tan^2 x - 1}{\tan x} = 0$$

$$\frac{1}{\tan x}(3 \tan^2 x - 1) = 0$$

$$\cot x(3 \tan^2 x - 1) = 0$$

$\cot x = 0 \qquad$ or $\quad 3 \tan^2 x - 1 = 0$

$$x = \frac{\pi}{2}, \frac{3\pi}{2} \qquad\qquad \tan^2 x = \frac{1}{3}$$

$$\tan x = \pm\frac{\sqrt{3}}{3}$$

$$x = \frac{\pi}{6}, \frac{5\pi}{6}, \frac{7\pi}{6}, \frac{11\pi}{6}$$

$$x = \frac{\pi}{6}, \frac{\pi}{2}, \frac{5\pi}{6}, \frac{7\pi}{6}, \frac{3\pi}{2}, \frac{11\pi}{6}$$

17. $\qquad\qquad \sin 4x = -2 \sin 2x$

$$\sin 4x + 2 \sin 2x = 0$$
$$2 \sin 2x \cos 2x + 2 \sin 2x = 0$$
$$2 \sin 2x(\cos 2x + 1) = 0$$

$2 \sin 2x = 0 \qquad$ or $\quad \cos 2x + 1 = 0$

$\sin 2x = 0 \qquad\qquad\qquad \cos 2x = -1$

$2x = n\pi \qquad\qquad\qquad 2x = \pi + 2n\pi$

$$x = \frac{n}{2}\pi \qquad\qquad\qquad x = \frac{\pi}{2} + n\pi$$

$$x = 0, \frac{\pi}{2}, \pi, \frac{3\pi}{2} \qquad\qquad x = \frac{\pi}{2}, \frac{3\pi}{2}$$

19. $f(x) = 6 \sin x \cos x$

$\qquad = 3(2 \sin x \cos x)$

$\qquad = 3 \sin 2x$

21. $g(x) = 4 - 8 \sin^2 x$

$\qquad = 4(1 - 2 \sin^2 x)$

$\qquad = 4 \cos 2x$

23. $\sin u = \dfrac{3}{5}$, $0 < u < \dfrac{\pi}{2}$ $\implies$ $\cos u = \dfrac{4}{5}$

$\sin 2u = 2 \sin u \cos u = 2 \cdot \dfrac{3}{5} \cdot \dfrac{4}{5} = \dfrac{24}{25}$

$\cos 2u = \cos^2 u - \sin^2 u = \dfrac{16}{25} - \dfrac{9}{25} = \dfrac{7}{25}$

$\tan 2u = \dfrac{2 \tan u}{1 - \tan^2 u} = \dfrac{2(3/4)}{1 - (9/16)} = \dfrac{24}{7}$

25. $\tan u = \dfrac{1}{2}$, $\pi < u < \dfrac{3\pi}{2}$ $\implies$ $\sin u = -\dfrac{1}{\sqrt{5}}$ and

$\cos u = -\dfrac{2}{\sqrt{5}}$

$\sin 2u = 2 \sin u \cos u = 2\left(-\dfrac{1}{\sqrt{5}}\right)\left(-\dfrac{2}{\sqrt{5}}\right) = \dfrac{4}{5}$

$\cos 2u = \cos^2 u - \sin^2 u = \left(-\dfrac{2}{\sqrt{5}}\right)^2 - \left(-\dfrac{1}{\sqrt{5}}\right)^2 = \dfrac{3}{5}$

$\tan 2u = \dfrac{2 \tan u}{1 - \tan^2 u} = \dfrac{2(1/2)}{1 - (1/4)} = \dfrac{4}{3}$

27. $\sec u = -\dfrac{5}{2}$, $\dfrac{\pi}{2} < u < \pi$ $\implies$ $\sin u = \dfrac{\sqrt{21}}{5}$ and $\cos u = -\dfrac{2}{5}$

$\sin 2u = 2 \sin u \cos u = 2\left(\dfrac{\sqrt{21}}{5}\right)\left(-\dfrac{2}{5}\right) = -\dfrac{4\sqrt{21}}{25}$

$\cos 2u = \cos^2 u - \sin^2 u = \left(-\dfrac{2}{5}\right)^2 - \left(\dfrac{\sqrt{21}}{5}\right)^2 = -\dfrac{17}{25}$

$\tan 2u = \dfrac{2 \tan u}{1 - \tan^2 u} = \dfrac{2(-\sqrt{21}/2)}{1 - (-\sqrt{21}/2)^2}$

$= \dfrac{-\sqrt{21}}{1 - 21/4} = \dfrac{4\sqrt{21}}{17}$

29. $\cos^4 x = (\cos^2 x)(\cos^2 x) = \left(\dfrac{1 + \cos 2x}{2}\right)\left(\dfrac{1 + \cos 2x}{2}\right) = \dfrac{1 + 2\cos 2x + \cos^2 2x}{4}$

$= \dfrac{1 + 2\cos 2x + (1 + \cos 4x)/2}{4}$

$= \dfrac{2 + 4\cos 2x + 1 + \cos 4x}{8}$

$= \dfrac{3 + 4\cos 2x + \cos 4x}{8}$

$= \dfrac{1}{8}(3 + 4\cos 2x + \cos 4x)$

31. $(\sin^2 x)(\cos^2 x) = \left(\dfrac{1 - \cos 2x}{2}\right)\left(\dfrac{1 + \cos 2x}{2}\right)$

$= \dfrac{1 - \cos^2 2x}{4}$

$= \dfrac{1}{4}\left(1 - \dfrac{1 + \cos 4x}{2}\right)$

$= \dfrac{1}{8}(2 - 1 - \cos 4x)$

$= \dfrac{1}{8}(1 - \cos 4x)$

33. $\sin^2 x \cos^4 x = \sin^2 x \cos^2 x \cos^2 x = \left(\dfrac{1 - \cos 2x}{2}\right)\left(\dfrac{1 + \cos 2x}{2}\right)\left(\dfrac{1 + \cos 2x}{2}\right)$

$$= \dfrac{1}{8}(1 - \cos 2x)(1 + \cos 2x)(1 + \cos 2x)$$

$$= \dfrac{1}{8}(1 - \cos^2 2x)(1 + \cos 2x)$$

$$= \dfrac{1}{8}(1 + \cos 2x - \cos^2 2x - \cos^3 2x)$$

$$= \dfrac{1}{8}\left[1 + \cos 2x - \left(\dfrac{1 + \cos 4x}{2}\right) - \cos 2x\left(\dfrac{1 + \cos 4x}{2}\right)\right]$$

$$= \dfrac{1}{16}[2 + 2\cos 2x - 1 - \cos 4x - \cos 2x - \cos 2x \cos 4x]$$

$$= \dfrac{1}{16}\left[1 + \cos 2x - \cos 4x - \left(\dfrac{1}{2}\cos 2x + \dfrac{1}{2}\cos 6x\right)\right]$$

$$= \dfrac{1}{32}(2 + 2\cos 2x - 2\cos 4x - \cos 2x - \cos 6x)$$

$$= \dfrac{1}{32}(2 + \cos 2x - 2\cos 4x - \cos 6x)$$

Figure for Exercises 35 – 39

$\sin \theta = \frac{5}{13}$

$\cos \theta = \frac{12}{13}$

35. $\cos \dfrac{\theta}{2} = \sqrt{\dfrac{1 + \cos \theta}{2}} = \sqrt{\dfrac{1 + 12/13}{2}} = \sqrt{\dfrac{25}{26}} = \dfrac{5}{\sqrt{26}}$

37. $\tan \dfrac{\theta}{2} = \dfrac{\sin \theta}{1 + \cos \theta} = \dfrac{5/13}{1 + 12/13} = \dfrac{5}{25} = \dfrac{1}{5}$

39. $\csc \dfrac{\theta}{2} = \dfrac{1}{\sin(\theta/2)} = \dfrac{1}{\sqrt{(1 - \cos \theta)/2}} = \dfrac{1}{\sqrt{\left(1 - \frac{12}{13}\right)/2}} = \dfrac{1}{\sqrt{1/26}} = \sqrt{26}$

41. $\sin 105° = \sin\left(\dfrac{1}{2} \cdot 210°\right) = \sqrt{\dfrac{1 - \cos 210°}{2}} = \sqrt{\dfrac{1 + (\sqrt{3}/2)}{2}} = \dfrac{1}{2}\sqrt{2 + \sqrt{3}}$

$\cos 105° = \cos\left(\dfrac{1}{2} \cdot 210°\right) = -\sqrt{\dfrac{1 + \cos 210°}{2}} = -\sqrt{\dfrac{1 - (\sqrt{3}/2)}{2}} = -\dfrac{1}{2}\sqrt{2 - \sqrt{3}}$

$\tan 105° = \tan\left(\dfrac{1}{2} \cdot 210°\right) = \dfrac{\sin 210°}{1 + \cos 210°} = \dfrac{-1/2}{1 - (\sqrt{3}/2)} = -2 - \sqrt{3}$

43. $\sin 112° 30' = \sin\left(\frac{1}{2} \cdot 225°\right) = \sqrt{\frac{1 - \cos 225°}{2}} = \sqrt{\frac{1 + (\sqrt{2}/2)}{2}} = \frac{1}{2}\sqrt{2 + \sqrt{2}}$

$\cos 112° 30' = \cos\left(\frac{1}{2} \cdot 225°\right) = -\sqrt{\frac{1 + \cos 225°}{2}} = -\sqrt{\frac{1 - (\sqrt{2}/2)}{2}} = -\frac{1}{2}\sqrt{2 - \sqrt{2}}$

$\tan 112° 30' = \tan\left(\frac{1}{2} \cdot 225°\right) = \frac{\sin 225°}{1 + \cos 225°} = \frac{-\sqrt{2}/2}{1 - (\sqrt{2}/2)} = -1 - \sqrt{2}$

45. $\sin \frac{\pi}{8} = \sin\left[\frac{1}{2}\left(\frac{\pi}{4}\right)\right] = \sqrt{\frac{1 - \cos(\pi/4)}{2}} = \frac{1}{2}\sqrt{2 - \sqrt{2}}$

$\cos \frac{\pi}{8} = \cos\left[\frac{1}{2}\left(\frac{\pi}{4}\right)\right] = \sqrt{\frac{1 + \cos(\pi/4)}{2}} = \frac{1}{2}\sqrt{2 + \sqrt{2}}$

$\tan \frac{\pi}{8} = \tan\left[\frac{1}{2}\left(\frac{\pi}{4}\right)\right] = \frac{\sin(\pi/4)}{1 + \cos(\pi/4)} = \frac{\sqrt{2}/2}{1 + (\sqrt{2}/2)} = \sqrt{2} - 1$

47. $\sin u = \frac{5}{13}, \frac{\pi}{2} < u < \pi \implies \cos u = -\frac{12}{13}$

$\sin\left(\frac{u}{2}\right) = \sqrt{\frac{1 - \cos u}{2}} = \sqrt{\frac{1 + (12/13)}{.2}} = \frac{5\sqrt{26}}{26}$

$\cos\left(\frac{u}{2}\right) = \sqrt{\frac{1 + \cos u}{2}} = \sqrt{\frac{1 - (12/13)}{2}} = \frac{\sqrt{26}}{26}$

$\tan\left(\frac{u}{2}\right) = \frac{\sin u}{1 + \cos u} = \frac{5/13}{1 - (12/13)} = \frac{5}{1} = 5$

49. $\tan u = -\frac{5}{8}, \frac{3\pi}{2} < u < 2\pi \implies \sin u = -\frac{5}{\sqrt{89}}$ and $\cos u = \frac{8}{\sqrt{89}}$

$\sin\left(\frac{u}{2}\right) = \sqrt{\frac{1 - \cos u}{2}} = \sqrt{\frac{1 - (8/\sqrt{89})}{2}}\sqrt{\frac{\sqrt{89} - 8}{2\sqrt{89}}} = \sqrt{\frac{89 - 8\sqrt{89}}{178}}$

$\cos\left(\frac{u}{2}\right) = -\sqrt{\frac{1 + \cos u}{2}} = -\sqrt{\frac{1 + (8/\sqrt{89})}{2}} = -\sqrt{\frac{\sqrt{89} + 8}{2\sqrt{89}}} = -\sqrt{\frac{89 + 8\sqrt{89}}{178}}$

$\tan\left(\frac{u}{2}\right) = \frac{1 - \cos u}{\sin u} = \frac{1 - (8/\sqrt{89})}{-5/\sqrt{89}} = \frac{8 - \sqrt{89}}{5}$

51. $\csc u = -\frac{5}{3}, \pi < u < \frac{3\pi}{2} \implies \sin u = -\frac{3}{5}$ and $\cos u = -\frac{4}{5}$

$\sin\left(\frac{u}{2}\right) = \sqrt{\frac{1 - \cos u}{2}} = \sqrt{\frac{1 + (4/5)}{2}} = \frac{3\sqrt{10}}{10}$

$\cos\left(\frac{u}{2}\right) = -\sqrt{\frac{1 + \cos u}{2}} = -\sqrt{\frac{1 - (4/5)}{2}} = -\frac{\sqrt{10}}{10}$

$\tan\left(\frac{u}{2}\right) = \frac{1 - \cos u}{\sin u} = \frac{1 + (4/5)}{-3/5} = -3$

53. $\sqrt{\dfrac{1 - \cos 6x}{2}} = |\sin 3x|$

55. $-\sqrt{\dfrac{1 - \cos 8x}{1 + \cos 8x}} = -\dfrac{\sqrt{(1 - \cos 8x)/2}}{\sqrt{(1 + \cos 8x)/2}}$

$$= -\left|\dfrac{\sin 4x}{\cos 4x}\right|$$

$$= -|\tan 4x|$$

57. $\sin\dfrac{x}{2} + \cos x = 0$

$\pm\sqrt{\dfrac{1 - \cos x}{2}} = -\cos x$

$\dfrac{1 - \cos x}{2} = \cos^2 x$

$0 = 2\cos^2 x + \cos x - 1$

$\quad = (2\cos x - 1)(\cos x + 1)$

$\cos x = \dfrac{1}{2} \quad$ or $\quad \cos x = -1$

$x = \dfrac{\pi}{3}, \dfrac{5\pi}{3} \qquad x = \pi$

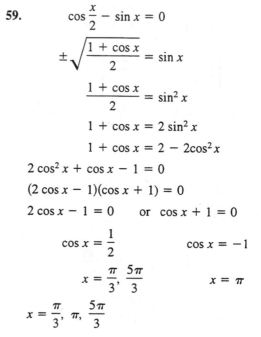

By checking these values in the original equation, we see that $x = \pi/3$ and $x = 5\pi/3$ are extraneous, and $x = \pi$ is the only solution.

59. $\cos\dfrac{x}{2} - \sin x = 0$

$\pm\sqrt{\dfrac{1 + \cos x}{2}} = \sin x$

$\dfrac{1 + \cos x}{2} = \sin^2 x$

$1 + \cos x = 2\sin^2 x$

$1 + \cos x = 2 - 2\cos^2 x$

$2\cos^2 x + \cos x - 1 = 0$

$(2\cos x - 1)(\cos x + 1) = 0$

$2\cos x - 1 = 0 \quad$ or $\quad \cos x + 1 = 0$

$\cos x = \dfrac{1}{2} \qquad\qquad \cos x = -1$

$x = \dfrac{\pi}{3}, \dfrac{5\pi}{3} \qquad\qquad x = \pi$

$x = \dfrac{\pi}{3}, \pi, \dfrac{5\pi}{3}$

$\pi/3$, π, and $5\pi/3$ are all solutions to the equation.

61. $6\sin\dfrac{\pi}{4}\cos\dfrac{\pi}{4} = 6 \cdot \dfrac{1}{2}\left[\sin\left(\dfrac{\pi}{4} + \dfrac{\pi}{4}\right) + \sin\left(\dfrac{\pi}{4} - \dfrac{\pi}{4}\right)\right] = 3\left(\sin\dfrac{\pi}{2} + \sin 0\right)$

63. $\sin 5\theta\cos 3\theta = \dfrac{1}{2}\left[\sin(5\theta + 3\theta) + \sin(5\theta - 3\theta) = \dfrac{1}{2}(\sin 8\theta + \sin 2\theta)\right.$

65. $5\cos(-5\beta)\cos 3\beta = 5 \cdot \dfrac{1}{2}\left[\cos(-5\beta - 3\beta) + \cos(-5\beta + 3\beta)\right] = \dfrac{5}{2}\left[\cos(-8\beta) + \cos(-2\beta)\right]$

$\qquad\qquad = \dfrac{5}{2}(\cos 8\beta + \cos 2\beta)$

67. $\sin(x + y)\sin(x - y) = \dfrac{1}{2}(\cos 2y - \cos 2x)$

69. $\sin(\theta + \pi)\cos(\theta - \pi) = \dfrac{1}{2}(\sin 2\theta + \sin 2\pi)$

71. $\sin 60° + \sin 30° = 2\sin\left(\dfrac{60° + 30°}{2}\right)\cos\left(\dfrac{60° - 30°}{2}\right) = 2\sin 45°\cos 15°$

73. $\cos\dfrac{3\pi}{4} - \cos\dfrac{\pi}{4} = -2\sin\left(\dfrac{(3\pi/4) + (\pi/4)}{2}\right)\sin\left(\dfrac{(3\pi/4) - (\pi/4)}{2}\right) = -2\sin\dfrac{\pi}{2}\sin\dfrac{\pi}{4}$

75. $\cos 6x + \cos 2x = 2\cos\left(\dfrac{6x + 2x}{2}\right)\cos\left(\dfrac{6x - 2x}{2}\right) = 2\cos 4x\cos 2x$

77. $\sin(\alpha + \beta) - \sin(\alpha - \beta) = 2\cos\left(\dfrac{\alpha + \beta + \alpha - \beta}{2}\right)\sin\left(\dfrac{\alpha + \beta - \alpha + \beta}{2}\right) = 2\cos\alpha\sin\beta$

79. $\cos(\phi + 2\pi) + \cos\phi = 2\cos\left(\dfrac{\phi + 2\pi + \phi}{2}\right)\cos\left(\dfrac{\phi + 2\pi - \phi}{2}\right) = 2\cos(\phi + \pi)\cos\pi$

81.

$$\sin 6x + \sin 2x = 0$$

$$2\sin\left(\frac{6x + 2x}{2}\right)\cos\left(\frac{6x - 2x}{2}\right) = 0$$

$$2(\sin 4x)\cos 2x = 0$$

$\sin 4x = 0 \quad$ or $\quad \cos 2x = 0$

$\quad 4x = n\pi \qquad\qquad 2x = \dfrac{\pi}{2} + n\pi$

$\quad x = \dfrac{n\pi}{4} \qquad\qquad x = \dfrac{\pi}{4} + \dfrac{n\pi}{2}$

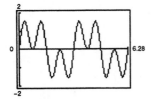

In the interval we have

$x = 0, \ \dfrac{\pi}{4}, \ \dfrac{\pi}{2}, \ \dfrac{3\pi}{4}, \ \pi, \ \dfrac{5\pi}{4}, \ \dfrac{3\pi}{2}, \ \dfrac{7\pi}{4}.$

83. $\dfrac{\cos 2x}{\sin 3x - \sin x} - 1 = 0$

$$\dfrac{\cos 2x}{\sin 3x - \sin x} = 1$$

$$\dfrac{\cos 2x}{2\cos 2x \sin x} = 1$$

$$2\sin x = 1$$

$$\sin x = \dfrac{1}{2}$$

$$x = \dfrac{\pi}{6}, \ \dfrac{5\pi}{6}$$

85. $\sin^2\alpha = \left(\dfrac{5}{13}\right)^2 = \dfrac{25}{169}$

$\sin^2\alpha = 1 - \cos^2\alpha = 1 - \left(\dfrac{12}{13}\right)^2 = 1 - \dfrac{144}{169} = \dfrac{25}{169}$

87. $\sin\alpha\cos\beta = \left(\dfrac{5}{13}\right)\left(\dfrac{4}{5}\right) = \dfrac{4}{13}$

$\sin\alpha\cos\beta = \cos\left(\dfrac{\pi}{2} - \alpha\right)\sin\left(\dfrac{\pi}{2} - \beta\right) = \left(\dfrac{5}{13}\right)\left(\dfrac{4}{5}\right) = \dfrac{4}{13}$

89. $\csc 2\theta = \dfrac{1}{\sin 2\theta}$

$= \dfrac{1}{2\sin\theta\cos\theta}$

$= \dfrac{1}{\sin\theta} \cdot \dfrac{1}{2\cos\theta}$

$= \dfrac{\csc\theta}{2\cos\theta}$

91. $\cos^2 2\alpha - \sin^2 2\alpha = \cos[2(2\alpha)]$

$= \cos 4\alpha$

93. $(\sin x + \cos x)^2 = \sin^2 x + 2\sin x \cos x + \cos^2 x$

$\qquad\qquad\qquad = (\sin^2 x + \cos^2 x) + 2\sin x \cos x$

$\qquad\qquad\qquad = 1 + \sin 2x$

95. $1 + \cos 10y = 1 + \cos^2 5y - \sin^2 5y$

$\qquad\qquad\quad = 1 + \cos^2 5y - (1 - \cos^2 5y)$

$\qquad\qquad\quad = 2\cos^2 5y$

97. $\sec \dfrac{u}{2} = \dfrac{1}{\cos(u/2)}$

$\qquad\quad = \pm\sqrt{\dfrac{2}{1 + \cos u}}$

$\qquad\quad = \pm\sqrt{\dfrac{2\sin u}{\sin u(1 + \cos u)}}$

$\qquad\quad = \pm\sqrt{\dfrac{2\sin u}{\sin u + \sin u \cos u}}$

$\qquad\quad = \pm\sqrt{\dfrac{(2\sin u)/(\cos u)}{(\sin u)/(\cos u) + (\sin u \cos u)/(\cos u)}}$

$\qquad\quad = \pm\sqrt{\dfrac{2\tan u}{\tan u + \sin u}}$

99. $\dfrac{\cos 4x + \cos 2x}{\sin 4x + \sin 2x} = \dfrac{2\cos\left(\dfrac{4x + 2x}{2}\right)\cos\left(\dfrac{4x - 2x}{2}\right)}{2\sin\left(\dfrac{4x + 2x}{2}\right)\cos\left(\dfrac{4x - 2x}{2}\right)}$

$\qquad\qquad\qquad\quad = \dfrac{2\cos 3x \cos x}{2\sin 3x \cos x}$

$\qquad\qquad\qquad\quad = \cot 3x$

101. $\dfrac{\cos t + \cos 3t}{\sin 3t - \sin t} = \dfrac{2\cos\left(\dfrac{4t}{2}\right)\cos\left(-\dfrac{2t}{2}\right)}{2\cos\left(\dfrac{4t}{2}\right)\sin\left(\dfrac{2t}{2}\right)}$

$\qquad\qquad\qquad\quad = \dfrac{\cos(-t)}{\sin(t)}$

$\qquad\qquad\qquad\quad = \dfrac{\cos(t)}{\sin(t)}$

$\qquad\qquad\qquad\quad = \cot t$

103. $\cos 3\beta = \cos(2\beta + \beta)$

$\qquad\qquad = \cos 2\beta \cos\beta - \sin 2\beta \sin\beta$

$\qquad\qquad = (\cos^2 \beta - \sin^2 \beta)\cos\beta - 2\sin\beta\cos\beta\sin\beta$

$\qquad\qquad = \cos^3 \beta - \sin^2 \beta \cos\beta - 2\sin^2 \beta \cos\beta$

$\qquad\qquad = \cos^3 \beta - 3\sin^2 \beta \cos\beta$

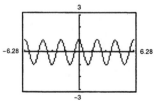

105. $\dfrac{\cos 4x - \cos 2x}{2 \sin 3x} = \dfrac{-2 \sin\left(\dfrac{4x + 2x}{2}\right) \sin\left(\dfrac{4x - 2x}{2}\right)}{2 \sin 3x}$

$\qquad\qquad\qquad = \dfrac{-2 \sin 3x \sin x}{2 \sin 3x}$

$\qquad\qquad\qquad = -\sin x$

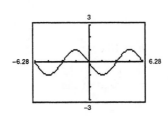

107. $\sin^2 x = \dfrac{1 - \cos 2x}{2} = \dfrac{1}{2} - \dfrac{\cos 2x}{2}$

109. (a) $y = 4 \sin \dfrac{x}{2} + \cos x$

Maximum: $(\pi, 3)$

(b) $\qquad 2 \cos \dfrac{x}{2} - \sin x = 0$

$\qquad 2\left(\pm\sqrt{\dfrac{1 + \cos x}{2}}\right) = \sin x$

$\qquad\qquad 4\left(\dfrac{1 + \cos x}{2}\right) = \sin^2 x$

$\qquad\qquad 2(1 + \cos x) = 1 - \cos^2 x$

$\qquad \cos^2 x + 2 \cos x + 1 = 0$

$\qquad\qquad\qquad (\cos x + 1)^2 = 0$

$\qquad\qquad\qquad\qquad \cos x = -1$

$\qquad\qquad\qquad\qquad\qquad x = \pi$

111. $f(x) = 2 \sin x \left[2 \cos^2(x/2) - 1\right]$

(a)

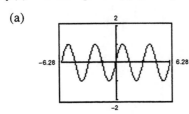

(b) and (c)

$2 \sin x [2 \cos^2 (x/2) - 1]$

$\qquad = 2 \sin x[(1 + \cos x) - 1]$

$\qquad = 2 \sin x(\cos x)$

$\qquad = 2 \sin x \cos x$

113. $\sin(2 \arcsin x) = 2 \sin(\arcsin x) \cos(\arcsin x) = 2x\sqrt{1 - x^2}$

115. (a) $A = \dfrac{1}{2}bh$

$$\cos\frac{\theta}{2} = \frac{h}{10} \implies h = 10\cos\frac{\theta}{2}$$

$$\sin\frac{\theta}{2} = \frac{(1/2)b}{10} \implies \frac{1}{2}b = 10\sin\frac{\theta}{2}$$

$$A = 10\sin\frac{\theta}{2}10\cos\frac{\theta}{2} \implies A = 100\sin\frac{\theta}{2}\cos\frac{\theta}{2}$$

(b) $A = 100\sin\dfrac{\theta}{2}\cos\dfrac{\theta}{2}$

$$A = 50\left(2\sin\frac{\theta}{2}\cos\frac{\theta}{2}\right)$$

$$A = 50\sin\theta$$

When $\theta = \pi/2$, $\sin\theta = 1 \implies$ the area is a maximum.

$$A = 50\sin\frac{\pi}{2} = 50(1) = 50 \text{ square feet}$$

117. Let x = profit for September, then $x + 0.16x$ = profit for October.

$$x + (x + 0.16x) = 507,600$$
$$2.16x = 507,600$$
$$x = 235,000$$
$$x + 0.16x = 272,600$$

Profit for September: $235,000

Profit for October: $276,600

119. Let x = number of gallons of 100% concentrate.

$$0.30(55 - x) + 1.00x = 0.50(55)$$
$$16.50 - 0.30x + x = 27.50$$
$$0.70x = 11$$
$$x \approx 15.7 \text{ gallons}$$

☐ Review Exercises for Chapter 5

Solutions to Odd-Numbered Exercises

1. $\dfrac{1}{\cot^2 x + 1} = \dfrac{1}{\csc^2 x} = \sin^2 x$

3. $\dfrac{\sin^2 \alpha - \cos^2 \alpha}{\sin^2 \alpha - \sin \alpha \cos \alpha} = \dfrac{(\sin \alpha + \cos \alpha)(\sin \alpha - \cos \alpha)}{\sin \alpha(\sin \alpha - \cos \alpha)}$

$\qquad = \dfrac{\sin \alpha + \cos \alpha}{\sin \alpha}$

$\qquad = 1 + \cot \alpha$

5. $\tan^2 \theta(\csc^2 \theta - 1) = \tan^2 \theta(\cot^2 \theta)$

$\qquad = \tan^2 \theta\left(\dfrac{1}{\tan^2 \theta}\right)$

$\qquad = 1$

7. $\dfrac{2 \tan(x + 1)}{1 - \tan^2(x + 1)} = \tan[2(x + 1)]$

$\qquad = \tan(2x + 2)$

9. $\tan x(1 - \sin^2 x) = \tan x \cos^2 x$

$\qquad = \dfrac{\sin x}{\cos x} \cdot \cos^2 x$

$\qquad = \sin x \cos x$

$\qquad = \dfrac{1}{2}(2 \sin x \cos x)$

$\qquad = \dfrac{1}{2} \sin 2x$

11. $\sec^2 x \cot x - \cot x = \cot x(\sec^2 x - 1)$

$\qquad = \cot x \tan^2 x$

$\qquad = \dfrac{1}{\tan x} \tan^2 x$

$\qquad = \tan x$

13. $\sin^5 x \cos^2 x = \sin^4 x \cos^2 x \sin x$

$\qquad = (1 - \cos^2 x)^2 \cos^2 x \sin x$

$\qquad = (1 - 2 \cos^2 x + \cos^4 x) \cos^2 x \sin x$

$\qquad = (\cos^2 x - 2 \cos^4 x + \cos^6 x)\sin x$

15. $\sin 3\theta \sin \theta = \frac{1}{2}[\cos(3\theta - \theta) - \cos(3\theta + \theta)]$

$\qquad = \frac{1}{2}(\cos 2\theta - \cos 4\theta)$

17. $\sqrt{\dfrac{1 - \sin \theta}{1 + \sin \theta}} = \sqrt{\dfrac{1 - \sin \theta}{1 + \sin \theta} \cdot \dfrac{1 - \sin \theta}{1 - \sin \theta}}$

$\qquad = \sqrt{\dfrac{(1 - \sin \theta)^2}{1 - \sin^2 \theta}} = \sqrt{\dfrac{(1 - \sin \theta)^2}{\cos^2 \theta}} = \dfrac{|1 - \sin \theta|}{|\cos \theta|} = \dfrac{1 - \sin \theta}{|\cos \theta|}$

Note: We can drop the absolute value on $1 - \sin \theta$ since it is always nonnegative.

19. $\cos 3x = \cos(2x + x)$

$\qquad = \cos 2x \cos x - \sin 2x \sin x$

$\qquad = (\cos^2 x - \sin^2 x) \cos x - 2 \sin x \cos x \sin x$

$\qquad = \cos^3 x - 3 \sin^2 x \cos x$

$\qquad = \cos^3 x - 3 \cos x(1 - \cos^2 x)$

$\qquad = \cos^3 x - 3 \cos x + 3 \cos^3 x$

$\qquad = 4 \cos^3 x - 3 \cos x$

21. $\cot\left(\dfrac{\pi}{2} - x\right) = \dfrac{\cos[(\pi/2) - x]}{\sin[(\pi/2) - x]}$

$\qquad\qquad = \dfrac{\cos(\pi/2) \cos x + \sin(\pi/2)\sin x}{\sin(\pi/2) \cos x - \sin x \cos(\pi/2)}$

$\qquad\qquad = \dfrac{\sin x}{\cos x}$

$\qquad\qquad = \tan x$

23. $\dfrac{\sec x - 1}{\tan x} = \dfrac{(1/\cos x) - 1}{\sin x/\cos x} = \dfrac{1 - \cos x}{\sin x} = \tan\dfrac{x}{2}$

25. $2 \sin y \cos y \sec 2y = (\sin 2y)(\sec 2y)$

$\qquad\qquad\qquad\quad = \dfrac{\sin 2y}{\cos 2y}$

$\qquad\qquad\qquad\quad = \tan 2y$

27. $\sin\left(x - \dfrac{3\pi}{2}\right) = \sin x \cos \dfrac{3\pi}{2} - \sin \dfrac{3\pi}{2} \cos x$

$\qquad\qquad\qquad = (\sin x)(0) - (-1)(\cos x)$

$\qquad\qquad\qquad = \cos x$

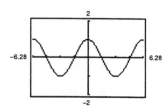

29. $\dfrac{1 - \cos 2x}{1 + \cos 2x} = \dfrac{1 - (1 - 2 \sin^2 x)}{1 + (2 \cos x^2 - 1)}$

$\qquad\qquad\quad = \dfrac{2 \sin^2 x}{2 \cos^2 x}$

$\qquad\qquad\quad = \tan^2 x$

31. $\sin \dfrac{5\pi}{12} = \sin\left(\dfrac{2\pi}{3} - \dfrac{\pi}{4}\right)$

$\qquad\quad = \sin\left(\dfrac{2\pi}{3}\right) \cos\left(\dfrac{\pi}{4}\right) - \cos \dfrac{2\pi}{3} \sin\left(\dfrac{\pi}{4}\right)$

$\qquad\quad = \left(\dfrac{\sqrt{3}}{2}\right)\left(\dfrac{\sqrt{2}}{2}\right) - \left(-\dfrac{1}{2}\right)\left(\dfrac{\sqrt{2}}{2}\right)$

$\qquad\quad = \dfrac{\sqrt{2}}{4}\left(\sqrt{3} + 1\right)$

33. $\cos(157°\,30') = \cos\dfrac{315°}{2} = -\sqrt{\dfrac{1 + \cos 315°}{2}} = -\sqrt{\dfrac{1 + \cos 45°}{2}}$

$\qquad\qquad\quad = -\sqrt{\dfrac{1 + \sqrt{2}/2}{2}} = -\sqrt{\dfrac{2 + \sqrt{2}}{4}} = -\dfrac{\sqrt{2 + \sqrt{2}}}{2}$

For Exercises 35–39

$$\sin u = \frac{3}{4}, \ u \text{ in Quadrant II} \implies \cos u = -\frac{\sqrt{7}}{4}$$

$$\cos v = -\frac{5}{13}, \ v \text{ in Quadrant II} \implies \sin v = \frac{12}{13}$$

35. $\sin(u + v) = \sin u \cos v + \cos u \sin v$

$$= \left(\frac{3}{4}\right)\left(-\frac{5}{13}\right) + \left(-\frac{\sqrt{7}}{4}\right)\left(\frac{12}{13}\right)$$

$$= -\frac{15}{52} - \frac{12\sqrt{7}}{52}$$

$$= \frac{-3(5 + 4\sqrt{7})}{52}$$

37. $\cos(u - v) = \cos u \cos v + \sin u \sin v$

$$= \left(-\frac{\sqrt{7}}{4}\right)\left(-\frac{5}{13}\right) + \left(\frac{3}{4}\right)\left(\frac{12}{13}\right)$$

$$= \frac{5\sqrt{7} + 36}{52}$$

39. $\cos \dfrac{u}{2} = \sqrt{\dfrac{1 + \cos u}{2}}$

$$= \sqrt{\frac{1 + (-\sqrt{7}/4)}{2}}$$

$$= \sqrt{\frac{4 - \sqrt{7}}{8}}$$

$$= \frac{1}{4}\sqrt{2(4 - \sqrt{7})}$$

41. If $\dfrac{\pi}{2} < \theta < \pi$, then $\cos \dfrac{\theta}{2} < 0$. False, if

$$\frac{\pi}{2} < \theta < \pi \implies \frac{\pi}{4} < \frac{\theta}{2} < \frac{\pi}{2},$$

which is in Quadrant I $\implies \cos(\theta/2) > 0$.

43. $4 \sin(-x) \cos(-x) = -2 \sin 2x$. True.

$$4 \sin(-x) \cos(-x) = 4(-\sin x)(\cos x) = -4 \sin x \cos x = -2(2 \sin x \cos x) = -2 \sin 2x$$

45.
$$\sin x - \tan x = 0$$
$$\sin x - \frac{\sin x}{\cos x} = 0$$
$$\sin x \cos x - \sin x = 0$$
$$\sin x(\cos x - 1) = 0$$
$$\sin x = 0 \quad \text{or} \quad \cos x - 1 = 0$$
$$x = 0, \pi \qquad \cos x = 1$$
$$x = 0$$

47.
$$\sin 2x + \sqrt{2} \sin x = 0$$
$$2 \sin x \cos x + \sqrt{2} \sin x = 0$$
$$\sin x(2 \cos x + \sqrt{2}) = 0$$
$$\sin x = 0 \quad \text{or} \quad 2 \cos x + \sqrt{2} = 0$$
$$x = 0, \pi \qquad \cos x = -\frac{\sqrt{2}}{2}$$
$$x = \frac{3\pi}{4}, \frac{5\pi}{4}$$

49.
$$\cos^2 x + \sin x = 1$$
$$1 - \sin^2 x + \sin x = 1$$
$$\sin x(\sin x - 1) = 0$$
$$\sin x = 0 \quad \text{or} \quad \sin x = 1$$
$$x = 0, \pi \qquad x = \frac{\pi}{2}$$

51. $\dfrac{1 + \sin x}{\cos x} + \dfrac{\cos x}{1 + \sin x} = 4$

$$(1 + \sin x)^2 + \cos^2 x = 4\cos x(1 + \sin x)$$

$$1 + 2\sin x + \sin^2 x + \cos^2 x = 4\cos x(1 + \sin x)$$

$$2 + 2\sin x - 4\cos x(1 + \sin x) = 0$$

$$2(1 + \sin x)(1 - 2\cos x) = 0$$

$$1 + \sin x = 0 \quad \text{or} \quad 1 - 2\cos x = 0$$

$$\sin x = -1 \qquad\qquad \cos x = \dfrac{1}{2}$$

$$x = \dfrac{3\pi}{2} \qquad\qquad x = \dfrac{\pi}{3}, \dfrac{5\pi}{3}$$

(extraneous solution)

53. $\tan^3 x - \tan^2 x + 3\tan x - 3 = 0$

$$\tan^2 x(\tan x - 1) + 3(\tan x - 1) = 0$$

$$(\tan^2 x + 3)(\tan x - 1) = 0$$

$$\tan^2 x + 3 = 0 \quad \text{or} \quad \tan x - 1 = 0$$

(No solution) or $\tan x = 1$

$$x = \dfrac{\pi}{4}, \dfrac{5\pi}{4}$$

55. False, $\sin \theta = \frac{1}{2}$ has an infinite number of solutions but is not an identity.

57. $\cos 3\theta + \cos 2\theta = 2\cos\!\left(\dfrac{3\theta + 2\theta}{2}\right)\cos\!\left(\dfrac{3\theta - 2\theta}{2}\right)$

$$= 2\cos\dfrac{5\theta}{2}\cos\dfrac{\theta}{2}$$

59. $\sin 3\alpha \sin 2\alpha = \frac{1}{2}[\cos(3\alpha - 2\alpha) - \cos(3\alpha + 2\alpha)]$

$$= \tfrac{1}{2}(\cos \alpha - \cos 5\alpha)$$

61. $\cos(2 \arccos 2x) = \cos 2\theta$

$$= \cos^2 \theta - \sin^2 \theta$$

$$= (2x)^2 - \left(\sqrt{1 - 4x^2}\right)^2$$

$$= 4x^2 - (1 - 4x^2)$$

$$= 8x^2 - 1$$

$\theta = \arccos 2x$

63. $\sin^{-1/2} \cos x = \dfrac{\cos x}{\sin^{1/2} x}$

$\qquad = \dfrac{\cos x}{\sqrt{\sin x}} \cdot \dfrac{\sqrt{\sin x}}{\sqrt{\sin x}}$

$\qquad = \dfrac{\cos x}{\sin x}\sqrt{\sin x}$

$\qquad = \cot x\sqrt{\sin x}$

65. $y = 1.5 \sin 8t - 0.5 \cos 8t$

(a) $a = \dfrac{3}{2}, \ b = -\dfrac{1}{2}, \ B = 8, \ c = \arctan\left(-\dfrac{1/2}{3/2}\right)$

$\quad y = \sqrt{(3/2)^2 + (-1/2)^2}\,\sin\left(8t + \arctan -\dfrac{1}{3}\right)$

$\quad y = \dfrac{1}{2}\sqrt{10}\,\sin\left(8t - \arctan\dfrac{1}{3}\right)$

(b) Amplitude: $\dfrac{1}{2}\sqrt{10}$ sin feet

(c) Frequency: $\dfrac{8}{2\pi} = \dfrac{4}{\pi}$ cycles per second

❑ Practice Test for Chapter 5

1 Find the value of the other five trigonometric functions, given $\tan x = \frac{4}{11}$, $\sec x < 0$.

2. Simplify $\dfrac{\sec^2 x + \csc^2 x}{\csc^2 x(1 + \tan^2 x)}$.

3. Rewrite as a single logarithm and simplify $\ln|\tan \theta| - \ln|\cot \theta|$.

4. True or false:

$$\cos\left(\frac{\pi}{2} - x\right) = \frac{1}{\csc x}$$

5. Factor and simplify: $\sin^4 x + (\sin^2 x)\cos^2 x$

6. Multiply and simplify: $(\csc x + 1)(\csc x - 1)$

7. Rationalize the denominator and simplify:

$$\frac{\cos^2 x}{1 - \sin x}$$

8. Verify:

$$\frac{1 + \cos \theta}{\sin \theta} + \frac{\sin \theta}{1 + \cos \theta} = 2\csc \theta$$

9. Verify:

$$\tan^4 x + 2\tan^2 x + 1 = \sec^4 x$$

10. Use the sum or difference formulas to determine:

   (a) $\sin 105°$ (b) $\tan 15°$

11. Simplify: $(\sin 42°)\cos 38° - (\cos 42°)\sin 38°$

12. Verify $\tan\left(\theta + \dfrac{\pi}{4}\right) = \dfrac{1 + \tan \theta}{1 - \tan \theta}$.

13. Write $\sin(\arcsin x - \arccos x)$ as an algebraic expression in x.

14. Use the double-angle formulas to determine:

   (a) $\cos 120°$ (b) $\tan 300°$

15. Use the half-angle formulas to determine:

   (a) $\sin 22.5°$ (d) $\tan \dfrac{\pi}{12}$

16. Given $\sin = 4/5$, θ lies in Quadrant II, find $\cos(\theta/2)$.

17. Use the power-reducing identities to write $(\sin^2 x)\cos^2 x$ in terms of the first power of cosine.

18. Rewrite as a sum: $6(\sin 5\theta)\cos 2\theta$.

19. Rewrite as a product:

$\sin(x + \pi) + \sin(x - \pi)$.

20. Verify $\dfrac{\sin 9x + \sin 5x}{\cos 9x - \cos 5x} = -\cot 2x$.

21. Verify:

$(\cos u)\sin v = \frac{1}{2}[\sin(u + v) - \sin(u - v)]$.

22. Find all solutions in the interval $[0, 2\pi)$:

$4\sin^2 x = 1$

23. Find all solutions in the interval $[0, 2\pi)$:

$\tan^2 \theta + \left(\sqrt{3} - 1\right)\tan\theta - \sqrt{3} = 0$

24. Find all solutions in the interval $[0, 2\pi)$:

$\sin 2x = \cos x$

25. Use the quadratic formula to find all solutions in the interval $[0, 2\pi)$:

$\tan^2 x - 6\tan x + 4 = 0$

CHAPTER 6
Additional Topics in Trigonometry

C H A P T E R 6
Additional Topics in Trigonometry

Section 6.1   Law of Sines

■ If ABC is any oblique triangle with sides a, b, and c, then

$$\frac{a}{\sin A} = \frac{b}{\sin B} = \frac{c}{\sin C}.$$

■ You should be able to use the Law of Sines to solve an oblique triangle for the remaining three parts, given:

(a) Two angles and any side (AAS or ASA)

(b) Two sides and an angle opposite one of them (SSA)

    1. If A is acute and $h = b \sin A$:

       (a) $a < h$, no triangle is possible.

       (b) $a = h$ or $a > b$, one triangle is possible.

       (c) $h < a < b$, two triangles are possible.

    2. If A is obtuse and $h = b \sin A$:

       (a) $a \le b$, no triangle is possible.

       (b) $a > b$, one triangle is possible.

■ The area of any triangle equals one-half the product of the lengths of two sides times the sine of their included angle.

$$A = \tfrac{1}{2}ab \sin C = \tfrac{1}{2}ac \sin B = \tfrac{1}{2}bc \sin A$$

Solutions to Odd-Numbered Exercises

1. Given: $A = 30°$, $B = 45°$, $a = 20$

$C = 180° - A - B = 105°$

$b = \dfrac{a}{\sin A}(\sin B) = \dfrac{20 \sin 45°}{\sin 30°} = 20\sqrt{2} \approx 28.28$

$c = \dfrac{a}{\sin A}(\sin C) = \dfrac{20 \sin 105°}{\sin 30°} \approx 38.64$

3. Given: $A = 10°$, $B = 60°$, $a = 7.5$

$C = 180° - A - B = 110°$

$b = \dfrac{a}{\sin A}(\sin B) = \dfrac{7.5}{\sin 10°}(\sin 60°) \approx 37.40$

$c = \dfrac{a}{\sin A}(\sin C) = \dfrac{7.5}{\sin 10°}(\sin 110°) \approx 40.59$

5. Given: $A = 36°$, $a = 8$, $b = 5$

$$\sin B = \frac{b \sin A}{a} = \frac{5 \sin 36°}{8} \approx 0.36737 \implies B \approx 21.55°$$

$$C = 180° - A - B \approx 180° - 36° - 21.55 = 122.45°$$

$$c = \frac{a}{\sin A}(\sin C) = \frac{8}{\sin 36°}(\sin 122.45°) \approx 11.49$$

7. Given: $A = 150°$, $C = 20°$, $a = 200$

$$B = 180° - A - C = 180° - 150° - 20° = 10°$$

$$b = \frac{a}{\sin A}(\sin B) = \frac{200}{\sin 150°}(\sin 10°) \approx 69.46$$

$$c = \frac{a}{\sin A}(\sin C) = \frac{200}{\sin 150°}(\sin 20°) \approx 136.81$$

9. Given: $A = 83°20'$, $C = 54.6°$, $c = 18.1$

$$B = 180° - A - C = 180° - 80°20' - 54°36' = 42°4'$$

$$a = \frac{c}{\sin C}(\sin A) = \frac{18.1}{\sin 54.6°}(\sin 83°20') \approx 22.05$$

$$b = \frac{c}{\sin C}(\sin B) = \frac{18.1}{\sin 54.6°}(\sin 42°4') \approx 14.88$$

11. Given: $B = 15°30'$, $a = 4.5$, $b = 6.8$

$$\sin A = \frac{a \sin B}{b} = \frac{4.5 \sin 15°30'}{6.8} \approx 0.17685 \implies A \approx 10°11'$$

$$C = 180° - A - B \approx 180° - 10°11' - 15°30' = 154°19'$$

$$c = \frac{b}{\sin B}(\sin C) = \frac{6.8}{\sin 15°30'}(\sin 154°19') \approx 11.03$$

13. Given: $C = 145°$, $b = 4$, $c = 14$

$$\sin B = \frac{b \sin C}{c} = \frac{4 \sin 145°}{14} \approx 0.1639 \implies B \approx 9.43°$$

$$A = 180° - B - C \approx 180° - 9.43° - 145° = 25.57°$$

$$a = \frac{c}{\sin C}(\sin A) \approx \frac{14}{\sin 145°}(\sin 25.57°) \approx 10.5$$

15. Given: $B = 110°15'$, $a = 48$, $b = 16$

$$\sin B = \frac{b \sin A}{a} = \frac{16 \sin 110°15'}{48} \approx 0.31273 \implies B \approx 18°13'$$

$$C = 180° - A - B \approx 180° - 110°15' - 18°13' = 51°32'$$

$$c = \frac{a}{\sin A}(\sin C) = \frac{48}{\sin 110°15'}(\sin 51°32') \approx 40.06$$

17. Given: $a = 4.5$, $b = 12.8$, $A = 58°$

$h = 12.8 \sin 58° \approx 10.86$

Since $a < h$, no triangle is formed.

19. Given: $a = 4.5$, $b = 5$, $A = 58°$

$$\sin B = \frac{b \sin A}{a} = \frac{5 \sin 58°}{4.5} \approx 0.9423 \implies B = 70.4° \text{ or } B = 109.6°$$

Case 1	Case 2
$B \approx 70.4°$	$B \approx 109.6°$
$C \approx 180° - 70.4° - 58° = 51.6°$	$C \approx 180° - 109.6° - 58° = 12.4°$
$c \approx \dfrac{4.5}{\sin 58°} (\sin 51.6°) \approx 4.16$	$c \approx \dfrac{4.5}{\sin 58°} (\sin 12.4°) \approx 1.14$

21. Given: $a = 125$, $b = 200$, $A = 110°$

No triangle is formed because A is obtuse and $a < b$.

23. Given: $A = 36°$, $a = 5$

(a) One solution if $b \le 5$ or $b = \dfrac{5}{\sin 36°}$

(b) Two solutions if $5 < b < \dfrac{5}{\sin 36°}$

(c) No solution is $b > \dfrac{5}{\sin 36°}$

25. (a)

(b) $\dfrac{16}{\sin 70°} = \dfrac{h}{\sin 32°}$

(c) $h = \dfrac{16 \sin 32°}{\sin 70°} \approx 9$ meters

27. $\dfrac{\sin(42° - \theta)}{10} = \dfrac{\sin 48°}{17}$

$\sin(42° - \theta) \approx 0.43714$

$\theta \approx 16.1°$

29. Given: $A = 74° - 28° = 46°$,

$B = 180° - 41° - 74° = 65°$, $c = 100$

$C = 180° - 46° - 65° = 69°$

$a = \dfrac{c}{\sin C} (\sin A) = \dfrac{100}{\sin 69°} (\sin 46°) \approx 77$ meters

31. (a)

(b) $\dfrac{x}{\sin 17.5°} = \dfrac{9000}{\sin 1.3°}$

$x \approx 119{,}289.1261$ feet ≈ 22.6 miles

(c) $\dfrac{y}{\sin 71.2°} = \dfrac{x}{\sin 90°}$

$y = x \sin 71.2° \approx 119{,}289.1261 \sin 71.2°$

$\approx 112{,}924.963$ feet ≈ 21.4 miles

(d) $z = x \sin 18.8° \approx 119{,}289.1261 \sin 18.8° \approx 37{,}443$ feet

33. $A = 65° - 28° = 37°$

$c = 30$

$B = 180° - 16.5° - 65° = 98.5°$

$C = 180° - 37° - 98.5° = 44.5°$

$a = \dfrac{c}{\sin C}(\sin A) = \dfrac{30}{\sin 44.5°}(\sin 37°) \approx 25.8$ km to B

$b = \dfrac{c}{\sin C}(\sin B) = \dfrac{30}{\sin 44.5°}(\sin 98.5°) \approx 42.3$ km to A

35. $A = 90° - 62° = 28°$

$B = 90° + 38° = 128°,\ c = 5$

$C = 180° - 128° - 28° = 24°$

$a = \dfrac{c}{\sin C}(\sin A) = \dfrac{5}{\sin 24°}(\sin 28°) \approx 5.77$

$d = a \sin(90° - 38°) \approx 5.77 \sin 52° \approx 4.55$ miles

37. (a) $\dfrac{\sin \alpha}{9} = \dfrac{\sin \beta}{18}$

(b)

$\sin \alpha = 0.5 \sin \beta$

$\alpha = \arcsin(0.5 \sin \beta)$

Domain: $0 < \beta < \pi$

Range: $0 < \alpha \le \dfrac{\pi}{6}$

(c) $\gamma = \pi - \alpha - \beta = \pi - \beta - \arcsin(0.5 \sin \beta)$

$\dfrac{c}{\sin \gamma} = \dfrac{18}{\sin \beta}$

$c = \dfrac{18 \sin \gamma}{\sin \beta} = \dfrac{18 \sin\left[\pi - \beta - \arcsin(0.5 \sin \beta)\right]}{\sin \beta}$

(d)

Domain: $0 < \beta < \pi$

Range: $9 < \alpha < 27$

(e)

β	0	0.4	0.8	1.2	1.6	2.0	2.4	2.8
α	0	0.1960	0.3669	0.4848	0.5234	0.4720	0.3445	0.1683
c	27	25.92	27.07	19.19	15.33	12.29	10.31	9.27

As $\beta \to 0$, $c \to 27$

As $\beta \to \pi$, $c \to 9$

39. Area $= \frac{1}{2}ab \sin C = \frac{1}{2}(4)(6) \sin 120° \approx 10.4$

41. Area $= \frac{1}{2}bc \sin A = \frac{1}{2}(57)(85) \sin 43°45' \approx 1675.2$

43. Area $= \frac{1}{2}ac \sin B = \frac{1}{2}(62)(20) \sin 130° \approx 474.9$

45. (a) $A = \dfrac{1}{2}(30)(20) \sin\left(\theta + \dfrac{\theta}{2}\right) - \dfrac{1}{2}(8)(20) \sin \dfrac{\theta}{2} - \dfrac{1}{2}(8)(30) \sin \theta$

$= 300 \sin \dfrac{3\theta}{2} - 80 \sin \dfrac{\theta}{2} - 120 \sin \theta$

$= 20\left[15 \sin \dfrac{3\theta}{2} - 4 \sin \dfrac{\theta}{2} - 6 \sin \theta\right]$

(b)

(c) Domain: $0 \le \theta \le 1.6690$

The domain would increase in length and the area would increase if the 8-centimeter line segment were decreased.

Section 6.2   Law of Cosines

■ If ABC is any oblique triangle with sides a, b, and c, the following equations are valid.

(a) $a^2 = b^2 + c^2 - 2bc \cos A$ or $\cos A = \dfrac{b^2 + c^2 - a^2}{2bc}$

(b) $b^2 = a^2 + c^2 - 2ac \cos B$ or $\cos B = \dfrac{a^2 + c^2 - b^2}{2ac}$

(c) $c^2 = a^2 + b^2 - 2ab \cos C$ or $\cos C = \dfrac{a^2 + b^2 - c^2}{2ab}$

■ You should be able to use the Law of Cosines to solve an oblique triangle for the remaining three parts, given:

(a) Three sides (SSS)

(b) Two sides and their included angle (SAS)

■ Given any triangle with sides of length a, b, and c, then the area of the triangle is

$$\text{Area} = \sqrt{s(s-a)(s-b)(s-c)}, \text{ where } s = \frac{a+b+c}{2}. \quad \text{(Heron's Formula)}$$

Solutions to Odd-Numbered Exercises

1. Given: $a = 6$, $b = 8$, $c = 12$

$\cos A = \dfrac{b^2 + c^2 - a^2}{2bc} = \dfrac{64 + 144 - 36}{2(8)(12)} \approx 0.8958 \implies A \approx 26.4°$

$\sin B = \dfrac{b \sin A}{a} \approx \dfrac{8 \sin 26.4°}{6} \approx 0.5928 \implies B \approx 36.3°$

$C \approx 180° - 26.4° - 36.3° = 117.3°$

3. Given: $A = 30°$, $b = 15$, $c = 30$

$a^2 = b^2 + c^2 - 2bc \cos A$

$\quad = 225 + 900 - 2(15)(30) \cos 30° \approx 18.5897$

$a \approx 18.6$

$\cos B = \dfrac{a^2 + c^2 - b^2}{2ac} \approx \dfrac{(18.6)^2 + 900 - 225}{2(18.6)(30)} \approx 0.9148$

$B \approx 23.8°$

$C \approx 180° - 30° - 23.8° = 126.2°$

5. Given: $a = 9$, $b = 12$, $c = 15$

$\cos C = \dfrac{a^2 + b^2 - c^2}{2ab} = \dfrac{81 + 144 - 225}{2(9)(12)} = 0 \implies C = 90°$

$\sin A = \dfrac{9}{15} = \dfrac{3}{5} \implies A \approx 36.9°$

$B \approx 180° - 90° - 36.9° = 53.1°$

7. Given: $a = 75.4$, $b = 52$, $c = 52$

$$\cos A = \frac{b^2 + c^2 - a^2}{2bc} = \frac{52^2 + 52^2 - 75.4^2}{2(52)(52)} = -0.05125 \implies A \approx 92.94°$$

$$\sin B = \frac{b \sin A}{a} \approx \frac{52(0.9987)}{75.4} \approx 0.68875 \implies B \approx 43.53°$$

$$C = B \approx 43.53°$$

9. Given: $A = 120°$, $b = 3$, $c = 10$

$$a^2 = b^2 + c^2 - 2bc \cos A = 9 + 100 - 60 \cos 120° = 139 \implies a \approx 11.79$$

$$\sin B = \frac{b \sin A}{a} \approx \frac{3 \sin 120°}{11.79} \approx 0.2204 \implies B \approx 12.7°$$

$$C = 180° - 120° - 12.7° = 47.3°$$

11. Given: $B = 8°45'$, $a = 25$, $c = 15$

$$b^2 = a^2 + c^2 - 2ac \cos B \approx 625 + 225 - 2(25)(15)(0.9884) \approx 108.7 \implies b \approx 10.4$$

$$\sin C = \frac{c \sin B}{b} \approx \frac{15(0.1521)}{10.43} \approx 0.2188 \implies C \approx 12.64° \approx 12°38'$$

$$A \approx 180° - 8°45' - 12°38' = 158°37'$$

13. Given: $C = 125°40'$, $a = 32$, $b = 32$

$$c^2 = a^2 + b^2 - 2ab \cos C \approx 32^2 + 32^2 - 2(32)(32)(-0.5831) \approx 3242.1 \implies c \approx 56.9$$

$$A = B \implies 2A = 180° - 125°40' = 54°20' \implies A = B = 27°10'$$

15.

$$d^2 = 4^2 + 6^2 - 2(4)(6) \cos 30°$$

$$d \approx 3.23$$

$$2\phi = 360° - 2(30°)$$

$$\phi = 150°$$

$$c^2 = 4^2 + 6^2 - 2(4)(6) \cos 150°$$

$$c \approx 9.67$$

17.

$$\cos \phi = \frac{10^2 + 14^2 - 20^2}{2(10)(14)}$$

$$\phi \approx 111.8°$$

$$2\theta \approx 360° - 2(111.8°)$$

$$\theta = 68.2°$$

$$d^2 = 10^2 + 14^2 - 2(10)(14) \cos 68.2°$$

$$d \approx 13.86$$

19. $\cos \alpha = \dfrac{(9)^2 + (10)^2 - (6)^2}{2(9)(10)}$

$\alpha \approx 36.3°$

$\cos \beta = \dfrac{6^2 + 10^2 - 9^2}{2(6)(10)}$

$\beta \approx 62.7°$

$z = 180° - \alpha - \beta \approx 81.0°$

$\mu = 180° - z \approx 99.0°$

$b^2 = 9^2 + 6^2 - 2(9)(6)(\cos 99.0°)$

$b \approx 11.58$

$\cos \omega \approx \dfrac{9^2 + 11.58^2 - 6^2}{2(9)(11.58)}$

$\omega \approx 30.8°$

$\theta = \alpha + \omega \approx 67.1°$

$\cos x \approx \dfrac{6^2 + 11.58^2 - 9^2}{2(6)(11.58)}$

$x \approx 50.2°$

$\phi = \beta + x \approx 112.9°$

21. $\cos B = \dfrac{1100^2 + 2500^2 - 2000^2}{2(1100)(2500)}$

$B \approx 51° \implies$ Bearing of N 39° E

$\cos C = \dfrac{1100^2 + 2000^2 - 2500^2}{2(1100)(2000)}$

$C \approx 103.7°$

$\alpha = 180° - 51° - 103.7° = 25.3° \implies$ Bearing of S 64.7° E

23.

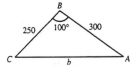

$b^2 = 250^2 + 300^2 - 2(250)(300) \cos 100°$

$b \approx 422.5$ meters

25.

The largest angle is across from the largest side.

$\cos C = \dfrac{650^2 + 575^2 - 725^2}{2(650)(575)}$

$C \approx 72.3°$

27. $C = 180° - 53° - 67° = 60°$

$c^2 = a^2 + b^2 - 2ab \cos C$

$\qquad = 36^2 + 48^2 - 2(36)(48)(0.5)$

$\qquad = 1872$

$\quad c \approx 43.3$ mi

29. (a) $\cos \theta = \dfrac{273^2 + 178^2 - 235^2}{2(273)(178)}$

$\qquad \theta \approx 58.4°$

Bearing: N 58.4° W

(b) $\cos \phi = \dfrac{235^2 + 178^2 - 273^2}{2(235)(178)}$

$\qquad \phi \approx 81.5°$

Bearing: S 81.5° W

31. $d^2 = 60.5^2 + 90^2 - 2(60.5)(90) \cos 45° \approx 4059.9 \implies d \approx 63.7$ ft

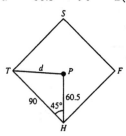

33. $\overline{RS} = \sqrt{8^2 + 10^2} = \sqrt{164} = 2\sqrt{41} \approx 12.8$ ft

$\overline{PQ} = \frac{1}{2}\sqrt{16^2 + 10^2} = \frac{1}{2}\sqrt{356} = \sqrt{89} \approx 9.4$ ft

$\tan P = \frac{10}{16}$

$\quad P = \arctan \frac{5}{8} \approx 32.0°$

$\overline{QS} \approx \sqrt{8^2 + 9.4^2 - 2(8)(9.4) \cos 32°} \approx \sqrt{24.81} \approx 5.0$ ft

35. (a) $7^2 = 1.5^2 + x^2 - 2(1.5)(x) \cos \theta$

$49 = 2.25 + x^2 - 3x \cos \theta$

(b) $x^2 - 3x \cos \theta = 46.75$

$$x^2 - 3x \cos \theta + \left(\frac{3 \cos \theta}{2}\right)^2 = 46.75 + \left(\frac{3 \cos \theta}{2}\right)^2$$

$$\left[x - \frac{3 \cos \theta}{2}\right]^2 = \frac{187}{4} - \frac{9 \cos^2 \theta}{4}$$

$$x - \frac{3 \cos \theta}{2} = \pm \sqrt{\frac{187 + 9 \cos^2 \theta}{4}}$$

Choosing the positive values of x, we have $x = \frac{1}{2}\left[3 \cos \theta + \sqrt{9 \cos^2 \theta + 187}\right]$.

(c)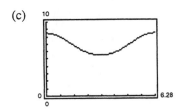

(d) When $\theta = 2\pi$, the piston has moved $2(2)(1.5) = 6$ inches.

37. $A = 180° - 40° - 20° = 120°$

$$\frac{x}{\sin 20°} = \frac{7}{\sin 120°}$$

$$x = \frac{7 \sin 20°}{\sin 120°}$$

$$x = 2.76 \text{ feet}$$

39. $a = 25, \; b = 55, \; c = 72, \; s = \dfrac{25 + 55 + 72}{2} = 76$

(a) $A = \sqrt{(76)(76 - 25)(76 - 55)(76 - 72)} \approx 570.60$

(b) $\cos C = \dfrac{a^2 + b^2 - c^2}{2ab} = \dfrac{25^2 + 55^2 - 72^2}{2(25)(55)} \implies C \approx 123.905°$

$2R = \dfrac{c}{\sin C} \approx \dfrac{72}{\sin 123.905°} \implies R \approx 43.3754$

$A = \pi R^2 \approx 5910.68$

(c) $r = \sqrt{\dfrac{(s - a)(s - b)(s - c)}{s}} = \sqrt{\dfrac{(51)(21)(4)}{76}} \approx 7.5079$

$A = \pi r^2 \approx 177.09$

41. $a = 5, \; b = 7, \; c = 10 \implies s = \dfrac{a + b + c}{2} = 11$

Area $= \sqrt{s(s - a)(s - b)(s - c)} = \sqrt{11(6)(4)(1)} \approx 16.25$

43. $a = 12,\ b = 15,\ c = 9 \implies s = \dfrac{12 + 15 + 9}{2} = 18$

Area $= \sqrt{18(6)(3)(9)} = 54$

45. $a = 20,\ b = 20,\ c = 10 \implies s = \dfrac{20 + 20 + 10}{2} = 25$

Area $= \sqrt{25(5)(5)(15)} \approx 96.82$

47. $a = 200,\ b = 500,\ c = 600 \implies s = \dfrac{200 + 500 + 600}{2} = 650$

Area $= \sqrt{650(450)(150)(50)} \approx 46{,}837.5$ sq ft

49. $\dfrac{1}{2}bc(1 + \cos A) = \dfrac{1}{2}bc\left[1 + \dfrac{b^2 + c^2 - a^2}{2bc} \right]$

$\qquad = \dfrac{1}{2}bc\left[\dfrac{2bc + b^2 + c^2 - a^2}{2bc} \right]$

$\qquad = \dfrac{1}{4}[(b + c)^2 - a^2]$

$\qquad = \dfrac{1}{4}[(b + c) + a][(b + c) - a]$

$\qquad = \dfrac{b + c + a}{2} \cdot \dfrac{b + c - a}{2}$

$\qquad = \dfrac{a + b + c}{2} \cdot \dfrac{-a + b + c}{2}$

51. Let $\theta = \arcsin 2x$, then

$\sin \theta = 2x = \dfrac{2x}{1}$ and $\sec \theta = \dfrac{1}{\sqrt{1 - 4x^2}}$.

53. Let $\theta = \arctan(x - 2)$, then

$\tan \theta = x - 2 = \dfrac{x - 2}{1}$ and $\cot \theta = \dfrac{1}{x - 2}$.

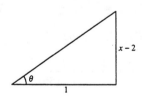

Section 6.3   Vectors in the Plane

■ A vector **v** is the collection of all directed line segments that are equivalent to a given directed line segment $\overrightarrow{PQ}$.

■ You should be able to *geometrically* perform the operations of vector addition and scalar multiplication.

■ The component form of the vector with initial point $P = (p_1, p_2)$ and terminal point $Q = (q_1, q_2)$ is

$$\overrightarrow{PQ} = \langle q_1 - p_1, q_2 - p_2 \rangle = \langle v_1, v_2 \rangle = \mathbf{v}.$$

■ The magnitude of $\mathbf{v} = \langle v_1, v_2 \rangle$ is given by $\|\mathbf{v}\| = \sqrt{v_1^2 + v_2^2}$.

■ You should be able to perform the operations of scalar multiplication and vector addition in component form.

■ You should know the following properties of vector addition and scalar multiplication.

   (a) $\mathbf{u} + \mathbf{v} = \mathbf{v} + \mathbf{u}$

   (b) $(\mathbf{u} + \mathbf{v}) + \mathbf{w} = \mathbf{u} + (\mathbf{v} + \mathbf{w})$

   (c) $\mathbf{u} + \phi = \mathbf{u}$

   (d) $\mathbf{u} + (-\mathbf{u}) = \phi$

   (e) $c(d\mathbf{u}) = (cd)\mathbf{u}$

   (f) $(c + d)\mathbf{u} = c\mathbf{u} + d\mathbf{u}$

   (g) $c(\mathbf{u} + \mathbf{v}) = c\mathbf{u} + c\mathbf{v}$

   (h) $1(\mathbf{u}) = \mathbf{u}, 0\mathbf{u} = \phi$

   (i) $\|c\mathbf{v}\| = |c|\,\|\mathbf{v}\|$

■ A unit vector in the direction of **v** is given $\mathbf{u} = \dfrac{\mathbf{v}}{\|\mathbf{v}\|}$.

■ The standard unit vectors are $\mathbf{i} = \langle 1, 0 \rangle$ and $\mathbf{j} = \langle 0, 1 \rangle$. $\mathbf{v} = \langle v_1, v_2 \rangle$ can be written as $\mathbf{v} = v_1\mathbf{i} + v_2\mathbf{j}$.

■ A vector **v** with magnitude $\|\mathbf{v}\|$ and direction θ can be written as $\mathbf{v} = a\mathbf{i} + b\mathbf{j} = \|\mathbf{v}\|(\cos\theta)\mathbf{i} + \|\mathbf{v}\|(\sin\theta)\mathbf{j}$ where $\tan\theta = b/a$.

Solutions to Odd-Numbered Exercises

1. Initial point: $(0, 0)$

   Terminal point: $(4, 3)$

   $\mathbf{v} = \langle 4 - 0, 3 - 0 \rangle = \langle 4, 3 \rangle$

   $\|\mathbf{v}\| = \sqrt{4^2 + 3^2} = 5$

3. Initial point: $(2, 2)$

   Terminal point: $(-1, 4)$

   $\mathbf{v} = \langle -1 - 2, 4 - 2 \rangle = \langle -3, 2 \rangle$

   $\|\mathbf{v}\| = \sqrt{(-3)^2 + 2^2} = \sqrt{13}$

5. Initial point: $(3, -2)$

   Terminal point: $(3, 3)$

   $\mathbf{v} = \langle 3 - 3, 3 - (-2) \rangle = \langle 0, 5 \rangle$

   $\|\mathbf{v}\| = \sqrt{0^2 + 5^2} = \sqrt{25} = 5$

7. Initial point: $(-1, 5)$

   Terminal point: $(15, 12)$

   $\mathbf{v} = \langle 15 - (-1), 12 - 5 \rangle = \langle 16, 7 \rangle$

   $\|\mathbf{v}\| = \sqrt{16^2 + 7^2} = \sqrt{305}$

9. Initial point: $(-3, -5)$

   Terminal point: $(5, 1)$

   $\mathbf{v} = \langle 5 - (-3), 1 - (-5) \rangle = \langle 8, 6 \rangle$

   $\|\mathbf{v}\| = \sqrt{8^2 + 6^2} = \sqrt{100} = 10$

11.

13.

15.

17. $\mathbf{u} = \langle 1, 2 \rangle, \mathbf{v} = \langle 3, 1 \rangle$

    (a) $\mathbf{u} + \mathbf{v} = \langle 4, 3 \rangle$

    (b) $\mathbf{u} - \mathbf{v} = \langle -2, 1 \rangle$

    (c) $2\mathbf{u} - 3\mathbf{v} = \langle 2, 4 \rangle - \langle 9, 3 \rangle = \langle -7, 1 \rangle$

19. $\mathbf{u} = \langle 4, -2 \rangle, \mathbf{v} = \langle 0, 0 \rangle$

    (a) $\mathbf{u} + \mathbf{v} = \langle 4, -2 \rangle$

    (b) $\mathbf{u} - \mathbf{v} = \langle 4, -2 \rangle$

    (c) $2\mathbf{u} - 3\mathbf{v} = \langle 8, -4 \rangle - \langle 0, 0 \rangle = \langle 8, -4 \rangle$

21. $\mathbf{u} = \mathbf{i} + \mathbf{j}, \mathbf{v} = 2\mathbf{i} - 3\mathbf{j}$

    (a) $\mathbf{u} + \mathbf{v} = 3\mathbf{i} - 2\mathbf{j}$

    (b) $\mathbf{u} - \mathbf{v} = -\mathbf{i} + 4\mathbf{j}$

    (c) $2\mathbf{u} - 3\mathbf{v} = (2\mathbf{i} + 2\mathbf{j}) - (6\mathbf{i} - 9\mathbf{j})$
                        $= -4\mathbf{i} + 11\mathbf{j}$

23. $\mathbf{u} = 2\mathbf{i}, \mathbf{v} = \mathbf{j}$

    (a) $\mathbf{u} + \mathbf{v} = 2\mathbf{i} + \mathbf{j}$

    (b) $\mathbf{u} - \mathbf{v} = 2\mathbf{i} - \mathbf{j}$

    (c) $2\mathbf{u} - 3\mathbf{v} = 4\mathbf{i} - 3\mathbf{j}$

25. $\mathbf{u} = \dfrac{1}{\|\mathbf{v}\|} \mathbf{v}$

    $= \dfrac{1}{\sqrt{5^2 + 0^2}} \langle 5, 0 \rangle$

    $= \dfrac{1}{5} \langle 5, 0 \rangle$

    $= \langle 1, 0 \rangle$

27. $\mathbf{u} = \dfrac{1}{\|\mathbf{v}\|} \mathbf{v}$

    $= \dfrac{1}{\sqrt{(-2)^2 + 2^2}} \langle -2, 2 \rangle$

    $= \dfrac{1}{2\sqrt{2}} \langle -2, 2 \rangle$

    $= \left\langle -\dfrac{1}{\sqrt{2}}, \dfrac{1}{\sqrt{2}} \right\rangle$

29. $\mathbf{u} = \dfrac{1}{\|\mathbf{v}\|} \mathbf{v}$

    $= \dfrac{1}{\sqrt{16 + 9}} (4\mathbf{i} - 3\mathbf{j}) = \dfrac{1}{5} (4\mathbf{i} - 3\mathbf{j})$

    $= \dfrac{4}{5}\mathbf{i} - \dfrac{3}{5}\mathbf{j}$

31. $\mathbf{u} = \dfrac{1}{\|\mathbf{v}\|} \mathbf{v} = \dfrac{1}{2} (2\mathbf{j}) = \mathbf{j}$

33. $5\left(\dfrac{1}{\|\mathbf{v}\|} \mathbf{v} \right) = 5\left(\dfrac{1}{\sqrt{3^2 + 3^2}} \langle 3, 3 \rangle \right)$

                $= 5\left(\dfrac{1}{3\sqrt{2}} \langle 3, 3 \rangle \right)$

                $= \left\langle \dfrac{5}{\sqrt{2}}, \dfrac{5}{\sqrt{2}} \right\rangle$

35. $7\left(\dfrac{1}{\|\mathbf{v}\|} \mathbf{v} \right) = 7\left(\dfrac{1}{\sqrt{(-3)^2 + 4^2}} \langle -3, 4 \rangle \right)$

                $= \dfrac{7}{5} \langle -3, 4 \rangle$

                $= \left\langle -\dfrac{21}{5}, \dfrac{28}{5} \right\rangle$

37. $\mathbf{v} = \frac{3}{2}\mathbf{u}$

$= \frac{3}{2}(2\mathbf{i} - \mathbf{j})$

$= 3\mathbf{i} - \frac{3}{2}\mathbf{j} = \langle 3, -\frac{3}{2} \rangle$

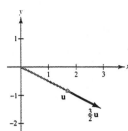

39. $\mathbf{v} = \mathbf{u} + 2\mathbf{w}$

$= (2\mathbf{i} - \mathbf{j}) + 2(\mathbf{i} + 2\mathbf{j})$

$= 4\mathbf{i} + 3\mathbf{j} = \langle 4, 3 \rangle$

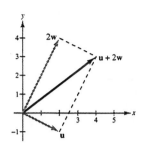

41. $\mathbf{v} = \frac{1}{2}(3\mathbf{u} + \mathbf{w})$

$= \frac{1}{2}(6\mathbf{i} - 3\mathbf{j} + \mathbf{i} + 2\mathbf{j})$

$= \frac{7}{2}\mathbf{i} - \frac{1}{2}\mathbf{j} = \langle \frac{7}{2}, -\frac{1}{2} \rangle$

43. $\mathbf{v} = 5(\cos 30°\mathbf{i} + \sin 30°\mathbf{j})$

$\|\mathbf{v}\| = 5, \ \theta = 30°$

45. $\mathbf{v} = 6\mathbf{i} - 6\mathbf{j}$

$\|\mathbf{v}\| = \sqrt{6^2 + (-6)^2} = \sqrt{72} = 6\sqrt{2}$

$\tan \theta = \frac{-6}{6} = -1$

Since $\mathbf{v}$ lies in Quadrant IV, $\theta = 315°$.

47. $\mathbf{v} = \langle 3\cos 0°, 3\sin 0° \rangle$

$= \langle 3, 0 \rangle$

49. $\mathbf{v} = \langle \cos 150°, \sin 150° \rangle$

$= \langle -\frac{\sqrt{3}}{2}, \frac{1}{2} \rangle$

51. $\mathbf{v} = \langle 3\sqrt{2}\cos 150°, \ 3\sqrt{2}\sin 150° \rangle$

$= \langle -\frac{3\sqrt{6}}{2}, \frac{3\sqrt{2}}{2} \rangle$

53. $\mathbf{v} = 2\left(\frac{1}{\sqrt{3^2 + 1^2}}\right)(\mathbf{i} + 3\mathbf{j})$

$= \frac{2}{\sqrt{10}}(\mathbf{i} + 3\mathbf{j})$

$= \frac{\sqrt{10}}{5}\mathbf{i} + \frac{3\sqrt{10}}{5}\mathbf{j} = \langle \frac{\sqrt{10}}{5}, \frac{3\sqrt{10}}{5} \rangle$

55. $\mathbf{u} = \langle 5\cos 0°, 5\sin 0° \rangle = \langle 5, 0 \rangle$

$\mathbf{v} = \langle 5\cos 90°, 5\sin 90° \rangle = \langle 0, 5 \rangle$

$\mathbf{u} + \mathbf{v} = \langle 5, 5 \rangle$

57. $\mathbf{u} = \langle 20\cos 45°, 20\sin 45° \rangle = \langle 10\sqrt{2}, 10\sqrt{2} \rangle$

$\mathbf{v} = \langle 50\cos 180°, 50\sin 180° \rangle = \langle -50, 0 \rangle$

$\mathbf{u} + \mathbf{v} = \langle 10\sqrt{2} - 50, 10\sqrt{2} \rangle$

59. $v = i + j$

$w = 2(i - j)$

$u = v - w = -i + 3j$

$\|v\| = \sqrt{2}$

$\|w\| = 2\sqrt{2}$

$\|v - w\| = \sqrt{10}$

$\cos \alpha = \dfrac{\|v\|^2 + \|w\|^2 - \|v - w\|^2}{2\|v\| \|w\|} = \dfrac{2 + 8 - 10}{2\sqrt{2} \cdot 2\sqrt{2}} = 0$

$\alpha = 90°$

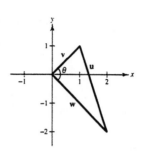

61. $v = i + j$

$w = 3i - j$

$u = v - w = -2i + 2j$

$\cos \alpha = \dfrac{\|v\|^2 + \|w\|^2 - \|v - w\|^2}{2\|v\| \|w\|} = \dfrac{2 + 10 - 8}{2\sqrt{2} \sqrt{10}} \approx 0.4472$

$\alpha = 63.4°$

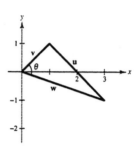

63. Force One: $u = 45i$

Force Two: $v = 60 \cos \theta i + 60 \sin \theta j$

Resultant Force: $u + v = (45 + 60 \cos \theta)i + 60 \sin \theta j$

$\|u + v\| = \sqrt{(45 + 60 \cos \theta)^2 + (60 \sin \theta)^2} = 90$

$$2025 + 5400 \cos \theta + 3600 = 8100$$

$$5400 \cos \theta = 2475$$

$$\cos \theta = \frac{2475}{5400} \approx 0.4583$$

$$\theta \approx 62.7°$$

65. (a) The angle between them is $0°$.

(b) The angle between them is $180°$.

(c) No. At most it can be equal to the sum when the angle between them is $0°$.

67. $u = 220i$

$v = (150 \cos 30°)i + (150 \sin 30°)j = 75\sqrt{3}i + 75j$

$u + v = (220 + 75\sqrt{3})i + 75j$

$\|u + v\| = \sqrt{(220 + 75\sqrt{3})^2 + 75^2} \approx 357.85$ newtons

$\tan \theta = \dfrac{75}{220 + 75\sqrt{3}} \implies \theta \approx 12.1°$

69. $\mathbf{u} = (75 \cos 30°)\mathbf{i} + (75 \sin 30°)\mathbf{j} \approx 64.95\mathbf{i} + 37.5\mathbf{j}$

$\mathbf{v} = (100 \cos 45°)\mathbf{i} + (100 \sin 45°)\mathbf{j} \approx 70.71\mathbf{i} + 70.71\mathbf{j}$

$\mathbf{w} = (125 \cos 120°)\mathbf{i} + (125 \sin 120°)\mathbf{j} \approx -62.5\mathbf{i} + 108.3\mathbf{j}$

$\mathbf{u} + \mathbf{v} + \mathbf{w} \approx 73.16\mathbf{i} + 216.5\mathbf{j}$

$\|\mathbf{u} + \mathbf{v} + \mathbf{w}\| \approx 228.5$ pounds

$\tan \theta \approx \dfrac{216.5}{73.16} \approx 2.9592$

$\theta \approx 71.3°$

71. Horizontal component of velocity: $80 \cos 40° \approx 61.28$ ft/sec

Vertical component of velocity: $80 \sin 40° \approx 51.42$ ft/sec

73. Cable $\overrightarrow{AC}$: $\mathbf{u} = \|\mathbf{u}\|(\cos 50°\mathbf{i} - \sin 50°\mathbf{j})$

Cable $\overrightarrow{BC}$: $\mathbf{u} = \|\mathbf{u}\|(\cos 30°\mathbf{i} - \sin 30°\mathbf{j})$

Resultant: $\mathbf{u} + \mathbf{v} = -1000\mathbf{j}$

$\|\mathbf{u}\| \cos 50° - \|\mathbf{v}\| \cos 30° = 0$

$-\|\mathbf{u}\| \sin 50° - \|\mathbf{v}\| \sin 30° = -2000$

Solving this system of equations yields:

$T_{AC} = \|\mathbf{u}\| \approx 1758.8$ pounds

$T_{BC} = \|\mathbf{v}\| \approx 1305.4$ pounds

75. Towline 1: $\mathbf{u} = \|\mathbf{u}\|(\cos 18°\mathbf{i} + \sin 18°\mathbf{j})$

Towline 2: $\mathbf{v} = \|\mathbf{u}\|(\cos 18°\mathbf{i} - \sin 18°\mathbf{j})$

Resultant: $\mathbf{u} + \mathbf{v} = 6000\mathbf{i}$

$\|\mathbf{u}\| \cos 18° + \|\mathbf{u}\| \cos 18° = 6000$

$\|\mathbf{u}\| \approx 3154.4$

Therefore, the tension on each towline is

$\|\mathbf{u}\| \approx 3154.4$ pounds.

77. Airspeed: $\mathbf{u} = (875 \cos 32°)\mathbf{i} - (875 \sin 32°)\mathbf{j}$

Groundspeed: $\mathbf{v} = (800 \cos 40°)\mathbf{i} - (800 \sin 40°)\mathbf{j}$

Wind: $\mathbf{w} = \mathbf{v} - \mathbf{u} = (800 \cos 40° - 875 \cos 32°)\mathbf{i} + (-800 \sin 40° + 875 \sin 32°)\mathbf{j}$

$\approx -129.2065\mathbf{i} - 50.5507\mathbf{j}$

Wind speed: $\|\mathbf{w}\| \approx \sqrt{(-129.2065)^2 + (-50.5507)^2}$

≈ 138.7 kilometers per hour

Wind direction: $\tan \theta \approx \dfrac{-50.5507}{-129.2065}$

$\theta \approx 21.4°$

N 21.4° E

79. $W = FD = (85 \cos 60°)(20) = 850$ ft/lb

81. True

83. False, $a = b = 0$.

85. Let $\mathbf{v} = (\cos\theta)\mathbf{i} + (\sin\theta)\mathbf{j}$.

$\|\mathbf{v}\| = \sqrt{\cos^2\theta + \sin^2\theta} = \sqrt{1} = 1$

Therefore, $\mathbf{v}$ is a unit vector for any value of θ.

87. $\mathbf{u} = \langle 5 - 1, 2 - 6 \rangle = \langle 4, -4 \rangle$

$\mathbf{v} = \langle 9 - 4, 4 - 5 \rangle = \langle 5, -1 \rangle$

$\mathbf{u} - \mathbf{v} = \langle -1, -3 \rangle$ or $\mathbf{v} - \mathbf{u} = \langle 1, 3 \rangle$

89. Let d be the distance from the bridge deck to the water level.

$$\frac{d}{\sin 55} = \frac{17.779}{\sin 90}$$

$$d \approx 14.6 \text{ meters}$$

91.
$$\sqrt{x^2 - 64} = \sqrt{(8\sec\theta)^2 - 64}$$
$$= \sqrt{64(\sec^2\theta - 1)}$$
$$= 8\sqrt{\tan^2\theta}$$
$$= 8\tan\theta \quad \text{for} \quad 0 < \theta < \frac{\pi}{2}$$

93.
$$\sqrt{x^2 + 36} = \sqrt{(6\tan\theta)^2 + 36}$$
$$= \sqrt{36(\tan^2\theta + 1)}$$
$$= 6\sqrt{\sec^2\theta}$$
$$= 6\sec\theta \quad \text{for} \quad 0 < \theta < \frac{\pi}{2}$$

Section 6.4   Vectors and Dot Products

■ Know the definition of the dot product of $\mathbf{u} = \langle u_1, u_2 \rangle$ and $\mathbf{v} = \langle v_1, v_2 \rangle$.

$\quad\quad \mathbf{u} \cdot \mathbf{v} = u_1 v_1 + u_2 v_2$

■ Know the following properties of the dot product:

1. $\mathbf{u} \cdot \mathbf{v} = \mathbf{v} \cdot \mathbf{u}$
2. $\mathbf{0} \cdot \mathbf{v} = 0$
3. $\mathbf{u} \cdot (\mathbf{v} + \mathbf{w}) = \mathbf{u} \cdot \mathbf{v} + \mathbf{u} \cdot \mathbf{w}$
4. $\mathbf{v} \cdot \mathbf{v} = \|\mathbf{v}\|^2$
5. $c(\mathbf{u} \cdot \mathbf{v}) = c\mathbf{u} \cdot \mathbf{v} = \mathbf{u} \cdot c\mathbf{v}$

■ If θ is the angle between two nonzero vectors $\mathbf{u}$ and $\mathbf{v}$, then

$$\cos\theta = \frac{\mathbf{u} \cdot \mathbf{v}}{\|\mathbf{u}\|\,\|\mathbf{v}\|}.$$

■ The vectors $\mathbf{u}$ and $\mathbf{v}$ are orthogonal if $\mathbf{u} \cdot \mathbf{v} = 0$.

■ Know the definition of vector components.

$\mathbf{u} = \mathbf{w}_1 + \mathbf{w}_2$ where $\mathbf{w}_1$ and $\mathbf{w}_2$ are orthogonal, and $\mathbf{w}_1$ is parallel to $\mathbf{v}$. $\mathbf{w}_1$ is called the projection of $\mathbf{u}$ onto $\mathbf{v}$

and is denoted by $\mathbf{w}_1 = \text{proj}_\mathbf{v}\mathbf{u} = \left(\dfrac{\mathbf{u} \cdot \mathbf{v}}{\|\mathbf{v}\|^2}\right)\mathbf{v}$. Then we have $\mathbf{w}_2 = \mathbf{u} - \mathbf{w}_1$.

■ Know the definition of work.

1. Projection form: $w = \|\text{proj}_{\overrightarrow{PQ}} \mathbf{F}\|\,\|\overrightarrow{PQ}\|$
2. Dot product form: $w = \mathbf{F} \cdot \overrightarrow{PQ}$

Solutions to Odd-Numbered Exercises

1. $\mathbf{u} = \langle 3, 4 \rangle$, $\mathbf{v} = \langle 2, -3 \rangle$

$\mathbf{u} \cdot \mathbf{v} = 3(2) + 4(-3) = -6$

3. $\mathbf{u} = 4\mathbf{i} - 2\mathbf{j}$, $\mathbf{v} = \mathbf{i} - \mathbf{j}$

$\mathbf{u} \cdot \mathbf{v} = 4(1) + (-2)(-1) = 6$

5. $\mathbf{u} = \langle 2, 2 \rangle$

$\mathbf{u} \cdot \mathbf{u} = 2(2) + 2(2) = 8$

The result is a scalar.

7. $\mathbf{u} = \langle 2, 2 \rangle$, $\mathbf{v} = \langle -3, 4 \rangle$

$(\mathbf{u} \cdot \mathbf{v})\mathbf{v} = [(2)(-3) + 2(4)]\langle -3, 4 \rangle$

$= 2\langle -3, 4 \rangle = \langle -6, 8 \rangle$

The result is a vector.

9. $\mathbf{u} = \langle -5, 12 \rangle$

$\|\mathbf{u}\| = \sqrt{\mathbf{u} \cdot \mathbf{u}} = \sqrt{(-5)^2 + 12^2} = 13$

11. $\mathbf{u} = 20\mathbf{i} + 25\mathbf{j}$

$\|\mathbf{u}\| = \sqrt{(20)^2 + (25)^2} = \sqrt{1025} = 5\sqrt{41}$

13. $\mathbf{u} = \langle 1245, 2600 \rangle$, $\mathbf{v} = \langle 12.20, 8.50 \rangle$

$\mathbf{u} \cdot \mathbf{v} = 1245(12.20) + 2600(8.50) = \$37,289$

This gives the total revenue that can be earned by selling all of the units.

15. $\mathbf{u} = \langle 1, 0 \rangle$, $\mathbf{v} = \langle 0, -2 \rangle$

$\cos \theta = \dfrac{\mathbf{u} \cdot \mathbf{v}}{\|\mathbf{u}\| \, \|\mathbf{v}\|} = \dfrac{0}{(1)(2)} = 0$

$\theta = 90°$

17. $\mathbf{u} = 3\mathbf{i} + 4\mathbf{j}$, $\mathbf{v} = -2\mathbf{j}$

$\cos \theta = \dfrac{\mathbf{u} \cdot \mathbf{v}}{\|\mathbf{u}\| \, \|\mathbf{v}\|} = -\dfrac{8}{(5)(2)}$

$\theta = \arccos\left(-\dfrac{4}{5}\right)$

$\theta \approx 143.13°$

19. $\mathbf{u} = \left(\cos\dfrac{\pi}{3}\right)\mathbf{i} + \left(\sin\dfrac{\pi}{3}\right)\mathbf{j} = \dfrac{1}{2}\mathbf{i} + \dfrac{\sqrt{3}}{2}\mathbf{j}$

$\mathbf{v} = \left(\cos\dfrac{3\pi}{4}\right)\mathbf{i} + \left(\sin\dfrac{3\pi}{4}\right)\mathbf{j} = -\dfrac{\sqrt{2}}{2}\mathbf{i} + \dfrac{\sqrt{2}}{2}\mathbf{j}$

$\|\mathbf{u}\| = \|\mathbf{v}\| = 1$

$\cos \theta = \dfrac{\mathbf{u} \cdot \mathbf{v}}{\|\mathbf{u}\| \, \|\mathbf{v}\|} = \mathbf{u} \cdot \mathbf{v} = \left(\dfrac{1}{2}\right)\left(-\dfrac{\sqrt{2}}{2}\right) + \left(\dfrac{\sqrt{3}}{2}\right)\left(\dfrac{\sqrt{2}}{2}\right) = \dfrac{-\sqrt{2} + \sqrt{6}}{4}$

$\theta = \arccos\left(\dfrac{-\sqrt{2} + \sqrt{6}}{4}\right) = 75° = \dfrac{5\pi}{12}$

21. $\mathbf{u} = 3\mathbf{i} + 4\mathbf{j}$, $\mathbf{v} = -7\mathbf{i} + 5\mathbf{j}$

$\cos \theta = \dfrac{\mathbf{u} \cdot \mathbf{v}}{\|\mathbf{u}\| \, \|\mathbf{v}\|} = -\dfrac{1}{(5)(\sqrt{74})} \implies \theta \approx 91.33°$

23. $\mathbf{u} = 5\mathbf{i} + 5\mathbf{j}$, $\mathbf{v} = -6\mathbf{i} + 6\mathbf{j}$

$\cos \theta = \dfrac{\mathbf{u} \cdot \mathbf{v}}{\|\mathbf{u}\| \, \|\mathbf{v}\|} = 0 \implies \theta = 90°$

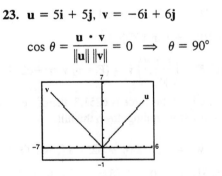

25. $P = (1, 2)$, $Q = (3, 4)$, $R = (2, 5)$

$\overrightarrow{PQ} = \langle 2, 2 \rangle$, $\overrightarrow{PR} = \langle 1, 3 \rangle$, $\overrightarrow{QR} = \langle -1, -1 \rangle$

$\cos \alpha = \dfrac{\overrightarrow{PQ} \cdot \overrightarrow{PR}}{\|\overrightarrow{PQ}\| \, \|\overrightarrow{PR}\|} = \dfrac{8}{(2\sqrt{2})(\sqrt{10})} \implies \alpha = \arccos\dfrac{2}{\sqrt{5}} \approx 26.6°$

$\cos \beta = \dfrac{\overrightarrow{PQ} \cdot \overrightarrow{QR}}{\|\overrightarrow{PQ}\| \, \|\overrightarrow{QR}\|} = 0 \implies \beta = 90°.$ Thus, $\gamma = 180° - 26.6° - 90° = 63.4°$.

27. $\mathbf{u} \cdot \mathbf{v} = \|\mathbf{u}\| \, \|\mathbf{v}\| \cos \theta$

$\qquad = (4)(10) \cos \dfrac{2\pi}{3}$

$\qquad = 40 \left(-\dfrac{1}{2} \right)$

$\qquad = -20$

29. $\mathbf{u} = \langle -12, 30 \rangle, \quad \mathbf{v} = \left\langle \dfrac{1}{2}, \, -\dfrac{5}{4} \right\rangle$

$\quad \mathbf{u} = -24\mathbf{v} \implies \mathbf{u}$ and $\mathbf{v}$ are parallel.

31. $\mathbf{u} = \frac{1}{4} (3\mathbf{i} - \mathbf{j}), \quad \mathbf{v} = 5\mathbf{i} + 6\mathbf{j}$

$\quad \mathbf{u} \neq k\mathbf{v} \implies$ Not parallel

$\quad \mathbf{u} \cdot \mathbf{v} \neq 0 \implies$ Not orthogonal

Neither

33. $\mathbf{u} = 2\mathbf{i} - 2\mathbf{j}, \quad \mathbf{v} = -\mathbf{i} - \mathbf{j}$

$\quad \mathbf{u} \cdot \mathbf{v} = 0 \implies \mathbf{u}$ and $\mathbf{v}$ are orthogonal.

35. $\mathbf{u} = \langle 3, 4 \rangle, \quad \mathbf{v} = \langle 8, 2 \rangle$

$\quad \mathbf{w}_1 = \text{proj}_{\mathbf{v}}\mathbf{u} = \left(\dfrac{\mathbf{u} \cdot \mathbf{v}}{\|\mathbf{v}\|^2} \right) \mathbf{v} = \left(\dfrac{32}{68} \right) \mathbf{v} = \dfrac{8}{17} \langle 8, \, 2 \rangle = \dfrac{16}{17} \langle 4, \, 1 \rangle$

$\quad \mathbf{w}_2 = \mathbf{u} - \mathbf{w}_1 = \langle 3, 4 \rangle - \dfrac{16}{17} \langle 4, 1 \rangle = \dfrac{13}{17} \langle -1, 4 \rangle$

37. $\mathbf{u} = \langle 0, 3 \rangle, \quad \mathbf{v} = \langle 2, 15 \rangle$

$\quad \mathbf{w}_1 = \text{proj}_{\mathbf{v}}\mathbf{u} = \left(\dfrac{\mathbf{u} \cdot \mathbf{v}}{\|\mathbf{v}\|^2} \right) \mathbf{v} = \dfrac{45}{229} \langle 2, 15 \rangle$

$\quad \mathbf{w}_2 = \mathbf{u} - \mathbf{w}_1 = \langle 0, 3 \rangle - \dfrac{45}{229} \langle 2, 15 \rangle = \left\langle -\dfrac{90}{229}, \dfrac{12}{229} \right\rangle = \dfrac{6}{229} \langle -15, 2 \rangle$

39. $\mathbf{u} = \langle 3, 5 \rangle$

For $\mathbf{v}$ to be orthogonal to $\mathbf{u}$, $\mathbf{u} \cdot \mathbf{v}$ must equal 0.

Two possibilities: $\langle -5, 3 \rangle$ and $\langle 5, -3 \rangle$

41. $\mathbf{u} = \frac{1}{2}\mathbf{i} - \frac{2}{3}\mathbf{j}$

For $\mathbf{u}$ and $\mathbf{v}$ to be orthogonal, $\mathbf{u} \cdot \mathbf{v}$ must equal 0.

Two possibilities: $\frac{2}{3}\mathbf{i} + \frac{1}{2}\mathbf{j}$ and $-\frac{2}{3}\mathbf{i} - \frac{1}{2}\mathbf{j}$

43. (a) $\mathbf{F} = -36{,}000\mathbf{j}$ Gravitational force

$\quad \mathbf{v} = (\cos 10°)\mathbf{i} + (\sin 10°)\mathbf{j}$

$\quad \mathbf{w}_1 = \text{proj}_{\mathbf{v}}\mathbf{F} = \left(\dfrac{\mathbf{F} \cdot \mathbf{v}}{\|\mathbf{v}\|^2} \right) \mathbf{v} = (\mathbf{F} \cdot \mathbf{v}) \, \mathbf{v} \approx -6251.3\mathbf{v}$

The magnitude of this force is 6251.3, therefore a force of 6251.3 pounds is needed to keep the truck from rolling down the hill.

(b) $\mathbf{w}_2 = \mathbf{F} - \mathbf{w}_1 = -36{,}000\mathbf{j} + 6251.3 \, (\cos 10°\mathbf{i} + \sin 10°\mathbf{j})$

$\qquad = [(6251.3 \cos 10°)\mathbf{i} + (6251.3 \sin 10° - 36{,}000)\mathbf{j}]$

$\quad \|\mathbf{w}_2\| \approx 35{,}453.1$ pounds

45. (a) $\mathbf{u} \cdot \mathbf{v} = 0 \implies \mathbf{u}$ and $\mathbf{v}$ are orthogonal and $\theta = \dfrac{\pi}{2}$

(b) $\mathbf{u} \cdot \mathbf{v} > 0 \implies \cos \theta > 0 \implies 0 \le \theta < \dfrac{\pi}{2}$

(c) $\mathbf{u} \cdot \mathbf{v} < 0 \implies \cos \theta < 0 \implies \dfrac{\pi}{2} < \theta \le \pi$

47. $\mathbf{w} = (245)(3) = 735$ Newton-meters

49. $\mathbf{w} = (\cos 30°)(45)(20) \approx 779.4$ foot-pounds

51. $\mathbf{w} = \| \text{proj}_{\overrightarrow{PQ}} \mathbf{v} \| \| \overrightarrow{PQ} \|$ where $\overrightarrow{PQ} = \langle 4, 7 \rangle$ and $\mathbf{v} = \langle 1, 4 \rangle$.

$$\text{proj}_{\overrightarrow{PQ}} \mathbf{v} = \left(\frac{\mathbf{v} \cdot \overrightarrow{PQ}}{\| \overrightarrow{PQ} \|^2} \right) \overrightarrow{PQ} = \left(\frac{32}{65} \right) \langle 4, 7 \rangle$$

$$\mathbf{w} = \| \text{proj}_{\overrightarrow{PQ}} \mathbf{v} \| \| \overrightarrow{PQ} \| = \left(\frac{32 \sqrt{65}}{65} \right) \left(\sqrt{65} \right) = 32$$

53. In a rhombus, $\| \mathbf{u} \| = \| \mathbf{v} \|$. The diagonals are $\mathbf{u} + \mathbf{v}$ and $\mathbf{u} - \mathbf{v}$.

$$(\mathbf{u} + \mathbf{v}) \cdot (\mathbf{u} - \mathbf{v}) = (\mathbf{u} + \mathbf{v}) \cdot \mathbf{u} - (\mathbf{u} + \mathbf{v}) \cdot \mathbf{v}$$
$$= \mathbf{u} \cdot \mathbf{u} + \mathbf{v} \cdot \mathbf{u} - \mathbf{u} \cdot \mathbf{v} - \mathbf{v} \cdot \mathbf{v}$$
$$= \| \mathbf{u} \|^2 - \| \mathbf{v} \|^2 = 0$$

Therefore, the diagonals are orthogonal.

55. (a) Let $\mathbf{v} = \langle v_1, v_2 \rangle$.

$\quad$ $\mathbf{0} \cdot \mathbf{v} = 0(v_1) + 0(v_2) = 0$

$\quad$ (b) Let $\mathbf{u} = \langle u_1, u_2 \rangle$, $\mathbf{v} = \langle v_1, v_2 \rangle$ and $\mathbf{w} = \langle w_1, w_2 \rangle$.

$\quad$ $\mathbf{u} \cdot (\mathbf{v} + \mathbf{w}) = \langle u_1, u_2 \rangle \cdot \langle v_1 + w_1, v_2 + w_2 \rangle$
$\quad\quad\quad\quad\quad = u_1(v_1 + w_1) + u_2(v_2 + w_2)$
$\quad\quad\quad\quad\quad = u_1 v_1 + u_1 w_1 + u_2 v_2 + u_2 w_2$
$\quad\quad\quad\quad\quad = (u_1 v_1 + u_2 v_2) + (u_1 w_1 + u_2 w_2)$
$\quad\quad\quad\quad\quad = \mathbf{u} \cdot \mathbf{v} + \mathbf{u} \cdot \mathbf{w}$

(c) Let $\mathbf{u} = \langle u_1, u_2 \rangle$ and $\mathbf{v} = \langle v_1, v_2 \rangle$.

$\quad$ $c(\mathbf{u} \cdot \mathbf{v}) = c(u_1 v_1 + u_2 v_2)$
$\quad\quad\quad\quad = c(u_1 v_1) + c(u_2 v_2)$
$\quad\quad\quad\quad = u_1(c v_1) + u_2(c v_2)$
$\quad\quad\quad\quad = \mathbf{u} \cdot (c\mathbf{v})$

Section 6.5   DeMoivre's Theorem

- ■ You should be able to graphically represent complex numbers and know the following facts about them.
- ■ The absolute value of the complex numbers $z = a + bi$ is $|z| = \sqrt{a^2 + b^2}$.
- ■ The trigonometric form of the complex number $z = a + bi$ is $z = r(\cos \theta + i \sin \theta)$ where

  (a) $a = r \cos \theta$

  (b) $b = r \sin \theta$

  (c) $r = \sqrt{a^2 + b^2}$; r is called the modulus of z.

  (d) $\tan \theta = \frac{b}{a}$; θ is called the argument of z.

- ■ Given $z_1 = r_1(\cos \theta_1 + i \sin \theta_1)$ and $z_2 = r_2(\cos \theta_2 + i \sin \theta_2)$:

  (a) $z_1 z_2 = r_1 r_2 [\cos(\theta_1 + \theta_2) + i \sin(\theta_1 + \theta_2)]$

  (b) $\frac{z_1}{z_2} = \frac{r_1}{r_2} [\cos(\theta_1 - \theta_2) + i \sin(\theta_1 - \theta_2)]$, $z_2 \neq 0$

- ■ You should know DeMoivre's Theorem: If $z = r(\cos \theta + i \sin \theta)$, then for any positive integer n,

  $\quad z^n = r^n (\cos n\theta + i \sin n\theta)$.

- ■ You should know that for any positive integer n, $z = r(\cos \theta + i \sin \theta)$ has n distinct nth roots given by

  $$\sqrt[n]{r} \left[\cos \left(\frac{\theta + 2\pi k}{n} \right) + i \sin \left(\frac{\theta + 2\pi k}{n} \right) \right]$$

  where $k = 0, 1, 2, \dots, n - 1$.

Solutions to Odd-Numbered Exercises

1. $|-5i| = \sqrt{0^2 + (-5)^2}$
$= \sqrt{25} = 5$

3. $|-4 + 4i| = \sqrt{(-4)^2 + (4)^2}$
$= \sqrt{32} = 4\sqrt{2}$

5. $|6 - 7i| = \sqrt{6^2 + (-7)^2}$
$= \sqrt{85}$

7. $z = 3i$

$r = \sqrt{0^2 + 3^2} = \sqrt{9} = 3$

$\tan \theta = \dfrac{3}{0}$, undefined $\implies \theta = \dfrac{\pi}{2}$

$z = 3\left(\cos \dfrac{\pi}{2} + i \sin \dfrac{\pi}{2}\right)$

9. $z = -2 - 2i$

$r = \sqrt{(-2)^2 + (-2)^2} = \sqrt{8} = 2\sqrt{2}$

$\tan \theta = \dfrac{-2}{-2} = 1$, θ is in Quadrant III.

$\theta = 225°$ or $\dfrac{5\pi}{4}$

$z = 2\sqrt{2}\left(\cos \dfrac{5\pi}{4} + i \sin \dfrac{5\pi}{4}\right)$

11. $z = 3 - 3i$

$r = \sqrt{3^2 + (-3)^2} = \sqrt{18} = 3\sqrt{2}$

$\tan \theta = \dfrac{-3}{3} = -1$, θ is in Quadrant IV $\implies \theta = \dfrac{7\pi}{4}$.

$z = 3\sqrt{2}\left(\cos \dfrac{7\pi}{4} + i \sin \dfrac{7\pi}{4}\right)$

13. $z = \sqrt{3} + i$

$r = \sqrt{\left(\sqrt{3}\right)^2 + 1^2} = \sqrt{4} = 2$

$\tan \theta = \dfrac{1}{\sqrt{3}} = \dfrac{\sqrt{3}}{3} \implies \theta = \dfrac{\pi}{6}$

$z = 2\left(\cos \dfrac{\pi}{6} + i \sin \dfrac{\pi}{6}\right)$

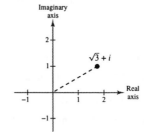

15. $z = -2(1 + \sqrt{3}i)$

$r = \sqrt{(-2)^2 + (-2\sqrt{3})^2} = \sqrt{16} = 4$

$\tan \theta = \dfrac{\sqrt{3}}{1} = \sqrt{3}$, θ is in Quadrant III $\Rightarrow$ $\theta = \dfrac{4\pi}{3}$.

$z = 4\left(\cos \dfrac{4\pi}{3} + i \sin \dfrac{4\pi}{3}\right)$

17. $z = 0 + 6i$

$r = \sqrt{0^2 + (6)^2} = \sqrt{36} = 6$

$\tan \theta = \dfrac{6}{0}$, undefined $\Rightarrow$ $\theta = \dfrac{\pi}{2}$

$z = 6\left(\cos \dfrac{\pi}{2} + i \sin \dfrac{\pi}{2}\right)$

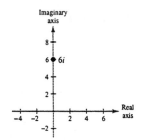

19. $z = -7 + 4i$

$r = \sqrt{(-7)^2 + (4)^2} = \sqrt{65}$

$\tan \theta = \dfrac{4}{-7}$, θ is in Quadrant II $\Rightarrow$ $\theta \approx 2.62$.

$z \approx \sqrt{65}\,(\cos 2.62 + i \sin 2.62)$

21. $z = 7 + 0i$

$r = \sqrt{(7)^2 + (0)^2} = \sqrt{49} = 7$

$\tan \theta = \dfrac{0}{7} = 0 \Rightarrow \theta = 0$

$z = 7\,(\cos 0 + i \sin 0)$

23. $z = 1 + 6i$

$r = \sqrt{1^2 + (6)^2} = \sqrt{37}$

$\tan \theta = \dfrac{6}{1} = 6 \Rightarrow \theta \approx 1.41$

$z \approx \sqrt{37}\,(\cos 1.41 + i \sin 1.41)$

25. $z = -3 - i$

$r = \sqrt{(-3)^2 + (-1)^2} = \sqrt{10}$

$\tan \theta = \dfrac{-1}{-3} = \dfrac{1}{3}$, θ is in Quadrant III $\Rightarrow$ $\theta \approx 3.46$.

$z \approx \sqrt{10}\,(\cos 3.46 + i \sin 3.46)$

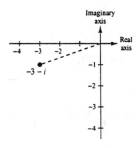

27. $z = 5 + 2i$

$r \approx 5.39$

$\theta \approx 0.38$

$z \approx 5.39(\cos 0.38 + i \sin 0.38)$

29. $z = 3\sqrt{2} - 7i$

$r \approx 8.19$

$\theta \approx -1.03 + 2\pi \approx 5.25$

$z \approx 8.19(\cos 5.25 + i \sin 5.25)$

31. $2(\cos 150° + i \sin 150°) = 2\left[-\dfrac{\sqrt{3}}{2} + i\left(\dfrac{1}{2}\right) \right]$

$\qquad\qquad\qquad\qquad = -\sqrt{3} + i$

33. $\dfrac{3}{2}(\cos 300° + i \sin 300°) = \dfrac{3}{2}\left[\dfrac{1}{2} + i\left(-\dfrac{\sqrt{3}}{2}\right) \right]$

$\qquad\qquad\qquad\qquad = \dfrac{3}{4} - \dfrac{3\sqrt{3}}{4}i$

35. $3.75\left(\cos \dfrac{3\pi}{4} + i \sin \dfrac{3\pi}{4}\right) = -\dfrac{15\sqrt{2}}{8} + \dfrac{15\sqrt{2}}{8}i$

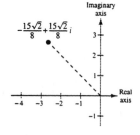

37. $4\left(\cos \dfrac{3\pi}{2} + i \sin \dfrac{3\pi}{2}\right) = 4(0 - i) = -4i$

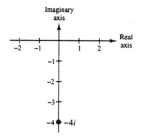

39. $3[\cos(18°45') + i \sin(18°45')] \approx 2.8408 + 0.9643i$

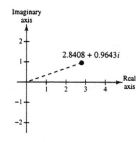

41. $5\left(\cos \dfrac{\pi}{9} + i \sin \dfrac{\pi}{9}\right) \approx 4.70 + 1.71i$

43. $4(\cos 216.5° + i \sin 216.5°) \approx -3.22 - 2.38i$

45. $\left[3\left(\cos \dfrac{\pi}{3} + i \sin \dfrac{\pi}{3}\right) \right]\left[4\left(\cos \dfrac{\pi}{6} + i \sin \dfrac{\pi}{6}\right) \right] = (3)(4)\left[\cos\left(\dfrac{\pi}{3} + \dfrac{\pi}{6}\right) + i \sin\left(\dfrac{\pi}{6} + \dfrac{\pi}{3}\right) \right]$

$\qquad\qquad\qquad\qquad\qquad\qquad\qquad = 12\left(\cos \dfrac{\pi}{2} + i \sin \dfrac{\pi}{2}\right)$

47. $\left[\frac{5}{3}(\cos 140° + i \sin 140°)\right]\left[\frac{2}{3}(\cos 60° + i \sin 60°)\right] = \left(\frac{5}{3}\right)\left(\frac{2}{3}\right)[\cos(140° + 60°) + i \sin(140° + 60°)]$

$$= \tfrac{10}{9}(\cos 200° + i \sin 200°)$$

49. $[0.45(\cos 310° + i \sin 310°)][0.60(\cos 200° + i \sin 200°)] = (0.45)(0.60)[\cos(310° + 200°) + i \sin(310° + 200°)]$

$$= 0.27(\cos 510° + i \sin 510°)$$

$$= 0.27(\cos 150° + i \sin 150°)$$

51. $\dfrac{\cos 40° + i \sin 40°}{\cos 10° + i \sin 10°} = \cos(40° - 10°) + i \sin(40° - 10°) = \cos 30° + i \sin 30°$

53. $\dfrac{\cos(5\pi/3) + i \sin(5\pi/3)}{\cos \pi + i \sin \pi} = \cos\left(\dfrac{5\pi}{3} - \pi\right) + i \sin\left(\dfrac{5\pi}{3} - \pi\right) = \cos\left(\dfrac{2\pi}{3}\right) + i \sin\left(\dfrac{2\pi}{3}\right)$

55. $\dfrac{12(\cos 52° + i \sin 52°)}{3(\cos 110° + i \sin 110°)} = 4[\cos(52° - 110°) + i \sin(52° - 110°)]$

$$= 4[\cos(-58°) + i \sin(-58°)]$$

57. (a) $2 + 2i = 2\sqrt{2}(\cos 45° + i \sin 45°)$

$1 - i = \sqrt{2}[\cos(-45°) + i \sin(-45°)]$

(b) $(2 + 2i)(1 - i) = [2\sqrt{2}(\cos 45° + i \sin 45°)][\sqrt{2}(\cos(-45°) + i \sin(-45°))] = 4(\cos 0° + i \sin 0°) = 4$

(c) $(2 + 2i)(1 - i) = 2 - 2i + 2i - 2i^2 = 2 + 2 = 4$

59. (a) $-2i = 2[\cos(-90°) + i \sin(-90°)]$

$1 + i = \sqrt{2}(\cos 45° + i \sin 45°)$

(b) $-2i(1 + i) = 2[\cos(-90°) + i \sin(-90°)]\left[\sqrt{2}(\cos 45° + i \sin 45°)\right]$

$$= 2\sqrt{2}[\cos(-45°) + i \sin(-45°)]$$

$$= 2\sqrt{2}\left[\frac{1}{\sqrt{2}} - \frac{1}{\sqrt{2}}i\right] = 2 - 2i$$

(c) $-2i(1 + i) = -2i - 2i^2 = -2i + 2 = 2 - 2i$

61. (a) $5 = 5(\cos 0° + i \sin 0°)$

$2 + 3i \approx \sqrt{13}(\cos 56.31° + i \sin 56.31°)$

(b) $\dfrac{5}{2 + 3i} \approx \dfrac{5(\cos 0° + i \sin 0°)}{\sqrt{13}(\cos 56.3° + i \sin 56.3°)} = \dfrac{5\sqrt{13}}{13}[\cos(-56.3°) + i \sin(-56.3°)] \approx 0.7694 - 1.154i$

(c) $\dfrac{5}{2 + 3i} = \dfrac{5}{2 + 3i} \cdot \dfrac{2 - 3i}{2 - 3i} = \dfrac{10 - 15i}{13} = \dfrac{10}{13} - \dfrac{15}{13}i \approx 0.7694 - 1.154i$

63. $\dfrac{z_1}{z_2} = \dfrac{r_1(\cos \theta_1 + i \sin \theta_1)}{r_2(\cos \theta_2 + i \sin \theta_2)} \cdot \dfrac{\cos \theta_2 + i \sin \theta_2}{\cos \theta_2 + i \sin \theta_2}$

$$= \dfrac{r_1}{r_2(\cos^2 \theta_2 + \sin^2 \theta_2)}[\cos \theta_1 \cos \theta_2 + \sin \theta_1 \sin \theta_2 + i(\sin \theta_1 \cos \theta_2 - \sin \theta_2 \cos \theta_1)]$$

$$= \dfrac{r_1}{r_2}[\cos(\theta_1 - \theta_2) + i \sin(\theta_1 - \theta_2)]$$

65. (a) $z\bar{z} = [r(\cos\theta + i\sin\theta)][r(\cos(-\theta) + i\sin(-\theta))]$

$\qquad = r^2[\cos(\theta - \theta) + i\sin(\theta - \theta)]$

$\qquad = r^2[\cos 0 + i\sin 0]$

$\qquad = r^2$

(b) $\dfrac{z}{\bar{z}} = \dfrac{r(\cos\theta + i\sin\theta)}{r[\cos(-\theta) + i\sin(-\theta)]}$

$\qquad = \dfrac{r}{r}[\cos(\theta - (-\theta)) + i\sin(\theta - (-\theta))]$

$\qquad = \cos 2\theta + i\sin 2\theta$

67. Let $z = x + iy$ such that:

$\qquad |z| = 2 \implies 2 = \sqrt{x^2 + y^2}$

$\qquad\qquad \implies 4 = x^2 + y^2 \text{: circle with radius of 2}$

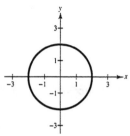

69. $(1 + i)^5 = \left[\sqrt{2}\left(\cos\dfrac{\pi}{4} + i\sin\dfrac{\pi}{4}\right)\right]^5$

$\qquad = (\sqrt{2})^5\left(\cos\dfrac{5\pi}{4} + i\sin\dfrac{5\pi}{4}\right)$

$\qquad = 4\sqrt{2}\left(-\dfrac{\sqrt{2}}{2} - \dfrac{\sqrt{2}}{2}i\right)$

$\qquad = -4 - 4i$

71. $(-1 + i)^{10} = \left[\sqrt{2}\left(\cos\dfrac{3\pi}{4} + i\sin\dfrac{3\pi}{4}\right)\right]^{10}$

$\qquad = (\sqrt{2})^{10}\left(\cos\dfrac{30\pi}{4} + i\sin\dfrac{30\pi}{4}\right)$

$\qquad = 32\left[\cos\left(\dfrac{3\pi}{2} + 6\pi\right) + i\sin\left(\dfrac{3\pi}{2} + 6\pi\right)\right]$

$\qquad = 32\left(\cos\dfrac{3\pi}{2} + i\sin\dfrac{3\pi}{2}\right)$

$\qquad = 32[0 + i(-1)]$

$\qquad = -32i$

73. $2(\sqrt{3} + i)^7 = 2\left[2\left(\cos\dfrac{\pi}{6} + i\sin\dfrac{\pi}{6}\right)\right]^7$

$\qquad = 2\left[2^7\left(\cos\dfrac{7\pi}{6} + i\sin\dfrac{7\pi}{6}\right)\right]$

$\qquad = 256\left(-\dfrac{\sqrt{3}}{2} - \dfrac{1}{2}i\right)$

$\qquad = -128\sqrt{3} - 128i$

75. $[5(\cos 20° + i\sin 20°)]^3 = 5^3(\cos 60° + i\sin 60°) = \dfrac{125}{2} + \dfrac{125\sqrt{3}}{2}i$

77. $\left(\cos\dfrac{5\pi}{4} + i\sin\dfrac{5\pi}{4}\right)^{10} = \cos\dfrac{25\pi}{2} + i\sin\dfrac{25\pi}{2}$

$$= \cos\left(12\pi + \dfrac{\pi}{2}\right) + i\sin\left(12\pi + \dfrac{\pi}{2}\right) = \cos\dfrac{\pi}{2} + i\sin\dfrac{\pi}{2} = i$$

79. $[5(\cos 3.2 + i\sin 3.2)]^4 = 5^4(\cos 12.8 + i\sin 12.8)$

$$\approx 608.02 + 144.69i$$

81. $(3 - 2i)^5 = -597 - 122i$

83. $[3(\cos 15° + i\sin 15°)]^4 = 81(\cos 60° + i\sin 60°)$

$$= \dfrac{81}{2} + \dfrac{8\sqrt{3}}{2}i$$

85. $\left[-\dfrac{1}{2}(1 + \sqrt{3}i)\right]^6 = \left[\cos\dfrac{4\pi}{3} + i\sin\dfrac{4\pi}{3}\right]^6$

$$= \cos 8\pi + i\sin 8\pi$$

$$= 1$$

87. (a) In trigonometric form we have:

$2(\cos 30° + i\sin 30°)$

$2(\cos 150° + i\sin 150°)$

$2(\cos 270° + i\sin 270°)$

(b) There are three roots evenly spaced around a circle of radius 2. Therefore, they represent the cube roots of some number of modulus 8. Cubing them shows that they are all cube roots of $8i$.

(c) $[2(\cos 30° + i\sin 30°)]^3 = 8i$

$[2(\cos 150° + i\sin 150°)]^3 = 8i$

$[2(\cos 270° + i\sin 270°)]^3 = 8i$

89. (a) Square roots of $5(\cos 120° + i\sin 120°)$:

$$\sqrt{5}\left[\cos\left(\dfrac{120° + 360°k}{2}\right) + i\sin\left(\dfrac{120° + 360°k}{2}\right)\right], \ k = 0, 1$$

$k = 0$: $\sqrt{5}(\cos 60° + i\sin 60°)$

$k = 1$: $\sqrt{5}(\cos 240° + i\sin 240°)$

(c) $\dfrac{\sqrt{5}}{2} + \dfrac{\sqrt{15}}{2}i, \ -\dfrac{\sqrt{5}}{2} - \dfrac{\sqrt{15}}{2}i$

(b)

91. (a) Fourth roots of $16\left(\cos\dfrac{4\pi}{3} + i\sin\dfrac{4\pi}{3}\right)$:

(b)

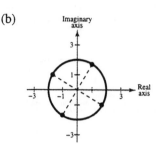

$$\sqrt[4]{16}\left[\cos\left(\frac{(4\pi/3) + 2k\pi}{4}\right) + i\sin\left(\frac{(4\pi/3) + 2k\pi}{4}\right)\right], \ k = 0, 1, 2, 3$$

$$k = 0: \ 2\left(\cos\frac{\pi}{3} + i\sin\frac{\pi}{3}\right)$$

$$k = 1: \ 2\left(\cos\frac{5\pi}{6} + i\sin\frac{5\pi}{6}\right)$$

$$k = 2: \ 2\left(\cos\frac{4\pi}{3} + i\sin\frac{4\pi}{3}\right)$$

$$k = 3: \ 2\left(\cos\frac{11\pi}{6} + i\sin\frac{11\pi}{6}\right)$$

(c) $1 + \sqrt{3}i, \ -\sqrt{3} + i, \ -1 - \sqrt{3}i, \ \sqrt{3} - i$

93. (a) Square roots of $-25i = 25\left(\cos\dfrac{3\pi}{2} + i\sin\dfrac{3\pi}{2}\right)$:

(b)

$$\sqrt{25}\left[\cos\left(\frac{(3\pi/2) + 2k\pi}{2}\right) + i\sin\left(\frac{(3\pi/2) + 2k\pi}{2}\right)\right], \ k = 0, 1$$

$$k = 0: \ 5\left(\cos\frac{3\pi}{4} + i\sin\frac{3\pi}{4}\right)$$

$$k = 1: \ 5\left(\cos\frac{7\pi}{4} + i\sin\frac{7\pi}{4}\right)$$

(c) $-\dfrac{5\sqrt{2}}{2} + \dfrac{5\sqrt{2}}{2}i, \ \dfrac{5\sqrt{2}}{2} - \dfrac{5\sqrt{2}}{2}i$

95. (a) Cube roots of $-\dfrac{125}{3}(1 + \sqrt{3}i) = 125\left(\cos\dfrac{4\pi}{3} + i\sin\dfrac{4\pi}{3}\right)$:

(b)

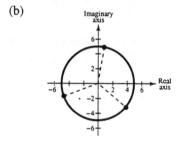

$$\sqrt[3]{125}\left[\cos\left(\frac{(4\pi/3) + 2k\pi}{3}\right) + i\sin\left(\frac{(4\pi/3) + 2k\pi}{3}\right)\right], \ k = 0, 1, 2$$

$$k = 0: \ 5\left(\cos\frac{4\pi}{9} + i\sin\frac{4\pi}{9}\right)$$

$$k = 1: \ 5\left(\cos\frac{10\pi}{9} + i\sin\frac{10\pi}{9}\right)$$

$$k = 2: \ 5\left(\cos\frac{16\pi}{9} + i\sin\frac{16\pi}{9}\right)$$

(c) $0.8682 + 4.924i, \ -4.698 - 1.710i, \ 3.830 - 3.214i$

97. (a) Cube roots of $8 = 8(\cos 0 + i \sin 0)$:

$$\sqrt[3]{8}\left[\cos\left(\frac{2k\pi}{3}\right) + i \sin\left(\frac{2k\pi}{3}\right)\right], \ k = 0, 1, 2$$

$k = 0$: $2(\cos 0 + i \sin 0)$

$k = 1$: $2\left(\cos\dfrac{2\pi}{3} + i \sin\dfrac{2\pi}{3}\right)$

$k = 2$: $2\left(\cos\dfrac{4\pi}{3} + i \sin\dfrac{4\pi}{3}\right)$

(c) $2, -1 + \sqrt{3}i, \ -1 - \sqrt{3}i$

(b)

99. (a) Fifth roots of $1 = \cos 0 + i \sin 0$:

$$\cos\left(\frac{2k\pi}{5}\right) + i \sin\left(\frac{2k\pi}{5}\right), k = 0, 1, 2, 3, 4$$

$k = 0$: $\cos 0 + i \sin 0$

$k = 1$: $\cos\dfrac{2\pi}{5} + i \sin\dfrac{2\pi}{5}$

$k = 2$: $\cos\dfrac{4\pi}{5} + i \sin\dfrac{4\pi}{5}$

$k = 3$: $\cos\dfrac{6\pi}{5} + i \sin\dfrac{6\pi}{5}$

$k = 4$: $\cos\dfrac{8\pi}{5} + i \sin\dfrac{8\pi}{5}$

(b)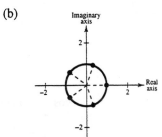

(c) $1, 0.3090 + 0.9511i, -0.8090 + 0.5878i, -0.8090 - 0.5878i, 0.3090 - 0.9511i$

101. (a) The cube roots of $-125 = 125(\cos 180° + i \sin 180°)$ are:

$5(\cos 60° + i \sin 60°)$

$5(\cos 180° + i \sin 180°)$

$5(\cos 300° + i \sin 300°)$

(b)

(c) $\dfrac{5}{2} + \dfrac{5\sqrt{3}}{2}i, \ -5, \ \dfrac{5}{2} - \dfrac{5\sqrt{3}}{2}i$

103. (a) The fifth roots of $128(-1 + i) = 128\sqrt{2}(\cos 135° + i \sin 135°)$ are:

$$2\sqrt[5]{4\sqrt{2}}(\cos 27° + i \sin 27°)$$

$$2\sqrt[5]{4\sqrt{2}}(\cos 99° + i \sin 99°)$$

$$2\sqrt[5]{4\sqrt{2}}(\cos 171° + i \sin 171°)$$

$$2\sqrt[5]{4\sqrt{2}}(\cos 243° + i \sin 243°)$$

$$2\sqrt[5]{4\sqrt{2}}(\cos 315° + i \sin 315°)$$

(b)

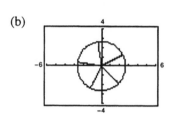

(c) $2.52 + 1.28i, -0.44 + 2.79i, -2.79 + 0.44i,$
$-1.28 - 2.52i, 2 - 2i$

105. $x^4 - i = 0$

$\qquad x^4 = i$

The solutions are the fourth roots of $i = \cos\dfrac{\pi}{2} + i \sin\dfrac{\pi}{2}$:

$$\sqrt[4]{1}\left[\cos\left(\frac{(\pi/2) + 2k\pi}{4}\right) + i \sin\left(\frac{(\pi/2) + 2k\pi}{4}\right)\right], \ k = 0, 1, 2, 3$$

$k = 0$: $\cos\dfrac{\pi}{8} + i \sin\dfrac{\pi}{8}$

$k = 1$: $\cos\dfrac{5\pi}{8} + i \sin\dfrac{5\pi}{8}$

$k = 2$: $\cos\dfrac{9\pi}{8} + i \sin\dfrac{9\pi}{8}$

$k = 3$: $\cos\dfrac{13\pi}{8} + i \sin\dfrac{13\pi}{8}$

107. $x^5 + 243 = 0$

$\qquad x^5 = -243$

The solutions are the fifth roots of $-243 = 243(\cos\pi + i \sin\pi)$:

$$\sqrt[5]{243}\left[\cos\left(\frac{\pi + 2k\pi}{5}\right) + i \sin\left(\frac{\pi + 2k\pi}{5}\right)\right], \ k = 0, 1, 2, 3, 4$$

$k = 0$: $3\left(\cos\dfrac{\pi}{5} + i \sin\dfrac{\pi}{5}\right)$

$k = 1$: $3\left(\cos\dfrac{3\pi}{5} + i \sin\dfrac{3\pi}{5}\right)$

$k = 2$: $3(\cos\pi + i \sin\pi) = -3$

$k = 3$: $3\left(\cos\dfrac{7\pi}{5} + i \sin\dfrac{7\pi}{5}\right)$

$k = 4$: $3\left(\cos\dfrac{9\pi}{5} + i \sin\dfrac{9\pi}{5}\right)$

109. $x^3 + 64i = 0$

$\qquad x^3 = -64i$

The solutions are the cube roots of $-64i = 64\left(\cos\dfrac{3\pi}{2} + i\sin\dfrac{3\pi}{2}\right)$:

$$\sqrt[3]{64}\left[\cos\left(\frac{(3\pi/2) + 2k\pi}{3}\right) + i\sin\left(\frac{(3\pi/2) + 2k\pi}{3}\right)\right],\ k = 0, 1, 2$$

$k = 0$: $4\left(\cos\dfrac{\pi}{2} + i\sin\dfrac{\pi}{2}\right) = 4i$

$k = 1$: $4\left(\cos\dfrac{7\pi}{6} + i\sin\dfrac{7\pi}{6}\right) = -2\sqrt{3} - 2i$

$k = 2$: $4\left(\cos\dfrac{11\pi}{6} + i\sin\dfrac{11\pi}{6}\right) = 2\sqrt{3} - 2i$

111. $x^3 - (1 - i) = 0$

$\qquad x^3 = 1 - i = \sqrt{2}(\cos 315° + i\sin 315°)$

The solutions are the cube roots of $1 - i$:

$$\sqrt[3]{\sqrt{2}}\left[\cos\left(\frac{315° + 360°k}{3}\right) + i\sin\left(\frac{315° + 360°k}{3}\right)\right],\ k = 0, 1, 2$$

$k = 0$: $\sqrt[6]{2}(\cos 105° + i\sin 105°)$

$k = 1$: $\sqrt[6]{2}(\cos 225° + i\sin 225°)$

$k = 2$: $\sqrt[6]{2}(\cos 345° + i\sin 345°)$

❑ Review Exercises for Chapter 6

Solutions to Odd-Numbered Exercises

1. Given: $a = 5$, $b = 8$, $c = 10$

$$\cos C = \frac{a^2 + b^2 - c^2}{2ab} = \frac{25 + 64 - 100}{80} \approx -0.1375 \implies C \approx 97.9°$$

$$\sin A = \frac{a\sin C}{c} \approx \frac{5(0.9905)}{10} \approx 0.4953 \implies A \approx 29.7°$$

$$B = 180° - A - C = 180° - 29.7° - 97.9° = 52.4°$$

3. Given: $A = 12°$, $B = 58°$, $a = 5$

$$C = 180° - A - B = 180° - 12° - 58° = 110°$$

$$b = \frac{a \sin B}{\sin A} = \frac{5 \sin 58°}{\sin 12°} \approx \frac{5(0.8480)}{0.2079} \approx 20.4$$

$$c = \frac{a \sin C}{\sin A} = \frac{5 \sin 110°}{\sin 12°} \approx \frac{5(0.9397)}{0.2079} \approx 22.6$$

5. Given: $B = 110°$, $a = 4$, $c = 4$

$$b^2 = a^2 + c^2 - 2ac \cos B \approx 16 + 16 - 2(4)(4)(-0.3420) \approx 42.94 \implies b \approx 6.6$$

$$\sin A = \frac{a \sin B}{b} \approx \frac{4 \sin 110°}{6.6} \approx \frac{4(0.9397)}{6.6} \approx 0.5736 \implies A \approx 35°$$

$$c = a \implies C = A \approx 35°$$

7. Given: $A = 75°$, $a = 2.5$, $b = 16.5$

$$\sin B = \frac{b \sin A}{a} = \frac{16.5 \sin 75°}{2.5} \approx \frac{16.5(0.9659)}{2.5} \approx 5.375 \implies \text{no triangle formed}$$

No solution

9. Given: $B = 115°$, $a = 7$, $b = 14.5$

$$\sin A = \frac{a \sin B}{b} = \frac{7 \sin 115°}{14.5} \approx \frac{7(0.9063)}{14.5} \approx 0.4375 \implies A \approx 25.9°$$

$$C \approx 180° - 115° - 25.9° = 39.1°$$

$$c^2 = a^2 + b^2 - 2ab \cos C \approx 7^2 + 14.5^2 - 2(7)(14.5)(0.7760) \approx 101.7 \implies c \approx 10.1$$

11. Given: $A = 15°$, $a = 5$, $b = 10$

$$\sin B = \frac{b \sin A}{a} = \frac{10 \sin 15°}{5} \approx \frac{10(0.2588)}{5} \approx 0.5176 \implies B \approx 31.2° \text{ or } 148.8°$$

Case 1: $B \approx 31.2°$ 　　　　　　　　　　　　　Case 2: $B \approx 148.8°$

$C \approx 180° - 15° - 31.2° = 133.8°$ 　　　　　$C \approx 180° - 15° - 148.8° = 16.2°$

$c = \dfrac{a \sin C}{\sin A} \approx 13.9$ 　　　　　　　　　　$c = \dfrac{a \sin C}{\sin A} \approx 5.39$

13. Given: $B = 150°$, $a = 10$, $c = 20$

$$b^2 = a^2 + c^2 - 2ac \cos B \approx 100 + 400 - 400(-0.8660) \approx 846.4 \implies b \approx 29.1$$

$$\sin C = \frac{c \sin B}{b} \approx \frac{20(0.5)}{29.09} \approx 0.3437 \implies C \approx 20.1°$$

$$A = 180° - B - C \approx 180° - 150° - 20.1° = 9.9°$$

15. Given: $B = 25°$, $a = 6.2$, $b = 4$

$$\sin A = \frac{a \sin B}{b} \approx 0.6551 \implies A \approx 40.9° \text{ or } 139.1°$$

Case 1: $A \approx 40.9°$ 　　　　　Case 2: $A \approx 139.1°$

$C \approx 180° - 25° - 40.9° = 114.1°$ 　$C \approx 180° - 25° - 139.1° = 15.9°$

$c \approx 8.6$ 　　　　　　　$c \approx 2.6$

17. $a = 4$, $b = 5$, $c = 7$

$$s = \frac{a + b + c}{2} = \frac{4 + 5 + 7}{2} = 8$$
$$\text{Area} = \sqrt{s(s-a)(s-b)(s-c)}$$
$$= \sqrt{8(4)(3)(1)} \approx 9.798$$

19. $A = 27°$, $b = 5$, $c = 8$

$$\text{Area} = \frac{1}{2}bc \sin A \approx \frac{1}{2}(5)(8)(0.4540) \approx 9.08$$

21. $\alpha = 180° - 31° = 149°$

$\phi = 180° - 149° - 17° = 14°$

$$x = \frac{50 \sin 17°}{\sin \phi} = \frac{50 \sin 17°}{\sin 14°} \approx 60.43$$

$h = x \sin 31°$

$\approx 60.43(0.5150) \approx 31.1$ meters

23. $\sin 28° = \dfrac{h}{75}$

$h = 75 \sin 28° \approx 35.21$ feet

$\cos 28° = \dfrac{x}{75}$

$x = 75 \cos 28° \approx 66.22$ feet

$\tan 45° = \dfrac{H}{x}$

$H = x \tan 45° \approx 66.22$ feet

Height of tree: $H - h \approx 31$ feet

25. $d^2 = 850^2 + 1060^2 - 2(850)(1060) \cos 72°$

$\approx 1,289,251$

$d \approx 1135$ miles

27. Initial point: $(-5, 4)$

Terminal point: $(2, -1)$

$\mathbf{v} = \langle 2 - (-5), -1 - 4 \rangle = \langle 7, -5 \rangle$

29. Initial point: $(0, 10)$

Terminal point: $(7, 3)$

$\mathbf{v} = \langle 7 - 0, 3 - 10 \rangle = \langle 7, -7 \rangle$

31. $\langle 8 \cos 120°, 8 \sin 120° \rangle = (-4, 4\sqrt{3})$

33. $\mathbf{v} = -10\mathbf{i} + 10\mathbf{j}$

$\|\mathbf{v}\| = \sqrt{(-10)^2 + (10)^2} = \sqrt{200} = 10\sqrt{2}$

$\tan \theta = \dfrac{10}{-10} = -1 \implies \theta = 135°$ since

$\mathbf{v}$ is in Quadrant II.

$\mathbf{v} = 10\sqrt{2}(\mathbf{i} \sin 135° + \mathbf{j} \cos 135°)$

35. $\mathbf{u} = 6\mathbf{i} - 5\mathbf{j}$

$\dfrac{1}{\|\mathbf{u}\|}\mathbf{u} = \dfrac{1}{\sqrt{6^2 + 5^2}}(6\mathbf{i} - 5\mathbf{j}) = \dfrac{6}{\sqrt{61}}\mathbf{i} - \dfrac{5}{\sqrt{61}}\mathbf{j}$

$= \left\langle \dfrac{6}{\sqrt{61}}, -\dfrac{5}{\sqrt{61}} \right\rangle$

37. $\mathbf{u} = 6\mathbf{i} - 5\mathbf{j}, \quad \mathbf{v} = 10\mathbf{i} + 3\mathbf{j}$

$4\mathbf{u} - 5\mathbf{v} = (24\mathbf{i} - 20\mathbf{j}) - (50\mathbf{i} + 15\mathbf{j}) = -26\mathbf{i} - 35\mathbf{j}$

$= \langle -26, -35 \rangle$

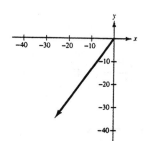

39. $\mathbf{u} = 15[(\cos 20°)\mathbf{i} + (\sin 20°)\mathbf{j}]$

$\mathbf{v} = 20[(\cos 63°)\mathbf{i} + (\sin 63°)\mathbf{j}]$

$\mathbf{u} + \mathbf{v} \approx 23.1752\mathbf{i} + 22.9504\mathbf{j}$

$\|\mathbf{u} + \mathbf{v}\| \approx 32.6161$

$\tan \theta \approx \dfrac{22.9504}{23.1752} \implies \theta \approx 44.72°$

41. $\tan \alpha = \dfrac{12}{5} \implies \sin \alpha = \dfrac{12}{13}$ and $\cos \alpha = \dfrac{5}{13}$

$\tan \beta = \dfrac{3}{4} \implies \sin(180° - \beta) = \dfrac{3}{5}$ and $\cos(180° - \beta) = -\dfrac{4}{5}$

$\mathbf{u} = 250\left(\dfrac{5}{13}\mathbf{i} + \dfrac{12}{13}\mathbf{j}\right)$

$\mathbf{v} = 100\left(-\dfrac{4}{5}\mathbf{i} + \dfrac{3}{5}\mathbf{j}\right)$

$\mathbf{w} = 200(0\mathbf{i} - \mathbf{j})$

$\mathbf{r} = \mathbf{u} + \mathbf{v} + \mathbf{w} = \left(\dfrac{1250}{13} - 80 + 0\right)\mathbf{i} + \left(\dfrac{3000}{13} + 60 - 200\right)\mathbf{j} = \dfrac{210}{13}\mathbf{i} + \dfrac{1180}{13}\mathbf{j}$

$\|\mathbf{r}\| = \sqrt{\left(\dfrac{210}{13}\right)^2 + \left(\dfrac{1180}{13}\right)^2} \approx 92.2 \text{ lb}$

$\tan \theta = \dfrac{1180}{210} \implies \theta \approx 79.9°$

43. Rope One: $\mathbf{u} = \|\mathbf{u}\|(\cos 30°\mathbf{i} - \sin 30°\mathbf{j}) = \|\mathbf{u}\|\left(\dfrac{\sqrt{3}}{2}\mathbf{i} - \dfrac{1}{2}\mathbf{j}\right)$

Rope Two: $\mathbf{v} = \|\mathbf{u}\|(-\cos 30°\mathbf{i} - \sin 30°\mathbf{j}) = \|\mathbf{u}\|\left(-\dfrac{\sqrt{3}}{2}\mathbf{i} - \dfrac{1}{2}\mathbf{j}\right)$

Resultant: $\mathbf{u} + \mathbf{v} = -\|\mathbf{u}\|\mathbf{j} = -180\mathbf{j}$

$\qquad\qquad \|\mathbf{u}\| = 180$

Therefore, the tension on each rope is $\|\mathbf{u}\| = 180$ lb.

45. Airspeed: $\mathbf{u} = 724(\cos 60°\mathbf{i} + \sin 60°\mathbf{j})$

$\qquad\qquad = 362(\mathbf{i} + \sqrt{3}\mathbf{j})$

Wind: $\mathbf{w} = 32\mathbf{i}$

Groundspeed $= \mathbf{u} + \mathbf{w} = (394\mathbf{i} + 362\sqrt{3}\mathbf{j})$

$\|\mathbf{u} + \mathbf{w}\| = \sqrt{(394)^2 + (326\sqrt{3})^2} \approx 740.5$ km/hr

$\tan\theta = \dfrac{362\sqrt{3}}{394} \implies \theta \approx 57.9°$

Bearing: N 32.1° E

47. $P(7, -4), Q(-3, 2)$

$\overrightarrow{PQ} = \langle -3 - 7, 2 - (-4) \rangle = \langle -10, 6 \rangle$

$\|\overrightarrow{PQ}\| = \sqrt{(-10)^2 + (6)^2} = \sqrt{136} = 2\sqrt{34}$

$\dfrac{\overrightarrow{PQ}}{\|\overrightarrow{PQ}\|} = \dfrac{1}{2\sqrt{34}}\langle -10, 6 \rangle = \dfrac{1}{\sqrt{34}}\langle -5, 3 \rangle$

49. $\mathbf{u} = \langle 39, -12 \rangle, \mathbf{v} = \langle -26, 8 \rangle$

$\mathbf{u} \cdot \mathbf{v} = 39(-26) + (-12)(8) = -1110 \neq 0 \implies \mathbf{u}$ and $\mathbf{v}$ are not orthogonal.

$\mathbf{v} = -\frac{2}{3}\mathbf{u} \implies \mathbf{u}$ and $\mathbf{v}$ are parallel.

51. $\mathbf{u} = \cos\dfrac{7\pi}{4}\mathbf{i} + \sin\dfrac{7\pi}{4}\mathbf{j} = \left\langle \dfrac{1}{\sqrt{2}}, -\dfrac{1}{\sqrt{2}} \right\rangle$

$\mathbf{v} = \cos\dfrac{5\pi}{6}\mathbf{i} + \sin\dfrac{5\pi}{6}\mathbf{j} = \left\langle -\dfrac{\sqrt{3}}{2}, \dfrac{1}{2} \right\rangle$

$\cos\theta = \dfrac{\mathbf{u} \cdot \mathbf{v}}{\|\mathbf{u}\|\,\|\mathbf{v}\|} = \dfrac{-\sqrt{3} - 1}{2\sqrt{2}} \Rightarrow \theta = \dfrac{11\pi}{12}$

53. $\mathbf{u} = \langle 2\sqrt{2}, -4 \rangle, \mathbf{v} = \langle -\sqrt{2}, 1 \rangle$

$\cos\theta = \dfrac{\mathbf{u} \cdot \mathbf{v}}{\|\mathbf{u}\|\,\|\mathbf{v}\|} = \dfrac{-8}{(\sqrt{24})(\sqrt{3})} \implies \theta \approx 160.5°$

55. $\mathbf{u} = \langle -4, 3 \rangle, \mathbf{v} = \langle -8, -2 \rangle$

$\text{proj}_{\mathbf{v}}\mathbf{u} = \left(\dfrac{\mathbf{u} \cdot \mathbf{v}}{\|\mathbf{v}\|^2}\right)\mathbf{v} = \left(\dfrac{26}{68}\right)\langle -8, -2 \rangle$

$\qquad\qquad = -\dfrac{13}{17}\langle 4, 1 \rangle$

57. $\mathbf{u} = \langle 2, 7 \rangle, \mathbf{v} = \langle 1, -1 \rangle$

$\text{proj}_{\mathbf{v}}\mathbf{u} = \left(\dfrac{\mathbf{u} \cdot \mathbf{v}}{\|\mathbf{v}\|^2}\right)\mathbf{v} = -\dfrac{5}{2}\langle 1, -1 \rangle$

59. $5 - 5i$

$r = \sqrt{5^2 + (-5)^2} = \sqrt{50} = 5\sqrt{2}$

$\tan \theta = \dfrac{-5}{5} = -1 \implies \theta \approx 315°$ since the complex number is in Quadrant IV.

$5 - 5i = 5\sqrt{2}(\cos 315° + i \sin 315°)$

61. $5 + 12i$

$r = \sqrt{5^2 + 12^2} = \sqrt{169} = 13$

$\tan \theta = \frac{12}{5} \implies \theta \approx 67.38°$ since the complex number is in Quadrant I.

$5 + 12i \approx 13(\cos 67.38° + i \sin 67.38°)$

63. $100(\cos 240° + i \sin 240°) = 100\left(-\dfrac{1}{2} - \dfrac{\sqrt{3}}{2}i\right)$

$\qquad\qquad\qquad\qquad\qquad\qquad = -50 - 50\sqrt{3}i$

65. $13(\cos 0 + i \sin 0) = 13(1 + 0i) = 13$

67. (a) $z_1 = 2\sqrt{3} - 2i = 4(\cos 330° + i \sin 330°)$

$\qquad z_2 = -10i = 10(\cos 270° + i \sin 270°)$

(b) $z_1 z_2 = [4(\cos 330° + i \sin 330°)][10(\cos 270° + i \sin 270°)]$

$\qquad\quad = 40(\cos 600° + i \sin 600°)$

$\qquad\quad = 40(\cos 240° + i \sin 240°)$

$\qquad\quad \approx -20.00 - 34.64i$

$\dfrac{z_1}{z_2} = \dfrac{4(\cos 330° + i \sin 330°)}{10(\cos 270° + i \sin 270°)}$

$\qquad = \dfrac{2}{5}(\cos 60° + i \sin 60°)$

69. $\left[5\left(\cos \dfrac{\pi}{12} + i \sin \dfrac{\pi}{12}\right)\right]^4 = 5^4\left(\cos \dfrac{4\pi}{12} + i \sin \dfrac{4\pi}{12}\right)$

$\qquad\qquad\qquad\qquad\qquad\qquad = 625\left(\cos \dfrac{\pi}{3} + i \sin \dfrac{\pi}{3}\right)$

$\qquad\qquad\qquad\qquad\qquad\qquad = 625\left(\dfrac{1}{2} + \dfrac{\sqrt{3}}{2}i\right)$

$\qquad\qquad\qquad\qquad\qquad\qquad = \dfrac{625}{2} + \dfrac{625\sqrt{3}}{2}i$

71. $(2 + 3i)^6 \approx [\sqrt{13}(\cos 56.3° + i \sin 56.3°)]^6$

$\qquad\qquad = 13^3(\cos 337.9° + i \sin 337.9°)$

$\qquad\qquad \approx 13^3(0.9263 - 0.3769i)$

$\qquad\qquad \approx 2035 - 828i$

73. (a) The trigonometric form of the three roots shown is:

$4(\cos 60° + i \sin 60°)$

$4(\cos 180° + i \sin 180°)$

$4(\cos 300° + i \sin 300°)$

(c) $[4(\cos 60° + i \sin 60°)]^3 = -64$

$[4(\cos 180° + i \sin 180°)]^3 = -64$

$[4(\cos 300° + i \sin 300°)]^3 = -64$

(b) Since there are three evenly spaced roots on the circle of radius 4, they are cube roots of a complex number of modulus $4^3 = 64$. Cubing them yields -64.

75. Sixth roots of $-729i = 729\left(\cos\dfrac{3\pi}{2} + i\sin\dfrac{3\pi}{2}\right)$:

$$\sqrt[6]{729}\left(\cos\frac{(3\pi/2) + 2k\pi}{6} + i\sin\frac{(3\pi/2) + 2k\pi}{6}\right),\ k = 0, 1, 2, 3, 4, 5$$

$k = 0:\ 3\left(\cos\dfrac{\pi}{4} + i\sin\dfrac{\pi}{4}\right)$

$k = 1:\ 3\left(\cos\dfrac{7\pi}{12} + i\sin\dfrac{7\pi}{12}\right)$

$k = 2:\ 3\left(\cos\dfrac{11\pi}{12} + i\sin\dfrac{11\pi}{12}\right)$

$k = 3:\ 3\left(\cos\dfrac{5\pi}{4} + i\sin\dfrac{5\pi}{4}\right)$

$k = 4:\ 3\left(\cos\dfrac{19\pi}{12} + i\sin\dfrac{19\pi}{12}\right)$

$k = 5:\ 3\left(\cos\dfrac{23\pi}{12} + i\sin\dfrac{23\pi}{12}\right)$

77. $x^4 + 81 = 0$

$\quad x^4 = -81$ Solve by finding the fourth roots of -81.

$\quad -81 = 81(\cos\pi + i\sin\pi)$

$$\sqrt[4]{-81} = \sqrt[4]{81}\left[\cos\left(\frac{\pi + 2\pi k}{4}\right) + i\sin\left(\frac{\pi + 2\pi k}{4}\right)\right],\ k = 0, 1, 2, 3$$

$k = 0:\ 3\left(\cos\dfrac{\pi}{4} + i\sin\dfrac{\pi}{4}\right) = \dfrac{3\sqrt{2}}{2} + \dfrac{3\sqrt{2}}{2}i$

$k = 1:\ 3\left(\cos\dfrac{3\pi}{4} + i\sin\dfrac{3\pi}{4}\right) = -\dfrac{3\sqrt{2}}{2} + \dfrac{3\sqrt{2}}{2}i$

$k = 2:\ 3\left(\cos\dfrac{5\pi}{4} + i\sin\dfrac{5\pi}{4}\right) = -\dfrac{3\sqrt{2}}{2} - \dfrac{3\sqrt{2}}{2}i$

$k = 3:\ 3\left(\cos\dfrac{7\pi}{4} + i\sin\dfrac{7\pi}{4}\right) = \dfrac{3\sqrt{2}}{2} - \dfrac{3\sqrt{2}}{2}i$

79. $x^3 + 8i = 0$

$\quad x^3 = -8i$ Solve by finding the cube roots of $-8i$.

$\quad -8i = 8\left(\cos\dfrac{3\pi}{2} + i\sin\dfrac{3\pi}{2}\right)$

$$\sqrt[3]{-8i} = \sqrt[3]{8}\left[\cos\frac{(3\pi/2) + 2\pi k}{3} + i\sin\frac{(3\pi/2) + 2\pi k}{3}\right],\ k = 0, 1, 2$$

$k = 0:\ 2\left(\cos\dfrac{\pi}{2} + i\sin\dfrac{\pi}{2}\right) = 2i$

$k = 1:\ 2\left(\cos\dfrac{7\pi}{6} + i\sin\dfrac{7\pi}{6}\right) = -\sqrt{3} - i$

$k = 2:\ 2\left(\cos\dfrac{11\pi}{6} + i\sin\dfrac{11\pi}{6}\right) = \sqrt{3} - i$

☐ Practice Test for Chapter 6

For Exercises 1 and 2, use the Law of Sines to find the remaining sides and angles of the triangle.

1. $A = 40°$, $B = 12°$, $b = 100$

2. $C = 150°$, $a = 5$, $c = 20$

3. Find the area of the triangle: $a = 3$, $b = 6$, $C = 130°$.

4. Determine the number of solutions to the triangle: $a = 10$, $b = 35$, $A = 22.5°$.

For Exercises 5 and 6, use the Law of Cosines to find the remaining sides and angles of the triangle.

5. $a = 49$, $b = 53$, $c = 38$

6. $C = 29°$, $a = 100$, $b = 300$

7. Use Heron's Formula to find the area of the triangle: $a = 4.1$, $b = 6.8$, $c = 5.5$.

8. A ship travels 40 miles due east, then adjusts its course 12° southward. After traveling 70 miles in that direction, how far is the ship from its point of departure?

9. $\mathbf{w} = 4\mathbf{u} - 7\mathbf{v}$ where $\mathbf{u} = 3\mathbf{i} + \mathbf{j}$ and $\mathbf{v} = -\mathbf{i} + 2\mathbf{j}$. Find $\mathbf{w}$.

10. Find a unit vector in the direction of $\mathbf{v} = 5\mathbf{i} - 3\mathbf{j}$.

11. Find the dot product and the angle between $\mathbf{u} = 6\mathbf{i} + 5\mathbf{j}$ and $\mathbf{v} = 2\mathbf{i} - 3\mathbf{j}$.

12. $\mathbf{v}$ is a vector of magnitude 4 making an angle of 30° with the positive x-axis. Find $\mathbf{v}$ in component form.

13. Find the projection of $\mathbf{u}$ onto $\mathbf{v}$ given $\mathbf{u} = \langle 3, -1 \rangle$ and $\mathbf{v} = \langle -2, 4 \rangle$.

14. Give the trigonometric form of $z = 5 - 5i$.

15. Give the standard form of $z = 6(\cos 225° + i \sin 225°)$

16. Multiply $[7(\cos 23° + i \sin 23°)][4(\cos 7° + i \sin 7°)]$.

17. Divide $\dfrac{9\left(\cos \dfrac{5\pi}{4} + i \sin \dfrac{5\pi}{4}\right)}{3(\cos \pi + i \sin \pi)}$.

18. Find $(2 + 2i)^8$.

19. Find the cube roots of $8\left(\cos \dfrac{\pi}{3} + i \sin \dfrac{\pi}{3}\right)$.

20. Find all the solutions to $x^4 + i = 0$.

C H A P T E R   7
Systems of Equations and Inequalities

C H A P T E R 7
Systems of Equations and Inequalities

Section 7.1 Solving Systems of Equations

- You should be able to solve systems of equations by the method of substitution.
  1. Solve one of the equations for one of the variables.
  2. Substitute this expression into the other equation and solve.
  3. Back-substitute into the first equation to find the value of the other variable.
  4. Check your answer in each of the original equations.
- You should be able to find solutions graphically. (See Example 5 in textbook.)

Solutions to Odd-Numbered Exercises

1. $2x + y = 6$ Equation 1

   $-x + y = 0$ Equation 2

Solve for y in Equation 1: $y = 6 - 2x$

Substitute for y in Equation 2: $-x + (6 - 2x) = 0$

Solve for x: $-3x + 6 = 0 \implies x = 2$

Back-substitute $x = 2$: $y = 6 - 2(2) = 2$

Answer: $(2, 2)$

3. $x - y = -4$ Equation 1

   $x^2 - y = -2$ Equation 2

Solve for y in Equation 1: $y = x + 4$

Substitute for y in Equation 2: $x^2 - (x + 4) = -2$

Solve for x: $x^2 - x - 2 = 0 \implies (x + 1)(x - 2) = 0 \implies x = -1, 2$

Back-substitute $x = -1$: $y = -1 + 4 = 3$

Back-substitute $x = 2$: $y = 2 + 4 = 6$

Answers: $(-1, 3), (2, 6)$

5. $x - 3y = 15$ Equation 1

$x^2 + y^2 = 25$ Equation 2

Solve for x in Equation 1: $x = 3y + 15$

Substitute for x in Equation 2: $(3y + 15)^2 + y^2 = 25$

Solve for y: $10y^2 + 90y + 200 = 0 \implies y^2 + 9y + 20 = 0 \implies (y + 5)(y + 4) = 0 \implies y = -5, -4$

Back-substitute $y = -5$: $x = 3(-5) + 15 = 0$

Back-substitute $y = -4$: $x = 3(-4) + 15 = 3$

Answers: $(0, -5), (3, -4)$

7. $x^2 + y = 0$ Equation 1

$x^2 - 4x - y = 0$ Equation 2

Solve for y in Equation 1: $y = -x^2$

Substitute for y in Equation 2: $x^2 - 4x - (-x^2) = 0$

Solve for x: $2x^2 - 4x = 0 \implies 2x(x - 2) = 0 \implies x = 0, 2$

Back-substitute $x = 0$: $y = -0^2 = 0$

Back-substitute $x = 2$: $y = -2^2 = -4$

Answers: $(0, 0), (2, -4)$

9. $x - 6y = -8$ Equation 1

$x^2 - 4y^3 = 0$ Equation 2

Solve for x in Equation 1: $x = 6y - 8$

Substitute for x in Equation 2: $(6y - 8)^2 - 4y^3 = 0$

Solve for y: $-4y^3 + 36y^2 - 96y + 64 = 0$

$$y^3 - 9y^2 + 24y - 16 = 0$$

$$(y - 1)(y - 4)^2 = 0 \implies y = 1, 4$$

Back-substitute $y = 1$: $x = 6(1) - 8 = -2$

Back-substitute $y = 4$: $x = 6(4) - 8 = 16$

Answers: $(-2, 1), (16, 4)$

11. $x - y = 0$ Equation 1

$5x - 3y = 10$ Equation 2

Solve for y in Equation 1: $y = x$

Substitute for y in Equation 2: $5x - 3x = 10$

Solve for x: $2x = 10 \implies x = 5$

Back-substitute in Equation 1: $y = x = 5$

Answer: $(5, 5)$

13. $2x - y + 2 = 0$ Equation 1

$4x + y - 5 = 0$ Equation 2

Solve for y in Equation 1: $y = 2x + 2$

Substitute for y in Equation 2: $4x + (2x + 2) - 5 = 0$

Solve for x: $4x + (2x + 2) - 5 = 0 \implies 6x - 3 = 0 \implies x = \frac{1}{2}$

Back-substitute $x = \frac{1}{2}$: $y = 2x + 2 = 2\left(\frac{1}{2}\right) + 2 = 3$

Answer: $\left(\frac{1}{2}, 3\right)$

15. $30x - 40y - 33 = 0$ Equation 1

$10x + 20y - 21 = 0$ Equation 2

Solve for x in Equation 2: $x = -2y + \frac{21}{10}$

Substitute for x in Equation 1: $30\left(-2y + \frac{21}{10}\right) - 40y - 33 = 0$

Solve for y: $-100y + 30 = 0 \implies y = \frac{3}{10}$

Back-substitute $y = \frac{3}{10}$: $x = -2y + \frac{21}{10} = -2\left(\frac{3}{10}\right) + \frac{21}{10} = \frac{3}{2}$

Answer: $\left(\frac{3}{2}, \frac{3}{10}\right)$

17. $\frac{1}{5}x + \frac{1}{2}y = 8$ Equation 1

$x + y = 20$ Equation 2

Solve for x in Equation 2: $x = 20 - y$

Substitute for x in Equation 1: $\frac{1}{5}(20 - y) + \frac{1}{2}y = 8$

Solve for y: $4 + \frac{3}{10}y = 8 \implies y = \frac{40}{3}$

Back-substitute $y = \frac{40}{3}$: $x = 20 - y = 20 - \frac{40}{3} = \frac{20}{3}$

Answer: $\left(\frac{20}{3}, \frac{40}{3}\right)$

19. $2x + y = 4$ Equation 1

$-4x + 2y = -12$ Equation 2

Solve for y in Equation 1: $y = 2x - 4$

Substitute for y in Equation 2: $-4x + 2(2x - 4) = -12$

Solve for x: $-8 \neq -12$ Inconsistent

No Solution.

21. $x - y = 0$ Equation 1

$2x + y = 0$ Equation 2

Solve for y in Equation 1: $y = x$

Substitute for y in Equation 2: $2x + x = 0$

Solve for x: $3x = 0 \implies x = 0$

Back-substitute $x = 0$: $y = x = 0$

Answer: $(0, 0)$

23. $-x + 2y = 2$

$3x + y = 15$

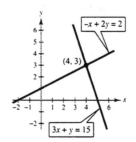

Point of intersection: $(4, 3)$

25. $x - 3y = -2$

$5x + 3y = 17$

Point of intersection: $\left(\frac{5}{2}, \frac{3}{2}\right)$

27. $x + y = 4$

$x^2 + y^2 - 4x = 0$

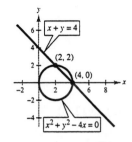

Points of intersection: $(2, 2)$, $(4, 0)$

29. $7x + 8y = 24 \implies y_1 = -\frac{7}{8}x + 3$

$x - 8y = 8 \implies y_2 = \frac{1}{8}x - 1$

Point of intersection: $\left(4, -\frac{1}{2}\right)$

31. $3x - 2y = 0 \implies y_1 = \frac{3}{2}x$

$x^2 - y^2 = 4 \implies y_2 = \sqrt{x^2 - 4}$

$y_3 = -\sqrt{x^2 - 4}$

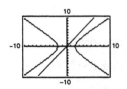

No points of intersection

Inconsistent

No solution

33. $x^2 + y^2 = 8 \implies y_1 = \sqrt{8 - x^2}$ and $y_2 = -\sqrt{8 - x^2}$

$y = x^2 \implies y_3 = x^2$

Points of intersection: $\left(\pm\sqrt{\dfrac{-1 + \sqrt{33}}{2}}, \dfrac{-1 + \sqrt{33}}{2}\right)$

$\approx (\pm 1.54, 2.37)$

Algebraically we have:

$$x^2 + (x^2)^2 = 8$$

$$x^4 + x^2 - 8 = 0$$

$$x^2 = \frac{-1 \pm \sqrt{1^2 - 4(1)(-8)}}{2(1)}$$

Use the positive value $\pm\sqrt{\dfrac{1 + \sqrt{33}}{2}}$

$$y = x^2 = \frac{-1 + \sqrt{33}}{2}$$

35. $y = e^x$

$x - y + 1 = 0 \implies y = x + 1$

Point of intersection: $(0, 1)$

37. $y = \sqrt{x}$

$y = x$

Points of intersection: $(0, 0)$, $(1, 1)$

39. $x^2 + y^2 = 169 \implies y_1 = \sqrt{169 - x^2}$ and $y_2 = -\sqrt{169 - x^2}$

$x^2 - 8y = 104 \implies y_3 = \frac{1}{8}x^2 - 13$

Points of intersection: $(0, -13)$, $(\pm 12, 5)$

41. $y = 2x$ Equation 1

$y = x^2 + 1$ Equation 2

Substitute for y in Equation 2: $2x = x^2 + 1$

Solve for x: $x^2 - 2x + 1 = (x - 1)^2 = 0 \implies x = 1$

Back-substitute $x = 1$ in Equation 1: $y = 2x = 2$

Answer: $(1, 2)$

43. $3x - 7y + 6 = 0$ Equation 1

$x^2 - y^2 = 4$ Equation 2

Solve for y in Equation 1: $y = \dfrac{3x + 6}{7}$

Solve for y in Equation 2: $x^2 - \left(\dfrac{3x + 6}{7}\right)^2 = 4$

Solve for x: $\quad x^2 - \left(\dfrac{9x^2 + 36x + 36}{49}\right) = 4$

$$49x^2 - (9x^2 + 36x + 36) = 196$$

$$40x^2 - 36x - 232 = 0$$

$4(10x - 29)(x + 2) = 0 \implies x = \dfrac{29}{10}, -2$

Back-substitute $x = \dfrac{29}{10}$: $y = \dfrac{3x + 6}{7} = \dfrac{3(29/10) + 6}{7} = \dfrac{21}{10}$

Back-substitute $x = -2$: $y = \dfrac{3x + 6}{7} = 0$

Answers: $\left(\dfrac{29}{10}, \dfrac{21}{10}\right)$, $(-2, 0)$

45. $x - 2y = 4$ Equation 1

$x^2 - y = 0$ Equation 2

Solve for y in Equation 2: $y = x^2$

Substitute for y in Equation 1: $x - 2x^2 = 4$

Solve for x: $0 = 2x^2 - x + 4$

No real solutions, the discriminant in the Quadratic Formula is negative.

Inconsistent

No real solution

47. $y - e^{-x} = 1 \implies y = e^{-x} + 1$

$y - \ln x = 3 \implies y = \ln x + 3$

Point of intersection: Approximately (0.287, 1.75)

49. $y = x^4 - 2x^2 + 1$ Equation 1

$y = 1 - x^2$ Equation 2

Substitute for y in Equation 1: $1 - x^2 = x^4 - 2x^2 + 1$

Solve for x: $x^4 - x^2 = 0 \implies x^2(x^2 - 1) = 0$

$\implies x = 0, \pm 1$

Back-substitute $x = 0$: $1 - x^2 = 1$

Back-substitute $x = 1$: $1 - x^2 = 1 - 1^2 = 0$

Back-substitute $x = -1$: $1 - x^2 = 1 - (-1)^2 = 0$

Answers: $(0, 1), (\pm 1, 0)$

51. $xy - 1 = 0$ Equation 1

$2x - 4y + 7 = 0$ Equation 2

Solve for y in Equation 1: $y = \dfrac{1}{x}$

Substitute for y in Equation 2: $2x - 4\left(\dfrac{1}{x}\right) + 7 = 0$

Solve for x: $2x^2 - 4 + 7x = 0 \implies (2x - 1)(x + 4) = 0 \implies x = \dfrac{1}{2}, -4$

Back-substitute $x = \dfrac{1}{2}$: $y = \dfrac{1}{1/2} = 2$

Back-substitute $x = -4$: $y = \dfrac{1}{-4} = -\dfrac{1}{4}$

Answers: $\left(\dfrac{1}{2}, 2\right), \left(-4, -\dfrac{1}{4}\right)$

53. The system has no solution if you arrive at a false statement, ie. $4 = 8$, or you have a quadratic equation with a negative discriminant, which would yield imaginary solutions.

55. $C = 8650x + 250,000, \ R = 9950x$

$R = C$

$9950x = 8650x + 250,000$

$1300x = 250,000$

$x \approx 192$ units

57. $C = 2.65x + 350,000, \ R = 4.15x$

$R = C$

$4.15x = 2.65x + 350,000$

$1.50x = 350,000$

$x \doteq 233,333$ units

59. $C = 3.45x + 16,000, \ R = 5.95x$

(a) $R = C$

$5.95x = 3.45x + 16,000$

$2.50x = 16,000$

$x \approx 6400$ units

(b) $P = R - C$

$6000 = 5.95x - (3.45x + 16,000)$

$6000 = 2.5x - 16,000$

$22000 = 2.5x$

$x \approx 8800$ units

61. (a) $x + y = 25,000$

$0.06x + 0.085y = 2000$

(b) $y_1 = 25,000 - x$

$y_2 = \dfrac{2000 - 0.06x}{0.085}$

As the amount at 6% increases, the amount at 8.5% decreases. The amount of interest is fixed at $2000.

(c) The point of intersection occurs when $x = 5000$, so the most that can be invested at 6% and still earn $2000 per year in interest is $5000.

63. $0.06x = 0.03x + 250$

$0.03x = 250$

$x \approx \$8333.33$

To make the straight commission offer the better offer, you would have to sell more than $8333.33 per week.

65. $V = (D - 4)^2, 5 \le D \le 40$ Doyle Log Rule

$V = 0.79D^2 - 2D - 4, 5 \le D \le 40$ Scribner Log Rule

(a)

(b) The graphs intersect when $D \approx 24.7$ inches.

(c) For large logs, Doyle's Log Rule gives a greater volume for a given diameter.

67. $2l + 2w = 30 \implies \quad l + w = 15$

$l = w + 3 \implies (w + 3) + 2 = 15$

$2w = 12$

$w = 6$

$l = w + 3 = 9$

Dimensions: 6 meters × 9 meters

69. $2l + 2w = 42 \implies l + w = 21$

$w = \frac{3}{4}l \implies l + \frac{3}{4}l = 21$

$\frac{7}{4}l = 21$

$l = 12$

$w = \frac{3}{4}l = 9$

Dimensions: 9 inches × 12 inches

71. $2l + 2w = 40 \implies \quad l + w = 20 \implies w = 20 - l$

$lw = 96 \implies l(20 - l) = 96$

$20l - l^2 = 96$

$0 = l^2 - 20l + 96$

$0 = (l - 8)(l - 12)$

$l = 8 \text{ or } l = 12$

$w = 12, w = 8$

Since the length is supposed to be greater than the width, we have $l = 12$ kilometers and $w = 8$ kilometers.

73. The point lies on the line through $(0, 10)$ and $\left(\sqrt{61}, 0\right)$. This line's equation is $y = -\dfrac{10}{\sqrt{61}}x + 10.$

Substitute for y in $\dfrac{x^2}{25} - \dfrac{y^2}{36} = 1.$

$$\frac{x^2}{25} - \frac{\left(-10/\sqrt{61}\,x + 10\right)^2}{36} = 1$$

$$36x^2 - 25\left(-\frac{10}{\sqrt{61}}x + 10\right)^2 = 900$$

$$36x^2 - 25\left(\frac{100}{61}x^2 - \frac{200}{\sqrt{61}}x + 100\right) = 900$$

$$-\frac{304}{61}x^2 + \frac{5000}{\sqrt{61}}x - 3400 = 0$$

By the Quadratic Formula we have $x \approx 122.91$ or $x \approx 5.55$. Only $x \approx 5.55$ agrees with the graph. The point of intersection is approximately $(5.55, 2.89)$.

75. $(0, 6.6), (1, 6.8), (2, 7.1), (3, 7.1)$

(a) Linear model: $f(t) = 0.18t + 6.63$

Quadratic model: $g(t) = -0.05t^2 + 0.33t + 6.58$

(b)

(c) Points of intersection: $(0.382, 6.70), (2.618, 7.10)$

(d) Linear model when
$t = 4$: $f(4) = 7.35$ million short tons.

Quadratic model when
$t = 4$: $g(4) = 7.1$ million short tons.

Since the sale of newsprint has been slowly decreasing (more papers are on-line now and many people would rather listen to the news than read it) the Quadratic model is probably more accurate.

77. $(-2, 7), (5, 5)$

$$m = \frac{5 - 7}{5 - (-2)} = -\frac{2}{7}$$

$$y - 7 = -\frac{2}{7}(x - (-2))$$

$$7y - 49 = -2x - 4$$

$$2x + 7y - 45 = 0$$

79. $(6, 3), (10, 3)$

$$m = \frac{3 - 3}{10 - 6} = 0 \implies \text{The line is horizontal.}$$

$$y = 3$$

81. $\left(\frac{3}{5}, 0\right), (4, 6)$

$$m = \frac{6 - 0}{4 - \frac{3}{5}} = \frac{6}{\frac{17}{5}} = \frac{30}{17}$$

$$y - 6 = \frac{30}{17}(x - 4)$$

$$17y - 102 = 30x - 120$$

$$0 = 30x - 17y - 18$$

Section 7.2   Two-Variable Linear Systems

- You should be able to solve a linear system by the method of elimination.
  1. Obtain coefficients for either x or y that differ only in sign. This is done by multiplying all the terms of one or both equations by appropriate constants.
  2. Add the equations to eliminate one of the variables and then solve for the remaining variable.
  3. Use back-substitution into either original equation and solve for the other variable.
  4. Check your answer.
- You should know that for a system of two linear equations, one of the following is true.
  1. There are infinitely many solutions; the lines are identical. The system is consistent.
  2. There is no solution; the lines are parallel. The system is inconsistent.
  3. There is one solution; the lines intersect at one point. The system is consistent.

Solutions to Odd-Numbered Exercises

1. $2x + y = 5$ Equation 1

   $x - y = 5$ Equation 2

   Add to eliminate y: $3x = 6 \implies x = 2$

   Substitute $x = 2$ in Equation 2: $2 - y = 1 \implies y = 1$

   Answer: $(2, 1)$

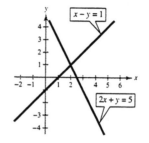

3. $x + y = 0$ Equation 1

   $3x + 2y = 1$ Equation 2

   Multiply Equation 1 by -2: $-2x - 2y = 0$

   Add this to Equation 2 to eliminate y: $x = 1$

   Substitute $x = 1$ in Equation 1: $1 + y = 0 \implies y = -1$

   Answer: $(1, -1)$

5. $x - y = 2$ Equation 1

   $-2x + 2y = 5$ Equation 2

   Multiply Equation 1 by 2: $2x - 2y = 4$

   Add this to Equation 2: $0 = 9$

   There are no solutions.

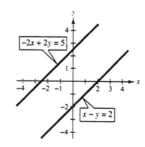

7. $3x - 2y = \quad 5$ Equation 1

$-6x + 4y = -10$ Equation 2

Multiply Equation 1 by 2 and add to Equation 2: $0 = 0$

The equations are dependent. There are infinitely many solutions.

9. $9x + 3y = 1$ Equation 1

$3x - 6y = 5$ Equation 2

Multiply Equation 2 by (-3): $9x + \quad 3y = \quad 1$

$\qquad\qquad\qquad\qquad -9x + 18y = -15$

Add to eliminate x: $21y = -14 \implies y = -\frac{2}{3}$

Substitute $y = -\frac{2}{3}$ in Equation 1: $9x + 3\left(-\frac{2}{3}\right) = 1$

$\qquad\qquad\qquad\qquad\qquad\qquad\qquad x = \frac{1}{3}$

Answer: $\left(\frac{1}{3}, -\frac{2}{3}\right)$

11. $x + 2y = 4$ Equation 1

$x - 2y = 1$ Equation 2

Add to eliminate y:

$\quad 2x = 5$

$\quad x = \frac{5}{2}$

Substitute $x = \frac{5}{2}$ in Equation 1:

$\quad \frac{5}{2} + 2y = 4 \implies y = \frac{3}{4}$

Answer: $\left(\frac{5}{2}, \frac{3}{4}\right)$

13. $2x + 3y = 18$ Equation 1

$5x - \quad y = 11$ Equation 2

Multiply Equation 2 by 3: $15x - 3y = 33$

Add this to Equation 1 to eliminate y:

$\quad 17x = 51 \implies x = 3$

Substitute $x = 3$ in Equation 1:

$\quad 6 + 3y = 18 \implies y = 4$

Answer: $(3, 4)$

15. $3x + 2y = 10$ Equation 1

$2x + 5y = \quad 3$ Equation 2

Multiply Equation 1 by 2 and Equation 2 by (-3):

$\quad 6x + \quad 4y = 20$

$\quad -6x - 15y = -9$

Add to eliminate x: $-11y = 11 \implies y = -1$

Substitute $y = -1$ in Equation 1:

$\quad 3x - 2 = 10 \implies x = 4$

Answer: $(4, -1)$

17. $2u + \quad v = 120$ Equation 1

$u + 2v = 120$ Equation 2

Multiply Equation 2 by (-2):

$\quad -2u - 4v = -240$

Add this to Equation 1 to eliminate u:

$\quad -3v = -120$

$\quad v = 40$

Substitute $v = 40$ in Equation 2:

$\quad u + 80 = 120 \implies u = 40$

Answer: $(40, 40)$

19. $6r - \quad 5s = 3$ Equation 1

$-12r + 10s = 5$ Equation 2

Multiply Equation 1 by 2: $12r - 10s = 6$

Add this to Equation 2 to eliminate r: $0 = 11$

Inconsistent

No solution

21. $\dfrac{x}{4} + \dfrac{y}{6} = 1$ Equation 1

$x - y = 3$ Equation 2

Multiply Equation 1 by 6: $\dfrac{3}{2}x + y = 6$

Add this to Equation 2 to eliminate y:

$\dfrac{5}{2}x = 9 \implies x = \dfrac{18}{5}$

Substitute $x = \dfrac{18}{5}$ in Equation 2:

$\dfrac{18}{5} - y = 3$

$y = \dfrac{3}{5}$

Answer: $\left(\dfrac{18}{5}, \dfrac{3}{5}\right)$

23. $\dfrac{x+3}{4} + \dfrac{y-1}{3} = 1$ Equation 1

$2x - y = 12$ Equation 2

Multiply Equation 1 by 12 and Equation 2 by 4:

$3x + 4y = 7$

$8x - 4y = 48$

Add to eliminate y: $11x = 55 \implies x = 5$

Substitute $x = 5$ into Equation 2:

$2(5) - y = 12 \implies y = -2$

Answer: $(5, -2)$

25. $2.5x - 3y = 1.5$ Equation 1

$10x - 12y = 6$ Equation 2

Multiply Equation 1 by (-4):

$-10x + 12y = -6$

Add this to Equation 2 to eliminate x:

$0 = 0$ (Dependent)

The solution set consists of all points lying

on the line $10x - 12y = 6$.

Let $x = a$, then $y = \dfrac{5}{6}a - \dfrac{1}{2}$.

Answer: $\left(a, \dfrac{5}{6}a - \dfrac{1}{2}\right)$, where a is any

real number.

27. $0.05x - 0.03y = 0.21$ Equation 1

$0.07x + 0.02y = 0.16$ Equation 2

Multiply Equation 1 by 200 and
Equation 2 by 300: $10x - 6y = 42$

$21x + 6y = 48$

Add to eliminate y: $31x = 90$

$x = \dfrac{90}{31}$

Substitute $x = \dfrac{90}{31}$ in Equation 2:

$0.07\left(\dfrac{90}{31}\right) + 0.02y = 0.16$

$y = -\dfrac{67}{31}$

Answer: $\left(\dfrac{90}{31}, -\dfrac{67}{31}\right)$

29. $4b + 3m = 3$ Equation 1

$3b + 11m = 13$ Equation 2

Multiply Equation 1 by 3 and Equation 2 by (-4):

$12b + 9m = 9$

$-12b - 44m = -52$

Add to eliminate b: $-35m = -43$

$m = \dfrac{43}{35}$

Substitute $m = \dfrac{43}{35}$ in Equation 1: $5b + 3\left(\dfrac{43}{35}\right) = 3 \implies b = -\dfrac{6}{35}$

Answer: $\left(-\dfrac{6}{35}, \dfrac{43}{35}\right)$

31. $\dfrac{1}{5}x - \dfrac{1}{3}y = 1$

$-3x + 5y = 9$

The lines are parallel. The system is inconsistent.

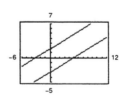

33. $2x - 5y = 0$

$\quad\; x - y = 3$

The system is consistent. There is one solution.

35. $8x + 9y = 42$

$\quad\; 6x - y = 16$

Answer: $(3, 2)$

37. $\quad\;\; 4y = -8$

$\quad 7x - 2y = 25$

Answer: $(3, -2)$

39. $3x - 5y = 7$ Equation 1

$\quad 2x + y = 9$ Equation 2

Multiply Equation 2 by 5:

$\quad 10x + 5y = 45$

Add this to Equation 1:

$\quad 13x = 52 \implies x = 4$

Back-substitute $x = 4$ into Equation 2:

$\quad 2(4) + y = 9 \implies y = 1$

Answer: $(4, 1)$

41. $y = 2x - 5$ Equation 1

$\quad y = 5x - 11$ Equation 2

Since both equations are solved for y, set them equal to one another and solve for x.

$\quad 2x - 5 = 5x - 11$

$\quad\quad\quad 6 = 3x$

$\quad\quad\quad 2 = x$

Back-substitute $x = 2$ into Equation 1:

$\quad y = 2(2) - 5 = -1$

Answer: $(2, -1)$

43. There are infinitely many systems that have the solution $\left(3, \frac{5}{2}\right)$. One possible system is:

$\quad 2(3) + 2\left(\frac{5}{2}\right) = 11 \implies 2x + 2y = 11$

$\quad\quad 3 - 4\left(\frac{5}{2}\right) = -7 \implies \quad x - 4y = -7$

45. $100y - x = \quad 200$ Equation 1

$\quad 99y - x = -198$ Equation 2

Subtract Equation 2 from Equation 1 to eliminate x: $y = 398$

Substitute $y = 398$ into Equation 1: $100(398) - x = 200 \implies x = 39{,}600$

Answer: $(39{,}600, \; 398)$

The lines are not parallel. The scale on the axes must be changed to see the point of intersection.

47. No, it is not possible for a consistent system of linear equations to have exactly two solutions. Either the lines will intersect once or they will coincide and then the system would have infinite solutions.

49. $4x - 8y = -3$ Equation 1

$2x + ky = 16$ Equation 2

Multiply Equation 2 by -2: $-4x - 2ky = -32$

Add this to Equation 1: $-8y - 2ky = -35$

The system in inconsistent if $-8y - 2ky = 0$. This occurs when $k = -4$.

51. Let $x =$ the air speed and $y =$ the wind speed.

$$3.6(x - y) = 1800 \quad \text{Equation 1}$$
$$6(x + y) = 1800 \quad \text{Equation 2}$$

$$
\begin{aligned}
x - y &= 500 \\
x + y &= 600 \\
\hline
2x &= 1100 \\
x &= 550 \\
550 + y &= 600 \\
y &= 50
\end{aligned}
$$

Answer: $x = 550$ mph, $y = 50$ mph

53. Let $x =$ the number of liters at 20%

   $y =$ the number of liters at 50%.

(a) $x + y = 10$

   $0.2x + 0.5y = 0.3(10)$

(b)   As x increases, y decreases.

(c) -2 Equation 1 $\quad -2x - 2y = -20$

   10 Equation 2 $\quad \dfrac{2x + 5y = 30}{}$

$$
\begin{aligned}
3y &= 10 \\
y &= \frac{10}{3} \\
x + \frac{10}{3} &= 10 \\
x &= \frac{20}{3}
\end{aligned}
$$

Answer: $x = 6\frac{2}{3}$ liters at 20%

   $y = 3\frac{1}{3}$ liters at 50%

55. Let $x =$ amount invested at 10.5%

   $y =$ amount invested at 12%.

$$
\begin{aligned}
x + y &= 12{,}000 \quad \text{Equation 1} \\
0.105x + 0.12y &= 1350 \quad \text{Equation 2}
\end{aligned}
$$

$$
\begin{aligned}
-12x - 12y &= -144{,}000 \\
10.5x + 12y &= 135{,}000 \\
\hline
-1.5x \quad\quad &= -9000 \\
x \quad\quad &= 6000 \\
6000 + y &= 12{,}000 \\
y &= 6000
\end{aligned}
$$

Answer: $y = \$6000$ at 12%

   $x = \$6000$ at 10.5%

57. Let x = number of adult tickets sold

y = number of child tickets sold.

$$x + y = 500 \qquad \text{Equation 1}$$
$$7.5x + 4y = \$3312.50 \qquad \text{Equation 2}$$

$$
\begin{aligned}
-4x - 4y &= -2000.00 \\
7.5x + 4y &= 3312.50 \\
\hline
3.5x &= 1312.50 \\
x &= 375 \\
375 + y &= 500 \\
y &= 125
\end{aligned}
$$

Answer: $x = 375$ adult tickets

$y = 125$ child tickets

59. Let x = distance one person drives

y = distance other person drives.

$$x + y = 300 \qquad \text{Equation 1}$$
$$y = 3x \qquad \text{Equation 2}$$
$$x + 3x = 300 \qquad \text{Use substitution}$$
$$4x = 300$$
$$x = 75$$
$$y = 3x = 225$$

Answer: 75 km and 225 km

61.
$$\text{Demand} = \text{Supply}$$
$$50 - 0.5x = 0.125x$$
$$50 = 0.625x$$
$$x = 80 \text{ units}$$
$$p = \$10$$
$$4x = 300$$
Answer: $(80, 10)$

63.
$$\text{Demand} = \text{Supply}$$
$$140 - 0.00002x = 80 + 0.00001x$$
$$60 = 0.00003x$$
$$x = 2{,}000{,}000 \text{ units}$$
$$p = \$100.00$$
Answer: $(2{,}000{,}000, 100)$

65.
$$
\begin{aligned}
5b + 10a &= 20.2 \;\Rightarrow\; -10b - 20a = -40.4 \\
10b + 30a &= 50.1 \;\Rightarrow\; 10b + 30a = 50.1 \\
&\hline
& 10a = 9.7 \\
& a = 0.97 \\
& b = 2.10
\end{aligned}
$$

Least squares regression line:

$$y = 0.97x + 2.10$$

67.
$$
\begin{aligned}
7b + 21a &= 35.1 \;\Rightarrow\; -21b - 63a = -105.3 \\
21b + 91a &= 114.2 \;\Rightarrow\; 21b + 91a = 114.2 \\
&\hline
& 28a = 8.9 \\
& a = \frac{89}{280} \\
& b = \frac{1137}{280}
\end{aligned}
$$

Least squares regression line:

$$y = \frac{1}{280}(89x + 1137)$$
$$y \approx 0.318x + 4.061$$

69. $(-2, 0), (0, 1), (2, 3)$

$3b = 4 \implies b = \frac{4}{3}$

$8a = 6 \implies a = \frac{3}{4}$

Least squares regression line:

$y = \frac{3}{4}x + \frac{4}{3}$

71. $(0, 4), (1, 3), (1, 1), (2, 0)$

$$\begin{aligned}
4b + 4a &= 8 \implies & 4b + 4a &= 8 \\
4b + 6a &= 4 \implies & \underline{-4b - 6a} &= \underline{-4} \\
& & -2a &= 4 \\
& & a &= -2 \\
& & b &= 4
\end{aligned}$$

Least squares regression line: $y = -2x + 4$

73. $(1.00, 450), (1.25, 375), (1.50, 330)$

$3b + 3.75a = 1155$

$3.75b + 4.8125a = 1413.75$

By elimination we have $a = -240$ and $b = 685$ and the least squares
regression line is $y = -240x + 685$. When $x = 1.40$, we have $y = -240(1.40) + 685 = 349$ units.

Section 7.3   Multivariable Linear Systems

■   You should know the operations that lead to equivalent systems of equations:

(a) Interchange any two equations.

(b) Multiply all terms of an equation by a nonzero constant.

(c) Replace an equation by the sum of itself and a constant multiple of any other equation in the system.

■   You should be able to use the method of elimination.

Solutions to Odd-Numbered Exercises

1.
$$\begin{aligned}
2x - y + 5z &= 24 & \text{Equation 1} \\
y + 2z &= 6 & \text{Equation 2} \\
z &= 4 & \text{Equation 3}
\end{aligned}$$

Back-substitute $z = 4$ into Equation 2.

$y + 2(4) = 6$

$z = -2$

Back-substitute $y = -2$ and $z = 4$ into Equation 1.

$2x - (-2) + 5(4) = 24$

$2x + 22 = 24$

$x = 1$

Answer: $(1, -2, 4)$

3.
$$\begin{aligned}
2x + y - 3z &= 10 & \text{Equation 1} \\
y &= 2 & \text{Equation 2} \\
y - z &= 4 & \text{Equation 3}
\end{aligned}$$

Back-substitute $y = 2$ into Equation 3.

$2 - z = 4$

$z = -2$

Back-substitute $y = 2$ and $z = -2$ into Equation 1.

$2x + 2 - 3(-2) = 10$

$2x + 8 = 10$

$x = 1$

Answer: $(1, 2, -2)$

5. $4x - 2y + z = 8$ Equation 1

$\qquad\quad 2z = 4$ Equation 2

$\qquad -y + z = 4$ Equation 3

From Equation 2 we have $z = 2$. Back-substitute $z = 2$ into Equation 3.

$$-y + 2 = 4$$
$$y = -2$$

Back-substitute $y = -2$ and $z = 2$ into Equation 1.

$$4x - 2(-2) + 2 = 8$$
$$4x + 6 = 8$$
$$x = \tfrac{1}{2}$$

Answer: $\left(\tfrac{1}{2}, -2, 2\right)$

9. $\quad x + y + z = \quad 6$ Equation 1

$\quad 2x - y + z = \quad 3$ Equation 2

$\quad 3x \quad - z = \quad 0$ Equation 3

$\quad x + y + z = \quad 6$

$\qquad -3y - z = -9$ -2Eq.1 + Eq.2

$\qquad -3y - 4z = -18$ -3Eq.1 + Eq.3

$\quad x + y + z = \quad 6$

$\qquad -3y - z = -9$

$\qquad\qquad -3z = -9$ $-$Eq.2 + Eq.3

$\qquad\qquad -3z = -9 \implies z = 3$

$\qquad -3y - 3 = -9 \implies y = 2$

$\quad x + 2 + 3 = \quad 6 \implies x = 1$

Answer: $(1, 2, 3)$

7. $\quad x - 2y + 3z = 5$ Equation 1

$\quad -x + 3y - 5z = 4$ Equation 2

$\quad 2x \qquad - 3z = 0$ Equation 3

Add Equation 1 to Equation 2.

$$y - 2z = 9$$

This is the first step in putting the system in row-echelon form.

11. $2x \qquad + 2z = 2$ Equation 1

$\quad 5x + 3y \qquad = 4$ Equation 2

$\quad 3x \qquad - z = 0$ Equation 3

$\quad x + y + z = 6$

$\quad x + 3y - 4z = 0$ -2Eq.1 + Eq.2

$\quad 2x \qquad + 2z = 2$ Interchange equations.

$\qquad 3y - 4z = 4$

$\quad x + 3y - 4z = 0$

$\qquad -6y + 10z = 2$ -2Eq.1 + Eq.2

$\qquad 3y - 4z = 4$

$\qquad -6y + 10z = 2$

$\qquad\qquad z = 5$ $\tfrac{1}{2}$Eq.2 + Eq.3

$\qquad\qquad z = 5$

$-6y + 10(5) = 2 \implies y = 8$

$x + 3(8) - 4(5) = 0 \implies x = -4$

Answer: $(-4, 8, 5)$

13. $\begin{aligned} 3x + 3y \qquad = \quad 9 \\ 2x \qquad - 3z = \quad 10 \\ 6y + 4z = -12 \end{aligned}$ Interchange equations.

$\begin{aligned} x + y \qquad = \quad 3 \\ 2x \qquad - 3z = \quad 10 \\ 6y + 4z = -12 \end{aligned}$ $\frac{1}{3}$Eq.1

$\begin{aligned} x + y \qquad = \quad 3 \\ -2y - 3z = \quad 4 \\ 6y + 4z = -12 \end{aligned}$ -2Eq.1 + Eq.2

$\begin{aligned} x + y \qquad = \quad 3 \\ -2y - 3z = \quad 4 \\ -5z = \quad 0 \end{aligned}$ 3Eq.2 + Eq.3

$-5x = 0 \Longrightarrow z = 0$

$-2y - 3(0) = 4 \Longrightarrow y = -2$

$x - 2 = 3 \Longrightarrow x = 5$

Answer: $(5, -2, 0)$

15. $\begin{aligned} x + y - 2z = \quad 3 \\ 3x - 2y + 4z = \quad 1 \\ 2x - 3y + 6z = \quad 8 \end{aligned}$ Interchange equations.

$\begin{aligned} x + y - 2z = \quad 3 \\ -5y + 10z = -8 \\ -5y + 10z = \quad 2 \end{aligned}$ $\begin{aligned} -3\text{Eq.1} + \text{Eq.2} \\ -2\text{Eq.1} + \text{Eq.3} \end{aligned}$

$\begin{aligned} x + y - 2z = \quad 3 \\ -5y + 10z = -8 \\ 0 = \quad 10 \end{aligned}$ $\rightarrow \leftarrow -\text{Eq.2} + \text{Eq.3}$

No solution, inconsistent

17. $\begin{aligned} 3x + 3y + 5z = \quad 1 \\ 3x + 5y + 9z = \quad 0 \\ 5x + 9y + 17z = \quad 0 \end{aligned}$

$\begin{aligned} 6x + 6y + 10z = \quad 2 \\ 3x + 5y + 9z = \quad 0 \\ 5x + 9y + 17z = \quad 0 \end{aligned}$ 2 Eq.1

$\begin{aligned} x - 3y - 7z = \quad 2 \\ 3x + 5y + 9z = \quad 0 \\ 5x + 9y + 17z = \quad 0 \end{aligned}$ $-$Eq.3 + Eq.1

$\begin{aligned} x - 3y - 7z = \quad 2 \\ 14y + 30z = -6 \\ 24y + 52z = -10 \end{aligned}$ $\begin{aligned} -3\text{Eq.1} + \text{Eq.2} \\ -5\text{Eq.1} + \text{Eq.3} \end{aligned}$

$\begin{aligned} x - 3y - 7z = \quad 2 \\ 84y + 180z = -36 \\ 84y + 182z = -35 \end{aligned}$ $\begin{aligned} 6\text{Eq.2} \\ 3.5\text{Eq.3} \end{aligned}$

$\begin{aligned} x - 3y - 7z = \quad 2 \\ 84y + 180z = -36 \\ 2z = \quad 1 \end{aligned}$ $-$Eq.2 + Eq.3

$2z = 1 \Longrightarrow x = \frac{1}{2}$

$84y + 180\left(\frac{1}{2}\right) = -36 \Longrightarrow y = \frac{1}{2}$

$x - 3\left(-\frac{3}{2}\right) - 7\left(\frac{1}{2}\right) = 2 \Longrightarrow x = 1$

Answer: $\left(1, -\frac{3}{2}, \frac{1}{2}\right)$

19.
$$x + 2y - 7z = -4$$
$$2x + y + z = 13$$
$$3x + 9y - 36z = -33$$

$$x + 2y - 7z = -4$$ $-2\text{Eq.2} + \text{Eq.2}$
$$-3y + 15z = 21$$ $-3\text{Eq.1} + \text{Eq.3}$
$$3y - 15z = -21$$

$$x + 2y - 7z = -4$$
$$-3y + 15z = 21$$
$$0 = 0$$ Eq.2 + Eq.3

$$x + 2y - 7z = -4$$
$$y - 5z = -7$$ $\frac{1}{3}\text{Eq.2}$
$$x + 3z = 10$$ $-2\text{Eq.2} + \text{Eq.1}$
$$y - 5z = -7$$

Let $z = a$, then:
$$y = 5a - 7$$
$$x = -3a + 10$$
Answer: $(-3a + 10, 5a - 7, a)$

21.
$$3x - 3y + 6z = 6$$
$$x + 2y - z = 5$$
$$5x - 8y + 13z = 7$$

$$x - y + 2z = 2$$ $\frac{1}{3}\text{Eq.1}$
$$3y - 3z = 3$$ $-\text{Eq.1} + \text{Eq.2}$
$$-3y + 3z = -3$$ $-5\text{Eq.1} + \text{Eq.3}$

$$x - y + 2z = 2$$
$$y - z = 1$$ $\frac{1}{3}\text{Eq.2}$
$$0 = 0$$ Eq.2 + Eq.3

$$x + z = 3$$ Eq.2 + Eq.1
$$y - z - 1$$

Let $z = a$, then:
$$y = a + 1$$
$$x = -a + 3$$

Answer: $(-a + 3, a + 1, a)$

23. $x - 2y + 5z = 2$
$$4x - z = 0$$
Let $z = a$, then $x = \frac{1}{4}a$.
$$\tfrac{1}{4}a - 2y + 5a = 2$$
$$a - 8y + 20a = 8$$
$$-8y = -21a + 8$$
$$y = \tfrac{21}{8}a - 1$$
Answer: $\left(\tfrac{1}{4}a, \tfrac{21}{8}a - 1, a\right)$
To avoid fractions, we could go back and let
$z = 8a$, then $4x - 8a = 0 \Rightarrow x = 2a$.
$$2a - 2y + 5(8a) = 2$$
$$-2y + 42a = 2$$
$$y = 21a - 1$$
Answer: $(2a, 21a - 1, 8a)$

25. $2x - 3y + z = -2$
$$-4x + 9y = 7$$

$$2x - 3y + z = -2$$
$$3y + 2z = 3$$ $2\text{Eq.1} + \text{Eq.2}$

$$2x + 3z = 1$$ Eq.2 + Eq.1
$$3y + 2z = 3$$

Let $x = a$, then:
$$y = -\tfrac{2}{3}a + 1$$
$$x = -\tfrac{3}{2}a + \tfrac{1}{2}$$
Answer: $\left(-\tfrac{3}{2}a + \tfrac{1}{2}, -\tfrac{2}{3}a + 1, a\right)$

27.

$$\begin{aligned}
x \quad\quad\quad + 3w &= 4 \\
2y - z - w &= 0 \\
3y \quad\quad - 2w &= 1 \\
2x - y + 4z \quad\quad &= 5
\end{aligned}$$

$$\begin{aligned}
x \quad\quad\quad + 3w &= 4 \\
2y - z - w &= 0 \\
3y \quad\quad - 2w &= 1 \\
-y + 4z - 6w &= -3 \quad -2\text{Eq.1} + \text{Eq.4}
\end{aligned}$$

$$\begin{aligned}
x \quad\quad\quad + 3w &= 4 \\
y - 4z + 6w &= 3 \quad -\text{Eq.4 and} \\
2y - z - w &= 0 \quad \text{interchange} \\
3y \quad\quad - 2w &= 1 \quad \text{the equations.}
\end{aligned}$$

$$\begin{aligned}
x \quad\quad\quad + 3w &= 4 \\
y - 4z + 6w &= 3 \\
7z - 13w &= -6 \quad -\text{Eq.2} + \text{Eq.3} \\
12z - 20w &= -8 \quad -3\text{Eq.2} + \text{Eq.4}
\end{aligned}$$

$$\begin{aligned}
x \quad\quad\quad + 3w &= 4 \\
y - 4z + 6w &= 3 \\
z - 3w &= -2 \quad -\tfrac{1}{2}\text{Eq.4} + \text{Eq.3} \\
12z - 20w &= -8
\end{aligned}$$

$$\begin{aligned}
x \quad\quad\quad + 3w &= 4 \\
y - 4z + 6w &= 3 \\
z - 3w &= -2 \\
16w &= 16 \quad -12\text{Eq.3} + \text{Eq.4}
\end{aligned}$$

$$\begin{aligned}
16w = 16 &\Rightarrow w = 1 \\
z - 3(1) = -2 &\Rightarrow z = 1 \\
y - 4(1) + 6(1) = 3 &\Rightarrow y = 1 \\
x + 3(1) = 4 &\Rightarrow x = 1
\end{aligned}$$

Answer: $(1, 1, 1, 1)$

29.

$$\begin{aligned}
x \quad\quad + 4z &= 1 \\
x + y + 10z &= 10 \\
2x - y + 2z &= -5
\end{aligned}$$

$$\begin{aligned}
x \quad\quad + 4z &= 1 \\
y + 6z &= 9 \quad -\text{Eq.1} + \text{Eq.2} \\
-y - 6z &= -7 \quad -2\text{Eq.1} + \text{Eq.3}
\end{aligned}$$

$$\begin{aligned}
x \quad\quad + 4z &= 1 \\
y + 6z &= 9 \\
0 &= 2 \quad \rightarrow \leftarrow \text{Eq.2} + \text{Eq.3}
\end{aligned}$$

No solution, inconsistent

31.

$$\begin{aligned}
2x + 3y \quad\quad &= 0 \\
4x + 3y - z &= 0 \\
8x + 3y + 3z &= 0
\end{aligned}$$

$$\begin{aligned}
2x + 3y \quad\quad &= 0 \\
-3y - z &= 0 \quad -2\text{Eq.1} + \text{Eq.2} \\
-9y + 3z &= 0 \quad -4\text{Eq.1} + \text{Eq.3}
\end{aligned}$$

$$\begin{aligned}
2x + 3y \quad\quad &= 0 \\
-3y - z &= 0 \\
6z &= 0 \quad -3\text{Eq.2} + \text{Eq.3}
\end{aligned}$$

$$\begin{aligned}
6z = 0 &\Rightarrow z = 0 \\
-3y - 0 = 0 &\Rightarrow y = 0 \\
2x + 3(0) = 0 &\Rightarrow x = 0
\end{aligned}$$

Answer: $(0, 0, 0)$

33.

$$\begin{aligned}
23x + 4y - z &= 0 \quad \text{Interchange equations.} \\
12x + 5y + z &= 0
\end{aligned}$$

$$\begin{aligned}
x + 6y + 3z &= 0 \quad 2\text{Eq.2} - \text{Eq.1} \\
-67y - 35z &= 0 \quad -12\text{Eq.1} + \text{Eq.2}
\end{aligned}$$

To avoid fractions, let $z = 67a$, then:

$$\begin{aligned}
-67y - 35(67a) &= 0 \\
y &= -35a \\
x + 6(-35a) + 3(67a) &= 0 \\
x &= 9a
\end{aligned}$$

Answer: $(9a, -35a, 67a)$

35. No, they are not equivalent. The constant in the second equation should be -11 and the coefficient of z in the third equation should be 2.

37. There are an infinite number of linear systems that have $(4, -1, 2)$ as their solution. One such system is as follows:

$$3(4) + (-1) - (2) = 9 \implies 3x + y - z = 9$$
$$(4) + 2(-1) - (2) = 0 \implies x + 2y - z = 0$$
$$-(4) + (-1) + 3(2) = 1 \implies -x + y + 3z = 1$$

39. $y = ax^2 + bx + c$ passing through $(0, 0)$, $(2, -2)$, $(4, 0)$

$(0, \ 0)$: $\quad 0 = \qquad\qquad c$

$(2, -2)$: $-2 = \ 4a + 2b + c \implies -1 = 2a + b$

$(4, \ 0)$: $\quad 0 = 16a + 4b + c \implies \quad 0 = 4a + b$

Answer: $a = \frac{1}{2}, b = -2, c = 0$

The equation of the parabola is $y = \frac{1}{2}x^2 - 2x$.

41. $y = ax^2 + bx + c$ passing through $(2, 0)$, $(3, -1)$, $(4, 0)$

$(2, \ 0)$: $\quad 0 = \ 4a + 2b + c \implies \quad 0 = -4a - 2b - c$

$(3, -1)$: $-1 = \ 9a + 3b + c \implies -1 = \quad 5a + b$

$(4, \ 0)$: $\quad 0 = 16a + 4b + c \implies \quad 0 = 12a + 2b$

Answer: $a = 1, b = -6, c = 8$

The equation of the parabola is $y = x^2 - 6x + 8$.

43. $x^2 + y^2 + Dx + Ey + F = 0$ passing through $(0, 0)$, $(2, 2)$, $(4, 0)$

$(0, 0)$: $\qquad\qquad F = 0$

$(2, 2)$: $\ 8 + 2D + 2E + F = 0 \implies D + E = -4$

$(4, 0)$: $16 + 4D \qquad + F = 0 \implies D = -4$ and $E = 0$

The equation of the circle is $x^2 + y^2 - 4x = 0$.

To graph, let $y_1 = \sqrt{4x - x^2}$ and $y_2 = -\sqrt{4x - x^2}$.

45. $x^2 + y^2 + Dx + Ey + F = 0$ passing through $(-3, -1)$, $(2, 4)$, $(-6, 8)$

$(-3, -1)$: $\ 10 - 3D - E + F = 0 \implies \ 10 = \ 3D + E - F$

$(\ 2, \ 4)$: $\ 20 + 2D + 4E + F = 0 \implies \ 20 = -2D - 4E - F$

$(-6, \ 8)$: $100 - 6D + 8E + F = 0 \implies 100 = \ 6D - 8E - F$

Answer: $D = 6, E = -8, F = 0$

The equation of the circle is $x^2 + y^2 + 6x - 8y = 0$.
To graph, complete the squares first, then solve for y.

$$(x^2 + 6x + 9) + (y^2 - 8y + 16) = 0 + 9 + 16$$
$$(x + 3)^2 + (y - 4)^2 = 25$$
$$(y - 4)^2 = 25 - (x + 3)^2$$
$$y - 4 = \pm\sqrt{25 - (x + 3)^2}$$
$$y = 4 \pm \sqrt{25 - (x + 3)^2}$$

Let $y_1 = 4 + \sqrt{25 - (x + 3)^2}$ and $y_2 = 4 - \sqrt{25 - (x + 3)^2}$.

47. $s = \frac{1}{2}at^2 + v_0t + s_0$

$(1, 128), (2, 80), (3, 0)$

$128 = \frac{1}{2}a + v_0 + s_0 \implies a + 2v_0 + 2s_0 = 256$

$80 = 2a + 2v_0 + s_0 \implies 2a + 2v_0 + s_0 = 80$

$0 = \frac{9}{2}a + 3v_0 + s_0 \implies 9a + 6v_0 + 2s_0 = 0$

Solving this system yields $a = -32$, $v_0 = 0$, $s_0 = 144$.

Thus, $s = \frac{1}{2}(-32)t^2 + (0)t + 144$

$\qquad = -16t^2 + 144.$

49. $s = \frac{1}{2}at^2 + v_0t + s_0$

$(1, 452), (2, 372), (3, 260)$

$452 = \frac{1}{2}a + v_0 + s_0 \implies a + 2v_0 + 2s_0 = 904$

$372 = 2a + 2v_0 + s_0 \implies 2a + 2v_0 + s_0 = 372$

$260 = \frac{9}{2}a + 3v_0 + s_0 \implies 9a + 6v_0 + 2s_0 = 520$

Solving this system yields $a = -32$, $v_0 = -32$, $s_0 = 500$.

Thus, $s = \frac{1}{2}(-32)t^2 + (-32)t + 500$

$\qquad = -16t^2 - 32t + 500.$

51. Let x = amount at 5%

Let y = amount at 6%

Let z = amount at 7%

$$x + y + z = 16{,}000$$
$$0.05x + 0.06y + 0.07z = 990$$
$$x + 3000 = z$$
$$y + 2000 = z$$

$$(z - 3000) + (z - 2000) + z = 16{,}000$$
$$3z = 21{,}000$$
$$z = 7000$$

$x = 4000$, $y = 5000$

Check: $0.05(4000) + 0.06(5000) + 0.07(7000) = 990$

Answer: $x = \$4000$ at 5%

$\qquad\quad y = \$5000$ at 6%

$\qquad\quad z = \$7000$ at 7%

53. Let x = amount at 8%

Let y = amount at 9%

Let z = amount at 10%

$$x + y + z = 775{,}000$$
$$0.08x + 0.09y + 0.10z = 67{,}500$$
$$x = 4z$$

$$y + 5z = 775{,}000$$
$$0.09y + 0.42z = 67{,}500$$
$$z = 75{,}000$$
$$y = 775{,}000 - 5z = 400{,}000$$
$$x = 4z = 300{,}000$$

Answer: $x = \$300{,}000$ at 8%
$\qquad\quad y = \$400{,}000$ at 9%
$\qquad\quad z = \$75{,}000$ at 10%

55. Let C = amount in certificates of deposit

Let M = amount in municipal bonds

Let B = amount in blue-chip stocks

Let G = amount in growth or speculative stocks

$$C + M + B + G = 500{,}000$$
$$0.10C + 0.08M + 0.12B + 0.13G = 0.10(500{,}000)$$
$$B + G = \tfrac{1}{4}(500{,}000)$$

This system has infinitely many solutions.

Let $G = s$, then $\quad B = 125{,}000 - s$
$$M = 125{,}000 + \tfrac{1}{2}s$$
$$C = 250{,}000 - \tfrac{1}{2}s$$

Answer:
$(250{,}000 - \tfrac{1}{2}s,\ 125{,}000 + \tfrac{1}{2}s,\ 125{,}000 - s,\ s)$,
where $0 \le s \le 125{,}000$

One possible solution is to let $s = 50{,}000$.
Certificates of deposit: $\$225{,}000$
Municipal bonds: $\$150{,}000$
Blue-chip stocks: $\$75{,}000$
Growth or speculative stocks: $\$50{,}000$

57. Let x = gallons of spray X

Let y = gallons of spray Y

Let z = gallons of spray Z

$\left.\begin{array}{l} \text{Chemical A: } \tfrac{1}{5}x + \tfrac{1}{2}z = 12 \\[4pt] \text{Chemical B: } \tfrac{2}{5}x + \tfrac{1}{2}z = 16 \end{array}\right\} \Rightarrow x = 20,\ z = 16$

Chemical C: $\tfrac{2}{5}x + y = 26 \quad \Rightarrow \quad y = 18$

Answer: 20 liters of spray X
18 liters of spray Y
16 liters of spray Z

59.

	Product	
Truck	A	B
Large	6	3
Medium	4	4
Small	0	3

Possible solutions:

(1) 4 medium trucks

(2) 2 large trucks, 1 medium truck, 2 small trucks

(3) 3 large trucks, 1 medium truck, 1 small truck

(4) 3 large trucks, 3 small trucks

61.
$$t_1 - 2t_2 = 0$$
$$t_1 \qquad\ - 2a = 128 \ \Rightarrow \ 2t_2 - 2a = 128$$
$$t_2 + a = 32 \ \Rightarrow\ \underline{-2t_2 - 2a = -64}$$
$$-4a = 64$$
$$a = -16$$
$$t_2 = 48$$
$$t_1 = 96$$

Answer: $t_1 = 96$ lb
$\qquad\quad t_2 = 48$ lb
$\qquad\quad a = -16$ ft/sec^2

63. $\dfrac{1}{x^3 - x} = \dfrac{A}{x} + \dfrac{B}{x - 1} + \dfrac{C}{x + 1}$

$1 = A(x + 1)(x - 1) + Bx(x + 1) + Cx(x - 1)$

$1 = Ax^2 - A + B^2 + Bx + Cx^2 - Cx$

$1 = (A + B + C)x^2 + (B - C)x - A$

By equating coefficients, we have:

$0 = A + B + C$

$0 = B - C$

$1 = -A \quad \Longrightarrow \quad A = -1$

$\qquad\qquad\qquad B + C = \ 1$

$\qquad\qquad\qquad \dfrac{B - C = \ 0}{2B \qquad = \ 1} \Longrightarrow B = \dfrac{1}{2}$

$\qquad\qquad\qquad\qquad\qquad C = \dfrac{1}{2}$

$\dfrac{A}{x} + \dfrac{B}{x - 1} + \dfrac{C}{x + 1} = \dfrac{-1}{x} + \dfrac{1/2}{x - 1} + \dfrac{1/2}{x + 1} = \dfrac{1}{2}\left(-\dfrac{2}{x} + \dfrac{1}{x - 1} + \dfrac{1}{x + 1}\right)$

65. $\dfrac{x^2 - 3x - 3}{x(x - 2)(x + 3)} = \dfrac{A}{x} + \dfrac{B}{x - 2} + \dfrac{C}{x + B}$

$x^2 - 3x - 3 = A(x - 2)(x + 3) + Bx(x + 3) + Cx(x - 2)$

$x^2 - 3x - 3 = Ax^2 + Ax - 6A + Bx^2 + 3Bx + Cx^2 - 2Cx$

$x^2 - 3x - 3 = (A + B + C)x^2 + (A + 3B - 2C)x - 6A$

By equating coefficients, we have:

$1 = A + B + C$

$-3 = A + 3B - 2C$

$-3 = -6A \qquad\qquad \Longrightarrow \quad A = \tfrac{1}{2}$

$\qquad\qquad\qquad \tfrac{1}{2} = \ B + \ C \Longrightarrow \ 1 = 2B + 2C$

$\qquad\qquad\qquad -\tfrac{7}{2} = 3B - 2C \Longrightarrow -\tfrac{7}{2} = 3B - 2C$

$\qquad\qquad\qquad\qquad\qquad\qquad \dfrac{}{-\tfrac{5}{2} = 5B}$

$\qquad\qquad\qquad\qquad\qquad\qquad B = -\tfrac{1}{2}$

$\qquad\qquad\qquad\qquad\qquad\qquad C = 1$

$\dfrac{x^2 - 3x - 3}{x(x - 2)(x + 3)} = \dfrac{1/2}{x} - \dfrac{1/2}{x - 2} + \dfrac{1}{x + 3} = \dfrac{1}{2}\left(\dfrac{1}{x} - \dfrac{1}{x - 2} + \dfrac{2}{x + 3}\right)$

67. Least squares regression parabola through $(-4, 5)$, $(-2, 6)$, $(2, 6)$, $(4, 2)$

$n = 4$

$$\sum x_i = 0 \qquad \sum y_i = 19$$

$$\sum x_i^2 = 40 \qquad \sum x_i^3 = 0$$

$$\sum x_i^4 = 544 \qquad \sum x_i y_i = -12$$

$$\sum x_i^2 y_i = 160$$

$$4c \ + \ 40a = \ 19$$
$$40b \qquad = -12$$
$$40c \ + 544a = \ 160$$

Solving this system yields $a = -\frac{5}{24}$, $b = -\frac{3}{10}$, and $c = \frac{41}{6}$. Thus, $y = -\frac{5}{24}x^2 - \frac{3}{10}x + \frac{41}{6}$.

69. Least squares regression parabola through $(0, 0)$, $(2, 2)$, $(3, 6)$, $(4, 12)$

$n = 4$

$$\sum x_i = 9 \qquad \sum y_i = 20$$

$$\sum x_i^2 = 29 \qquad \sum x_i^3 = 99$$

$$\sum x_i^4 = 353 \qquad \sum x_i y_i = 70$$

$$\sum x_i^2 y_i = 254$$

$$4c + \ 9b + \ 29a = \ 20$$
$$9c + 29b + \ 99a = \ 70$$
$$29c + 99b + 353a = 254$$

Solving this system yields $a = 1$, $b = -1$, and $c = 0$. Thus, $y = x^2 - x$.

71. (a) Least squares regression parabola through $(20, 25)$, $(30, 55)$, $(40, 105)$, $(50, 188)$, $(60, 300)$

$n = 5$

$$\sum x_i = 200 \qquad \sum y_i = 673$$

$$\sum x_i^2 = 9000 \qquad \sum x_i^3 = 440{,}000$$

$$\sum x_i^4 = 22{,}740{,}000 \qquad \sum x_i y_i = 33{,}750$$

$$\sum x_i^2 y_i = 1{,}777{,}500$$

$$5c + \qquad 200b + \qquad 9000a = \qquad 673$$
$$200c + \qquad 9000b + \qquad 440{,}000a = \qquad 33{,}750$$
$$9000c + 440{,}000b + 22{,}740{,}000a = 1{,}777{,}500$$

Solving this system yields $a \approx 0.14$, $b \approx -4.43$, and $c \approx 58.40$.
Thus, $y = 0.14x^2 - 4.43x + 58.40$.

(b)

(c) When $x = 70$, $y \approx 434.3$ feet.

73. $\left.\begin{array}{r} y + \lambda = 0 \\ x + \lambda = 0 \end{array}\right\} \implies x = y = -\lambda$

$x + y - 10 = 0 \implies 2x - 10 = 0$

$x = 5$

$y = 5$

$\lambda = -5$

75. $2x - 2x\lambda = 0 \implies 2x(1 - \lambda) = 0 \implies \lambda = 1 \text{ or } x = 0$

$-2y + \lambda = 0 \implies 2y = \lambda \implies y = \dfrac{1}{2}$

$y - x^2 = 0 \implies x^2 = y \implies x = \pm\sqrt{\dfrac{1}{2}} = \pm\dfrac{\sqrt{2}}{2}$

Answer: $x = \pm\dfrac{\sqrt{2}}{2} \text{ or } x = 0$

$y = \dfrac{1}{2} \text{ or } y = 0$

$\lambda = 1 \text{ or } \lambda = 0$

77. The slope represents the average increase in sales per year.

79. $(0.075)(85) = 6.375$

81. $(0.005)(n) = 400$

$n = 80,000$

Section 7.4   Systems of Inequalities

■   You should be able to sketch the graph of an inequality in two variables.

    (a) Replace the inequality with an equal sign and graph the equation. Use a dashed line for $<$ or $>$, a solid line for $\le$ or $\ge$.

    (b) Test a point in each region formed by the graph. If the point satisfies the inequality, shade the whole region.

Solutions to Odd-Numbered Exercises

1. $x \ge 2$

Using a solid line, graph the vertical line $x = 2$ and shade to the right of this line.

3. $y \ge -1$

Using a solid line, graph the horizontal line $y = -1$ and shade above this line.

5. $y < 2 - x$

Using a dashed line, graph $y = 2 - x$, and then shade below the line. $\big($Use $(0, 0)$ as a test point.$\big)$

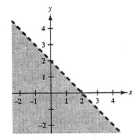

7. $2y - x \geq 4$

Using a solid line, graph $2y - x = 4$, and then shade above the line. $\big($Use $(0, 0)$ as a test point.$\big)$

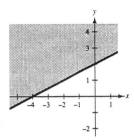

9. $(x + 1)^2 + (y - 2)^2 < 9$

Using a dashed line, sketch the circle $(x + 1)^2 + (y - 2)^2 = 9$.

Center: $(-1, 2)$

Radius: 3

Test point: $(0, 0)$. Shade the inside of the circle.

11. $y \leq \dfrac{1}{1 + x^2}$

Using a solid line, graph $y = \dfrac{1}{1 + x^2}$, and then shade below the curve. $\big($Use $(0, 0)$ as a test point.$\big)$

13. $y \geq \dfrac{2}{3}x - 1$

15. $x^2 + 5y - 10 \leq 0$

$$y \leq 2 - \frac{x^2}{5}$$

17. The line through $(-4, 0)$ and $(0, 2)$ is $y = \frac{1}{2}x + 2$. For the shaded region below the line, we have $y \leq \frac{1}{2}x + 2$.

19. The line through $(0, 2)$ and $(3, 0)$ is $y = -\frac{2}{3}x + 2$. For the shaded region above the line, we have

$$y \geq -\frac{2}{3}x + 2$$

$$3y \geq -2x + 6$$

$$2x + 3y \geq 6$$

$$\frac{x}{3} + \frac{y}{2} \geq 1$$

21. $x + y \leq 1$

$-x + y \leq 1$

$y \geq 0$

First, find the points of intersection of each pair of equations.

Vertex A	Vertex B	Vertex C
$x + y = 1$	$x + y = 1$	$-x + y = 1$
$-x + y = 1$	$y = 0$	$y = 0$
$(0, 1)$	$(1, 0)$	$(-1, 0)$

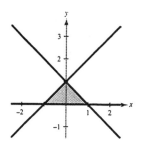

23. $x + y \leq 5$

$x \geq 2$

$y \geq 0$

First, find the points of intersection of each pair of equations.

Vertex A	Vertex B	Vertex C
$x + y = 5$	$x + y = 5$	$x = 2$
$x = 2$	$y = 0$	$y = 0$
$(2, 3)$	$(5, 0)$	$(2, 0)$

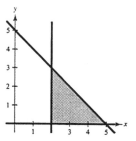

25. $-3x + 2y < 6$

$x - 4y > -2$

$2x + y < 3$

First, find the points of intersection of each pair of equations.

Vertex *A*	Vertex *B*	Vertex *C*
$-3x + 2y = 6$	$-3x + 2y = 6$	$x - 4y = -2$
$x - 4y = -2$	$2x + y = 3$	$2x + y = 3$
$(-2, 0)$	$(0, 3)$	$\left(\frac{10}{9}, \frac{7}{9}\right)$

27. $2x + y > 2$

$6x + 3y < 2$

The lines are parallel. There are no points of intersection. There is no region common to both inequalities.

29. $\quad x \qquad \geq 1$

$\qquad x - 2y \leq 3$

$\qquad 3x + 2y \geq 9$

$\qquad x + \ y \leq 6$

First, find the points of intersection of each pair of equations.

Vertex A	Vertex B	Vertex C
$x = 1$	$x = 1$	$x = 1$
$x - 2y = 3$	$3x + 2y = 9$	$x + y = 6$
$(1, -1)$	$(1, 3)$	$(1, 5)$

Vertex D	Vertex E	Vertex F
$x - 2y = 3$	$x - 2y = 3$	$3x + 2y = 9$
$3x + 2y = 9$	$x + \ y = 6$	$x + \ y = 6$
$(3, 0)$	$(5, 1)$	$(-3, 9)$

By shading each inequality, we find that the vertices of the region are $(1, 5)$, $(1, 3)$, $(3, 0)$, and $(5, 1)$.

31. $x^2 + y^2 \leq 9$

$\quad x^2 + y^2 \geq 1$

There are no points of intersection. The region common to both inequalities is the region between the circles.

33. $x > y^2$

$\quad x < y + 2$

Points of intersection:

$$y^2 = y + 2$$

$$y^2 - y - 2 = 0$$

$$(y + 1)(y - 2) = 0$$

$$y = -1, 2$$

$(1, -1), (4, 2)$

35. $y \leq \sqrt{3x} + 1$

$\quad y \geq x^2 + 1$

37. $y < x^3 - 2x + 1$

$\quad y > -2x$

$\quad x \leq 1$

39. $\quad x^2 y \geq 1$

$\quad 0 < x \leq 4$

$\quad y \leq 4$

41. $y \le -x + 4 \implies \dfrac{x}{4} + \dfrac{y}{4} \le 1$

   $x \ge 0$ ⟶ $x \ge 0$

   $y \ge 0$ ⟶ $y \ge 0$

43. Line through points $(0, 4)$ and $(4, 0)$: $y = 4 - x$

   Line through points $(0, 2)$ and $(8, 0)$: $y = 2 - \frac{1}{4}x$

   $y \ge 4 - x$

   $y \ge 2 - \frac{1}{4}x$

   $x \ge 0$

   $y \ge 0$

45. $x^2 + y^2 \le 16$

   $x \ge 0$

   $y \ge 0$

47. Rectangular region with vertices at $(2, 1)$, $(5, 1)$, $(5, 7)$, and $(2, 7)$

   $x \ge 2$

   $x \le 5$

   $y \ge 1$

   $y \le 7$

   Thus, $2 \le x \le 5$, $1 \le y \le 7$.

49. Triangle with vertices at $(0, 0)$, $(5, 0)$, $(2, 3)$

   $(0, 0)$, $(5, 0)$ Line: $y \ge 0$

   $(0, 0)$, $(2, 3)$ Line: $y \le \frac{3}{2}x$

   $(2, 3)$, $(5, 0)$ Line: $y \le -x + 5$

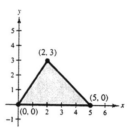

51. Assembly center constraint: $x + \frac{3}{2}y \le 12$

   Finishing center constraint: $\frac{4}{3}x + \frac{3}{2}y \le 15$

   Point of intersection: $(9, 2)$

   Physical constraints: $x \ge 0$ and $y \ge 0$

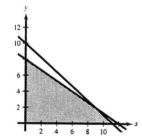

53. Account constraints: $x \ge 5000$

   $y \ge 5000$

   $2x \le y$

   $x + y \le 20,000$

55. x = number of ounces of food X

   y = number of ounces of food Y

   Calcium: $20x + 10y \ge 280$

   Iron: $15x + 10y \ge 160$

   Vitamin B: $10x + 20y \ge 180$

   $x \ge 0$

   $y \ge 0$

57.

$$xy \geq 500 \qquad \text{Body-building space}$$

$$2x + \pi y \geq 125 \qquad \text{Track (Two semi-circles and two lengths)}$$

$$x \geq 0 \qquad \text{Physical constraint}$$

$$y \geq 0 \qquad \text{Physical constraint}$$

59.   Demand = Supply

$$50 - 0.5x = 0.125x$$

$$50 = 0.625x$$

$$80 = x$$

$$10 = p$$

Point of equilibrium: (80, 10)

The consumer surplus is the area of the triangle bounded by

$$p \leq 50 - 0.5x$$

$$p \geq 10$$

$$x \geq 0.$$

Consumer surplus $= \frac{1}{2}(\text{base})(\text{height}) = \frac{1}{2}(80)(40) = \$1600$

The producer surplus is the area of the triangle bounded by

$$p \geq 0.125x$$

$$p \leq 10$$

$$x \geq 0.$$

Producer surplus $= \frac{1}{2}(\text{base})(\text{height}) = \frac{1}{2}(80)(10) = \$400$

61.   Demand = Supply

$$140 - 0.00002x = 80 + 0.00001x$$

$$60 = 0.00003x$$

$$2{,}000{,}000 = x$$

$$100 = p$$

Point of equilibrium: (2,000,000, 100)

The consumer surplus is the area of the triangle bounded by

$$p \leq 140 - 0.00002x$$

$$p \geq 100$$

$$x \geq 0.$$

Consumer surplus $= \frac{1}{2}$(base)(height) $= \frac{1}{2}$(2,000,000)(40) $= \$40{,}000{,}000$ or \$40 million

The producer surplus is the area of the triangle bounded by

$$p \geq 80 + 0.00001x$$

$$p \leq 100$$

$$x \geq 0.$$

Producer surplus $= \frac{1}{2}$(base)(height) $= \frac{1}{2}$(2,000,000)(20) $= \$20{,}000{,}000$ or \$20 million

63. Test a point on either side of the boundary.

Section 7.5   Linear Programming

■   To solve a linear programming problem:
1. Sketch the solution set for the system of constraints.
2. Find the vertices of the region.
3. Test the objective function at each of the vertices.

Solutions to Odd-Numbered Exercises

1. $z = 4x + 5y$

At (0, 6): $z = 4(0) + 5(6) = 30$

At (0, 0): $z = 4(0) + 5(0) = 0$

At (6, 0): $z = 4(6) + 5(0) = 24$

The minimum value is 0 at (0, 0).
The maximum value is 30 at (0, 6).

3. $z = 10x + 6y$

At (0, 6): $z = 10(0) + 6(6) = 36$

At (0, 0): $z = 10(0) + 6(0) = 0$

At (6, 0): $z = 10(6) + 6(0) = 60$

The minimum value is 0 at (0, 0).
The maximum value is 60 at (6, 0).

5. $z = 3x + 2y$

    At $(0, 5)$: $z = 3(0) + 2(5) = 10$

    At $(4, 0)$: $z = 3(4) + 2(0) = 12$

    At $(3, 4)$: $z = 3(3) + 2(4) = 17$

    At $(0, 0)$: $z = 3(0) + 2(0) = 0$

    The minimum value is 0 at $(0, 0)$.
    The maximum value is 17 at $(3, 4)$.

7. $z = 5x + 0.5y$

    At $(0, 5)$: $z = 5(0) + \frac{5}{2} = \frac{5}{2}$

    At $(4, 0)$: $z = 5(4) + \frac{0}{2} = 20$

    At $(3, 4)$: $z = 5(3) + \frac{4}{2} = 17$

    At $(0, 0)$: $z = 5(0) + \frac{0}{2} = 0$

    The minimum value is 0 at $(0, 0)$.
    The maximum value is 20 at $(4, 0)$.

9. $z = 10x + 7y$

    At $(0, 45)$: $z = 10(0) + 7(45) = 315$

    At $(30, 45)$: $z = 10(30) + 7(45) = 615$

    At $(60, 20)$: $z = 10(60) + 7(20) = 740$

    At $(60, 0)$: $z = 10(60) + 7(0) = 600$

    At $(0, 0)$: $z = 10(0) + 7(0) = 0$

    The minimum value is 0 at $(0, 0)$.
    The maximum value is 740 at $(60, 20)$.

11. $z = 25x + 30y$

    At $(0, 45)$: $z = 25(0) + 30(45) = 1350$

    At $(30, 45)$: $z = 25(30) + 30(45) = 2100$

    At $(60, 20)$: $z = 25(60) + 30(20) = 2100$

    At $(60, 0)$: $z = 25(60) + 30(0) = 1500$

    At $(0, 0)$: $z = 25(0) + 30(0) = 0$

    The minimum value is 0 at $(0, 0)$.
    The maximum value is 2100 at any point along the
    line segment connecting $(30, 45)$ and $(60, 20)$.

13. $z = 6x + 10y$

    At $(0, 2)$: $z = 6(0) + 10(2) = 20$

    At $(5, 0)$: $z = 6(5) + 10(0) = 30$

    At $(0, 0)$: $z = 6(0) + 10(0) = 0$

    The minimum value is 0 at $(0, 0)$.
    The maximum value is 30 at $(5, 0)$.

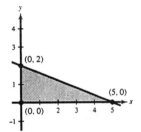

15. $z = 9z + 24y$

    At $(0, 2)$: $z = 9(0) + 24(2) = 48$

    At $(5, 0)$: $z = 9(5) + 24(0) = 45$

    At $(0, 0)$: $z = 9(0) + 24(0) = 0$

    The minimum value is 0 at $(0, 0)$.
    The maximum value is 48 at $(0, 2)$.

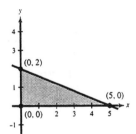

17. $z = 4x + 5y$

    At $(10, 0)$: $z = 4(10) + 5(0) = 40$

    At $(5, 3)$: $z = 4(5) + 5(3) = 35$

    At $(0, 8)$: $z = 4(0) + 5(8) = 40$

    The minimum value is 35 at $(5, 3)$.
    C is unbounded. Therefore, there is no maximum.

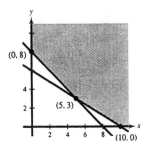

19. $z = 2x + 7y$

At $(10, 0)$: $z = 2(10) + 7(0) = 20$

At $(5, 3)$: $z = 2(5) + 7(3) = 31$

At $(0, 8)$: $z = 2(0) + 7(8) = 56$

The minimum value is 20 at $(10, 0)$.
C is unbounded. Therefore, there is no maximum.

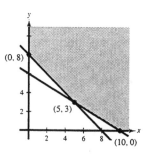

21. $z = 4x + y$

At $(36, 0)$: $z = 4(36) + 0 = 144$

At $(40, 0)$: $z = 4(40) + 0 = 160$

At $(24, 8)$: $z = 4(24) + 8 = 104$

The minimum value is 104 at $(24, 8)$.
The maximum value is 160 at $(40, 0)$.

23. $z = x + 4y$

At $(36, 0)$: $z = 36 + 4(0) = 36$

At $(40, 0)$: $z = 40 + 4(0) = 40$

At $(24, 8)$: $z = 24 + 4(8) = 56$

The minimum value is 36 at $(36, 0)$.
The maximum value is 56 at $(24, 8)$.

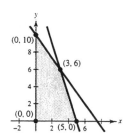

Figure for Exercises 25 and 27

25. $z = 2x + y$

At $(0, 10)$: $z = 2(0) + (10) = 10$

At $(3, 6)$: $z = 2(3) + (6) = 12$

At $(5, 0)$: $z = 2(5) + (0) = 10$

At $(0, 0)$: $z = 2(0) + (0) = 0$

The maximum value is 12 at $(3, 6)$.

27. $z = x + y$

At $(0, 10)$: $z = (0) + (10) = 10$

At $(3, 6)$: $z = (3) + (6) = 9$

At $(5, 0)$: $z = (5) + (0) = 5$

At $(0, 0)$: $z = (0) + (0) = 0$

The maximum value is 10 at $(0, 10)$.

Figure for Exercises 29 and 31

29. $z = x + 5y$

At $(0, 5)$: $z = 0 + 5(5) = 25$

At $\left(\frac{22}{3}, \frac{19}{6}\right)$: $z = \frac{22}{3} + 5\left(\frac{19}{6}\right) = \frac{139}{6}$

At $\left(\frac{21}{2}, 0\right)$: $z = \frac{21}{2} + 5(0) = \frac{21}{2}$

At $(0, 0)$: $z = 0 + 5(0) = 0$

The maximum value is 25 at $(0, 5)$.

31. $z = 4x + 5y$

At $(0, 5)$: $z = 4(0) + 5(5) = 25$

At $\left(\frac{22}{3}, \frac{19}{6}\right)$: $z = 4\left(\frac{22}{3}\right) + 5\left(\frac{19}{6}\right) = \frac{271}{6}$

At $\left(\frac{21}{2}, 0\right)$: $z = 4\left(\frac{21}{2}\right) + 5(0) = 42$

At $(0, 0)$: $z = 4(0) + 5(0) = 0$

The maximum value is $\frac{271}{6}$ at $\left(\frac{22}{3}, \frac{19}{6}\right)$.

33. There are an infinite number of objective functions that would have a maximum at $(0, 4)$. One such objective function is $z = x + 5y$.

35. There are an infinite number of objective functions that would have a maximum at $(5, 0)$. One such objective function is $z = 4x + y$.

37. $x =$ number of Model A

$y =$ number of Model B

Constraints: $2x + 2.5y \le 4000$

$\qquad\qquad\quad 4x + y \le 4800$

$\qquad\quad x + 0.75y \le 1500$

$\qquad\qquad\qquad\qquad x \ge 0$

$\qquad\qquad\qquad\qquad y \ge 0$

Objective function: $P = 45x + 50y$

Vertices: $(0, 0)$, $(0, 1600)$, $(750, 1000)$, $(1050, 600)$, $(1200, 0)$

At $(0, 0)$:　　$P = 45(0) + 50(0) = 0$

At $(0, 1600)$:　$P = 45(0) + 50(1600) = 80,000$

At $(750, 1000)$: $P = 45(750) + 50(1000) = 83,750$

At $(1050, 600)$: $P = 45(1050) + 50(600) = 77,250$

At $(1200, 0)$:　$P = 45(1200) + 50(0) = 54,000$

The maximum profit of \$83,750 occurs when 750 units of Model A and 1000 units of Model B are produced.

39. x = number of $250 models

y = number of $400 models

Constraints: $250x + 400y \le 70{,}000$

$$x + y \le 250$$

$$x \ge 0$$

$$y \ge 0$$

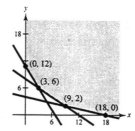

Objective function: $P = 45x + 50y$

Vertices: $(0, 175)$, $(200, 50)$, $(250, 0)$, $(0, 0)$

At $(0, 175)$: $P = 45(0) + 50(175) = 8750$

At $(200, 50)$: $P = 45(200) + 50(50) = 11{,}500$

At $(250, 0)$: $P = 45(250) + 50(0) = 11{,}250$

At $(0, 0)$: $P = 45(0) + 50(0) = 0$

To maximize the profit, the merchant should stock 200 units of the model costing $250 and 50 units of the model costing $400. Then the maximum profit would be $11,500.

41. x = number of bags of Brand X

y = number of bags of Brand Y

Constraints: $2x + y \ge 12$

$$2x + 9y \ge 36$$

$$2x + 3y \ge 24$$

$$x \ge 0$$

$$y \ge 0$$

Objective function: $C = 25x + 20y$

Vertices: $(0, 12)$, $(3, 6)$, $(9, 2)$, $(18, 0)$

At $(0, 12)$: $C = 25(0) + 20(12) = 240$

At $(3, 6)$: $C = 25(3) + 20(6) = 195$

At $(9, 2)$: $C = 25(9) + 20(2) = 265$

At $(18, 0)$: $C = 25(18) + 20(0) = 450$

To minimize cost, use three bags of Brand X and six bags of Brand Y for a total cost of $195.

43. $x =$ the number of audits, and $y =$ the number of tax returns.

Objective function: Maximize $R = 2000x + 300y$.

Constraints: $100x + 12.5y \leq 900$
$$10x + 2.5y \leq 100$$
$$x \geq 0, y \geq 0$$

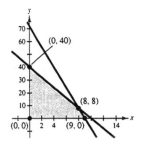

Vertex	Value of $R = 2000x + 300y$
$(0, 0)$	$R = 2000(0) + 300(0) = 0$
$(0, 40)$	$R = 2000(0) + 300(40) = 12,000$
$(8, 8)$	$R = 2000(8) + 300(8) = 18,400$, maximum value
$(9, 0)$	$R = 2000(9) + 300(0) = 18,000$

The revenue will be maximum if the firm does 8 audits and 8 tax returns each week. Maximum revenue is \$18,400.

45. Objective function: $z = 2.5x + y$

Constraints: $x \geq 0, y \geq 0, 3x + 5y \leq 15, 5x + 2y \leq 10$

At $(0, 0)$: $z = 0$

At $(2, 0)$: $z = 5$

At $\left(\frac{20}{19}, \frac{45}{19}\right)$: $z = \frac{95}{19} = 5$

At $(0, 3)$: $z = 3$

z is the maximum at any point on the line $5x + 2y = 10$ between the points $(2, 0)$ and $\left(\frac{20}{19}, \frac{45}{19}\right)$.

47. Objective function: $z = -x + 2y$

Constraints: $x \geq 0, y \geq 0, x \leq 10, x + y \leq 7$

At $(0, 0)$: $z = -0 + 2(0) = 0$

At $(0, 7)$: $z = -0 + 2(7) = 14$

At $(7, 0)$: $z = -7 + 2(0) = -7$

The constraint $x \leq 10$ is extraneous.

The maximum value of 14 occurs at $(0, 7)$.

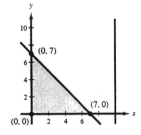

49. Objective function: $z = 3x + 4y$

Constraints: $x \geq 0, y \geq 0, x + y \leq 1, 2x + y \leq 4$

The constraint $2x + y \leq 4$ is extraneous.
The maximum value of $z = 4$ occurs at $(0, 1)$.

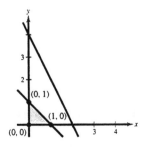

51. Constraints: $x \geq 0$, $y \geq 0$, $x + 3y \leq 15$, $4x + y \leq 16$

Vertex	Value of $z = 3x + ty$
$(0, 0)$	$z = 0$
$(0, 5)$	$z = 5t$
$(3, 4)$	$z = 9 + 4t$
$(4, 0)$	$z = 12$

(a) For the maximum value to be at $(0, 5)$, $z = 5t$ must be greater than or equal to $z = 9 + 4t$ and $z = 12$.

$$5t \geq 9 + 4t \quad \text{and} \quad 5t \geq 12$$
$$t \geq 9 \qquad\qquad t \geq \tfrac{12}{5}$$

Thus, $t \geq 9$.

(b) For the maximum value to be at $(3, 4)$, $z = 9 + 4t$ must be greater than or equal to $z = 5t$ and $z = 12$.

$$9 + 4t \geq 5t \quad \text{and} \quad 9 + 4t \geq 12$$
$$9 \geq t \qquad\qquad 4t \geq 3$$
$$\qquad\qquad t \geq \tfrac{3}{4}$$

Thus, $\tfrac{3}{4} \leq t \leq 9$.

53. $\dfrac{\dfrac{9}{x}}{\left(\dfrac{6}{x} + 2\right)} = \dfrac{\dfrac{9}{x}}{\dfrac{6 + 2x}{x}} = \dfrac{9}{x} \cdot \dfrac{x}{2(3 + x)} = \dfrac{9}{2(3 + x)} = \dfrac{9}{2(x + 3)}, x \neq 0$

55. $\dfrac{\left(\dfrac{4}{x^2 - 9} + \dfrac{2}{x - 2}\right)}{\left(\dfrac{1}{x + 3} + \dfrac{1}{x - 3}\right)} = \dfrac{\dfrac{4(x - 2) + 2(x^2 - 9)}{(x - 2)(x^2 - 9)}}{\dfrac{(x - 3) + (x + 3)}{x^2 - 9}}$

$\qquad = \dfrac{2x^2 + 4x - 26}{(x - 2)(x^2 - 9)} \cdot \dfrac{x^2 - 9}{2x}$

$\qquad = \dfrac{2(x^2 + 2x - 13)}{(x - 2)(2x)}$

$\qquad = \dfrac{x^2 + 2x - 13}{x(x - 2)}, x \neq \pm 3$

❏ Review Exercises for Chapter 7

Solutions to Odd-Numbered Exercises

1. $x + y = 2 \implies y = 2 - x$

$x - y = 0 \implies x - (2 - x) = 0$

$\qquad\qquad\qquad 2x - 2 = 0$

$\qquad\qquad\qquad\qquad x = 1$

$\qquad\qquad\qquad\qquad y = 2 - 1 = 1$

Solution: $(1, 1)$

3. $x^2 - y^2 = 9$

$x - y = 1 \implies x = y + 1$

$(y + 1)^2 - y^2 = 9$

$\qquad\quad 2y + 1 = 9$

$\qquad\qquad\quad y = 4$

$\qquad\qquad\quad x = 5$

Solution: $(5, 4)$

5. $y = 2x^2$

$y = x^4 - 2x^2 \implies 2x^2 = x^4 - 2x^2$

$\qquad\qquad\qquad\qquad 0 = x^4 - 4x^2$

$\qquad\qquad\qquad\qquad 0 = x^2(x^2 - 4)$

$\qquad\qquad\qquad\qquad 0 = x^2(x + 2)(x - 2)$

$\qquad\qquad\qquad\qquad x = 0, x = -2, x = 2$

$\qquad\qquad\qquad\qquad y = 0, y = 8, y = 8$

Solutions: $(0, 0), (-2, 8), (2, 8)$

7. $y^2 - 2y + x = 0 \implies (y - 1)^2 = 1 - x \implies y = 1 \pm \sqrt{1 - x}$

$\qquad x + y = 0 \implies y = -x$

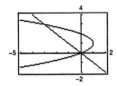

Points of intersection: $(0, 0)$ and $(-3, 3)$

9. $y = 2(6 - x)$

$y = 2^{x-2}$

Point of intersection: $(4, 4)$

11. $\qquad 2x - y = 2 \implies 16x - 8y = 16$

$\qquad 6x + 8y = 39 \implies \underline{6x + 8y = 39}$

$\qquad\qquad\qquad\qquad\qquad 22x = 55$

$\qquad\qquad\qquad\qquad\qquad x = \frac{55}{22} = \frac{5}{2}$

$\qquad\qquad\qquad\qquad\qquad y = 3$

Solution: $\left(\frac{5}{2}, 3\right)$

13. $0.2x + 0.3y = 0.14 \implies 20x + 30y = 14 \implies 20x + 30y = 14$

$0.4x + 0.5y = 0.20 \implies 4x + 5y = 2 \implies -20x - 25y = -10$

$\qquad\qquad\qquad\qquad\qquad\qquad\qquad\qquad\qquad \underline{}$

$\qquad\qquad\qquad\qquad\qquad\qquad\qquad\qquad\qquad\quad 5y = 4$

$\qquad\qquad\qquad\qquad\qquad\qquad\qquad\qquad\qquad\quad y = \frac{4}{5}$

$\qquad\qquad\qquad\qquad\qquad\qquad\qquad\qquad\qquad\quad x = -\frac{1}{2}$

Solution: $\left(-\frac{1}{2}, \frac{4}{5}\right) = (-0.5, 0.8)$

15. $\qquad 3x - 2y = 0 \implies 3x - 2y = 0$

$\qquad 3x + 2(y + 5) = 10 \implies \underline{3x + 2y = 0}$

$\qquad\qquad\qquad\qquad\qquad\qquad 6x = 0$

$\qquad\qquad\qquad\qquad\qquad\qquad x = 0$

$\qquad\qquad\qquad\qquad\qquad\qquad\qquad y = 0$

Solution: $(0, 0)$

17. $1.25x - 2y = 3.5 \implies 5x - 8y = 14$

$\qquad 5x - 8y = 14 \implies -5x + 8y = -14$

$\qquad\qquad\qquad\qquad\qquad\qquad\qquad 0 = 0$

Infinite solutions

Let $y = a$, then $5x - 8a = 14 \implies x = \frac{14}{5} + \frac{8}{5}a$.

Solution: $\left(\frac{14}{5} + \frac{8}{5}a, a\right)$

19. There are infinite linear systems with the solution $\left(\frac{4}{3}, 3\right)$. One possible solution is:

$$3\left(\tfrac{4}{3}\right) + 3 = 7 \implies 3x + y = 7$$

$$-6\left(\tfrac{4}{3}\right) + 3(3) = 1 \implies -6x + 3y = 1$$

21. Revenue $= 4.95x$

Cost $= 2.85x + 10{,}000$

Break even when Revenue $=$ Cost

$$4.95x = 2.85x + 10{,}000$$

$$2.10x = 10{,}000$$

$$x \approx 4762 \text{ units}$$

23. Let $x = $ the amount of 75% solution, and $y = $ amount of 50% solution.

$$x + y = 100 \implies y = 100 - x$$

$$0.75x + 0.50y = 0.60(100)$$

$$0.75x + 0.50(100 - x) = 60$$

$$0.75x + 50 - 0.50x = 60$$

$$0.25x = 10$$

$$x = 40$$

$$y = 100 - x = 60$$

Answer: 40 liters of 75% solution, 60 liters of 60% solution.

25. Let $x = $ speed of the slower plane

Let $y = $ speed of the faster plane

Then, distance of first plane $+$ distance of second plane $= 275$ miles

(rate of first plane)(time) $+$ (rate of second plane)(time) $= 275$ miles

$$x\left(\tfrac{40}{60}\right) + y\left(\tfrac{40}{60}\right) = 275$$

$$y = x + 25$$

$$\tfrac{2}{3}x + \tfrac{2}{3}(x + 25) = 275$$

$$4x + 50 = 825$$

$$4x = 775$$

$$x = 193.75 \text{ mph}$$

$$y = x + 25 = 218.75 \text{ mph}$$

27.   Demand = Supply

$$37 - 0.0002x = 22 + 0.00001x$$

$$15 = 0.00021x$$

$$x = \frac{500,000}{7}, p = \frac{159}{7}$$

Point of equilibrium: $\left(\dfrac{500,000}{7}, \dfrac{159}{7}\right)$

29.

$$\begin{aligned} x + 2y + 6z &= 4 \\ -3x + 2y - z &= -4 \\ 4x + 2z &= 16 \end{aligned}$$

$$\begin{aligned} x + 2y + 6z &= 4 \\ 8y + 17z &= 8 \quad \text{3Eq.1 + Eq.2} \\ -8y - 22z &= 0 \quad -\text{4Eq.1 + Eq.3} \end{aligned}$$

$$\begin{aligned} x + 2y + 6z &= 4 \\ 8y + 17z &= 8 \\ -5z &= 8 \quad \text{Eq.2 + Eq.3} \\ z &= -\tfrac{8}{5} = -1.6 \end{aligned}$$

$$8y + 17(-1.6) = 8 \implies y = 4.4$$

$$x + 2(4.4) + 6(-1.6) = 4 \implies x = 4.8$$

Solution: $(4.8, 4.4, -1.6)$

31.

$$\begin{aligned} x - 2y + z &= -6 \\ 2x - 3y &= -7 \\ -x + 3y - 3z &= 11 \end{aligned}$$

$$\begin{aligned} x - 2y + z &= -6 \\ y - 2z &= 5 \quad -\text{2Eq.1 + Eq.2} \\ y - 2z &= 5 \quad \text{Eq.1 + Eq.3} \end{aligned}$$

$$\begin{aligned} x - 2y + z &= -6 \\ y - 2z &= 5 \\ 0 &= 0 \quad -\text{Eq.2 + Eq.3} \end{aligned}$$

Let $z = a$, then:

$$y = 2a + 5$$

$$x - 2(2a + 5) + a = -6$$

$$x - 3a - 10 = -6$$

$$x = 3a + 4$$

Solution: $(3a + 4, 2a + 5, a)$ where a is any real number.

33. $\begin{aligned} 2x + 5y - 19z &= 34 \implies \\ 3x + 8y - 31z &= 54 \implies \end{aligned}$ $\begin{aligned} 6x + 15y - 57z &= 102 \\ -6x - 16y + 62z &= -108 \\ \hline -y + 5z &= -6 \end{aligned}$

Let $z = a$. Then:

$$y = 5a + 6$$

$$x = \tfrac{1}{2}[34 - 5(5a + 6) + 19a] = -3a + 2$$

Solution: $(-3a + 2, 5a + 6, a)$ where a is any real number.

35. There are an infinite number of linear systems with the solution $(4, -1, 3)$.
One possible system is as follows:

$$2(4) + (-1) - 2(3) = 1 \implies 2x + y - 2z = 1$$
$$(4) + (-1) - (3) = 0 \implies x + y - z = 0$$
$$2(4) - 3(-1) - 2(3) = 5 \implies 2x - 3y - 2z = 5$$

37. $y = ax^2 + bx + c$ through $(0, -5), (1, -2),$ and $(2, 5)$.

$$(0,-5): -5 = c \implies c = -5$$
$$(1,-2): -2 = a + b + c \implies a + b = 3$$
$$(2, 5): 5 = 4a + 2b + c \implies 2a + b = 5$$

$$2a + b = 5$$
$$-a - b = -3$$
$$a = 2$$
$$b = 1$$

The equation of the parabola is $y = 2x^2 + x - 5$.

39. $x^2 + y^2 + Dx + Ey + F = 0$ through $(-1, -2), (5, -2)$ and $(2, 1)$.

$$(-1,-2): 5 - D - 2E + F = 0 \implies D + 2E - F = 5$$
$$(5,-2): 29 + 5D - 2E + F = 0 \implies 5D - 2E + F = -29$$
$$(2, 1): 5 + 2D + 2E + F = 0 \implies 2D + E + F = -5$$

From the first two equations we have

$$6D = -24$$
$$D = -4.$$

Substituting $D = -4$ into the second and third equations yields:

$$-20 - 2E + F = -29 \implies -2E + F = -9$$
$$-8 + E + F = -5 \implies -E - F = -3$$
$$\overline{ -3E = -12}$$
$$E = 4$$
$$F = -1$$

The equation of the circle is $x^2 + y^2 - 4x + 4y - 1 = 0$.

41. From the following chart we obtain our system of equations.

	A	B	C
Mixture X	$\frac{1}{5}$	$\frac{2}{5}$	$\frac{2}{5}$
Mixture Y	0	0	1
Mixture Z	$\frac{1}{3}$	$\frac{1}{3}$	$\frac{1}{3}$
Desired Mixture	$\frac{6}{27}$	$\frac{8}{27}$	$\frac{13}{27}$

$$\left. \begin{array}{l} \frac{1}{5}x + \frac{1}{3}z = \frac{6}{27} \\ \frac{2}{5}x + \frac{1}{3}z = \frac{8}{27} \end{array} \right\} \; x = \frac{10}{27}, z = \frac{12}{27}$$

$$\frac{2}{5}x + y + \frac{1}{3}z = \frac{13}{27} \implies y = \frac{5}{27}$$

To obtain the desired mixture, use 10 gallons of X, 5 gallons of Y, and 12 gallons of Z.

43. $5b + 10a = 17.8 \implies -10b - 20a = -35.6$

$10b + 30a = 45.7 \implies \underline{\quad 10b + 30a = \quad 45.7 \quad}$

$$10a = \quad 10.1$$
$$a = \quad 1.01$$
$$b = \quad 1.54$$

Least squares regression line: $y = 1.01x + 1.54$

45. (a) $\quad 7b + \quad 156.8a = 169.5$

$\quad 156.8b + 3522.78a = 3806.8$

By elimination we have $a \approx 0.956$, $b \approx 2.799$.

The least squares regression line is $y = 0.956x + 2.779$.

(b)
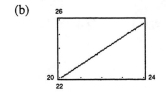

(c) The line is a good model for the data.

(d) A one year change in x (the women's ages) results in y (men's ages) changing 0.956 year.

47. $x + 2y \le 160$

$3x + \quad y \le 180$

$\quad\quad x \ge 0$

$\quad\quad y \ge 0$

Vertex A	Vertex B	Vertex C	Vertex D	Vertex E	Vertex F
$x + 2y = 160$	$x + 2y = 160$	$3x + y = 180$	$x = 0$	$x + 2y = 160$	$3x + y = 180$
$3x + y = 180$	$x = 0$	$y = 0$	$y = 0$	$y = 0$	$x = 0$
$(40, 60)$	$(0, 80)$	$(60, 0)$	$(0, 0)$	$(160, 0)$	$(0, 180)$
				Outside the region	Outside the region

49. $3x + 2y \geq 24$

$x + 2y \geq 12$

$2 \leq x \leq 15$

$y \leq 15$

Vertex A	Vertex B	Vertex C	Vertex D	Vertex E
$3x + 2y = 24$	$3x + 2y = 24$	$3x + 2y = 24$	$3x + 2y = 24$	$x + 2y = 12$
$x + 2y = 12$	$x = 2$	$x = 15$	$y = 15$	$x = 2$
$(6, 3)$	$(2, 9)$	$\left(15, -\frac{21}{2}\right)$	$(-2, 15)$	$(2, 5)$
		Outside the region	Outside the region	Outside the region

Vertex F	Vertex G	Vertex H	Vertex I
$x + 2y = 12$	$x + 2y = 12$	$x = 2$	$x = 15$
$x = 15$	$y = 15$	$y = 15$	$y = 15$
$\left(15, -\frac{3}{2}\right)$	$(-18, 15)$	$(2, 15)$	$(15, 15)$
	Outside the region		

51. $y < x + 1$

$y > x^2 - 1$

Vertices:

$x + 1 = x^2 - 1$

$\quad 0 = x^2 - x - 2 = (x + 1)(x - 2)$

$x = -1$ or $x = 2$

$y = 0 \qquad y = 3$

$(-1, 0) \qquad (2, 3)$

53. $2x - 3y \geq 0$

$2x - y \leq 8$

$y \geq 0$

Vertex A	Vertex B	Vertex C
$2x - 3y = 0$	$2x - 3y = 0$	$2x - y = 8$
$2x - y = 8$	$y = 0$	$y = 0$
$(6, 4)$	$(0, 0)$	$(4, 0)$

55.

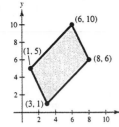

Line through $(1, 5)$, $(3, 1)$: $2x + y = 7$

Line through $(1, 5)$, $(6, 10)$: $-x + y = 4$

Line through $(6, 10)$, $(8, 6)$: $2x + y = 22$

Line through $(8, 6)$, $(3, 1)$: $-x + y = -2$

System of inequalities:

$$-x + y \leq 4$$
$$2x + y \leq 22$$
$$-x + y \geq -2$$
$$2x + y \geq 7$$

57. Let $x =$ the number of bushels for Harrisburg, and $y =$ the number of bushels for Philadelphia.

$$x \geq 400$$
$$y \geq 600$$
$$x + y \leq 1500$$

59.

$$\text{Demand} = \text{Supply}$$
$$160 - 0.0001x = 70 + 0.0002x$$
$$90 = 0.0003x$$
$$x = 300{,}000 \text{ units}$$
$$p = \$130$$

Point of equilibrium: $(300{,}000, 130)$

Consumer surplus: $\frac{1}{2}(300{,}000)(30) = \$4{,}500{,}000$

Producer surplus: $\frac{1}{2}(300{,}000)(60) = \$9{,}000{,}000$

61. Maximize $z = 3x + 4y$ subject to the following constraints.

$$x \geq 0$$
$$y \geq 0$$
$$2x + 5y \leq 50$$
$$4x + y \leq 28$$

Vertex	Value of $z = 3x + 4y$
$(0, 0)$	$z = 0$
$(0, 10)$	$z = 40$
$(5, 8)$	$z = 47$, maximum value
$(7, 0)$	$z = 21$

63. Minimize $z = 1.75x + 2.25y$ subject to the following constraints.

$$2x + y \geq 25$$
$$3x + 2y \geq 45$$
$$x \geq 0$$
$$y \geq 0$$

Vertex	Value of $z = 1.75x + 2.25y$
$(0, 25)$	$z = 56.25$
$(5, 15)$	$z = 42.5$
$(15, 0)$	$z = 26.25$, minimum value

65. Let $x =$ number of haircuts
Let $y =$ number of perms
Maximize $R = 17x + 60y$ subject to the following constraints.

$$x \geq 0$$
$$y \geq 0$$
$$\left(\tfrac{20}{60}\right)x + \left(\tfrac{70}{60}\right)y \leq 24 \implies 2x + 7y \leq 144$$

Vertex	Value of $R = 17x + 60y$
$(0, 0)$	$R = 0$
$(72, 0)$	$R = 1224$
$\left(0, \tfrac{144}{7}\right)$	$R \approx 1234.29$, maximum value

The revenue is maximum when $y = \frac{144}{7} \approx 20$ perms. (Round down since the student cannot work more than 24 hours. Note: Since we rounded down, the student would have enough time left to do 2 haircuts.)

67. Let $x =$ the number of bags of Brand X, and $y =$ the number of bags of Brand Y.
Objective function: Minimize $C = 15x + 30y$
Constraints: $8x + 2y \geq 16$

$$x + y \geq 5$$
$$2x + 7y \geq 20$$
$$x \geq 0, y \geq 0$$

Vertex	Value of $C = 15x + 30y$
$(0, 8)$	$C = 15(0) + 30(8) = 240$
$(1, 4)$	$C = 15(1) + 30(4) = 135$
$(3, 2)$	$C = 15(3) + 30(2) = 105$, minimum value
$(10, 0)$	$C = 15(10) + 30(0) = 150$

To minimize cost, use three bags of Brand X and two bags of Brand Y.

The cost is $105.

❏ Practice Test for Chapter 7

For Exercises 1–3, solve the given system by the method of substitution.

1. $x + y = 1$

$3x - y = 15$

2. $x - 3y = -3$

$x^2 + 6y = 5$

3. $x + y + z = 6$

$2x - y + 3z = 0$

$5x + 2y - z = -3$

4. Find the two numbers whose sum is 110 and product is 2800.

5. Find the dimensions of a rectangle if its perimeter is 170 feet and its area is 2800 square feet.

For Exercises 6–8, solve the linear system by elimination.

6. $2x + 15y = 4$

$x - 3y = 23$

7. $x + y = 2$

$38x - 19y = 7$

8. $0.4x + 0.5y = 0.112$

$0.3x - 0.7y = -0.131$

9. Herbert invests $17,000 in two funds that pay 11% and 13% simple interest, respectively. If he receives $2080 in yearly interest, how much is invested in each fund?

10. Find the least squares regression line for the points $(4, 3)$, $(1, 1)$, $(-1, -2)$, and $(-2, -1)$.

For Exercises 11–13, solve the system of equations.

11. $x + y \qquad = -2$

   $2x - y + z = \;\;11$

   $\qquad 4y - 3z = -20$

12. $4x - y + 5z = 4$

   $2x + y - z = 0$

   $2x + 4y + 8z = 0$

13. $3x + 2y - z = 5$

   $6x - y + 5z = 2$

14. Find the equation of the parabola $y = ax^2 + bx + c$ passing through the points $(0, -1)$, $(1, 4)$ and $(2, 13)$.

15. Find the position equation $s = \frac{1}{2}at^2 + v_0 t + s_0$ given that $s = 12$ feet after 1 second, $s = 5$ feet after 2 seconds, and $s = 4$ after 3 seconds.

16. Graph $x^2 + y^2 \geq 9$.

17. Graph the solution of the system.

   $x + y \leq 6$

   $x \geq 2$

   $y \geq 0$

18. Derive a set of inequalities to describe the triangle with vertices $(0, 0)$, $(0, 7)$, and $(2, 3)$.

19. Find the maximum value of the objective function, $z = 30z + 26y$, subject to the following constraints.

   $x \geq \;0$

   $y \geq \;0$

   $2x + 3y \leq 21$

   $5x + 3y \leq 30$

20. Graph the system of inequalities.

   $x^2 + y^2 \leq 4$

   $(x - 2)^2 + y^2 \geq 4$

CHAPTER 8
Matrices and Determinants

CHAPTER 8
Matrices and Determinants

Section 8.1   Matrices and Systems of Equations

- ■ You should be able to use elementary row operations to produce a row-echelon form (or reduced row-echelon form) of a matrix.
    1. Interchange two rows.
    2. Multiply a row by a nonzero constant.
    3. Add a multiple of one row to another row.
- ■ You should be able to use either Gaussian elimination with back-substitution or Gauss-Jordan elimination to solve a system of linear equations.

Solutions to Odd-Numbered Exercises

1. Since the matrix has three rows and two columns, its order is 3×2.

3. Since the matrix has three rows and one column, its order is 3×1.

5. Since the matrix has two rows and two columns, its order is 2×2.

7. $4x - 3y = -5$
$-x + 3y = 12$

$$\begin{bmatrix} 4 & -3 & \vdots & -5 \\ -1 & 3 & \vdots & 12 \end{bmatrix}$$

9. $x + 10y - 2z = 2$
$5x - 3y + 4z = 0$
$2x + y = 6$

$$\begin{bmatrix} 1 & 10 & -2 & \vdots & 2 \\ 5 & -3 & 4 & \vdots & 0 \\ 2 & 1 & 0 & \vdots & 6 \end{bmatrix}$$

11. $$\begin{bmatrix} 1 & 2 & \vdots & 7 \\ 2 & -3 & \vdots & 4 \end{bmatrix}$$

$x + 2y = 7$
$2x - 3y = 4$

13. $$\begin{bmatrix} 2 & 0 & 5 & \vdots & -12 \\ 0 & 1 & -2 & \vdots & 7 \\ 6 & 3 & 0 & \vdots & 2 \end{bmatrix}$$

$2x \quad + 5z = -12$
$\quad y - 2z = \quad 7$
$6x + 3y \quad = \quad 2$

15. $$\begin{bmatrix} 1 & 0 & 0 & 0 \\ 0 & 1 & 1 & 5 \\ 0 & 0 & 0 & 0 \end{bmatrix}$$

This matrix is in reduced row-echelon form.

17. $$\begin{bmatrix} 2 & 0 & 4 & 0 \\ 0 & -1 & 3 & 6 \\ 0 & 0 & 1 & 5 \end{bmatrix}$$

The first nonzero entries in rows one and two are not one. The matrix is not in row-echelon form.

19. $$\begin{bmatrix} 1 & 4 & 3 \\ 2 & 10 & 5 \end{bmatrix}$$

$-2R_1 + R_2 \rightarrow \begin{bmatrix} 1 & 4 & 3 \\ 0 & \boxed{2} & -1 \end{bmatrix}$

21. $$\begin{bmatrix} 1 & 1 & 4 & -1 \\ 3 & 8 & 10 & 3 \\ -2 & 1 & 12 & 6 \end{bmatrix}$$

$\begin{matrix} -3R_1 + R_2 \rightarrow \\ 2R_1 + R_3 \rightarrow \end{matrix} \begin{bmatrix} 1 & 1 & 4 & -1 \\ 0 & 5 & \boxed{-2} & \boxed{6} \\ 0 & 3 & \boxed{20} & \boxed{4} \end{bmatrix}$

$\frac{1}{5}R_2 \rightarrow \begin{bmatrix} 1 & 1 & 4 & -1 \\ 0 & 1 & -\frac{2}{5} & \frac{6}{5} \\ 0 & 3 & 20 & 4 \end{bmatrix}$

23. $\begin{bmatrix} 1 & 2 & 3 \\ 2 & -1 & -4 \\ 3 & 1 & -1 \end{bmatrix}$

(a) $\begin{bmatrix} 1 & 2 & 3 \\ 0 & -5 & -10 \\ 3 & 1 & -1 \end{bmatrix}$ (b) $\begin{bmatrix} 1 & 2 & 3 \\ 0 & -5 & -10 \\ 0 & -5 & -10 \end{bmatrix}$ (c) $\begin{bmatrix} 1 & 2 & 3 \\ 0 & -5 & -10 \\ 0 & 0 & 0 \end{bmatrix}$

(d) $\begin{bmatrix} 1 & 2 & 3 \\ 0 & 1 & 2 \\ 0 & 0 & 0 \end{bmatrix}$ (e) $\begin{bmatrix} 1 & 0 & -1 \\ 0 & 1 & 2 \\ 0 & 0 & 0 \end{bmatrix}$ This matrix is in reduced row-echelon form.

25. $\begin{bmatrix} 1 & 1 & 0 & 5 \\ -2 & -1 & 2 & -10 \\ 3 & 6 & 7 & 14 \end{bmatrix}$

$\begin{matrix} 2R_1 + R_2 \to \\ -3R_1 + R_3 \to \end{matrix} \begin{bmatrix} 1 & 1 & 0 & 5 \\ 0 & 1 & 2 & 0 \\ 0 & 3 & 7 & -1 \end{bmatrix}$

$-3R_2 + R_3 \to \begin{bmatrix} 1 & 1 & 0 & 5 \\ 0 & 1 & 2 & 0 \\ 0 & 0 & 1 & -1 \end{bmatrix}$

27. $\begin{bmatrix} 1 & -1 & -1 & 1 \\ 5 & -4 & 1 & 8 \\ -6 & 8 & 18 & 0 \end{bmatrix}$

$\begin{matrix} -5R_1 + R_2 \to \\ 6R_1 + R_3 \to \end{matrix} \begin{bmatrix} 1 & -1 & -1 & 1 \\ 0 & 1 & 6 & 3 \\ 0 & 2 & 12 & 6 \end{bmatrix}$

$-2R_2 + R_3 \to \begin{bmatrix} 1 & -1 & -1 & 1 \\ 0 & 1 & 6 & 3 \\ 0 & 0 & 0 & 0 \end{bmatrix}$

29. $\begin{bmatrix} 3 & 3 & 3 \\ -1 & 0 & -4 \\ 2 & 4 & -2 \end{bmatrix}$

$\frac{1}{3}R_1 \to \begin{bmatrix} 1 & 1 & 1 \\ -1 & 0 & -4 \\ 2 & 4 & -2 \end{bmatrix}$

$\begin{matrix} R_1 + R_2 \to \\ -2R_1 + R_3 \to \end{matrix} \begin{bmatrix} 1 & 1 & 1 \\ 0 & 1 & -3 \\ 0 & 2 & -4 \end{bmatrix}$

$\begin{matrix} -R_2 + R_1 \to \\ -2R_2 + R_3 \to \end{matrix} \begin{bmatrix} 1 & 0 & 4 \\ 0 & 1 & -3 \\ 0 & 0 & 2 \end{bmatrix}$

$\frac{1}{2}R_3 \to \begin{bmatrix} 1 & 0 & 4 \\ 0 & 1 & -3 \\ 0 & 0 & 1 \end{bmatrix}$

$\begin{matrix} -4R_3 + R_1 \to \\ 3R_3 + R_2 \to \end{matrix} \begin{bmatrix} 1 & 0 & 0 \\ 0 & 1 & 0 \\ 0 & 0 & 1 \end{bmatrix}$

31. $\begin{bmatrix} 1 & 2 & 3 & -5 \\ 1 & 2 & 4 & -9 \\ -2 & -4 & -4 & 3 \\ 4 & 8 & 11 & -14 \end{bmatrix}$

$\begin{matrix} -R_1 + R_2 \to \\ 2R_1 + R_3 \to \\ -4R_1 + R_4 \to \end{matrix} \begin{bmatrix} 1 & 2 & 3 & -5 \\ 0 & 0 & 1 & -4 \\ 0 & 0 & 2 & -7 \\ 0 & 0 & -1 & 6 \end{bmatrix}$

$\begin{matrix} -3R_2 + R_1 \to \\ \\ -R_2 + R_3 \to \\ R_2 + R_4 \to \end{matrix} \begin{bmatrix} 1 & 2 & 0 & 7 \\ 0 & 0 & 1 & -4 \\ 0 & 0 & 0 & 1 \\ 0 & 0 & 0 & 2 \end{bmatrix}$

$\begin{matrix} -7R_3 + R_1 \to \\ 4R_3 + R_2 \to \\ \\ -2R_3 + R_4 \to \end{matrix} \begin{bmatrix} 1 & 2 & 0 & 0 \\ 0 & 0 & 1 & 0 \\ 0 & 0 & 0 & 1 \\ 0 & 0 & 0 & 0 \end{bmatrix}$

33. $\quad x - 2y = \;\;4$

$\qquad\qquad y = -3$

$\quad x - 2(-3) = \;\;4$

$\qquad\qquad x = -2$

Answer: $(-2, -3)$

35. $x - y + 2z = 4$

$y - z = 2$

$z = -2$

$y - (-2) = 2$

$y = 0$

$x - 0 + 2(-2) = 4$

$x = 8$

Answer: $(8, 0, -2)$

37. $\begin{bmatrix} 1 & 0 & \vdots & 7 \\ 0 & 1 & \vdots & -5 \end{bmatrix}$

$x = 7$

$y = -5$

Answer: $(7, -5)$

39. $\begin{bmatrix} 1 & 0 & 0 & \vdots & -4 \\ 0 & 1 & 0 & \vdots & -8 \\ 0 & 0 & 1 & \vdots & 2 \end{bmatrix}$

$x = -4$

$y = -8$

$z = 2$

Answer: $(-4, -8, 2)$

41. $x + 2y = 7$

$2x + y = 8$

$\begin{bmatrix} 1 & 2 & \vdots & 7 \\ 2 & 1 & \vdots & 8 \end{bmatrix}$

$-2R_1 + R_2 \rightarrow \begin{bmatrix} 1 & 2 & \vdots & 7 \\ 0 & -3 & \vdots & -6 \end{bmatrix}$

$-\frac{1}{3}R_2 \rightarrow \begin{bmatrix} 1 & 2 & \vdots & 7 \\ 0 & 1 & \vdots & 2 \end{bmatrix}$

$y = 2$

$x + 2(2) = 7 \implies x = 3$

Answer: $(3, 2)$

43. $-3x + 5y = -22$

$3x + 4y = 4$

$4x - 8y = 32$

$\begin{bmatrix} -3 & 5 & \vdots & -22 \\ 3 & 4 & \vdots & 4 \\ 4 & -8 & \vdots & 32 \end{bmatrix}$

$R_3 + R_1 \rightarrow \begin{bmatrix} 1 & -3 & \vdots & 10 \\ 3 & 4 & \vdots & 4 \\ 4 & -8 & \vdots & 32 \end{bmatrix}$

$\begin{array}{c} -3R_1 + R_2 \rightarrow \\ -4R_1 + R_3 \rightarrow \end{array} \begin{bmatrix} 1 & -3 & \vdots & 10 \\ 0 & 13 & \vdots & -26 \\ 0 & 4 & \vdots & -8 \end{bmatrix}$

$\begin{array}{c} \frac{1}{13}R_2 \rightarrow \\ -4R_2 + R_3 \rightarrow \end{array} \begin{bmatrix} 1 & -3 & \vdots & 10 \\ 0 & 1 & \vdots & -2 \\ 0 & 0 & \vdots & 0 \end{bmatrix}$

$y = -2$

$x - 3(-2) = 10 \implies x = 4$

Answer: $(4, -2)$

45. $8x - 4y = 7$

$5x + 2y = 1$

$\begin{bmatrix} 8 & -4 & \vdots & 7 \\ 5 & 2 & \vdots & 1 \end{bmatrix}$

$\begin{array}{c} 3R_1 \rightarrow \\ 5R_2 \rightarrow \end{array} \begin{bmatrix} 24 & -12 & \vdots & 21 \\ 25 & 10 & \vdots & 5 \end{bmatrix}$

$-R_2 + R_1 \rightarrow \begin{bmatrix} -1 & -22 & \vdots & 16 \\ 25 & 10 & \vdots & 5 \end{bmatrix}$

$25R_1 + R_2 \rightarrow \begin{bmatrix} -1 & -22 & \vdots & 16 \\ 0 & -540 & \vdots & 405 \end{bmatrix}$

$\begin{array}{c} -R_1 \rightarrow \\ -\frac{1}{540}R_2 \rightarrow \end{array} \begin{bmatrix} 1 & 22 & \vdots & -16 \\ 0 & 1 & \vdots & -\frac{3}{4} \end{bmatrix}$

$y = -\frac{3}{4}$

$x + 22\left(-\frac{3}{4}\right) = -16 \implies x = \frac{1}{2}$

Answer: $\left(\frac{1}{2}, -\frac{3}{4}\right)$

47. $-x + 2y = 1.5$

$2x - 4y = 3.0$

$\begin{bmatrix} -1 & 2 & \vdots & 1.5 \\ 2 & -4 & \vdots & 3.0 \end{bmatrix}$

$2R_1 + R_2 \rightarrow \begin{bmatrix} -1 & 2 & \vdots & 1.5 \\ 0 & 0 & \vdots & 6.0 \end{bmatrix}$

The system is inconsistent and there is no solution.

49. $\begin{aligned} x\quad\;\; - 3z &= -2 \\ 3x + y - 2z &= 5 \\ 2x + 2y + z &= 4 \end{aligned}$

$$\begin{bmatrix} 1 & 0 & -3 & \vdots & -2 \\ 3 & 1 & -2 & \vdots & 5 \\ 2 & 2 & 1 & \vdots & 4 \end{bmatrix}$$

$\begin{aligned} -3R_1 + R_2 &\to \\ -2R_1 + R_3 &\to \end{aligned}$ $\begin{bmatrix} 1 & 0 & -3 & \vdots & -2 \\ 0 & 1 & 7 & \vdots & 11 \\ 0 & 2 & 7 & \vdots & 8 \end{bmatrix}$

$-2R_2 + R_3 \to$ $\begin{bmatrix} 1 & 0 & -3 & \vdots & -2 \\ 0 & 1 & 7 & \vdots & 11 \\ 0 & 0 & -7 & \vdots & -14 \end{bmatrix}$

$-\frac{1}{7}R_3 \to$ $\begin{bmatrix} 1 & 0 & -3 & \vdots & -2 \\ 0 & 1 & 7 & \vdots & 11 \\ 0 & 0 & 1 & \vdots & 2 \end{bmatrix}$

$z = 2$

$y + 7(2) = 11 \implies y = -3$

$x - 3(2) = -2 \implies x = 4$

Answer: $(4, -3, 2)$

51. $\begin{aligned} x + y - 5z &= 3 \\ x\quad\;\; - 2z &= 1 \\ 2x - y - z &= 0 \end{aligned}$

$$\begin{bmatrix} 1 & 1 & -5 & \vdots & 3 \\ 1 & 0 & -2 & \vdots & 1 \\ 2 & -1 & -1 & \vdots & 0 \end{bmatrix}$$

$\begin{aligned} -R_1 + R_2 &\to \\ -2R_1 + R_3 &\to \end{aligned}$ $\begin{bmatrix} 1 & 1 & -5 & \vdots & 3 \\ 0 & -1 & 3 & \vdots & -2 \\ 0 & -3 & 9 & \vdots & -6 \end{bmatrix}$

$-3R_2 + R_3 \to$ $\begin{bmatrix} 1 & 1 & -5 & \vdots & 3 \\ 0 & -1 & 3 & \vdots & -2 \\ 0 & 0 & 0 & \vdots & 0 \end{bmatrix}$

$\begin{aligned} R_2 + R_1 &\to \\ -R_2 &\to \end{aligned}$ $\begin{bmatrix} 1 & 0 & -2 & \vdots & 1 \\ 0 & 1 & -3 & \vdots & 2 \\ 0 & 0 & 0 & \vdots & 0 \end{bmatrix}$

$z = a$

$y - 3a = 2 \implies y = 3a + 2$

$x - 2a = 1 \implies x = 2a + 1$

Answer: $(2a + 1, 3a + 2, a)$

53. $\begin{aligned} x + 2y + z &= 8 \\ 3x + 7y + 6z &= 26 \end{aligned}$

$$\begin{bmatrix} 1 & 2 & 1 & \vdots & 8 \\ 3 & 7 & 6 & \vdots & 26 \end{bmatrix}$$

$-3R_1 + R_2 \to$ $\begin{bmatrix} 1 & 2 & 1 & \vdots & 8 \\ 0 & 1 & 3 & \vdots & 2 \end{bmatrix}$

$-2R_2 + R_1 \to$ $\begin{bmatrix} 1 & 0 & -5 & \vdots & 4 \\ 0 & 1 & 3 & \vdots & 2 \end{bmatrix}$

$z = a$

$y + 3a = 2 \implies y = -3a + 2$

$x - 5a = 4 \implies x = 5a + 4$

Answer: $(5a + 4, -3a + 2, a)$

55. $\begin{aligned} x + 2y &= 0 \\ -x - y &= 0 \end{aligned}$

$$\begin{bmatrix} 1 & 2 & \vdots & 0 \\ -1 & -1 & \vdots & 0 \end{bmatrix}$$

$R_1 + R_2 \to$ $\begin{bmatrix} 1 & 2 & \vdots & 0 \\ 0 & 1 & \vdots & 0 \end{bmatrix}$

$y = 0, \; x + 2(0) = 0 \implies x = 0$

Answer: $(0, 0)$

57. $\begin{aligned} 3x + 3y + 12z &= 6 \\ x + y + 4z &= 2 \\ 2x + 5y + 20z &= 10 \\ -x + 2y + 8z &= 4 \end{aligned}$ $\begin{bmatrix} 3 & 3 & 12 & \vdots & 6 \\ 1 & 1 & 4 & \vdots & 2 \\ 2 & 5 & 20 & \vdots & 10 \\ -1 & 2 & 8 & \vdots & 4 \end{bmatrix} \implies \begin{bmatrix} 1 & 0 & 0 & \vdots & 0 \\ 0 & 0 & 0 & \vdots & 0 \\ 0 & 1 & 4 & \vdots & 2 \\ 0 & 0 & 0 & \vdots & 0 \end{bmatrix}$

$z = a$

$y = -4a + 2$

$x = 0$

Answer: $(0, -4a + 2, a)$

59. $2x + y - z + 2w = -6$
$3x + 4y + w = 1$
$ x + 5y + 2z + 6w = -3$
$5x + 2y - z - w = 3$

$$\begin{bmatrix} 2 & 1 & -1 & 2 & \vdots & -6 \\ 3 & 4 & 0 & 1 & \vdots & 1 \\ 1 & 5 & 2 & 6 & \vdots & -3 \\ 5 & 2 & -1 & -1 & \vdots & 3 \end{bmatrix} \Rightarrow \begin{bmatrix} 1 & 5 & 2 & 6 & \vdots & -3 \\ 0 & 1 & -1 & -3 & \vdots & 2 \\ 0 & 0 & 238 & 629 & \vdots & -306 \\ 0 & 0 & 0 & -71 & \vdots & 142 \end{bmatrix}$$

$x = 1$
$y = 0$
$z = 4$
$w = -2$

Answer: $(1, 0, 4, -2)$

61. $x + y + z = 0$
$2x + 3y + z = 0$
$3x + 5y + z = 0$

$$\begin{bmatrix} 1 & 1 & 1 & \vdots & 0 \\ 2 & 3 & 1 & \vdots & 0 \\ 3 & 5 & 1 & \vdots & 0 \end{bmatrix} \Rightarrow \begin{bmatrix} 1 & 0 & 2 & \vdots & 0 \\ 0 & 1 & -1 & \vdots & 0 \\ 0 & 0 & 0 & \vdots & 0 \end{bmatrix}$$

$z = a$
$y = a$
$x = -2a$

Answer: $(-2a, a, a)$

63. $z = a$
$y = -4a + 1$
$x = -3a - 2$

One possible system is:

$x + y + 7z = (-3a - 2) + (-4a + 1) + 7a = -1$
$x + 2y + 11z = (-3a - 2) + 2(-4a + 1) + 11a = -0$
$2x + y + 10z = 2(-3a - 2) + (-4a + 1) + 10a = -3$

65. $x =$ amount at 8%, $y =$ amount at 9%, $z =$ amount at 12%

$x + y + z = 1,500,000$
$0.08x + 0.09y + 0.12z = 133,000$
$x - 4z = 0$

$$\begin{bmatrix} 1 & 1 & 1 & \vdots & 1,500,000 \\ 0.08 & 0.09 & 0.12 & \vdots & 133,000 \\ 1 & 0 & -4 & \vdots & 0 \end{bmatrix}$$

$\begin{matrix} -0.08R_1 + R_2 \rightarrow \\ -R_1 + R_3 \rightarrow \end{matrix}$ $\begin{bmatrix} 1 & 1 & 1 & \vdots & 1,500,000 \\ 0 & 0.01 & 0.04 & \vdots & 13,000 \\ 0 & -1 & -5 & \vdots & -1,500,000 \end{bmatrix}$

$\begin{matrix} 100R_2 \rightarrow \\ R_2 + R_3 \rightarrow \end{matrix}$ $\begin{bmatrix} 1 & 1 & 1 & \vdots & 1,500,000 \\ 0 & 1 & 4 & \vdots & 1,300,000 \\ 0 & 0 & -1 & \vdots & -200,000 \end{bmatrix}$

$-z = -200,000 \Rightarrow z = 200,000$
$y + 4(200,000) = 1,300,000 \Rightarrow y = 500,000$
$x + (500,000) + (200,000) = 1,500,000 \Rightarrow x = 800,000$

Answer: $800,000 at 8%, $500,000 at 9%, $200,000 at 12%

67. $\dfrac{4x^2}{(x+1)^2(x-1)} = \dfrac{A}{x-1} + \dfrac{B}{x+1} + \dfrac{C}{(x+1)^2}$

$4x^2 = A(x+1)^2 + B(x+1)(x-1) + C(x-1)$

Let $x = 1$: $4 = 4A \implies A = 1$

Let $x = -1$: $4 = -2C \implies C = -2$

Let $x = 0$: $0 = A - B - C \implies 0 = 1 - B - (-2) \implies B = 3$

Thus, $\dfrac{4x^2}{(x+1)^2(x-1)} = \dfrac{1}{x-1} + \dfrac{3}{x+1} - \dfrac{2}{(x+1)^2}$.

69. $f(x) = ax^2 + bx + c$

$f(1) = a + b + c = 8$

$f(2) = 4a + 2b + c = 13$

$f(3) = 9a + 3b + c = 20$

$$\begin{bmatrix} 1 & 1 & 1 & \vdots & 8 \\ 4 & 2 & 1 & \vdots & 13 \\ 9 & 3 & 1 & \vdots & 20 \end{bmatrix}$$

$$\begin{matrix} \\ -4R_1 + R_2 \rightarrow \\ -9R_1 + R_3 \rightarrow \end{matrix} \begin{bmatrix} 1 & 1 & 1 & \vdots & 8 \\ 0 & -2 & -3 & \vdots & -19 \\ 0 & -6 & -8 & \vdots & -52 \end{bmatrix}$$

$$\begin{matrix} \\ -\frac{1}{2}R_2 \rightarrow \\ -3R_2 + R_3 \rightarrow \end{matrix} \begin{bmatrix} 1 & 1 & 1 & \vdots & 8 \\ 0 & 1 & \frac{3}{2} & \vdots & \frac{19}{2} \\ 0 & 0 & 1 & \vdots & 5 \end{bmatrix}$$

$c = 5$

$b + \frac{3}{2}(5) = \frac{19}{2} \implies b = 2$

$a + 2 + 5 = 8 \implies a = 1$

Answer: $y = x^2 + 2x + 5$

71. (a) $(0, 5.0),\ (15, 9.6),\ (30, 12.4)$

$f(x) = ax^2 + bx + c$

$f(0) = c = 5$

$f(15) = 225a + 15b + c = 9.6 \implies 225a + 15b = 4.6$

$f(30) = 900a + 30b + c = 12.4 \implies 900a + 30b = 7.4$

$$\begin{bmatrix} 225 & 15 & \vdots & 4.6 \\ 900 & 30 & \vdots & 7.4 \end{bmatrix}$$

$$\begin{matrix} \frac{1}{225}R_1 \rightarrow \\ -900R_1 + R_2 \rightarrow \end{matrix} \begin{bmatrix} 1 & \frac{1}{15} & \vdots & \frac{23}{1125} \\ 0 & -30 & \vdots & -11 \end{bmatrix}$$

$-30b = -11 \implies b = \dfrac{11}{30} \approx 0.367$

$1 + \dfrac{1}{15}\left(\dfrac{11}{30}\right) = \dfrac{23}{1125} \implies a = -\dfrac{1}{250} = -0.004$

Thus, $y = -0.004x^2 + 0.367x + 5$.

— CONTINUED —

71. — CONTINUED —

(b)

The maximum height is approximately 13 feet and the ball strikes the ground at approximately 104 feet.

(c) The maximum occurs at the vertex.

$$-\frac{b}{2a} = \frac{-0.367}{2(-0.004)} = 45.875$$

$$f(45.875) = -0.004(45.875)^2 + 0.367(45.875) + 5 = 13.418 \text{ feet}$$

The ball strikes the ground when $y = 0$.

$$-0.004x^2 + 0.367x + 5 = 0$$

By the Quadratic Formula and using the positive value for x we have $x \approx 103.793$ feet.

73. (a) $x_1 + x_3 = 600$

$x_1 = x_2 + x_4 \implies x_1 - x_2 - x_4 = 0$

$x_2 + x_5 = 500$

$x_3 + x_6 = 600$

$x_4 + x_7 = x_6 \implies x_4 - x_6 + x_7 = 0$

$x_5 + x_7 = 500$

$$\begin{bmatrix} 1 & 0 & 1 & 0 & 0 & 0 & 0 & \vdots & 600 \\ 1 & -1 & 0 & -1 & 0 & 0 & 0 & \vdots & 0 \\ 0 & 1 & 0 & 0 & 1 & 0 & 0 & \vdots & 500 \\ 0 & 0 & 1 & 0 & 0 & 1 & 0 & \vdots & 600 \\ 0 & 0 & 0 & 1 & 0 & -1 & 1 & \vdots & 0 \\ 0 & 0 & 0 & 0 & 1 & 0 & 1 & \vdots & 500 \end{bmatrix}$$

$$\begin{matrix} \\ -R_1 + R_2 \to \\ R_2 + R_3 \to \\ R_3 + R_4 \to \\ R_4 + R_5 \to \\ -R_5 + R_6 \to \end{matrix} \begin{bmatrix} 1 & 0 & 1 & 0 & 0 & 0 & 0 & \vdots & 600 \\ 0 & -1 & -1 & -1 & 0 & 0 & 0 & \vdots & -600 \\ 0 & 0 & -1 & -1 & 1 & 0 & 0 & \vdots & -100 \\ 0 & 0 & 0 & -1 & 1 & 1 & 0 & \vdots & 500 \\ 0 & 0 & 0 & 0 & 1 & 0 & 1 & \vdots & 500 \\ 0 & 0 & 0 & 0 & 0 & 0 & 0 & \vdots & 0 \end{bmatrix}$$

$$\begin{matrix} \\ -R_3 + R_2 \to \\ -R_4 + R_3 \to \\ -R_4 \to \\ \\ \end{matrix} \begin{bmatrix} 1 & 0 & 1 & 0 & 0 & 0 & 0 & \vdots & 600 \\ 0 & -1 & 0 & 0 & -1 & 0 & 0 & \vdots & -500 \\ 0 & 0 & -1 & 0 & 0 & -1 & 0 & \vdots & -600 \\ 0 & 0 & 0 & 1 & -1 & -1 & 0 & \vdots & -500 \\ 0 & 0 & 0 & 0 & 1 & 0 & 1 & \vdots & 500 \\ 0 & 0 & 0 & 0 & 0 & 0 & 0 & \vdots & 0 \end{bmatrix}$$

Let $x_7 = t$ and $x_6 = s$, then $x_5 = 500 - t$,
$x_4 = -500 + s + (500 - t) = s - t$,
$x_3 = 600 - s, x_2 = 500 - (500 - t) = t, x_1 = 600 - (600 - s) = s$.

Answer: $(s, t, 600 - s, s - t, 500 - t, s, t)$

(b) $s = 0, t = 0$: $x_1 = 0, x_2 = 0, x_3 = 600, x_4 = 0, x_5 = 500, x_6 = 0, x_7 = 0$

(c) $s = 0, t = -500$: $x_1 = 0, x_2 = -500, x_3 = 600, x_4 = 500, x_5 = 1000, x_6 = 0, x_7 = -500$

75. $f(x) = 2^{x-1}$

x	-1	0	1	2	3
y	$\frac{1}{4}$	$\frac{1}{2}$	1	2	4

77. $h(x) = \log_2(x - 1) \implies 2^y = x - 1 \implies 2^y + 1 = x$

x	$\frac{3}{2}$	2	3	5	9
y	-1	0	1	2	3

Vertical asymptote: $x = 1$

Section 8.2   Operations with Matrices

- $A = B$ if and only if they have the same order and $a_{ij} = b_{ij}$.
- You should be able to perform the operations of matrix addition, scalar multiplication, and matrix multiplication.
- Some properties of matrix addition and scalar multiplication are:
  - (a) $A + B = B + A$
  - (b) $A + (B + C) = (A + B) + C$
  - (c) $(cd)A = c(dA)$
  - (d) $1A = A$
  - (e) $c(A + B) = cA + cB$
  - (f) $(c + d)A = cA + dA$
- You should remember that $AB \neq BA$ in general.

Solutions to Odd-Numbered Exercises

1. $x = -4, \ y = 22$

3. $2x + 1 = 5, \ 3y - 5 = 4$

$x = 2, \ y = 3$

5. (a) $A + B = \begin{bmatrix} 1 & -1 \\ 2 & -1 \end{bmatrix} + \begin{bmatrix} 2 & -1 \\ -1 & 8 \end{bmatrix} = \begin{bmatrix} 1+2 & -1-1 \\ 2-1 & -1+8 \end{bmatrix} = \begin{bmatrix} 3 & -2 \\ 1 & 7 \end{bmatrix}$

(b) $A - B = \begin{bmatrix} 1 & -1 \\ 2 & -1 \end{bmatrix} - \begin{bmatrix} 2 & -1 \\ -1 & 8 \end{bmatrix} = \begin{bmatrix} 1-2 & -1+1 \\ 2+1 & -1-8 \end{bmatrix} = \begin{bmatrix} -1 & 0 \\ 3 & -9 \end{bmatrix}$

— CONTINUED —

5. — CONTINUED —

(c) $3A = 3\begin{bmatrix} 1 & -1 \\ 2 & -1 \end{bmatrix} = \begin{bmatrix} 3(1) & 3(-1) \\ 3(2) & 3(-1) \end{bmatrix} = \begin{bmatrix} 3 & -3 \\ 6 & -3 \end{bmatrix}$

(d) $3A - 2B = \begin{bmatrix} 3 & -3 \\ 6 & -3 \end{bmatrix} - 2\begin{bmatrix} 2 & -1 \\ -1 & 8 \end{bmatrix} = \begin{bmatrix} 3 & -3 \\ 6 & -3 \end{bmatrix} + \begin{bmatrix} -4 & 2 \\ 2 & -16 \end{bmatrix} = \begin{bmatrix} -1 & -1 \\ 8 & -19 \end{bmatrix}$

7. $A = \begin{bmatrix} 6 & -1 \\ 2 & 4 \\ -3 & 5 \end{bmatrix}, B = \begin{bmatrix} 1 & 4 \\ -1 & 5 \\ 1 & 10 \end{bmatrix}$

(a) $A + B = \begin{bmatrix} 7 & 3 \\ 1 & 9 \\ -2 & 15 \end{bmatrix}$ (b) $A - B = \begin{bmatrix} 5 & -5 \\ 3 & -1 \\ -4 & -5 \end{bmatrix}$ (c) $3A = \begin{bmatrix} 18 & -3 \\ 6 & 12 \\ -9 & 15 \end{bmatrix}$

(d) $3A - 2B = \begin{bmatrix} 18 & -3 \\ 6 & 12 \\ -9 & 15 \end{bmatrix} - \begin{bmatrix} 2 & 8 \\ -2 & 10 \\ 2 & 20 \end{bmatrix} = \begin{bmatrix} 16 & -11 \\ 8 & 2 \\ -11 & -5 \end{bmatrix}$

9. $A = \begin{bmatrix} 2 & 2 & -1 & 0 & 1 \\ 1 & 1 & -2 & 0 & -1 \end{bmatrix}, B = \begin{bmatrix} 1 & 1 & -1 & 1 & 0 \\ -3 & 4 & 9 & -6 & -7 \end{bmatrix}$

(a) $A + B = \begin{bmatrix} 3 & 3 & -2 & 1 & 1 \\ -2 & 5 & 7 & -6 & -8 \end{bmatrix}$

(b) $A - B = \begin{bmatrix} 1 & 1 & 0 & -1 & 1 \\ 4 & -3 & -11 & 6 & 6 \end{bmatrix}$

(c) $3A = \begin{bmatrix} 6 & 6 & -3 & 0 & 3 \\ 3 & 3 & -6 & 0 & -3 \end{bmatrix}$

(d) $3A - 2B = \begin{bmatrix} 6 & 6 & -3 & 0 & 3 \\ 3 & 3 & -6 & 0 & -3 \end{bmatrix} - \begin{bmatrix} 2 & 2 & -2 & 2 & 0 \\ -6 & 8 & 18 & -12 & -14 \end{bmatrix} = \begin{bmatrix} 4 & 4 & -1 & -2 & 3 \\ 9 & -5 & -24 & 12 & 11 \end{bmatrix}$

11. $X = 3\begin{bmatrix} -2 & -1 \\ 1 & 0 \\ 3 & 4 \end{bmatrix} - 2\begin{bmatrix} 0 & 3 \\ 2 & 0 \\ -4 & -1 \end{bmatrix} = \begin{bmatrix} -6 & -3 \\ 3 & 0 \\ 9 & -12 \end{bmatrix} - \begin{bmatrix} 0 & 6 \\ 4 & 0 \\ -8 & -2 \end{bmatrix} = \begin{bmatrix} -6 & -9 \\ -1 & 0 \\ 17 & -10 \end{bmatrix}$

13. $X = -\frac{3}{2}A + \frac{1}{2}B = -\frac{3}{2}\begin{bmatrix} -2 & -1 \\ 1 & 0 \\ 3 & -4 \end{bmatrix} + \frac{1}{2}\begin{bmatrix} 0 & 3 \\ 2 & 0 \\ -4 & -1 \end{bmatrix} = \begin{bmatrix} 3 & 3 \\ -\frac{1}{2} & 0 \\ -\frac{13}{2} & \frac{11}{2} \end{bmatrix}$

15. (a) $AB = \begin{bmatrix} 1 & 2 \\ 4 & 2 \end{bmatrix}\begin{bmatrix} 2 & -1 \\ -1 & 8 \end{bmatrix} = \begin{bmatrix} 2-2 & -1+16 \\ 8-2 & -4+16 \end{bmatrix} = \begin{bmatrix} 0 & 15 \\ 6 & 12 \end{bmatrix}$

(b) $BA = \begin{bmatrix} 2 & -1 \\ -1 & 8 \end{bmatrix}\begin{bmatrix} 1 & 2 \\ 4 & 2 \end{bmatrix} = \begin{bmatrix} 2-4 & 4-2 \\ -1+32 & -2+16 \end{bmatrix} = \begin{bmatrix} -2 & 2 \\ 31 & 14 \end{bmatrix}$

(c) $A^2 = \begin{bmatrix} 1 & 2 \\ 4 & 2 \end{bmatrix}\begin{bmatrix} 1 & 2 \\ 4 & 2 \end{bmatrix} = \begin{bmatrix} 1+8 & 2+4 \\ 4+8 & 8+4 \end{bmatrix} = \begin{bmatrix} 9 & 6 \\ 12 & 12 \end{bmatrix}$

17. (a) $AB = \begin{bmatrix} 3 & -1 \\ 1 & 3 \end{bmatrix}\begin{bmatrix} 1 & -3 \\ 3 & 1 \end{bmatrix} = \begin{bmatrix} 3-3 & -9-1 \\ 1+9 & -3+3 \end{bmatrix} = \begin{bmatrix} 0 & -10 \\ 10 & 0 \end{bmatrix}$

(b) $BA = \begin{bmatrix} 1 & -3 \\ 3 & 1 \end{bmatrix}\begin{bmatrix} 3 & -1 \\ 1 & 3 \end{bmatrix} = \begin{bmatrix} 3-3 & -1-9 \\ 9+1 & -3+3 \end{bmatrix} = \begin{bmatrix} 0 & -10 \\ 10 & 0 \end{bmatrix}$

(c) $A^2 = \begin{bmatrix} 3 & -1 \\ 1 & 3 \end{bmatrix}\begin{bmatrix} 3 & -1 \\ 1 & 3 \end{bmatrix} = \begin{bmatrix} 9-1 & -3-3 \\ 3+3 & -1+9 \end{bmatrix} = \begin{bmatrix} 8 & -6 \\ 6 & 8 \end{bmatrix}$

19. (a) $AB = \begin{bmatrix} 1 & -1 & 7 \\ 2 & -1 & 8 \\ 3 & 1 & -1 \end{bmatrix}\begin{bmatrix} 1 & 1 & 2 \\ 2 & 1 & 1 \\ 1 & -3 & 2 \end{bmatrix} = \begin{bmatrix} 1-2+7 & 1-1-21 & 2-1+14 \\ 2-2+8 & 2-1-24 & 4-1+16 \\ 3+2-1 & 3+1+3 & 6+1-2 \end{bmatrix} = \begin{bmatrix} 6 & -21 & 15 \\ 8 & -23 & 19 \\ 4 & 7 & 5 \end{bmatrix}$

(b) $BA = \begin{bmatrix} 1 & 1 & 2 \\ 2 & 1 & 1 \\ 1 & -3 & 2 \end{bmatrix}\begin{bmatrix} 1 & -1 & 7 \\ 2 & -1 & 8 \\ 3 & 1 & -1 \end{bmatrix} = \begin{bmatrix} 1+2+6 & -1-1+2 & 7+8-2 \\ 2+2+3 & -2-1+1 & 14+8-1 \\ 1-6+6 & -1+3+2 & 7-24-2 \end{bmatrix} = \begin{bmatrix} 9 & 0 & 13 \\ 7 & -2 & 21 \\ 1 & 4 & -19 \end{bmatrix}$

(c) $A^2 = \begin{bmatrix} 1 & -1 & 7 \\ 2 & -1 & 8 \\ 3 & 1 & -1 \end{bmatrix}\begin{bmatrix} 1 & -1 & 7 \\ 2 & -1 & 8 \\ 3 & 1 & -1 \end{bmatrix} = \begin{bmatrix} 1-2+21 & -1+1+7 & 7-8-7 \\ 2-2+24 & -2+1+8 & 14-8-8 \\ 3+2-3 & -3-1-1 & 21+8+1 \end{bmatrix} = \begin{bmatrix} 20 & 7 & -8 \\ 24 & 7 & -2 \\ 2 & -5 & 30 \end{bmatrix}$

21. A is 3×2 and B is $3 \times 3 \implies AB$ is not defined.

23. A is 3×2, B is $2 \times 2 \implies AB$ is 3×2.

$AB = \begin{bmatrix} -1 & 3 \\ 4 & -5 \\ 0 & 2 \end{bmatrix}\begin{bmatrix} 1 & 2 \\ 0 & 7 \end{bmatrix} = \begin{bmatrix} -1 & 19 \\ 4 & -27 \\ 0 & 14 \end{bmatrix}$

25. A is 3×3, B is $3 \times 3 \implies AB$ is 3×3.

$AB = \begin{bmatrix} 5 & 0 & 0 \\ 0 & -8 & 0 \\ 0 & 0 & 7 \end{bmatrix}\begin{bmatrix} \frac{1}{5} & 0 & 0 \\ 0 & -\frac{1}{8} & 0 \\ 0 & 0 & \frac{1}{2} \end{bmatrix} = \begin{bmatrix} 1 & 0 & 0 \\ 0 & 1 & 0 \\ 0 & 0 & \frac{7}{2} \end{bmatrix}$

27. A is 2×1, B is $1 \times 4 \implies AB$ is 2×4.

$\begin{bmatrix} 10 \\ 12 \end{bmatrix}\begin{bmatrix} 6 & -2 & 1 & 6 \end{bmatrix} = \begin{bmatrix} 60 & -20 & 10 & 60 \\ 72 & -24 & 12 & 72 \end{bmatrix}$

29. $\begin{bmatrix} 5 & 6 & -3 \\ -2 & 5 & 1 \\ 10 & -5 & 5 \end{bmatrix}\begin{bmatrix} 1 & -1 & 2 \\ 8 & 1 & 4 \\ 4 & -2 & 9 \end{bmatrix} = \begin{bmatrix} 41 & 7 & 7 \\ 42 & 5 & 25 \\ -10 & -25 & 45 \end{bmatrix}$

31. $\begin{bmatrix} -3 & 8 & -6 & 8 \\ -12 & 15 & 9 & 6 \\ 5 & -1 & 1 & 5 \end{bmatrix}\begin{bmatrix} 3 & 1 & 6 \\ 24 & 15 & 14 \\ 16 & 10 & 21 \\ 8 & -4 & 10 \end{bmatrix} = \begin{bmatrix} 151 & 25 & 48 \\ 516 & 279 & 387 \\ 47 & -20 & 87 \end{bmatrix}$

33. A is 2×4 and B is $2 \times 4 \implies AB$ is not defined.

35. $A = \begin{bmatrix} -1 & 1 \\ -2 & 1 \end{bmatrix}$, $X = \begin{bmatrix} x \\ y \end{bmatrix}$, $B = \begin{bmatrix} 4 \\ 0 \end{bmatrix}$

By Gauss-Jordan elimination on

$$\begin{bmatrix} -1 & 1 & \vdots & 4 \\ -2 & 1 & \vdots & 0 \end{bmatrix}$$

$$\begin{array}{c} -R_1 \rightarrow \\ 2R_1 + R_2 \rightarrow \end{array} \begin{bmatrix} 1 & -1 & \vdots & -4 \\ 0 & -1 & \vdots & -8 \end{bmatrix}$$

$$\begin{array}{c} R_2 + R_1 \rightarrow \\ -R_2 \rightarrow \end{array} \begin{bmatrix} 1 & 0 & \vdots & 4 \\ 0 & 1 & \vdots & 8 \end{bmatrix}$$

we have $x = 4$ and $y = 8$.

37. $A = \begin{bmatrix} 2 & 3 \\ 1 & 4 \end{bmatrix}$, $X = \begin{bmatrix} x \\ y \end{bmatrix}$, $B = \begin{bmatrix} 5 \\ 10 \end{bmatrix}$

By Gauss-Jordan elimination on

$$\begin{bmatrix} 1 & 4 & \vdots & 10 \\ 2 & 3 & \vdots & 5 \end{bmatrix}$$

$$-2R_1 + R_2 \rightarrow \begin{bmatrix} 1 & 4 & \vdots & 10 \\ 0 & -5 & \vdots & -15 \end{bmatrix}$$

$$\begin{array}{c} -4R_2 + R_1 \rightarrow \\ -\frac{1}{5}R_2 \rightarrow \end{array} \begin{bmatrix} 1 & 0 & \vdots & -2 \\ 0 & 1 & \vdots & 3 \end{bmatrix}$$

we have $x = -2$ and $y = 3$.

39. $A = \begin{bmatrix} 2 & 0 \\ 4 & 5 \end{bmatrix}$

$$f(A) = A^2 - 5A + 2 = \begin{bmatrix} 2 & 0 \\ 4 & 5 \end{bmatrix}\begin{bmatrix} 2 & 0 \\ 4 & 5 \end{bmatrix} - 5\begin{bmatrix} 2 & 4 \\ 0 & 5 \end{bmatrix} + 2\begin{bmatrix} 1 & 0 \\ 0 & 1 \end{bmatrix} = \begin{bmatrix} -4 & 0 \\ 8 & 2 \end{bmatrix}$$

41. $A = \begin{bmatrix} 3 & 1 & 4 \\ 0 & 2 & 6 \\ 0 & 0 & 5 \end{bmatrix}$

$$f(A) = \begin{bmatrix} 3 & 1 & 4 \\ 0 & 2 & 6 \\ 0 & 0 & 5 \end{bmatrix}^3 - 10\begin{bmatrix} 3 & 1 & 4 \\ 0 & 2 & 6 \\ 0 & 0 & 5 \end{bmatrix}^2 + 31\begin{bmatrix} 3 & 1 & 4 \\ 0 & 2 & 6 \\ 0 & 0 & 5 \end{bmatrix} - 30\begin{bmatrix} 1 & 0 & 0 \\ 0 & 1 & 0 \\ 0 & 0 & 1 \end{bmatrix} = \begin{bmatrix} 0 & 0 & 0 \\ 0 & 0 & 0 \\ 0 & 0 & 0 \end{bmatrix}$$

43. $AC = \begin{bmatrix} 0 & 1 \\ 0 & 1 \end{bmatrix}\begin{bmatrix} 2 & 3 \\ 2 & 3 \end{bmatrix} = \begin{bmatrix} 2 & 3 \\ 2 & 3 \end{bmatrix}$

$BC = \begin{bmatrix} 1 & 0 \\ 1 & 0 \end{bmatrix}\begin{bmatrix} 2 & 3 \\ 2 & 3 \end{bmatrix} = \begin{bmatrix} 2 & 3 \\ 2 & 3 \end{bmatrix}$

Thus, $AC = BC$ even though $A \neq B$.

For 45–53, A is of order 2×3, B is of order 2×3, C is of order 3×2 and D is of order 2×2.

45. $A + 2C$ is not possible. A and C are not of the same order.

47. AB is not possible. The number of columns of A does not equal the number of rows of B.

49. $BC - D$ is possible. The resulting order is 2×2.

51. (CA) is 3×3 so $(CA)D$ is not possible.

53. $D(A - 3B)$ is possible. The resulting order is 2×3.

55. $1.20\begin{bmatrix} 60 & 40 & 20 \\ 30 & 90 & 60 \end{bmatrix} = \begin{bmatrix} 72 & 48 & 24 \\ 36 & 108 & 72 \end{bmatrix}$

57. $BA = \begin{bmatrix} 3.75 & 7.00 \end{bmatrix}\begin{bmatrix} 100 & 75 & 75 \\ 125 & 150 & 100 \end{bmatrix} = \begin{bmatrix} \$1250.00 & \$1331.25 & \$981.25 \end{bmatrix}$

The entries in the last matrix represent the profits for both crops at the three outlets.

59. $ST = \begin{bmatrix} 3 & 2 & 2 & 3 & 0 \\ 0 & 2 & 3 & 4 & 3 \\ 4 & 2 & 1 & 3 & 2 \end{bmatrix} \begin{bmatrix} 840 & 1100 \\ 1200 & 1350 \\ 1450 & 1650 \\ 2650 & 3000 \\ 3050 & 3200 \end{bmatrix} = \begin{bmatrix} \$15,770 & \$18,300 \\ \$26,500 & \$29,250 \\ \$21,260 & \$24,150 \end{bmatrix}$

The entries represent the wholesale and retail inventory values of the inventories at the three outlets.

61. $ST = \begin{bmatrix} 1 & 0.5 & 0.2 \\ 1.6 & 1.0 & 0.2 \\ 2.5 & 2.0 & 0.4 \end{bmatrix} \begin{bmatrix} 12 & 10 \\ 9 & 8 \\ 6 & 5 \end{bmatrix} = \begin{bmatrix} \$17.70 & \$15.00 \\ \$29.40 & \$25.00 \\ \$50.40 & \$43.00 \end{bmatrix}$

This represents the labor cost for each boat size at each plant.

63. $A^2 = \begin{bmatrix} i & 0 \\ 0 & i \end{bmatrix} \begin{bmatrix} i & 0 \\ 0 & i \end{bmatrix} = \begin{bmatrix} -1 & 0 \\ 0 & -1 \end{bmatrix}$ and $i^2 = -1$

$A^3 = A^2A = \begin{bmatrix} -1 & 0 \\ 0 & -1 \end{bmatrix} \begin{bmatrix} i & 0 \\ 0 & i \end{bmatrix} = \begin{bmatrix} -i & 0 \\ 0 & -i \end{bmatrix}$ and $i^3 = -i$

$A^4 = A^3A = \begin{bmatrix} -i & 0 \\ 0 & -i \end{bmatrix} \begin{bmatrix} i & 0 \\ 0 & i \end{bmatrix} = \begin{bmatrix} 1 & 0 \\ 0 & 1 \end{bmatrix}$ and $i^4 = 1$

65. The product of two diagonal matrices of the same order is a diagonal matrix whose entries are the products of the corresponding diagonal entries of A and B.

Section 8.3   The Inverse of a Square Matrix

■ You should be able to find the inverse, if it exists, of a square matrix.

(a) Write the $n \times 2n$ matrix that consists of the given matrix A on the left and the $n \times n$ identity matrix I on the right to obtain $[A \vdots I]$. Note that we separate the matrices A and I by a dotted line. We call this process **adjoining** the matrices A and I.

(b) If possible, row reduce A to I using elementary row operations of the *entire* matrix $[A \vdots I]$. The result will be the matrix $[I \vdots A^{-1}]$. If this is not possible, then A is not invertible.

(c) Check your work by multiplying to see that $AA^{-1} = I = A^{-1}A$.

■ You should be able to use inverse matrices to solve systems of equation.

Solutions to Odd-Numbered Exercises

1. $AB = \begin{bmatrix} 2 & 1 \\ 5 & 3 \end{bmatrix} \begin{bmatrix} 3 & -1 \\ -5 & 2 \end{bmatrix} = \begin{bmatrix} 2(3) + 1(-5) & 2(-1) + 1(2) \\ 5(3) + 3(-5) & 5(-1) + 3(2) \end{bmatrix} = \begin{bmatrix} 1 & 0 \\ 0 & 1 \end{bmatrix}$

$BA = \begin{bmatrix} 3 & -1 \\ -5 & 2 \end{bmatrix} \begin{bmatrix} 2 & 1 \\ 5 & 3 \end{bmatrix} = \begin{bmatrix} 3(2) + (-1)(5) & 3(1) + (-1)(3) \\ -5(2) + 2(5) & -5(1) + 2(3) \end{bmatrix} = \begin{bmatrix} 1 & 0 \\ 0 & 1 \end{bmatrix}$

3. $AB = \begin{bmatrix} 1 & 2 \\ 3 & 4 \end{bmatrix} \begin{bmatrix} -2 & 1 \\ \frac{3}{2} & -\frac{1}{2} \end{bmatrix} = \begin{bmatrix} -2+3 & 1-1 \\ -6+6 & 3-2 \end{bmatrix} = \begin{bmatrix} 1 & 0 \\ 0 & 1 \end{bmatrix}$

$BA = \begin{bmatrix} -2 & 1 \\ \frac{3}{2} & -\frac{1}{2} \end{bmatrix} \begin{bmatrix} 1 & 2 \\ 3 & 4 \end{bmatrix} = \begin{bmatrix} -2+3 & -4+4 \\ \frac{3}{2} - \frac{3}{2} & 3-2 \end{bmatrix} = \begin{bmatrix} 1 & 0 \\ 0 & 1 \end{bmatrix}$

5. $AB = \frac{1}{3} \begin{bmatrix} -2 & 2 & 3 \\ 1 & -1 & 0 \\ 0 & 1 & 4 \end{bmatrix} \begin{bmatrix} -4 & -5 & 3 \\ -4 & -8 & 3 \\ 1 & 2 & 0 \end{bmatrix} = \frac{1}{3} \begin{bmatrix} -8+8+3 & 10-16+6 & -6+6 \\ -4+4 & -5+8 & 3-3 \\ -4+4 & -8+8 & 3 \end{bmatrix}$

$= \frac{1}{3} \begin{bmatrix} 3 & 0 & 0 \\ 0 & 3 & 0 \\ 0 & 0 & 3 \end{bmatrix} = \begin{bmatrix} 1 & 0 & 0 \\ 0 & 1 & 0 \\ 0 & 0 & 1 \end{bmatrix}$

$BA = \frac{1}{3} \begin{bmatrix} -4 & -5 & 3 \\ -4 & -8 & 3 \\ 1 & 2 & 0 \end{bmatrix} \begin{bmatrix} -2 & 2 & 3 \\ 1 & -1 & 0 \\ 0 & 1 & 4 \end{bmatrix} = \frac{1}{3} \begin{bmatrix} 8-5 & -8+5+3 & -12+12 \\ 8-8 & -8+8+3 & -12+12 \\ -2+2 & 2-2 & 3 \end{bmatrix} = \begin{bmatrix} 1 & 0 & 0 \\ 0 & 1 & 0 \\ 0 & 0 & 1 \end{bmatrix}$

7. $AB = \begin{bmatrix} 2 & 0 & 1 & 1 \\ 3 & 0 & 0 & 1 \\ -1 & 1 & -2 & 1 \\ 4 & -1 & 1 & 0 \end{bmatrix} \begin{bmatrix} -1 & 2 & -1 & -1 \\ -4 & 9 & -5 & -6 \\ 0 & 1 & -1 & -1 \\ 3 & -5 & 3 & 3 \end{bmatrix} = \begin{bmatrix} 1 & 0 & 0 & 0 \\ 0 & 1 & 0 & 0 \\ 0 & 0 & 1 & 0 \\ 0 & 0 & 0 & 1 \end{bmatrix}$

$BA = \begin{bmatrix} -1 & 2 & -1 & -1 \\ -4 & 9 & -5 & -6 \\ 0 & 1 & -1 & -1 \\ 3 & -5 & 3 & 3 \end{bmatrix} \begin{bmatrix} 2 & 0 & 1 & 1 \\ 3 & 0 & 0 & 1 \\ -1 & 1 & -2 & 1 \\ 4 & -1 & 1 & 0 \end{bmatrix} = \begin{bmatrix} 1 & 0 & 0 & 0 \\ 0 & 1 & 0 & 0 \\ 0 & 0 & 1 & 0 \\ 0 & 0 & 0 & 1 \end{bmatrix}$

9. $[A \;\vdots\; I] = \begin{bmatrix} 2 & 0 & \vdots & 1 & 0 \\ 0 & 3 & \vdots & 0 & 1 \end{bmatrix}$

$\begin{matrix} \frac{1}{2}R_1 \to \\ \frac{1}{3}R_2 \to \end{matrix} \begin{bmatrix} 1 & 0 & \vdots & \frac{1}{2} & 0 \\ 0 & 1 & \vdots & 0 & \frac{1}{3} \end{bmatrix} = [I \;\vdots\; A^{-1}]$

$A^{-1} = \begin{bmatrix} \frac{1}{2} & 0 \\ 0 & \frac{1}{3} \end{bmatrix} = \frac{1}{6} \begin{bmatrix} 3 & 0 \\ 0 & 2 \end{bmatrix}$

11. $[A \;\vdots\; I] = \begin{bmatrix} 1 & -2 & \vdots & 1 & 0 \\ 2 & -3 & \vdots & 0 & 1 \end{bmatrix}$

$-2R_1 + R_2 \to \begin{bmatrix} 1 & -2 & \vdots & 1 & 0 \\ 0 & 1 & \vdots & -2 & 1 \end{bmatrix}$

$2R_2 + R_1 \to \begin{bmatrix} 1 & 0 & \vdots & -3 & 2 \\ 0 & 1 & \vdots & -2 & 1 \end{bmatrix} = [I \;\vdots\; A^{-1}]$

$A^{-1} = \begin{bmatrix} -3 & 2 \\ -2 & 1 \end{bmatrix}$

13. $[A \ \vdots \ I] = \begin{bmatrix} -1 & 1 & \vdots & 1 & 0 \\ -2 & 1 & \vdots & 0 & 1 \end{bmatrix}$

$-2R_1 + R_2 \rightarrow \begin{bmatrix} -1 & 1 & \vdots & 1 & 0 \\ 0 & -1 & \vdots & -2 & 1 \end{bmatrix}$

$R_2 + R_1 \rightarrow \begin{bmatrix} -1 & 0 & \vdots & -1 & 1 \\ 0 & -1 & \vdots & -2 & 1 \end{bmatrix}$

$\begin{matrix} -R_1 \rightarrow \\ -R_2 \rightarrow \end{matrix} \begin{bmatrix} 1 & 0 & \vdots & 1 & -1 \\ 0 & 1 & \vdots & 2 & -1 \end{bmatrix} = [I \ \vdots \ A^{-1}]$

$A^{-1} = \begin{bmatrix} 1 & -1 \\ 2 & -1 \end{bmatrix}$

15. $[A \ \vdots \ I] = \begin{bmatrix} 2 & 4 & \vdots & 1 & 0 \\ 4 & 8 & \vdots & 0 & 1 \end{bmatrix}$

$-2R_1 + R_2 \rightarrow \begin{bmatrix} 2 & 4 & \vdots & 1 & 0 \\ 0 & 0 & \vdots & -2 & 1 \end{bmatrix}$

The two zeros in the second row imply that the inverse does not exist.

17. $A = \begin{bmatrix} 2 & 7 & 1 \\ -3 & -9 & 2 \end{bmatrix}$

A has no inverse because it is not square.

19. $\begin{bmatrix} 1 & 1 & 1 & \vdots & 1 & 0 & 0 \\ 3 & 5 & 4 & \vdots & 0 & 1 & 0 \\ 3 & 6 & 5 & \vdots & 0 & 0 & 1 \end{bmatrix}$

$\begin{matrix} -3R_1 + R_2 \rightarrow \\ -3R_1 + R_3 \rightarrow \end{matrix} \begin{bmatrix} 1 & 1 & 1 & \vdots & 1 & 0 & 0 \\ 0 & 2 & 1 & \vdots & -3 & 1 & 0 \\ 0 & 3 & 2 & \vdots & -3 & 0 & 1 \end{bmatrix}$

$\begin{matrix} -R_2 + R_1 \rightarrow \\ \frac{1}{2}R_2 \rightarrow \\ -3R_2 + R_3 \rightarrow \end{matrix} \begin{bmatrix} 1 & 0 & \frac{1}{2} & \vdots & \frac{5}{2} & -\frac{1}{2} & 0 \\ 0 & 1 & \frac{1}{2} & \vdots & -\frac{3}{2} & \frac{1}{2} & 0 \\ 0 & 0 & \frac{1}{2} & \vdots & \frac{3}{2} & -\frac{3}{2} & 1 \end{bmatrix}$

$\begin{matrix} -R_3 + R_1 \rightarrow \\ -R_3 + R_2 \rightarrow \\ 2R_3 \rightarrow \end{matrix} \begin{bmatrix} 1 & 0 & 0 & \vdots & 1 & 1 & -1 \\ 0 & 1 & 0 & \vdots & -3 & 2 & -1 \\ 0 & 0 & 1 & \vdots & 3 & -3 & 2 \end{bmatrix}$

$A^{-1} = \begin{bmatrix} 1 & 1 & -1 \\ -3 & 2 & -1 \\ 3 & -3 & 2 \end{bmatrix}$

21. $[A \; \vdots \; I] = \begin{bmatrix} 1 & 0 \cdot & 0 & \vdots & 1 & 0 & 0 \\ 3 & 4 & 0 & \vdots & 0 & 1 & 0 \\ 2 & 5 & 5 & \vdots & 0 & 0 & 1 \end{bmatrix}$

$\begin{matrix} -3R_1 + R_2 \rightarrow \\ -2R_1 + R_3 \rightarrow \end{matrix} \begin{bmatrix} 1 & 0 & 0 & \vdots & 1 & 0 & 0 \\ 0 & 4 & 0 & \vdots & -3 & 1 & 0 \\ 0 & 5 & 5 & \vdots & -2 & 0 & 1 \end{bmatrix}$

$-\frac{5}{4}R_2 + R_3 \rightarrow \begin{bmatrix} 1 & 0 & 0 & \vdots & 1 & 0 & 0 \\ 0 & 4 & 0 & \vdots & -3 & 1 & 0 \\ 0 & 0 & 5 & \vdots & \frac{7}{4} & -\frac{5}{4} & 1 \end{bmatrix}$

$\begin{matrix} \frac{1}{4}R_2 \rightarrow \\ \frac{1}{5}R_3 \rightarrow \end{matrix} \begin{bmatrix} 1 & 0 & 0 & \vdots & 1 & 0 & 0 \\ 0 & 1 & 0 & \vdots & -\frac{3}{4} & \frac{1}{4} & 0 \\ 0 & 0 & 1 & \vdots & \frac{7}{20} & -\frac{1}{4} & \frac{1}{5} \end{bmatrix} = [I \; \vdots \; A^{-1}]$

$A^{-1} = \frac{1}{20} \begin{bmatrix} 20 & 0 & 0 \\ -15 & 5 & 0 \\ 7 & -5 & 4 \end{bmatrix} = \begin{bmatrix} 1 & 0 & 0 \\ -0.75 & 0.25 & 0 \\ 0.35 & -0.25 & 0.2 \end{bmatrix}$

23. $[A \; \vdots \; I] = \begin{bmatrix} -8 & 0 & 0 & 0 & \vdots & 1 & 0 & 0 & 0 \\ 0 & 1 & 0 & 0 & \vdots & 0 & 1 & 0 & 0 \\ 0 & 0 & 4 & 0 & \vdots & 0 & 0 & 1 & 0 \\ 0 & 0 & 0 & -5 & \vdots & 0 & 0 & 0 & 1 \end{bmatrix}$

$\begin{matrix} -\frac{1}{8}R_1 \rightarrow \\ \\ \frac{1}{4}R_3 \rightarrow \\ -\frac{1}{5}R_4 \rightarrow \end{matrix} \begin{bmatrix} 1 & 0 & 0 & 0 & \vdots & -\frac{1}{8} & 0 & 0 & 0 \\ 0 & 1 & 0 & 0 & \vdots & 0 & 1 & 0 & 0 \\ 0 & 0 & 1 & 0 & \vdots & 0 & 0 & \frac{1}{4} & 0 \\ 0 & 0 & 0 & 1 & \vdots & 0 & 0 & 0 & -\frac{1}{5} \end{bmatrix} = [I \; \vdots \; A^{-1}]$

$A^{-1} = \begin{bmatrix} -\frac{1}{8} & 0 & 0 & 0 \\ 0 & 1 & 0 & 0 \\ 0 & 0 & \frac{1}{4} & 0 \\ 0 & 0 & 0 & -\frac{1}{5} \end{bmatrix}$

25. $A = \begin{bmatrix} 1 & 2 & -1 \\ 3 & 7 & -10 \\ -5 & -7 & -15 \end{bmatrix}$

$A^{-1} = \begin{bmatrix} -175 & 37 & -13 \\ 95 & -20 & 7 \\ 14 & -3 & 1 \end{bmatrix}$

27. $A = \begin{bmatrix} 1 & 1 & 2 \\ 3 & 1 & 0 \\ -2 & 0 & 3 \end{bmatrix}$

$A^{-1} = \frac{1}{2} \begin{bmatrix} -3 & 3 & 2 \\ 9 & -7 & -6 \\ -2 & 2 & 2 \end{bmatrix}$

29. $A = \begin{bmatrix} 0.1 & 0.2 & 0.3 \\ -0.3 & 0.2 & 0.2 \\ 0.5 & 0.4 & 0.4 \end{bmatrix}$

$A^{-1} = \frac{5}{11} \begin{bmatrix} 0 & -4 & 2 \\ -22 & 11 & 11 \\ 22 & -6 & -8 \end{bmatrix}$

31. $A = \begin{bmatrix} 1 & 0 & 3 & 0 \\ 0 & 2 & 0 & 4 \\ 1 & 0 & 3 & 0 \\ 0 & 2 & 0 & 4 \end{bmatrix}$

A^{-1} does not exist.

33. $A = \begin{bmatrix} 1 & -2 & -1 & -2 \\ 3 & -5 & -2 & -3 \\ 2 & -5 & -2 & -5 \\ -1 & 4 & 4 & 11 \end{bmatrix}$

$A^{-1} = \begin{bmatrix} -24 & 7 & 1 & -2 \\ -10 & 3 & 0 & -1 \\ -29 & 7 & 3 & -2 \\ 12 & -3 & -1 & 1 \end{bmatrix}$

35. $AA^{-1} = \begin{bmatrix} a & b \\ c & d \end{bmatrix} \left(\dfrac{1}{ad-bc} \right) \begin{bmatrix} d & -b \\ -c & a \end{bmatrix} = \dfrac{1}{ad-bc} \begin{bmatrix} a & b \\ c & d \end{bmatrix} \begin{bmatrix} d & -b \\ -c & a \end{bmatrix}$

$= \dfrac{1}{ad-bc} \begin{bmatrix} ad-bc & 0 \\ 0 & ad-bc \end{bmatrix} = \begin{bmatrix} 1 & 0 \\ 0 & 1 \end{bmatrix}$

$A^{-1}A = \dfrac{1}{ad-bc} \begin{bmatrix} d & -b \\ -c & a \end{bmatrix} \begin{bmatrix} a & b \\ c & d \end{bmatrix} = \dfrac{1}{ad-bc} \begin{bmatrix} ad-bc & 0 \\ 0 & ad-bc \end{bmatrix} = \begin{bmatrix} 1 & 0 \\ 0 & 1 \end{bmatrix}$

37. $\begin{bmatrix} x \\ y \end{bmatrix} = \begin{bmatrix} -3 & 2 \\ -2 & 1 \end{bmatrix} \begin{bmatrix} 5 \\ 10 \end{bmatrix} = \begin{bmatrix} 5 \\ 0 \end{bmatrix}$

Answer: $(5, 0)$

39. $\begin{bmatrix} x \\ y \end{bmatrix} = \begin{bmatrix} -3 & 2 \\ -2 & 1 \end{bmatrix} = \begin{bmatrix} 4 \\ 2 \end{bmatrix} = \begin{bmatrix} -8 \\ -6 \end{bmatrix}$

Answer: $(-8, -6)$

41. $\begin{bmatrix} x \\ y \\ z \end{bmatrix} = \begin{bmatrix} 1 & 1 & -1 \\ -3 & 2 & -1 \\ 3 & -3 & 2 \end{bmatrix} \begin{bmatrix} 0 \\ 5 \\ 2 \end{bmatrix} = \begin{bmatrix} 3 \\ 8 \\ -11 \end{bmatrix}$

Answer: $(3, 8, -11)$

43. $\begin{bmatrix} x_1 \\ x_2 \\ x_3 \\ x_4 \end{bmatrix} = \begin{bmatrix} -24 & 7 & 1 & -2 \\ -10 & 3 & 0 & -1 \\ -29 & 7 & 3 & -2 \\ 12 & -3 & -1 & 1 \end{bmatrix} \begin{bmatrix} 0 \\ 1 \\ -1 \\ 2 \end{bmatrix} = \begin{bmatrix} 2 \\ 1 \\ 0 \\ 0 \end{bmatrix}$

Answer: $(2, 1, 0, 0)$

45. $A = \begin{bmatrix} 3 & 4 \\ 5 & 3 \end{bmatrix}$

$A^{-1} = \dfrac{1}{9-20} \begin{bmatrix} 3 & -4 \\ -5 & 3 \end{bmatrix}$

$\begin{bmatrix} x \\ y \end{bmatrix} = -\dfrac{1}{11} \begin{bmatrix} 3 & -4 \\ -5 & 3 \end{bmatrix} \begin{bmatrix} -2 \\ 4 \end{bmatrix} = -\dfrac{1}{11} \begin{bmatrix} -22 \\ 22 \end{bmatrix} = \begin{bmatrix} 2 \\ -2 \end{bmatrix}$

Answer: $(2, -2)$

47. $A = \begin{bmatrix} -0.4 & 0.8 \\ 2 & -4 \end{bmatrix}$

$A^{-1} = \dfrac{1}{1.6-1.6} \begin{bmatrix} -4 & -0.8 \\ -2 & -0.4 \end{bmatrix}$

A^{-1} does not exist.

No solution

49. $A = \begin{bmatrix} 3 & 6 \\ 6 & 14 \end{bmatrix}$

$A^{-1} = \dfrac{1}{42-36} \begin{bmatrix} 14 & -6 \\ -6 & 3 \end{bmatrix}$

$\begin{bmatrix} x \\ y \end{bmatrix} = \dfrac{1}{6} \begin{bmatrix} 14 & -6 \\ -6 & 3 \end{bmatrix} \begin{bmatrix} 6 \\ 11 \end{bmatrix} = \dfrac{1}{6} \begin{bmatrix} 18 \\ -3 \end{bmatrix} = \begin{bmatrix} 3 \\ -\frac{1}{2} \end{bmatrix}$

Answer: $\left(3, -\frac{1}{2}\right)$

51. $A = \begin{bmatrix} 4 & -1 & 1 \\ 2 & 2 & 3 \\ 5 & -2 & 6 \end{bmatrix}$

$A^{-1} = \frac{1}{55}\begin{bmatrix} 18 & 4 & -5 \\ 3 & 19 & -10 \\ -14 & 3 & 10 \end{bmatrix}$

$\begin{bmatrix} x \\ y \\ z \end{bmatrix} = \frac{1}{55}\begin{bmatrix} 18 & 4 & -5 \\ 3 & 19 & -10 \\ -14 & 3 & 10 \end{bmatrix}\begin{bmatrix} -5 \\ 10 \\ 1 \end{bmatrix} = \frac{1}{55}\begin{bmatrix} -55 \\ 165 \\ 110 \end{bmatrix} = \begin{bmatrix} -1 \\ 3 \\ 2 \end{bmatrix}$

Answer: $(-1, 3, 2)$

53. $A = \begin{bmatrix} 5 & -3 & 2 \\ 2 & 2 & -3 \\ 1 & -7 & 8 \end{bmatrix}$ A^{-1} does not exist.

No solution

55. $A = \begin{bmatrix} 7 & -3 & 0 & 2 \\ -2 & 1 & 0 & -1 \\ 4 & 0 & 1 & -2 \\ -1 & 1 & 0 & -1 \end{bmatrix}$

$A^{-1} = \begin{bmatrix} 0 & -1 & 0 & 1 \\ -1 & -5 & 0 & 3 \\ -2 & -4 & 1 & -2 \\ -1 & -4 & 0 & 1 \end{bmatrix}$

$\begin{bmatrix} x \\ y \\ z \\ w \end{bmatrix} = \begin{bmatrix} 0 & -1 & 0 & 1 \\ -1 & -5 & 0 & 3 \\ -2 & -4 & 1 & -2 \\ -1 & -4 & 0 & 1 \end{bmatrix}\begin{bmatrix} 41 \\ -13 \\ 12 \\ -8 \end{bmatrix} = \begin{bmatrix} 5 \\ 0 \\ -2 \\ 3 \end{bmatrix}$

Answer: $(5, 0, -2, 3)$

For 57–59 use $A = \begin{bmatrix} 1 & 1 & 1 \\ 0.065 & 0.07 & 0.09 \\ 0 & 2 & -1 \end{bmatrix}$ Using the methods of this section, we have $A^{-1} = \frac{1}{11}\begin{bmatrix} 50 & -600 & -4 \\ -13 & 200 & 5 \\ -26 & 400 & -1 \end{bmatrix}$

57. $X = A^{-1}B = \frac{1}{11}\begin{bmatrix} 50 & -600 & -4 \\ -13 & 200 & 5 \\ -26 & 400 & -1 \end{bmatrix}\begin{bmatrix} 25,000 \\ 1900 \\ 0 \end{bmatrix} = \begin{bmatrix} 10,000 \\ 5000 \\ 10,000 \end{bmatrix}$

Answer: $10,000 in AAA bonds, $5000 in A bonds, $10,000 in B bonds

59. $X = A^{-1}B = \frac{1}{11}\begin{bmatrix} 50 & -600 & -4 \\ -13 & 200 & 5 \\ -26 & 400 & -1 \end{bmatrix}\begin{bmatrix} 12,000 \\ 835 \\ 0 \end{bmatrix} = \begin{bmatrix} 9000 \\ 1000 \\ 2000 \end{bmatrix}$

Answer: $9000 in AAA bonds, $1000 in A bonds, $2000 in B bonds

61. The inverse matrix remained the same for each system.

63. $A = \begin{bmatrix} 2 & 0 & 4 \\ 0 & 1 & 4 \\ 1 & 1 & -1 \end{bmatrix}$

$A^{-1} = \frac{1}{14} \begin{bmatrix} 5 & -4 & 4 \\ -4 & 6 & 8 \\ 1 & 2 & -2 \end{bmatrix}$

$\begin{bmatrix} I_1 \\ I_2 \\ I_3 \end{bmatrix} = \frac{1}{14} \begin{bmatrix} 5 & -4 & 4 \\ -4 & 6 & 8 \\ 1 & 2 & -2 \end{bmatrix} \begin{bmatrix} 14 \\ 10 \\ 0 \end{bmatrix} = \begin{bmatrix} -3 \\ 8 \\ 5 \end{bmatrix}$

Answer: $I_1 = -3$ amps, $I_2 = 8$ amps, $I_3 = 5$ amps

65. (a) Given $A = \begin{bmatrix} a_{11} & 0 \\ 0 & a_{22} \end{bmatrix}$, $A^{-1} = \begin{bmatrix} \dfrac{1}{a_{11}} & 0 \\ 0 & \dfrac{1}{a_{22}} \end{bmatrix}$

Given $A = \begin{bmatrix} a_{11} & 0 & 0 \\ 0 & a_{22} & 0 \\ 0 & 0 & a_{33} \end{bmatrix}$ $A^{-1} = \begin{bmatrix} \dfrac{1}{a_{11}} & 0 & 0 \\ 0 & \dfrac{1}{a_{22}} & 0 \\ 0 & 0 & \dfrac{1}{a_{33}} \end{bmatrix}$

(b) In general, the inverse of the diagonal matrix A is

$$\begin{bmatrix} \dfrac{1}{a_{11}} & 0 & 0 & \cdots & 0 \\ 0 & \dfrac{1}{a_{22}} & 0 & \cdots & 0 \\ 0 & 0 & \dfrac{1}{a_{33}} & \cdots & 0 \\ \vdots & \vdots & \vdots & \cdots & \vdots \\ 0 & 0 & 0 & \cdots & \dfrac{1}{a_{33}} \end{bmatrix}$$

67. Men: $s = 1.279 - 0.0049(22) \approx 1.171$ minutes

Women: $s = 1.411 - 0.0078(22) \approx 1.239$ minutes

69. $3^{x/2} = 315$

$\ln 3^{x/2} = \ln 315$

$\dfrac{x}{2} \ln 3 = \ln 315$

$x = \dfrac{2 \ln 315}{\ln 3} \approx 10.47$

71. $\log_2 x - 2 = 4.5$

$\log_2 x = 6.5$

$x = 2^{6.5} \approx 90.51$

Section 8.4   The Determinant of a Square Matrix

- You should be able to determine the determinant of a matrix of order 2×2 by using the products of the diagonals.
- You should be able to use expansion by cofactors to find the determinant of a matrix of order 3 or greater.
- The determinant of a triangular matrix equals the product of the entries on the main diagonal.

Solutions to Odd-Numbered Exercises

1. 5

3. $\begin{vmatrix} 2 & 1 \\ 3 & 4 \end{vmatrix} = 2(4) - 1(3) = 8 - 3 = 5$

5. $\begin{vmatrix} 5 & 2 \\ -6 & 3 \end{vmatrix} = 5(3) - 2(-6) = 15 + 12 = 27$

7. $\begin{vmatrix} -7 & 6 \\ \frac{1}{2} & 3 \end{vmatrix} = -7(3) - 6\left(\frac{1}{2}\right) = -21 - 3 = -24$

9. $\begin{vmatrix} 2 & 6 \\ 0 & 3 \end{vmatrix} = 2(3) - 6(0) = 6$

11. $\begin{vmatrix} 2 & -1 & 0 \\ 4 & 2 & 1 \\ 4 & 2 & 1 \end{vmatrix} = 2\begin{vmatrix} 2 & 1 \\ 2 & 1 \end{vmatrix} - 4\begin{vmatrix} -1 & 0 \\ 2 & 1 \end{vmatrix} + 4\begin{vmatrix} -1 & 0 \\ 2 & 1 \end{vmatrix} = 2(0) - 4(-1) + 4(-1) = 0$

13. $\begin{vmatrix} 6 & 3 & -7 \\ 0 & 0 & 0 \\ 4 & -6 & 3 \end{vmatrix} = 0\begin{vmatrix} 3 & -7 \\ -6 & 3 \end{vmatrix} - 0\begin{vmatrix} 6 & -7 \\ 4 & 3 \end{vmatrix} + 0\begin{vmatrix} 6 & 3 \\ 4 & -6 \end{vmatrix} = 0$

15. $\begin{vmatrix} -1 & 2 & 5 \\ 0 & 3 & 4 \\ 0 & 0 & 3 \end{vmatrix} = (-1)(3)(3) = -9$ (Upper Triangular)

17. $\begin{vmatrix} 0.3 & 0.2 & 0.2 \\ 0.2 & 0.2 & 0.2 \\ -0.4 & 0.4 & 0.3 \end{vmatrix} = -0.002$

19. $\begin{vmatrix} 1 & 4 & -2 \\ 3 & 6 & -6 \\ -2 & 1 & 4 \end{vmatrix} = 0$

21. $\begin{bmatrix} 3 & 4 \\ 2 & -5 \end{bmatrix}$

(a) $M_{11} = -5$

$M_{12} = 2$

$M_{21} = 4$

$M_{22} = 3$

(b) $C_{11} = M_{11} = -5$

$C_{12} = -M_{12} = -2$

$C_{21} = -M_{21} = -4$

$C_{22} = M_{22} = 3$

23. $\begin{bmatrix} 3 & -2 & 8 \\ 3 & 2 & -6 \\ -1 & 3 & 6 \end{bmatrix}$

(a) $M_{11} = \begin{vmatrix} 2 & -6 \\ 3 & 6 \end{vmatrix} = 12 + 18 = 30$

$M_{12} = \begin{vmatrix} 3 & -6 \\ -1 & 6 \end{vmatrix} = 18 - 6 = 12$

$M_{13} = \begin{vmatrix} 3 & 2 \\ -1 & 3 \end{vmatrix} = 9 + 2 = 11$

$M_{21} = \begin{vmatrix} -2 & 8 \\ 3 & 6 \end{vmatrix} = -12 - 24 = -36$

$M_{22} = \begin{vmatrix} 3 & 8 \\ -1 & 6 \end{vmatrix} = 18 + 8 = 26$

$M_{23} = \begin{vmatrix} 3 & -2 \\ -1 & 3 \end{vmatrix} = 9 - 2 = 7$

$M_{31} = \begin{vmatrix} -2 & 8 \\ 2 & -6 \end{vmatrix} = 12 - 16 = -4$

$M_{32} = \begin{vmatrix} 3 & 8 \\ 3 & -6 \end{vmatrix} = -18 - 24 = -42$

$M_{33} = \begin{vmatrix} 3 & -2 \\ 3 & 2 \end{vmatrix} = 6 + 6 = 12$

(b) $C_{11} = (-1)^2 M_{11} = 30$

$C_{12} = (-1)^3 M_{12} = -12$

$C_{13} = (-1)^4 M_{13} = 11$

$C_{21} = (-1)^3 M_{21} = 36$

$C_{22} = (-1)^4 M_{22} = 26$

$C_{23} = (-1)^5 M_{23} = -7$

$C_{31} = (-1)^4 M_{31} = -4$

$C_{32} = (-1)^5 M_{32} = 42$

$C_{33} = (-1)^6 M_{33} = 12$

25. (a) $\begin{vmatrix} -3 & 2 & 1 \\ 4 & 5 & 6 \\ 2 & -3 & 1 \end{vmatrix} = -3\begin{vmatrix} 5 & 6 \\ -3 & 1 \end{vmatrix} - 2\begin{vmatrix} 4 & 6 \\ 2 & 1 \end{vmatrix} + \begin{vmatrix} 4 & 5 \\ 2 & -3 \end{vmatrix} = -3(23) - 2(-8) - 22 = -75$

(b) $\begin{vmatrix} -3 & 2 & 1 \\ 4 & 5 & 6 \\ 2 & -3 & 1 \end{vmatrix} = -2\begin{vmatrix} 4 & 6 \\ 2 & 1 \end{vmatrix} + 5\begin{vmatrix} -3 & 1 \\ 2 & 1 \end{vmatrix} + 3\begin{vmatrix} -3 & 1 \\ 4 & 6 \end{vmatrix} = -2(-8) + 5(-5) + 3(-22) = -75$

27. (a) $\begin{vmatrix} 5 & 0 & -3 \\ 0 & 12 & 4 \\ 1 & 6 & 3 \end{vmatrix} = 0\begin{vmatrix} 0 & -3 \\ 6 & 3 \end{vmatrix} + 12\begin{vmatrix} 5 & -3 \\ 1 & 3 \end{vmatrix} - 4\begin{vmatrix} 5 & 0 \\ 1 & 6 \end{vmatrix} = 0(18) + 12(18) - 4(30) = 96$

(b) $\begin{vmatrix} 5 & 0 & -3 \\ 0 & 12 & 4 \\ 1 & 6 & 3 \end{vmatrix} = 0\begin{vmatrix} 0 & 4 \\ 1 & 3 \end{vmatrix} + 12\begin{vmatrix} 5 & -3 \\ 1 & 3 \end{vmatrix} - 6\begin{vmatrix} 5 & -3 \\ 0 & 4 \end{vmatrix} = 0(-4) + 12(18) - 6(20) = 96$

29. (a)
$$\begin{vmatrix} 6 & 0 & -3 & 5 \\ 4 & 13 & 6 & -8 \\ -1 & 0 & 7 & 4 \\ 8 & 6 & 0 & 2 \end{vmatrix} = -4\begin{vmatrix} 0 & -3 & 5 \\ 0 & 7 & 4 \\ 6 & 0 & 2 \end{vmatrix} + 13\begin{vmatrix} 6 & -3 & 5 \\ -1 & 7 & 4 \\ 8 & 0 & 2 \end{vmatrix} - 6\begin{vmatrix} 6 & 0 & 5 \\ -1 & 0 & 4 \\ 8 & 6 & 2 \end{vmatrix} - 8\begin{vmatrix} 6 & 0 & -3 \\ -1 & 0 & 7 \\ 8 & 6 & 0 \end{vmatrix}$$

$$= -4(-282) + 13(-298) - 6(-174) - 8(-234) = 170$$

(b)
$$\begin{vmatrix} 6 & 0 & -3 & 5 \\ 4 & 13 & 6 & -8 \\ -1 & 0 & 7 & 4 \\ 8 & 6 & 0 & 2 \end{vmatrix} = 0\begin{vmatrix} 4 & 6 & -8 \\ -1 & 7 & 4 \\ 8 & 0 & 2 \end{vmatrix} + 13\begin{vmatrix} 6 & -3 & 5 \\ -1 & 7 & 4 \\ 8 & 0 & 2 \end{vmatrix} + 0\begin{vmatrix} 6 & -3 & 5 \\ 4 & 6 & -8 \\ 8 & 0 & 2 \end{vmatrix} + 6\begin{vmatrix} 6 & -3 & 5 \\ 4 & 6 & -8 \\ -1 & 7 & 4 \end{vmatrix}$$

$$= 0 + 13(-298) + 0 + 6(674) = 170$$

31. Expand by Column 3.

$$\begin{vmatrix} 1 & 4 & -2 \\ 3 & 2 & 0 \\ -1 & 4 & 3 \end{vmatrix} = -2\begin{vmatrix} 3 & 2 \\ -1 & 4 \end{vmatrix} + 3\begin{vmatrix} 1 & 4 \\ 3 & 2 \end{vmatrix} = -2(14) + 3(-10) = -58$$

33.
$$\begin{vmatrix} 2 & 4 & 6 \\ 0 & 3 & 1 \\ 0 & 0 & -5 \end{vmatrix} = (2)(3)(-5) = -30 \quad \text{(Upper Triangular)}$$

35. Expand by Column 3.

$$\begin{vmatrix} 2 & 6 & 6 & 2 \\ 2 & 7 & 3 & 6 \\ 1 & 5 & 0 & 1 \\ 3 & 7 & 0 & 7 \end{vmatrix} = 6\begin{vmatrix} 2 & 7 & 6 \\ 1 & 5 & 1 \\ 3 & 7 & 7 \end{vmatrix} - 3\begin{vmatrix} 2 & 6 & 2 \\ 1 & 5 & 1 \\ 3 & 7 & 7 \end{vmatrix} = 6(-20) - 3(16) = -168$$

37. Expand by Column 1.

$$\begin{vmatrix} 5 & 3 & 0 & 6 \\ 4 & 6 & 4 & 12 \\ 0 & 2 & -3 & 4 \\ 0 & 1 & -2 & 2 \end{vmatrix} = 5\begin{vmatrix} 6 & 4 & 12 \\ 2 & -3 & 4 \\ 1 & -2 & 2 \end{vmatrix} - 4\begin{vmatrix} 3 & 0 & 6 \\ 2 & -3 & 4 \\ 1 & -2 & 2 \end{vmatrix} = 5(0) - 4(0) = 0$$

39. Expand by Column 2, then by Column 4.

$$\begin{vmatrix} 3 & 2 & 4 & -1 & 5 \\ -2 & 0 & 1 & 3 & 2 \\ 1 & 0 & 0 & 4 & 0 \\ 6 & 0 & 2 & -1 & 0 \\ 3 & 0 & 5 & 1 & 0 \end{vmatrix} = -2\begin{vmatrix} -2 & 1 & 3 & 2 \\ 1 & 0 & 4 & 0 \\ 6 & 2 & -1 & 0 \\ 3 & 5 & 1 & 0 \end{vmatrix} = (-2)(-2)\begin{vmatrix} 1 & 0 & 4 \\ 6 & 2 & -1 \\ 3 & 5 & 1 \end{vmatrix} = 4(103) = 412$$

41. $\begin{vmatrix} 3 & 8 & -7 \\ 0 & -5 & 4 \\ 8 & 1 & 6 \end{vmatrix} = -126$

43. $\begin{vmatrix} 7 & 0 & -14 \\ -2 & 5 & 4 \\ -6 & 2 & 12 \end{vmatrix} = 0$

45. $\begin{vmatrix} 1 & -1 & 8 & 4 \\ 2 & 6 & 0 & -4 \\ 2 & 0 & 2 & 6 \\ 0 & 2 & 8 & 0 \end{vmatrix} = -336$

47. $\begin{vmatrix} 3 & -2 & 4 & 3 & 1 \\ -1 & 0 & 2 & 1 & 0 \\ 5 & -1 & 0 & 3 & 2 \\ 4 & 7 & -8 & 0 & 0 \\ 1 & 2 & 3 & 0 & 2 \end{vmatrix} = 410$

49. $\begin{vmatrix} w & x \\ y & z \end{vmatrix} = wz - xy$

$-\begin{vmatrix} y & z \\ w & x \end{vmatrix} = -(xy - wz) = wz - xy$

Thus, $\begin{vmatrix} w & x \\ y & z \end{vmatrix} = -\begin{vmatrix} y & z \\ w & x \end{vmatrix}$.

51. $\begin{vmatrix} w & x \\ y & z \end{vmatrix} = wz - xy$

$\begin{vmatrix} w & x + cw \\ y & z + cy \end{vmatrix} = w(z + cy) - y(x + cw) = wz - xy$

Thus, $\begin{vmatrix} w & x \\ y & z \end{vmatrix} = \begin{vmatrix} w & x + cw \\ y & z + cy \end{vmatrix}$.

53. $\begin{vmatrix} 1 & x & x^2 \\ 1 & y & y^2 \\ 1 & z & z^2 \end{vmatrix} = \begin{vmatrix} y & y^2 \\ z & z^2 \end{vmatrix} - \begin{vmatrix} x & x^2 \\ z & z^2 \end{vmatrix} + \begin{vmatrix} x & x^2 \\ y & y^2 \end{vmatrix}$

$= (yz^2 - y^2z) - (xz^2 - x^2z) + (xy^2 - x^2y)$
$= yz^2 - xz^2 - y^2z + x^2z + xy(y - x)$
$= z^2(y - x) - z(y^2 - x^2) + xy(y - x)$
$= z^2(y - x) - z(y - x)(y + x) + xy(y - x)$
$= (y - x)[z^2 - z(y + x) + xy]$
$= (y - x)[z^2 - zy - zx + xy]$
$= (y - x)[z^2 - zx - zy + xy]$
$= (y - x)[z(z - x) - y(z - x)]$
$= (y - x)(z - x)(z - y)$

55. $= \begin{vmatrix} x - 1 & 2 \\ 3 & x - 2 \end{vmatrix} = 0$

$(x - 1)(x - 2) - 6 = 0$
$x^2 - 3x - 4 = 0$
$(x + 1)(x - 4) = 0$
$x = -1 \text{ or } x = 4$

57. $\begin{vmatrix} 4u & -1 \\ -1 & 2v \end{vmatrix} = 8uv - 1$

59. $\begin{vmatrix} e^{2x} & e^{3x} \\ 2e^{2x} & 3e^{3x} \end{vmatrix} = 3e^{5x} - 2e^{5x} = e^{5x}$

61. $\begin{vmatrix} x & \ln x \\ 1 & \dfrac{1}{x} \end{vmatrix} = 1 - \ln x$

63. (a) $\begin{vmatrix} -1 & 0 \\ 0 & 3 \end{vmatrix} = -3$ (b) $\begin{vmatrix} 2 & 0 \\ 0 & -1 \end{vmatrix} = -2$

(c) $\begin{bmatrix} -1 & 0 \\ 0 & 3 \end{bmatrix} \begin{bmatrix} 2 & 0 \\ 0 & -1 \end{bmatrix} = \begin{bmatrix} -2 & 0 \\ 0 & -3 \end{bmatrix}$ (d) $\begin{vmatrix} -2 & 0 \\ 0 & -3 \end{vmatrix} = 6$

65. (a) $\begin{vmatrix} -1 & 2 & 1 \\ 1 & 0 & 1 \\ 0 & 1 & 0 \end{vmatrix} = 2$ (b) $\begin{vmatrix} -1 & 0 & 0 \\ 0 & 2 & 0 \\ 0 & 0 & 3 \end{vmatrix} = -6$

(c) $\begin{bmatrix} -1 & 2 & 1 \\ 1 & 0 & 1 \\ 0 & 1 & 0 \end{bmatrix} \begin{bmatrix} -1 & 0 & 0 \\ 0 & 2 & 0 \\ 0 & 0 & 3 \end{bmatrix} = \begin{bmatrix} 1 & 4 & 3 \\ -1 & 0 & 3 \\ 0 & 2 & 0 \end{bmatrix}$

(d) $\begin{vmatrix} 1 & 4 & 3 \\ -1 & 0 & 3 \\ 0 & 2 & 0 \end{vmatrix} = -12$

67. Let $A = \begin{bmatrix} 1 & 3 \\ -2 & 4 \end{bmatrix}$ and $B = \begin{bmatrix} -4 & 0 \\ 3 & 5 \end{bmatrix}$.

$|A| = \begin{vmatrix} 1 & 3 \\ -2 & 4 \end{vmatrix} = 10, \; |B| = \begin{vmatrix} -4 & 0 \\ 3 & 5 \end{vmatrix} = -20, \; |A| + |B| = -10$

$A + B = \begin{bmatrix} -3 & 3 \\ 1 & 9 \end{bmatrix}, \; |A + B| = \begin{vmatrix} -3 & 3 \\ 1 & 9 \end{vmatrix} = -30$

Thus, $|A + B| \neq |A| + |B|$. Your answer may differ, depending on how you choose A and B.

69. A square matrix is a square array of numbers. A determinant of a square matrix is a real number.

71. Parabola

Vertex: $(0, 3)$

Focus: $(2, 3)$

Horizontal axis: $(y - k)^2 = 4p(x - h)$

$p = 2$

$(y - 3)^2 = 4(2)(x - 0)$

$(y - 3)^2 = 8x$

73. Ellipse

Vertices: $(\pm 8, 0)$

Foci: $(\pm 6, 0)$

Horizontal major axis

Center: $(0, 0)$

$a = 8, c = 6, b = \sqrt{64 - 36} = \sqrt{28}$

$\dfrac{x^2}{a^2} + \dfrac{y^2}{b^2} = 1$

$\dfrac{x^2}{64} + \dfrac{y^2}{28} = 1$

Section 8.5   Applications of Matrices and Determinants

■ You should be able to use Cramer's Rule to solve a system of linear equations.

■ Now you should be able to solve a system of linear equations by substitution, elimination, elementary row operations on an augmented matrix, using the inverse matrix, or Cramer's Rule.

■ You should be able to find the area of a triangle with vertices (x_1, y_1), (x_2, y_2), and (x_3, y_3).

$$\text{Area} = \pm\frac{1}{2}\begin{vmatrix} x_1 & y_1 & 1 \\ x_2 & y_2 & 1 \\ x_3 & y_3 & 1 \end{vmatrix}$$

The $\pm$ symbol indicates that the appropriate sign should be chosen so that the area is positive.

■ You should be able to test to see if three points, (x_1, y_1), (x_2, y_2), and (x_3, y_3), are collinear.

$$\begin{vmatrix} x_1 & y_1 & 1 \\ x_2 & y_2 & 1 \\ x_3 & y_3 & 1 \end{vmatrix} = 0, \text{ if and only if they are collinear.}$$

■ You should be able to find the equation of the line through (x_1, y_1) and (x_2, y_2) by evaluating.

$$\begin{vmatrix} x & y & 1 \\ x_1 & y_1 & 1 \\ x_2 & y_2 & 1 \end{vmatrix} = 0$$

■ You should be able to encode and decode messages by using an invertible $n \times n$ matrix.

Solutions to Odd-Numbered Exercises

1. $3x + 4y = -2$

$5x + 3y = 4$

$$x = \dfrac{\begin{vmatrix} -2 & 4 \\ 4 & 3 \end{vmatrix}}{\begin{vmatrix} 3 & 4 \\ 5 & 3 \end{vmatrix}} = \dfrac{-22}{-11} = 2$$

$$y = \dfrac{\begin{vmatrix} 3 & -2 \\ 5 & 4 \end{vmatrix}}{\begin{vmatrix} 3 & 4 \\ 5 & 3 \end{vmatrix}} = -\dfrac{22}{11} = -2$$

Answer: $(2, -2)$

3. $4x - y + z = -5$

$2x + 2y + 3z = 10$

$5x - 2y + 6z = 1$

$$D = \begin{vmatrix} 4 & -1 & 1 \\ 2 & 2 & 3 \\ 5 & -2 & 6 \end{vmatrix} = 55$$

$$x = \dfrac{\begin{vmatrix} -5 & -1 & 1 \\ 10 & 2 & 3 \\ 1 & -2 & 6 \end{vmatrix}}{55} = \dfrac{-55}{55} = -1$$

$$y = \dfrac{\begin{vmatrix} 4 & -5 & 1 \\ 2 & 10 & 3 \\ 5 & 1 & 6 \end{vmatrix}}{55} = \dfrac{165}{55} = 3$$

$$z = \dfrac{\begin{vmatrix} 4 & -1 & -5 \\ 2 & 2 & 10 \\ 5 & -2 & 1 \end{vmatrix}}{55} = \dfrac{110}{55} = 2$$

Answer: $(-1, 3, 2)$

5. $3x + 3y + 5z = 1$
$3x + 5y + 9z = 2$ $D = \begin{vmatrix} 3 & 3 & 5 \\ 3 & 5 & 9 \\ 5 & 9 & 17 \end{vmatrix} = 4$
$5x + 9y + 17z = 4$

$$x = \dfrac{\begin{vmatrix} 1 & 3 & 5 \\ 2 & 5 & 9 \\ 4 & 9 & 17 \end{vmatrix}}{4} = 0, \quad y = \dfrac{\begin{vmatrix} 3 & 1 & 5 \\ 3 & 2 & 9 \\ 5 & 4 & 17 \end{vmatrix}}{4} = -\dfrac{1}{2}, \quad z = \dfrac{\begin{vmatrix} 3 & 3 & 1 \\ 3 & 5 & 2 \\ 5 & 9 & 4 \end{vmatrix}}{4} = \dfrac{1}{2}$$

Answer: $\left(0, -\frac{1}{2}, \frac{1}{2}\right)$

7. Vertices: $(0, 0), \ (3, 1), \ (1, 5)$

$$\text{Area} = \frac{1}{2}\begin{vmatrix} 0 & 0 & 1 \\ 3 & 1 & 1 \\ 1 & 5 & 1 \end{vmatrix} = \frac{1}{2}\begin{vmatrix} 3 & 1 \\ 1 & 5 \end{vmatrix} = 7 \text{ square units}$$

9. Vertices: $(-2, -3), \ (2, -3), \ (0, 4)$

$$\text{Area} = \frac{1}{2}\begin{vmatrix} -2 & -3 & 1 \\ 2 & -3 & 1 \\ 0 & 4 & 1 \end{vmatrix} = \frac{1}{2}\left(-2\begin{vmatrix} -3 & 1 \\ 4 & 1 \end{vmatrix} - 2\begin{vmatrix} -3 & 1 \\ 4 & 1 \end{vmatrix}\right) = \frac{1}{2}(14 + 14) = 14 \text{ square units}$$

11. Vertices: $\left(0, \frac{1}{2}\right), \ \left(\frac{5}{2}, 0\right), \ (4, 3)$

$$\text{Area} = \frac{1}{2}\begin{vmatrix} 0 & \frac{1}{2} & 1 \\ \frac{5}{2} & 0 & 1 \\ 4 & 3 & 1 \end{vmatrix} = \frac{1}{2}\left(2 + \frac{15}{2} - \frac{5}{4}\right) = \frac{33}{8} \text{ square units}$$

13. Vertices: $(-2, 4), \ (2, 3), \ (-1, 5)$

$$\text{Area} = \frac{1}{2}\begin{vmatrix} -2 & 4 & 1 \\ 2 & 3 & 1 \\ -1 & 5 & 1 \end{vmatrix} = \frac{1}{2}\left[\begin{vmatrix} 2 & 3 \\ -1 & 5 \end{vmatrix} - \begin{vmatrix} -2 & 4 \\ -1 & 5 \end{vmatrix} + \begin{vmatrix} -2 & 4 \\ 2 & 3 \end{vmatrix}\right] = \frac{5}{2} \text{ square units}$$

15. Vertices: $(-3, 5), \ (2, 6), \ (3, -5)$

$$\text{Area} = -\frac{1}{2}\begin{vmatrix} -3 & 5 & 1 \\ 2 & 6 & 1 \\ 3 & -5 & 1 \end{vmatrix} = -\frac{1}{2}\left[\begin{vmatrix} 2 & 6 \\ 3 & -5 \end{vmatrix} - \begin{vmatrix} -3 & 5 \\ 3 & -5 \end{vmatrix} + \begin{vmatrix} -3 & 5 \\ 2 & 6 \end{vmatrix}\right] = 28 \text{ square units}$$

17. $4 = \pm\dfrac{1}{2}\begin{vmatrix} -5 & 1 & 1 \\ 0 & 2 & 1 \\ -2 & x & 1 \end{vmatrix}$

$\pm 8 = -5\begin{vmatrix} 2 & 1 \\ x & 1 \end{vmatrix} - 2\begin{vmatrix} 1 & 1 \\ 2 & 1 \end{vmatrix}$

$\pm 8 = -5(2 - x) - 2(-1)$

$\pm 8 = 5x - 8$

$x = \dfrac{8 \pm 8}{5}$

$x = \dfrac{16}{5}$ OR $x = 0$

19. Vertices: $(0, 25)$, $(10, 0)$, $(28, 5)$

Area $= \dfrac{1}{2}\begin{vmatrix} 0 & 25 & 1 \\ 10 & 0 & 1 \\ 28 & 5 & 1 \end{vmatrix} = 250$ square miles

21. Points: $(3, -1)$, $(0, -3)$, $(12, 5)$

$\begin{vmatrix} 3 & -1 & 1 \\ 0 & -3 & 1 \\ 12 & 5 & 1 \end{vmatrix} = 3\begin{vmatrix} -3 & 1 \\ 5 & 1 \end{vmatrix} + 12\begin{vmatrix} -1 & 1 \\ -3 & 1 \end{vmatrix} = 0$

The points are collinear.

23. Points: $\left(2, -\frac{1}{2}\right)$, $(-4, 4)$, $(6, -3)$

$\begin{vmatrix} 2 & -\frac{1}{2} & 1 \\ -4 & 4 & 1 \\ 6 & -3 & 1 \end{vmatrix} = \begin{vmatrix} -4 & 4 \\ 6 & -3 \end{vmatrix} - \begin{vmatrix} 2 & -\frac{1}{2} \\ 6 & -3 \end{vmatrix} + \begin{vmatrix} 2 & -\frac{1}{2} \\ -4 & 4 \end{vmatrix} = -3 \neq 0$

The points are not collinear.

25. Points: $(0, 2)$, $(1, 2.4)$, $(-1, 1.6)$

$\begin{vmatrix} 0 & 2 & 1 \\ 1 & 2.4 & 1 \\ -1 & 1.6 & 1 \end{vmatrix} = -2\begin{vmatrix} 1 & 1 \\ -1 & 1 \end{vmatrix} + \begin{vmatrix} 1 & 2.4 \\ -1 & 1.6 \end{vmatrix} = 0$

The points are collinear.

27. Points: $(0, 0)$, $(5, 3)$

Equation: $\begin{vmatrix} x & y & 1 \\ 0 & 0 & 1 \\ 5 & 3 & 1 \end{vmatrix} = 5y - 3x = 0 \Rightarrow 3x - 5y = 0$

29. Points: $(-4, 3)$, $(2, 1)$

Equation: $\begin{vmatrix} x & y & 1 \\ -4 & 3 & 1 \\ 2 & 1 & 1 \end{vmatrix} = 2x - 6y - 10 = 0 \Rightarrow x + 3y - 5 = 0$

31. Points: $\left(-\frac{1}{2}, 3\right)$, $\left(\frac{5}{2}, 1\right)$

Equation: $\begin{vmatrix} x & y & 1 \\ -\frac{1}{2} & 3 & 1 \\ \frac{5}{2} & 1 & 1 \end{vmatrix} = 2x + 3y - 8 = 0$

33. $\begin{vmatrix} 2 & -5 & 1 \\ 4 & x & 1 \\ 5 & -2 & 1 \end{vmatrix} = 0$

$2\begin{vmatrix} x & 1 \\ -2 & 1 \end{vmatrix} + 5\begin{vmatrix} 4 & 1 \\ 5 & 1 \end{vmatrix} + \begin{vmatrix} 4 & x \\ 5 & -2 \end{vmatrix} = 0$

$2(x + 2) + 5(-1) + (-8 - 5x) = 0$

$$-3x - 9 = 0$$

$$x = -3$$

35. The uncoded row matrices are the rows of the 7×3 matrix on the left.

$$
\begin{matrix}
\text{T} & \text{R} & 0 \\
\text{U} & \text{B} & \text{L} \\
\text{E} & & \text{I} \\
\text{N} & & \text{R} \\
\text{I} & \text{V} & \text{E} \\
\text{R} & & \text{C} \\
\text{I} & \text{T} & \text{Y}
\end{matrix}
\begin{bmatrix}
20 & 18 & 15 \\
21 & 2 & 12 \\
5 & 0 & 9 \\
14 & 0 & 18 \\
9 & 22 & 5 \\
18 & 0 & 3 \\
9 & 20 & 25
\end{bmatrix}
\begin{bmatrix}
1 & -1 & 0 \\
1 & 0 & -1 \\
-6 & 2 & 3
\end{bmatrix}
=
\begin{bmatrix}
-52 & 10 & 27 \\
-49 & 3 & 34 \\
-49 & 13 & 27 \\
-94 & 22 & 54 \\
1 & 1 & -7 \\
0 & -12 & 9 \\
-121 & 41 & 55
\end{bmatrix}
$$

Answer: $[-52, 10, 27], [-49, 3, 34], [-49, 13, 27], [-94, 22, 54], [1, 1, -7], [0, -12, 9], [-121, 41, 55]$

In Exercises 37–39, use the matrix $A = \begin{bmatrix} 1 & 2 & 2 \\ 3 & 7 & 9 \\ -1 & -4 & -7 \end{bmatrix}$.

37. L A N   D I N G _ S U C C   E S S   F U L

[12 1 14] [4 9 14] [7 0 19] [21 3 3] [5 19 19] [6 21 12]

$[12 \quad 1 \quad 14] A = [\quad 1 \quad -25 \quad -65]$

$[4 \quad 9 \quad 14] A = [\quad 17 \quad 15 \quad -9]$

$[7 \quad 0 \quad 19] A = [-12 \quad -62 \quad -119]$

$[21 \quad 3 \quad 3] A = [\quad 27 \quad 51 \quad 48]$

$[5 \quad 19 \quad 19] A = [\quad 43 \quad 67 \quad 48]$

$[6 \quad 21 \quad 12] A = [\quad 57 \quad 111 \quad 117]$

Cryptogram: 1 −25 −65 17 15 −9 −12 −62 −119 27 51 48 43 67 48 57 111 117

39. H A P P Y _ B I R T H D A Y _

[8 1 16] [16 25 0] [2 9 18] [20 8 4] [1 25 0]

$[\,8\quad 1\quad 16\,]\,A = [\,5\quad -41\quad -87\,]$

$[\,16\quad 25\quad 0\,]\,A = [\,91\quad 207\quad 257\,]$

$[\,2\quad 9\quad 18\,]\,A = [\,11\quad -5\quad -41\,]$

$[\,20\quad 8\quad 4\,]\,A = [\,40\quad 80\quad 84\,]$

$[\,1\quad 25\quad 0\,]\,A = [\,76\quad 177\quad 227\,]$

Cryptogram: -5 -41 -87 91 207 257 11 -5 -41 40 80 84 76 177 227

41. $A^{-1} = \begin{bmatrix} 1 & 2 \\ 3 & 5 \end{bmatrix}^{-1} = \begin{bmatrix} -5 & 2 \\ 3 & -1 \end{bmatrix}$

$\begin{bmatrix} 11 & 21 \\ 64 & 112 \\ 25 & 50 \\ 29 & 53 \\ 23 & 46 \\ 40 & 75 \\ 55 & 92 \end{bmatrix} \begin{bmatrix} -5 & 2 \\ 3 & -1 \end{bmatrix} = \begin{bmatrix} 8 & 1 \\ 16 & 16 \\ 25 & 0 \\ 14 & 5 \\ 23 & 0 \\ 25 & 5 \\ 1 & 18 \end{bmatrix}$
H A
P P
Y
N E
W
Y E
A R

Message: HAPPY NEW YEAR

43. $A^{-1} = \begin{bmatrix} 1 & 2 & 2 \\ 3 & 7 & 9 \\ -1 & -4 & -7 \end{bmatrix}^{-1} = \begin{bmatrix} -13 & 6 & 4 \\ 12 & -5 & -3 \\ -5 & 2 & 1 \end{bmatrix}$

$\begin{bmatrix} 20 & 17 & -15 \\ -12 & -56 & -104 \\ 1 & -25 & -65 \\ 62 & 143 & 181 \end{bmatrix} \begin{bmatrix} -13 & 6 & 4 \\ 12 & -5 & -3 \\ -5 & 2 & 1 \end{bmatrix} = \begin{bmatrix} 19 & 5 & 14 \\ 4 & 0 & 16 \\ 12 & 1 & 14 \\ 5 & 19 & 0 \end{bmatrix}$
S E N
D P
L A N
E S

Message: SEND PLANES

45. Let A be the 2×2 matrix needed to decode the message.

$\begin{bmatrix} -18 & -18 \\ 1 & 16 \end{bmatrix} A = \begin{bmatrix} 0 & 18 \\ 15 & 14 \end{bmatrix}$ R
O N

$A = \begin{bmatrix} -18 & -18 \\ 1 & 16 \end{bmatrix}^{-1} \begin{bmatrix} 0 & 18 \\ 15 & 14 \end{bmatrix} = \begin{bmatrix} -\frac{8}{135} & -\frac{1}{15} \\ \frac{1}{270} & \frac{1}{15} \end{bmatrix} \begin{bmatrix} 0 & 18 \\ 15 & 14 \end{bmatrix} = \begin{bmatrix} -1 & -2 \\ 1 & 1 \end{bmatrix}$

$\begin{bmatrix} 8 & 21 \\ -15 & -10 \\ -13 & -13 \\ 5 & 10 \\ 5 & 25 \\ 5 & 19 \\ -1 & 6 \\ 20 & 40 \\ -18 & -18 \\ 1 & 16 \end{bmatrix} \begin{bmatrix} -1 & -2 \\ 1 & 1 \end{bmatrix} = \begin{bmatrix} 13 & 5 \\ 5 & 20 \\ 0 & 13 \\ 5 & 0 \\ 20 & 15 \\ 14 & 9 \\ 7 & 8 \\ 20 & 0 \\ 0 & 18 \\ 15 & 14 \end{bmatrix}$
M E
E T
 M
E
T O
N I
G H
T
 R
O N

Message: MEET ME TONIGHT RON

☐ Review Exercises for Chapter 8

Solutions to Odd-Numbered Exercises

1. $\begin{bmatrix} 3 & -10 & \vdots & 15 \\ 5 & 4 & \vdots & 22 \end{bmatrix}$

3. $\begin{bmatrix} 5 & 1 & 7 & \vdots & -9 \\ 4 & 2 & 0 & \vdots & 10 \\ 9 & 4 & 2 & \vdots & 3 \end{bmatrix}$ $\quad \begin{aligned} 5x + y + 7z &= -9 \\ 4x + 2y &= 10 \\ 9x + 4y + 2z &= 3 \end{aligned}$

5. $\begin{bmatrix} 0 & 1 & 1 \\ 1 & 2 & 3 \\ 2 & 2 & 2 \end{bmatrix}$

$\begin{array}{l} R_1 + R_2 \to \\ -R_1 + R_2 \to \\ -2R_1 + R_3 \to \end{array} \begin{bmatrix} 1 & 3 & 4 \\ 0 & -1 & -1 \\ 0 & -4 & -6 \end{bmatrix}$

$\begin{array}{l} 3R_2 + R_1 \to \\ -R_2 \to \\ -4R_2 + R_3 \to \end{array} \begin{bmatrix} 1 & 0 & 1 \\ 0 & 1 & 1 \\ 0 & 0 & -2 \end{bmatrix}$

$\begin{array}{l} -R_3 + R_1 \to \\ -R_3 + R_2 \to \\ -\frac{1}{2}R_3 \to \end{array} \begin{bmatrix} 1 & 0 & 0 \\ 0 & 1 & 0 \\ 0 & 0 & 1 \end{bmatrix}$

7. $\begin{bmatrix} 5 & 4 & \vdots & 2 \\ -1 & 1 & \vdots & -22 \end{bmatrix}$

$\begin{array}{l} 4R_2 + R_1 \to \\ R_1 + R_2 \to \end{array} \begin{bmatrix} 1 & 8 & \vdots & -86 \\ 0 & 9 & \vdots & -108 \end{bmatrix}$

$\begin{array}{l} -8R_2 + R_1 \to \\ \frac{1}{9}R_2 \to \end{array} \begin{bmatrix} 1 & 0 & \vdots & 10 \\ 0 & 1 & \vdots & -12 \end{bmatrix}$

$x = 10, \ y = -12$

Answer: $(10, -12)$

9. $\begin{bmatrix} 2 & 1 & \vdots & 0.3 \\ 3 & -1 & \vdots & -1.3 \end{bmatrix}$

$\begin{array}{l} R_2 - R_1 \to \\ -3R_1 + R_2 \to \end{array} \begin{bmatrix} 1 & -2 & \vdots & -1.6 \\ 0 & 5 & \vdots & 3.5 \end{bmatrix}$

$\begin{array}{l} 2R_2 + R_1 \to \\ \frac{1}{5}R_2 \to \end{array} \begin{bmatrix} 1 & 0 & \vdots & -0.2 \\ 0 & 1 & \vdots & 0.7 \end{bmatrix}$

$x = -0.2, \ y = 0.7$

Answer: $(-0.2, 0.7)$

11. $\begin{bmatrix} -1 & 1 & 2 & \vdots & 1 \\ 2 & 3 & 1 & \vdots & -2 \\ 5 & 4 & 2 & \vdots & 4 \end{bmatrix}$

$\begin{array}{l} -R_1 \to \\ 2R_1 + R_2 \to \\ 5R_1 + R_3 \to \end{array} \begin{bmatrix} 1 & -1 & -2 & \vdots & -1 \\ 0 & 5 & 5 & \vdots & 0 \\ 0 & 9 & 12 & \vdots & 9 \end{bmatrix}$

$\begin{array}{l} R_2 + R_1 \to \\ \frac{1}{5}R_2 \to \\ -9R_2 + R_3 \to \end{array} \begin{bmatrix} 1 & 0 & -1 & \vdots & -1 \\ 0 & 1 & 1 & \vdots & 0 \\ 0 & 0 & 3 & \vdots & 9 \end{bmatrix}$

$\begin{array}{l} R_3 + R_1 \to \\ -R_3 + R_2 \to \\ \frac{1}{3}R_3 \to \end{array} \begin{bmatrix} 1 & 0 & 0 & \vdots & 2 \\ 0 & 1 & 0 & \vdots & -3 \\ 0 & 0 & 1 & \vdots & 3 \end{bmatrix}$

$x = 2, \ y = -3, \ z = 3$

Answer: $(2, \ -3, \ 3)$

13. $\begin{bmatrix} 4 & 4 & 4 & \vdots & 5 \\ 4 & -2 & -8 & \vdots & 1 \\ 5 & 3 & 8 & \vdots & 6 \end{bmatrix}$

$\begin{array}{l} R_3 - R_1 \to \\ -4R_1 + R_2 \to \\ -5R_1 + R_3 \to \end{array} \begin{bmatrix} 1 & -1 & 4 & \vdots & 1 \\ 0 & 2 & -24 & \vdots & -3 \\ 0 & 8 & -12 & \vdots & 1 \end{bmatrix}$

$\begin{array}{l} R_2 + R_1 \to \\ \frac{1}{2}R_2 \to \\ -8R_2 + R_3 \to \end{array} \begin{bmatrix} 1 & 0 & -8 & \vdots & -\frac{1}{2} \\ 0 & 1 & -12 & \vdots & -\frac{3}{2} \\ 0 & 0 & 84 & \vdots & 13 \end{bmatrix}$

$\begin{array}{l} 8R_3 + R_1 \to \\ 12R_3 + R_2 \to \\ \frac{1}{84}R_3 \to \end{array} \begin{bmatrix} 1 & 0 & 0 & \vdots & \frac{31}{42} \\ 0 & 1 & 0 & \vdots & \frac{5}{14} \\ 0 & 0 & 1 & \vdots & \frac{13}{84} \end{bmatrix}$

$x = \frac{31}{42}, \ y = \frac{5}{14}, \ z = \frac{13}{84}$

Answer: $\left(\frac{31}{42}, \frac{5}{14}, \frac{13}{84} \right)$

15.
$$\begin{bmatrix} 2 & 1 & 2 & \vdots & 4 \\ 2 & 2 & 0 & \vdots & 5 \\ 2 & -1 & 6 & \vdots & 2 \end{bmatrix}$$

$$\begin{matrix} \\ -R_1 + R_2 \rightarrow \\ -R_1 + R_3 \rightarrow \end{matrix} \begin{bmatrix} 2 & 1 & 2 & \vdots & 4 \\ 0 & 1 & -2 & \vdots & 1 \\ 0 & -2 & 4 & \vdots & -2 \end{bmatrix}$$

$$\begin{matrix} -R_2 + R_1 \rightarrow \\ \\ 2R_2 + R_3 \rightarrow \end{matrix} \begin{bmatrix} 2 & 0 & 4 & \vdots & 3 \\ 0 & 1 & -2 & \vdots & 1 \\ 0 & 0 & 0 & \vdots & 0 \end{bmatrix}$$

Let $z = a$, then:

$y - 2a = 1 \implies y = 2a + 1$

$2x + 4a = 3 \implies x = -2a + \frac{3}{2}$

Answer: $\left(-2a + \frac{3}{2}, 2a + 1, a\right)$

17.
$$\begin{bmatrix} 1 & 2 & 6 & \vdots & 1 \\ 2 & 5 & 15 & \vdots & 4 \\ 3 & 1 & 3 & \vdots & -6 \end{bmatrix}$$

$$\begin{matrix} \\ -2R_1 + R_2 \rightarrow \\ -3R_1 + R_3 \rightarrow \end{matrix} \begin{bmatrix} 1 & 2 & 6 & \vdots & 1 \\ 0 & 1 & 3 & \vdots & 2 \\ 0 & -5 & -15 & \vdots & -9 \end{bmatrix}$$

$$\begin{matrix} -2R_2 + R_1 \rightarrow \\ \\ 5R_2 + R_3 \rightarrow \end{matrix} \begin{bmatrix} 1 & 0 & 0 & \vdots & -3 \\ 0 & 1 & 3 & \vdots & 2 \\ 0 & 0 & 0 & \vdots & 1 \end{bmatrix}$$

$x = -3$

$y + 3z = 2$

$0 = 1$

Inconsistent, no solution

19. If a system of linear equations has a unique solution, the augmented matrix reduces to a form in which the number of rows with nonzero entries on the coefficient side of the matrix equals the number of variables.

21. $\begin{bmatrix} 2 & 1 & 0 \\ 0 & 5 & -4 \end{bmatrix} - 3\begin{bmatrix} 5 & 3 & -6 \\ 0 & -2 & 5 \end{bmatrix} = \begin{bmatrix} 2 & 1 & 0 \\ 0 & 5 & -4 \end{bmatrix} - \begin{bmatrix} 15 & 9 & -18 \\ 0 & -6 & 15 \end{bmatrix}$

$= \begin{bmatrix} -13 & -8 & 18 \\ 0 & 11 & -19 \end{bmatrix}$

23. $\begin{bmatrix} 1 & 2 \\ 5 & -4 \\ 6 & 0 \end{bmatrix}\begin{bmatrix} 6 & -2 & 8 \\ 4 & 0 & 0 \end{bmatrix} = \begin{bmatrix} 1(6) + 2(4) & 1(-2) + 2(0) & 1(8) + 2(0) \\ 5(6) + (-4)(4) & 5(-2) + (-4)(0) & 5(8) + (-4)(0) \\ 6(6) + (0)(4) & 6(-2) + (0)(0) & 6(8) + (0)(0) \end{bmatrix}$

$= \begin{bmatrix} 14 & -2 & 8 \\ 14 & -10 & 40 \\ 36 & -12 & 48 \end{bmatrix}$

25. $\begin{bmatrix} 1 & 5 & 6 \\ 2 & -4 & 0 \end{bmatrix}\begin{bmatrix} 6 & 4 \\ -2 & 0 \\ 8 & 0 \end{bmatrix} = \begin{bmatrix} 1(6) + 5(-2) + 6(8) & 1(4) + 5(0) + 6(0) \\ 2(6) - 4(-2) + 0(8) & 2(4) - 4(0) + 0(0) \end{bmatrix}$

$= \begin{bmatrix} 44 & 4 \\ 20 & 8 \end{bmatrix}$

27. $\begin{bmatrix} 1 & 3 & 2 \\ 0 & 2 & -4 \\ 0 & 0 & 3 \end{bmatrix}\begin{bmatrix} 4 & -3 & 2 \\ 0 & 3 & -1 \\ 0 & 0 & 2 \end{bmatrix} = \begin{bmatrix} 1(4) & 1(-3) + 3(3) & 1(2) + 3(-1) + 2(2) \\ 0 & 2(3) & 2(-1) + (-4)(2) \\ 0 & 0 & 3(2) \end{bmatrix}$

$= \begin{bmatrix} 4 & 6 & 3 \\ 0 & 6 & -10 \\ 0 & 0 & 6 \end{bmatrix}$

29. $3\begin{bmatrix} 8 & -2 & 5 \\ 1 & 3 & -1 \end{bmatrix} + 6\begin{bmatrix} 4 & -2 & -3 \\ 2 & 7 & 6 \end{bmatrix} = \begin{bmatrix} 48 & -18 & -3 \\ 15 & 51 & 33 \end{bmatrix}$

31. $\begin{bmatrix} 4 & 1 \\ 11 & -7 \\ 12 & 3 \end{bmatrix}\begin{bmatrix} 3 & -5 & 6 \\ 2 & -2 & -2 \end{bmatrix} = \begin{bmatrix} 14 & -22 & 22 \\ 19 & -41 & 80 \\ 42 & -66 & 66 \end{bmatrix}$

33. $X = 3A - 2B = 3\begin{bmatrix} -4 & 0 \\ 1 & -5 \\ -3 & 2 \end{bmatrix} - 2\begin{bmatrix} 1 & 2 \\ -2 & 1 \\ 4 & 4 \end{bmatrix} = \begin{bmatrix} -14 & -4 \\ 7 & -17 \\ -17 & -2 \end{bmatrix}$

35. $X = \frac{1}{3}[B - 2A] = \frac{1}{3}\left(\begin{bmatrix} 1 & 2 \\ -2 & 1 \\ 4 & 4 \end{bmatrix} - 2\begin{bmatrix} -4 & 0 \\ 1 & -5 \\ -3 & 2 \end{bmatrix}\right) = \frac{1}{3}\begin{bmatrix} 9 & 2 \\ -4 & 11 \\ 10 & 0 \end{bmatrix}$

37. $\begin{bmatrix} 5 & 4 \\ -1 & 1 \end{bmatrix}\begin{bmatrix} x \\ y \end{bmatrix} = \begin{bmatrix} 2 \\ -22 \end{bmatrix}$

$\begin{bmatrix} 5x + 4y \\ -x + y \end{bmatrix} = \begin{bmatrix} 2 \\ -22 \end{bmatrix}$

$5x + 4y = 2$

$-x + 4y = -22$

39. $\begin{bmatrix} 2 & 6 \\ 3 & -6 \end{bmatrix}^{-1} = \begin{bmatrix} \frac{1}{5} & \frac{1}{5} \\ \frac{1}{10} & -\frac{1}{15} \end{bmatrix}$

41. $\begin{bmatrix} 2 & 0 & 3 \\ -1 & 1 & 1 \\ 2 & -2 & 1 \end{bmatrix}^{-1} = \begin{bmatrix} \frac{1}{2} & -1 & -\frac{1}{2} \\ \frac{1}{2} & -\frac{2}{3} & -\frac{5}{6} \\ 0 & \frac{2}{3} & \frac{1}{3} \end{bmatrix}$

43. $\begin{vmatrix} 50 & -30 \\ 10 & 5 \end{vmatrix} = 50(5) - (-30)(10) = 550$

45. $\begin{vmatrix} 3 & 0 & -4 & 0 \\ 0 & 8 & 1 & 2 \\ 6 & 1 & 8 & 2 \\ 0 & 3 & -4 & 1 \end{vmatrix} = 3\begin{vmatrix} 8 & 1 & 2 \\ 1 & 8 & 2 \\ 3 & -4 & 1 \end{vmatrix} + (-4)\begin{vmatrix} 0 & 8 & 2 \\ 6 & 1 & 2 \\ 0 & 3 & 1 \end{vmatrix}$ (Expansion along Row 1)

$= 3[8(8 - (-8)) - 1(1 - 6) + 2(-4 - 24)] - 4[0 - 6(8 - 6) + 0]$

$= 3[128 + 5 - 56] - 4[-12]$

$= 279$

47. $x + 2y = -1$

$3x + 4y = -5$

$\begin{bmatrix} 1 & 2 \\ 3 & 4 \end{bmatrix}^{-1} = \begin{bmatrix} -2 & 1 \\ \frac{3}{2} & -\frac{1}{2} \end{bmatrix}$

$\begin{bmatrix} x \\ y \end{bmatrix} = \begin{bmatrix} -2 & 1 \\ \frac{3}{2} & -\frac{1}{2} \end{bmatrix}\begin{bmatrix} -1 \\ -5 \end{bmatrix} = \begin{bmatrix} -3 \\ 1 \end{bmatrix}$

$x = -3, y = 1$

Answer: $(-3, 1)$

49. $-3x - 3y - 4z = 2$

$y + z = -1$

$4x + 3y + 4z = -1$

$\begin{bmatrix} -3 & -3 & -4 \\ 0 & 1 & 1 \\ 4 & 3 & 4 \end{bmatrix}^{-1} = \begin{bmatrix} 1 & 0 & 1 \\ 4 & 4 & 3 \\ -4 & -3 & -3 \end{bmatrix}$

$\begin{bmatrix} x \\ y \\ z \end{bmatrix} = \begin{bmatrix} 1 & 0 & 1 \\ 4 & 4 & 3 \\ -4 & -3 & -3 \end{bmatrix}\begin{bmatrix} 2 \\ -1 \\ -1 \end{bmatrix} = \begin{bmatrix} 1 \\ 1 \\ -2 \end{bmatrix}$

$x = 1, y = 1, z = -2$

Answer: $(1, 1, -2)$

51.
$$x + 3y + 2z = 2$$
$$-2x - 5y - z = 10$$
$$2x + 4y = -12$$

$$\begin{bmatrix} 1 & 3 & 2 \\ -2 & -5 & -1 \\ 2 & 4 & 0 \end{bmatrix}^{-1} = \begin{bmatrix} 2 & 4 & \frac{7}{2} \\ -1 & -2 & -\frac{3}{2} \\ 1 & 1 & \frac{1}{2} \end{bmatrix}$$

$$\begin{bmatrix} x \\ y \\ z \end{bmatrix} = \begin{bmatrix} 1 & 0 & 1 \\ 4 & 4 & 3 \\ -4 & -3 & -3 \end{bmatrix} \begin{bmatrix} 2 \\ -1 \\ -1 \end{bmatrix} = \begin{bmatrix} 1 \\ 1 \\ -2 \end{bmatrix}$$

$$x = 2, y = -4, z = 6$$

Answer: $(2, -4, 6)$

53.
$$-x + y + z = 6$$
$$4x - 3y + z = 20$$
$$2x - y + 3z = 8$$

$$\begin{bmatrix} -1 & 1 & 1 \\ 4 & -3 & 1 \\ 2 & -1 & 3 \end{bmatrix}^{-1} \text{ does not exist}$$

The system is inconsistent and has no solution.

55. x = number of carnations, y = number of roses

$$x + y = 12$$
$$0.75x + 1.50y = 12.00$$

$$x = \frac{\begin{vmatrix} 12 & 1 \\ 12 & 1.50 \end{vmatrix}}{\begin{vmatrix} 1 & 1 \\ 0.75 & 1.50 \end{vmatrix}} = \frac{6}{0.75} = 8$$

$$y = \frac{\begin{vmatrix} 1 & 12 \\ 0.75 & 12 \end{vmatrix}}{\begin{vmatrix} 1 & 1 \\ 0.75 & 1.50 \end{vmatrix}} = \frac{3}{0.75} = 4$$

Answer: 8 carnations, 4 roses

57. $(-1, 2), (0, 3), (1, 6)$

$$f(x) = ax^2 + bx + c$$
$$f(-1) = a - b + c = 2$$
$$f(0) = c = 3$$
$$f(1) = a + b + c = 6$$

$$D = \begin{vmatrix} 1 & -1 & 1 \\ 0 & 0 & 1 \\ 1 & 1 & 1 \end{vmatrix} = -2$$

$$a = \frac{\begin{vmatrix} 2 & -1 & 1 \\ 3 & 0 & 1 \\ 6 & 1 & 1 \end{vmatrix}}{-2} = \frac{-2}{-2} = 1$$

$$b = \frac{\begin{vmatrix} 1 & 2 & 1 \\ 0 & 3 & 1 \\ 1 & 6 & 1 \end{vmatrix}}{-2} = \frac{-4}{-2} = 2; c = 3$$

Thus, $y = x^2 + 2x + 3$.

59.
$$13a + 91b = 1107$$
$$91a + 819b = 8404.7$$

(a) $a \approx 59.9, \ b \approx 3.6$

$$y = 59.9 + 3.6t$$

(b)

(c) The median price of one-family homes sold in the United States has been increasing by an average of 3.6 thousand dollars ($3600) each year.

(d) $y(15) = 59.9 + 3.6(15) = 113.9$ which corresponds to a price of \$113,900.

61. $(1, 0),\ (5, 0),\ (5, 8)$

$$\text{Area} = \frac{1}{2}\begin{vmatrix} 1 & 0 & 1 \\ 5 & 0 & 1 \\ 5 & 8 & 1 \end{vmatrix} = \frac{1}{2}(32)$$

$$= 16 \text{ square units}$$

63. $(1, 2),\ (4, -5),\ (3, 2)$

$$\text{Area} = \frac{1}{2}\begin{vmatrix} 1 & 2 & 1 \\ 4 & -5 & 1 \\ 3 & 1 & 1 \end{vmatrix} = \frac{1}{2}(14)$$

$$= 7 \text{ square units}$$

65. $(-4, 0),\ (4, 4)$

$$\begin{vmatrix} x & y & 1 \\ -4 & 0 & 1 \\ 4 & 4 & 1 \end{vmatrix} = 0$$

$$-4x + 8y - 16 = 0$$

$$x - 2y + 4 = 0$$

67. $\left(-\frac{5}{2}, 3\right),\ \left(\frac{7}{2}, 1\right)$

$$\begin{vmatrix} x & y & 1 \\ -\frac{5}{2} & 3 & 1 \\ \frac{7}{2} & 1 & 1 \end{vmatrix} = 0$$

$$2x + 6y - 13 = 0$$

69. Expansion by Row 3

$$\begin{vmatrix} a_{11} & a_{12} & a_{13} \\ a_{21} & a_{22} & a_{23} \\ a_{31}+c_1 & a_{32}+c_2 & a_{33}+c_3 \end{vmatrix} = (a_{31}+c_1)\begin{vmatrix} a_{12} & a_{13} \\ a_{22} & a_{23} \end{vmatrix} - (a_{32}+c_2)\begin{vmatrix} a_{11} & a_{13} \\ a_{21} & a_{23} \end{vmatrix} + (a_{33}+c_3)\begin{vmatrix} a_{11} & a_{12} \\ a_{21} & a_{22} \end{vmatrix}$$

$$= a_{31}\begin{vmatrix} a_{12} & a_{13} \\ a_{22} & a_{23} \end{vmatrix} - a_{32}\begin{vmatrix} a_{11} & a_{13} \\ a_{21} & a_{23} \end{vmatrix} + a_{33}\begin{vmatrix} a_{11} & a_{12} \\ a_{21} & a_{22} \end{vmatrix} + c_1\begin{vmatrix} a_{12} & a_{13} \\ a_{22} & a_{23} \end{vmatrix}$$

$$- c_2\begin{vmatrix} a_{11} & a_{13} \\ a_{21} & a_{23} \end{vmatrix} + c_3\begin{vmatrix} a_{11} & a_{12} \\ a_{21} & a_{22} \end{vmatrix}$$

$$= \begin{vmatrix} a_{11} & a_{12} & a_{13} \\ a_{21} & a_{22} & a_{23} \\ a_{31} & a_{32} & a_{33} \end{vmatrix} + \begin{vmatrix} a_{11} & a_{12} & a_{13} \\ a_{21} & a_{22} & a_{23} \\ c_1 & c_2 & c_3 \end{vmatrix}$$

Note: Expand each of these matrices by Row 3 to see the previous step.

❑ **Practice Test for Chapter 8**

1. Put the matrix in reduced echelon form.

$$\begin{bmatrix} 1 & -2 & 4 \\ 3 & -5 & 9 \end{bmatrix}$$

For Exercises 2–4, use matrices to solve the system of equations.

2. $3x + 5y = 3$
 $2x - y = -11$

3. $2x + 3y = -3$
 $3x + 2y = 8$
 $x + y = 1$

4. $x + 3z = -5$
 $2x + y = 0$
 $3x + y - z = 3$

5. Multiply $\begin{bmatrix} 1 & 4 & 5 \\ 2 & 0 & -3 \end{bmatrix} \begin{bmatrix} 1 & 6 \\ 0 & -7 \\ -1 & 2 \end{bmatrix}$.

6. Given $A = \begin{bmatrix} 9 & 1 \\ -4 & 8 \end{bmatrix}$ and $B = \begin{bmatrix} 6 & -2 \\ 3 & 5 \end{bmatrix}$, find $3A - 5B$.

7. Find $f(A)$:

$$f(x) = x^2 - 7x + 8, \quad A = \begin{bmatrix} 3 & 0 \\ 7 & 1 \end{bmatrix}.$$

8. True or false:

$(A + B)(A + 3B) = A^2 + 4AB + 3B^2$ where A and B are matrices.

(Assume that A^2, AB, and B^2 exist.)

For Exercises 9–10, find the inverse of the matrix, if it exists.

9. $\begin{bmatrix} 1 & 2 \\ 3 & 5 \end{bmatrix}$

10. $\begin{bmatrix} 1 & 1 & 1 \\ 3 & 6 & 5 \\ 6 & 10 & 8 \end{bmatrix}$

11. Use an inverse matrix to solve the systems.

(a) $x + 2y = 4$
  $3x + 5y = 1$

(b) $x + 2y = 3$
  $3x + 5y = -2$

For Exercises 12–14, find the determinant of the matrix.

12. $\begin{bmatrix} 6 & -1 \\ 3 & 4 \end{bmatrix}$

13. $\begin{bmatrix} 1 & 3 & -1 \\ 5 & 9 & 0 \\ 6 & 2 & -5 \end{bmatrix}$

14. $\begin{bmatrix} 1 & 4 & 2 & 3 \\ 0 & 1 & -2 & 0 \\ 3 & 5 & -1 & 1 \\ 2 & 0 & 6 & 1 \end{bmatrix}$

15. Evaluate $\begin{vmatrix} 6 & 4 & 3 & 0 & 6 \\ 0 & 5 & 1 & 4 & 8 \\ 0 & 0 & 2 & 7 & 3 \\ 0 & 0 & 0 & 9 & 2 \\ 0 & 0 & 0 & 0 & 1 \end{vmatrix}$

16. Use a determinant to find the area of the triangle with vertices $(0, 7)$, $(5, 0)$, and $(3, 9)$.

17. Find the equation of the line through $(2, 7)$ and $(-1, 4)$.

For Exercises 18–20, use Cramer's Rule to find the indicated value.

18. Find x.

$6x - 7y = 4$

$2x + 5y = 11$

19. Find z.

$3x + z = 1$

$ y + 4z = 3$

$x - y = 2$

20. Find y.

$721.4x - 29.1y = 33.77$

$45.9x + 105.6y = 19.85$

CHAPTER 9
Sequences and Probability

CHAPTER 9
Sequences and Probability

Section 9.1   Sequences and Summation Notation

■ Given the general nth term in a sequence, you should be able to find, or list, some of the terms.

■ You should be able to find an expression for the nth term of a sequence.

■ You should be able to use and evaluate factorials.

■ You should be able to use sigma notation for a sum.

Solutions to Odd-Numbered Exercises

1. $a_n = 2n + 1$

$a_1 = 2(1) + 1 = 3$

$a_2 = 2(2) + 1 = 5$

$a_3 = 2(3) + 1 = 7$

$a_4 = 2(4) + 1 = 9$

$a_5 = 2(5) + 1 = 11$

3. $a_n = 2^n$

$a_1 = 2^1 = 2$

$a_2 = 2^2 = 4$

$a_3 = 2^3 = 8$

$a_4 = 2^4 = 16$

$a_5 = 2^5 = 32$

5. $a_n = (-2)^n$

$a_1 = (-2)^1 = -2$

$a_2 = (-2)^2 = 4$

$a_3 = (-2)^3 = -8$

$a_4 = (-2)^4 = 16$

$a_5 = (-2)^5 = -32$

7. $a_n = \dfrac{n+1}{n}$

$a_1 = \dfrac{1+1}{1} = 2$

$a_2 = \dfrac{3}{2}$

$a_3 = \dfrac{4}{3}$

$a_4 = \dfrac{5}{4}$

$a_5 = \dfrac{6}{5}$

9. $a_n = \dfrac{6n}{3n^2 - 1}$

$a_1 = \dfrac{6(1)}{3(1)^2 - 1} = 3$

$a_2 = \dfrac{6(2)}{3(2)^2 - 1} = \dfrac{12}{11}$

$a_3 = \dfrac{6(3)}{3(3)^2 - 1} = \dfrac{9}{13}$

$a_4 = \dfrac{6(4)}{3(4)^2 - 1} = \dfrac{24}{47}$

$a_5 = \dfrac{6(5)}{3(5)^2 - 1} = \dfrac{15}{37}$

11. $a_n = \dfrac{1 + (-1)^n}{n}$

$a_1 = 0$

$a_2 = \dfrac{2}{2} = 1$

$a_3 = 0$

$a_4 = \dfrac{2}{4} = \dfrac{1}{2}$

$a_5 = 0$

13. $a_n = 3 - \dfrac{1}{2^n}$

$a_1 = 3 - \dfrac{1}{2} = \dfrac{5}{2}$

$a_2 = 3 - \dfrac{1}{4} = \dfrac{11}{4}$

$a_3 = 3 - \dfrac{1}{8} = \dfrac{23}{8}$

$a_4 = 3 - \dfrac{1}{16} = \dfrac{47}{16}$

$a_5 = 3 - \dfrac{1}{32} = \dfrac{95}{32}$

15. $a_n = \dfrac{1}{n^{3/2}}$

$a_1 = \dfrac{1}{1} = 1$

$a_2 = \dfrac{1}{2^{3/2}}$

$a_3 = \dfrac{1}{3^{3/2}}$

$a_4 = \dfrac{1}{4^{3/2}} = \dfrac{1}{8}$

$a_5 = \dfrac{1}{5^{3/2}}$

17. $a_n = \dfrac{3^n}{n!}$

$a_1 = \dfrac{3^1}{1!} = \dfrac{3}{1} = 3$

$a_2 = \dfrac{3^2}{2!} = \dfrac{9}{2}$

$a_3 = \dfrac{27}{6} = \dfrac{9}{2}$

$a_4 = \dfrac{81}{24} = \dfrac{27}{8}$

$a_5 = \dfrac{243}{120} = \dfrac{81}{40}$

19. $a_n = \dfrac{(-1)^n}{n^2}$

$a_1 = -\dfrac{1}{1} = -1$

$a_2 = \dfrac{1}{4}$

$a_3 = -\dfrac{1}{9}$

$a_4 = \dfrac{1}{16}$

$a_5 = -\dfrac{1}{25}$

21. $a_n = \dfrac{2}{3}$

$a_1 = \dfrac{2}{3}$

$a_2 = \dfrac{2}{3}$

$a_3 = \dfrac{2}{3}$

$a_4 = \dfrac{2}{3}$

$a_5 = \dfrac{2}{3}$

23. $a_{25} = (-1)^{25}(3(25) - 2) = -73$

25. $a_1 = 28$ and $a_{k+1} = a_k - 4$

$a_1 = 28$

$a_2 = a_1 - 4 = 28 - 4 = 24$

$a_3 = a_2 - 4 = 24 - 4 = 20$

$a_4 = a_3 - 4 = 20 - 4 = 16$

$a_5 = a_4 - 4 = 16 - 4 = 12$

27. $a_1 = 3$ and $a_{k+1} = 2(a_k - 1)$

$a_1 = 3$

$a_2 = 2(a_1 - 1) = 2(3 - 1) = 4$

$a_3 = 2(a_2 - 1) = 2(4 - 1) = 6$

$a_4 = 2(a_3 - 1) = 2(6 - 1) = 10$

$a_5 = 2(a_4 - 1) = 2(10 - 1) = 18$

29. $a_n = \dfrac{2}{3}n$

31. $a_n = 16(-0.5)^{n-1}$

33. $a_n = \dfrac{2n}{n+1}$

35. $a_n = \dfrac{8}{n+1}$

$a_n \to 0$ as $n \to \infty$

$a_1 = 4,\ a_{10} = \dfrac{8}{11}$

Matches graph (c).

37. $a_n = 4(0.5)^{n-1}$

$a_n \to 0$ as $n \to \infty$

$a_1 = 4,\ a_{10} \approx 0.008$

Matches graph (d).

39. $\dfrac{4!}{6!} = \dfrac{4!}{6 \cdot 5 \cdot 4!} = \dfrac{1}{30}$

41. $\dfrac{10!}{8!} = \dfrac{10 \cdot 9 \cdot 8!}{8!} = 90$

43. $\dfrac{(n+1)!}{n!} = \dfrac{(n+1)n!}{n!} = n+1$

45. $\dfrac{(2n-1)!}{(2n+1)!} = \dfrac{(2n-1)!}{(2n+1)(2n)(2n-1)!}$

$= \dfrac{1}{2n(2n+1)}$

47. $1, 4, 7, 10, 13, \ldots$

$a_n = 1 + (n-1)3 = 3n - 2$

49. $0, 3, 8, 15, 24, \ldots$

$a_n = n^2 - 1$

51. $\dfrac{2}{3}, \dfrac{3}{4}, \dfrac{4}{5}, \dfrac{5}{6}, \dfrac{6}{7}, \ldots$

$a_n = \dfrac{n+1}{n+2}$

53. $\dfrac{1}{2}, \dfrac{-1}{4}, \dfrac{1}{8}, \dfrac{-1}{16}, \ldots$

$a_n = \dfrac{(-1)^{n+1}}{2^n}$

55. $1 + \dfrac{1}{1}, 1 + \dfrac{1}{2}, 1 + \dfrac{1}{3}, 1 + \dfrac{1}{4}, 1 + \dfrac{1}{5}, \ldots$

$a_n = 1 + \dfrac{1}{n}$

57. $1, \dfrac{1}{2}, \dfrac{1}{6}, \dfrac{1}{24}, \dfrac{1}{120}, \ldots$

$a_n = \dfrac{1}{n!}$

59. $1, -1, 1, -1, 1, \ldots$

$a_n = (-1)^{n+1}$

61. $a_1 = 6$ and $a_{k+1} = a_k + 2$

$a_1 = 6$

$a_2 = a_1 + 2 = 6 + 2 = 8$

$a_3 = a_2 + 2 = 8 + 2 = 10$

$a_4 = a_3 + 2 = 10 + 2 = 12$

$a_5 = a_4 + 2 = 12 + 2 = 14$

In general, $a_n = 2n + 4$.

63. $a_1 = 81$ and $a_{k+1} = \dfrac{1}{3}a_k$

$a_1 = 81$

$a_2 = \dfrac{1}{3}a_1 = \dfrac{1}{3}(81) = 27$

$a_3 = \dfrac{1}{3}a_2 = \dfrac{1}{3}(27) = 9$

$a_4 = \dfrac{1}{3}a_3 = \dfrac{1}{3}(9) = 3$

$a_5 = \dfrac{1}{3}a_4 = \dfrac{1}{3}(3) = 1$

In general, $a_n = 81\left(\dfrac{1}{3}\right)^{n-1} = 81(3)\left(\dfrac{1}{3}\right)^n = \dfrac{243}{3^n}$.

65. $\displaystyle\sum_{i=1}^{5}(2i+1) = (2+1)+(4+1)+(6+1)+(8+1)+(10+1) = 35$

67. $\displaystyle\sum_{k=1}^{4}10 = 10 + 10 + 10 + 10 = 40$

69. $\displaystyle\sum_{i=0}^{4}i^2 = 0^2 + 1^2 + 2^2 + 3^2 + 4^2 = 30$

71. $\displaystyle\sum_{k=0}^{3}\frac{1}{k^2+1}=\frac{1}{1}+\frac{1}{1+1}+\frac{1}{4+1}+\frac{1}{9+1}=\frac{9}{5}$

73. $\displaystyle\sum_{i=1}^{4}[(i-1)^2+(i+1)^3]=[(0)^2+(2)^3]+[(1)^2+(3)^3]+[(2)^2+(4)^3]+[(3)^2+(5)^3]=238$

75. $\displaystyle\sum_{i=1}^{4}2^i=2^1+2^2+2^3+2^4=30$ **77.** $\displaystyle\sum_{j=1}^{6}(24-3j)=81$

79. $\displaystyle\sum_{k=0}^{4}\frac{(-1)^k}{k+1}=1-\frac{1}{2}+\frac{1}{3}-\frac{1}{4}+\frac{1}{5}=\frac{47}{60}$

81. $\displaystyle\frac{1}{3(1)}+\frac{1}{3(2)}+\frac{1}{3(3)}+\cdots+\frac{1}{3(9)}=\sum_{i=1}^{9}\frac{1}{3i}$

83. $\displaystyle\left[2\left(\frac{1}{8}\right)+3\right]+\left[2\left(\frac{2}{8}\right)+3\right]+\left[2\left(\frac{3}{8}\right)+3\right]+\cdots+\left[2\left(\frac{8}{8}\right)+3\right]=\sum_{i=1}^{8}\left[2\left(\frac{i}{8}\right)+3\right]$

85. $\displaystyle 3-9+27-81+243-729=\sum_{i=1}^{6}(-1)^{i+1}3^i$

87. $\displaystyle\frac{1}{1^2}-\frac{1}{2^2}+\frac{1}{3^2}-\frac{1}{4^2}+\cdots-\frac{1}{20^2}=\sum_{i=1}^{20}\frac{(-1)^{i+1}}{i^2}$

89. $\displaystyle\frac{1}{4}+\frac{3}{8}+\frac{7}{16}+\frac{15}{32}+\frac{31}{64}=\sum_{i=1}^{5}\frac{2^i-1}{2^{i+1}}$

91. $A_n=5000\left(1+\dfrac{0.08}{4}\right)^n$, $n=1,2,3,\ldots$

    (a) $A_1=\$5100.00$

       $A_2=\$5202.00$

       $A_3=\$5306.04$

       $A_4=\$5412.16$

       $A_5=\$5520.40$

       $A_6=\$5630.81$

       $A_7=\$5743.43$

       $A_8=\$5858.30$

    (b) $A_{40}=\$11{,}040.20$

93. $a_n=510.13+16.37n+3.23n^2$, $n=1,\ldots,11$

    $a_1=529.73$

    $a_2=555.79$

    $a_3=588.31$

    $a_4=627.29$

    $a_5=672.73$

    $a_6=724.63$

    $a_7=782.99$

    $a_8=847.81$

    $a_9=919.09$

    $a_{10}=996.83$

    $a_{11}=1081.03$

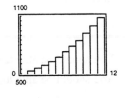

95. $\displaystyle\sum_{n=5}^{14}(129.9+0.9n^3)=\$11{,}131.5$ million

97. $a_1 = 1, a_2 = 1, \ a_{k+2} = a_{k+1} + a_k$

$a_1 = 1$	$b_1 = \frac{1}{1} = 1$
$a_2 = 1$	$b_2 = \frac{2}{1} = 2$
$a_3 = 1 + 1 = 2$	$b_3 = \frac{3}{2}$
$a_4 = 2 + 1 = 3$	$b_4 = \frac{5}{3}$
$a_5 = 3 + 2 = 5$	$b_5 = \frac{8}{5}$
$a_6 = 5 + 3 = 8$	$b_6 = \frac{13}{8}$
$a_7 = 8 + 5 = 13$	$b_7 = \frac{21}{13}$
$a_8 = 13 + 8 = 21$	$b_8 = \frac{34}{21}$
$a_9 = 21 + 13 = 34$	$b_9 = \frac{55}{34}$
$a_{10} = 34 + 21 = 55$	$b_{10} = \frac{89}{55}$
$a_{11} = 55 + 34 = 89$	
$a_{12} = 89 + 55 = 144$	

99. $\dfrac{327.15 + 785.69 + 433.04 + 265.38 + 604.12 + 590.30}{6} \approx \$500.95$

101. $\displaystyle\sum_{i=1}^{n}(x_i - \bar{x}) = \sum_{i=1}^{n} x_i - \sum_{i=1}^{n} \bar{x}$

$\displaystyle \qquad\qquad = \sum_{i=1}^{n} x_i - n\bar{x}$

$\displaystyle \qquad\qquad = \sum_{i=1}^{n} x_i - n\left(\frac{1}{n}\sum_{i=1}^{n} x_i\right)$

$\displaystyle \qquad\qquad = 0$

103. True, $\displaystyle\sum_{i=1}^{4}(i^2 + 2i) = \sum_{i=1}^{4} i^2 + 2\sum_{i=1}^{4} i$

by the properties of sums.

Section 9.2   Arithmetic Sequences

> ■   You should be able to recognize an arithmetic sequence, find its common difference, and find its nth term.
>
> ■   You should be able to find the nth partial sum of an arithmetic sequence by using the formula
>
> $$S_n = \frac{n}{2}(a_1 + a_n).$$

Solutions to Odd-Numbered Exercises

1. $10, \ 8, \ 6, \ 4, \ 2, \ldots$

Arithmetic sequence, $d = -2$

3. $1, \ 2, \ 4, \ 8, \ 16, \ 32, \ldots$

Not an arithmetic sequence

5. $\frac{9}{4}, \ 2, \ \frac{7}{4}, \ \frac{3}{2}, \ \frac{5}{4}, \ 1, \ldots$

Arithmetic sequence, $d = -\frac{1}{4}$

7. $-12, \ -8, \ -4, \ 0, \ 4, \ldots$

Arithmetic sequence, $d = 4$

9. $5.3, \ 5.7, \ 6.1, \ 6.5, \ 6.9, \ldots$

Arithmetic sequence, $d = 0.4$

11. $a_n = 5 + 3n$

$8, \ 11, \ 14, \ 17, \ 20$

Arithmetic sequence, $d = 3$

13. $a_n = \dfrac{1}{n+1}$

$\dfrac{1}{2}, \dfrac{1}{3}, \dfrac{1}{4}, \dfrac{1}{5}, \dfrac{1}{6}$

Not an arithmetic sequence

15. $a_n = 100 - 3n$

97, 94, 91, 88, 85

Arithmetic sequence, $d = -3$

17. $a_n = 3 + \dfrac{(-1)^n 2}{n}$

$1, 4, \dfrac{7}{3}, \dfrac{7}{2}, \dfrac{13}{5}$

Not an arithmetic sequence

19. $a_1 = 15, \ a_{k+1} = a_k + 4$

$a_2 = 15 + 4 = 19$

$a_3 = 19 + 4 = 23$

$a_4 = 23 + 4 = 27$

$a_5 = 27 + 4 = 31$

$a_n = 11 + 4n$

21. $a_1 = 200, \ a_{k+1} = a_k - 10$

$a_2 = 200 - 10 = 190$

$a_3 = 190 - 10 = 180$

$a_4 = 180 - 10 = 170$

$a_5 = 170 - 10 = 160$

$a_n = 210 - 10n$

23. $a_1 = \dfrac{3}{2}, \ a_{k+1} = a_k - \dfrac{1}{4}$

$a_2 = \dfrac{3}{2} - \dfrac{1}{4} = \dfrac{5}{4}$

$a_3 = \dfrac{5}{4} - \dfrac{1}{4} = 1$

$a_4 = 1 - \dfrac{1}{4} = \dfrac{3}{4}$

$a_5 = \dfrac{3}{4} - \dfrac{1}{4} = \dfrac{1}{2}$

$a_n = \dfrac{7}{4} - \dfrac{1}{4}n$

25. $a_1 = 5, \ d = 6$

$a_1 = 5$

$a_2 = 5 + 6 = 11$

$a_3 = 11 + 6 = 17$

$a_4 = 17 + 6 = 23$

$a_5 = 23 + 6 = 29$

27. $a_1 = -2.6, \ d = -0.4$

$a_1 = -2.6$

$a_2 = -2.6 + (-0.4) = -3.0$

$a_3 = -3.0 + (-0.4) = -3.4$

$a_4 = -3.4 + (-0.4) = -3.8$

$a_5 = -3.8 + (-0.4) = -4.2$

29. $a_1 = 2, \ a_{12} = 46$

$46 = 2 + (12 - 1)d$

$44 = 11d$

$4 = d$

$a_1 = 2$

$a_2 = 2 + 4 = 6$

$a_3 = 6 + 4 = 10$

$a_4 = 10 + 4 = 14$

$a_5 = 14 + 4 = 18$

31. $a_8 = 26, \ a_{12} = 42$

$26 = a_8 = a_1 + (n - 1)d = a_1 + 7d$

$42 = a_{12} = a_1 + (n - 1)d = a_1 + 11d$

Answer: $d = 4, \ a_1 = -2$

$a_1 = -2$

$a_2 = -2 + 4 = 2$

$a_3 = 2 + 4 = 6$

$a_4 = 6 + 4 = 10$

$a_5 = 10 + 4 = 14$

33. $a_1 = 1, \ d = 3$

$a_n = a_1 + (n - 1)d = 1 + (n - 1)(3)$

35. $a_1 = 100, \ d = -8$

$a_n = a_1 + (n - 1)d = 100 + (n - 1)(-8)$

37. $a_1 = x, \ d = 2x$

$a_n = a_1 + (n - 1)d = x + (n - 1)(2x)$

39. $4, \dfrac{3}{2}, -1, -\dfrac{7}{2}, \ldots$

$d = -\dfrac{5}{2}$

$a_n = a_1 + (n - 1)d = 4 + (n - 1)\left(-\dfrac{5}{2}\right)$

41. $a_1 = 5, \ a_4 = 15$

$a_4 = a_1 + 3d \ \Longrightarrow \ 15 = 5 + 3d \ \Longrightarrow \ d = \dfrac{10}{3}$

$a_n = a_1 + (n - 1)d = 5 + (n - 1)\left(\dfrac{10}{3}\right)$

43. $a_3 = 94, \ a_6 = 85$

$a_6 = a_3 + 3d \ \Longrightarrow \ 85 = 94 + 3d \ \Longrightarrow \ d = -3$

$a_1 = a_3 - 2d \ \Longrightarrow \ a_1 = 94 - 2(-3) = 100$

$a_n = a_1 + (n - 1)d = 100 + (n - 1)(-3)$

45. $a_n = -\frac{2}{3}n + 6$

$d = -\frac{2}{3}$ so the sequence is decreasing, and $a_1 = 5\frac{1}{3}$. Matches (b).

47. $a_n = 2 + \frac{3}{4}n$

$d = \frac{3}{4}$ so the sequence is increasing, and $a_1 = 2\frac{3}{4}$. Matches (c).

49. $a_n = 15 - \frac{3}{2}n$

51. $a_n = 0.2n + 3$

53. Since $a_n = dn + c$, its geometric pattern is linear.

55. 8, 20, 32, 44, . . .

$a_1 = 8,\ d = 12,\ n = 10$

$a_{10} = 8 + 9(12) = 116$

$S_{10} = \frac{10}{2}(8 + 116) = 620$

57. −6, −2, 2, 6, . . .

$a_1 = -6,\ d = 4,\ n = 50$

$a_{50} = -6 + 49(4) = 190$

$S_{50} = \frac{50}{2}(-6 + 190) = 4600$

59. 40, 37, 34, 31, . . .

$a_1 = 40,\ d = -3,\ n = 10$

$a_{10} = 40 + 9(-3) = 13$

$S_{10} = \frac{10}{2}(40 + 13) = 265$

61. $a_1 = 100,\ a_{25} = 220,\ n = 25$

$S_n = \frac{n}{2}[a_1 + a_n]$

$S_{25} = \frac{25}{2}(100 + 220) = 4000$

63. $a_1 = 1,\ a_{50} = 50,\ n = 50$

$\sum_{n=1}^{50} n = \frac{50}{2}(1 + 50) = 1275$

65. $a_1 = 5,\ a_{100} = 500,\ n = 100$

$\sum_{n=1}^{100} 5n = \frac{100}{2}(5 + 500) = 25,250$

67. $\sum_{n=11}^{30} n - \sum_{n=1}^{10} n = \frac{20}{2}(11 + 30) - \frac{10}{2}(1 + 10) = 355$

69. $a_1 = 4,\ a_{500} = 503,\ n = 500$

$\sum_{n=1}^{500} (n + 3) = \frac{500}{2}(4 + 503) = 126,750$

71. $a_1 = 7,\ a_{20} = 45,\ n = 20$

$\sum_{n=1}^{20} (2n + 5) = \frac{20}{2}(7 + 45) = 520$

73. $a_0 = 1000,\ a_{50} = 750,\ n = 51$

$\sum_{n=0}^{50} (100 - 5n) = \frac{51}{2}(1000 + 750) = 44,625$

75. $a_1 = \frac{742}{3},\ a_{60} = 90,\ n = 60$

$\sum_{i=1}^{60} \left(250 - \frac{8}{3}i\right) = \frac{60}{2}\left(\frac{742}{3} + 90\right) = 10,120$

77. $a_1 = 1,\ a_{100} = 199,\ n = 100$

$\sum_{n=1}^{100} (2n - 1) = \frac{100}{2}(1 + 199) = 10,000$

79. (a) $a_1 = 32,500,\ d = 1500$

$a_6 = a_1 + 5d = 32,500 + 5(1500) = \$40,000$

(b) $S_6 = \frac{6}{2}[32,500 + 40,000] = \$217,500$

81. $a_1 = 20,\ d = 4,\ n = 30$

$a_{30} = 20 + 29(4) = 136$

$S_{30} = \frac{30}{2}(20 + 136) = 2340$ seats

83. $a_1 = 14,\ a_{18} = 31$

$S_{18} = \frac{18}{2}(14 + 31) = 405$ bricks

85. (a) $1 + 3 = 4$

$\quad\quad 1 + 3 + 5 = 9$

$\quad\quad 1 + 3 + 5 + 7 = 16$

$\quad\quad 1 + 3 + 5 + 7 + 9 = 25$

$\quad\quad 1 + 3 + 5 + 7 + 9 + 11 = 36$

(b) $S_n = n^2$

$\quad S_7 = 1 + 3 + 5 + 7 + 9 + 11 + 13 = 49 = 7^2$

(c) $S_n = \dfrac{n}{2}[1 + (2n - 1)] = \dfrac{n}{2}(2n) = n^2$

87. $S_{20} = \frac{20}{2}\{a_1 + [a_1 + (20 - 1)(3)]\} = 650$

$\quad\quad 10(2a_1 + 57) = 650$

$\quad\quad\quad 2a_1 + 57 = 65$

$\quad\quad\quad\quad\quad 2a_1 = 8$

$\quad\quad\quad\quad\quad\; a_1 = 4$

Section 9.3   Geometric Sequences

■ You should be able to identify a geometric sequence, find its common ratio, and find the *n*th term.

■ You should be able to find the *n*th partial sum of a geometric sequence with common ratio *r* using the formula.

$$S_n = a_1\left(\frac{1 - r^n}{1 - r}\right)$$

■ You should know that if $|r| < 1$, then

$$\sum_{n=1}^{\infty} a_1 r^{n-1} = \frac{a_1}{1 - r}.$$

Solutions to Odd-Numbered Exercises

1. $5, \; 15, \; 45, \; 135, \ldots$

Geometric sequence, $r = 3$

3. $3, \; 12, \; 21, \; 30, \ldots$

Not a geometric sequence

Note: It is an arithmetic sequence with $d = 9$.

5. $1, \; -\frac{1}{2}, \; \frac{1}{4}, \; -\frac{1}{8}, \ldots$

Geometric sequence, $r = -\frac{1}{2}$

7. $\frac{1}{2}, \; \frac{2}{3}, \; \frac{3}{4}, \; \frac{4}{5}, \ldots$

Not a geometric sequence

9. $1, \; \frac{1}{2}, \; \frac{1}{3}, \; \frac{1}{4}, \ldots$

Not a geometric sequence

11. $a_1 = 2, \; r = 3$

$\quad a_1 = 2$

$\quad a_2 = 2(3) = 6$

$\quad a_3 = 6(3) = 18$

$\quad a_4 = 18(3) = 54$

$\quad a_5 = 54(3) = 162$

13. $a_1 = 1, \; r = \frac{1}{2}$

$\quad a_1 = 1$

$\quad a_2 = 1\left(\frac{1}{2}\right) = \frac{1}{2}$

$\quad a_3 = \frac{1}{2}\left(\frac{1}{2}\right) = \frac{1}{4}$

$\quad a_4 = \frac{1}{4}\left(\frac{1}{2}\right) = \frac{1}{8}$

$\quad a_5 = \frac{1}{8}\left(\frac{1}{2}\right) = \frac{1}{16}$

15. $a_1 = 5, \; r = -\frac{1}{10}$

$\quad a_1 = 5$

$\quad a_2 = 5\left(-\frac{1}{10}\right) = -\frac{1}{2}$

$\quad a_3 = \left(-\frac{1}{2}\right)\left(-\frac{1}{10}\right) = \frac{1}{20}$

$\quad a_4 = \frac{1}{20}\left(-\frac{1}{10}\right) = -\frac{1}{200}$

$\quad a_5 = \left(-\frac{1}{200}\right)\left(-\frac{1}{10}\right) = \frac{1}{2000}$

17. $a_1 = 1$, $r = e$

    $a_1 = 1$

    $a_2 = 1(e) = e$

    $a_3 = (e)(e) = e^2$

    $a_4 = (e^2)(e) = e^3$

    $a_5 = (e^3)(e) = e^4$

19. $a_1 = 3$, $r = \dfrac{x}{2}$

    $a_1 = 3$

    $a_2 = 3\left(\dfrac{x}{2}\right) = \dfrac{3x}{2}$

    $a_3 = \left(\dfrac{3x}{2}\right)\left(\dfrac{x}{2}\right) = \dfrac{3x^2}{4}$

    $a_4 = \left(\dfrac{3x^2}{4}\right)\left(\dfrac{x}{2}\right) = \dfrac{3x^3}{8}$

    $a_5 = \left(\dfrac{3x^3}{8}\right)\left(\dfrac{x}{2}\right) = \dfrac{3x^4}{16}$

21. $a_1 = 64$, $a_{k+1} = \dfrac{1}{2}a_k$

    $a_1 = 64$

    $a_2 = \dfrac{1}{2}(64) = 32$

    $a_3 = \dfrac{1}{2}(32) = 16$

    $a_4 = \dfrac{1}{2}(16) = 8$

    $a_5 = \dfrac{1}{2}(8) = 4$

    $a_n = 64\left(\dfrac{1}{2}\right)^{n-1} = 128\left(\dfrac{1}{2}\right)^n$

23. $a_1 = 4$, $a_{k+1} = 3a_k$

    $a_1 = 4$

    $a_2 = 3(4) = 12$

    $a_3 = 3(12) = 36$

    $a_4 = 3(36) = 108$

    $a_5 = 3(108) = 324$

    $a_n = 4(3)^{n-1} = \dfrac{4}{3}(3)^n$

25. $a_k = 6$, $a_{k+1} = -\dfrac{3}{2}a_k$

    $a_1 = 6$

    $a_2 = -\dfrac{3}{2}(6) = -9$

    $a_3 = -\dfrac{3}{2}(-9) = \dfrac{27}{2}$

    $a_4 = -\dfrac{3}{2}\left(\dfrac{27}{2}\right) = -\dfrac{81}{4}$

    $a_5 = -\dfrac{3}{2}\left(-\dfrac{81}{4}\right) = \dfrac{243}{8}$

    $a_n = 6\left(-\dfrac{3}{2}\right)^{n-1}$ or $a_n = -4\left(-\dfrac{3}{2}\right)^n$

27. $a_1 = 4$, $r = \dfrac{1}{2}$, $n = 10$

    $a_n = a_1 r^{n-1}$

    $a_{10} = 4\left(\dfrac{1}{2}\right)^9 = \left(\dfrac{1}{2}\right)^7 = \dfrac{1}{128}$

29. $a_1 = 6$, $r = -\dfrac{1}{3}$, $n = 12$

    $a_n = a_1 r^{n-1}$

    $a_{12} = 6\left(-\dfrac{1}{3}\right)^{11} = \dfrac{-2}{3^{10}}$

31. $a_1 = 100$, $r = e^x$, $n = 9$

    $a_n = a_1 r^{n-1}$

    $a_9 = 100(e^x)^8 = 100e^{8x}$

33. $a_1 = 500$, $r = 1.02$, $n = 40$

    $a_n = a_1 r^{n-1}$

    $a_{40} = 500(1.02)^{39} \approx 1082.37$

35. $a_1 = 16$, $a_4 = \dfrac{27}{4}$, $n = 3$

    $\dfrac{27}{4} = 16r^3 \implies r = \dfrac{3}{4}$

    $a_n = a_1 r^{n-1}$

    $a_3 = 16\left(\dfrac{3}{4}\right)^2 = 9$

37. $a_2 = a_1 r = -18 \implies a_1 = \dfrac{-18}{r}$

    $a_5 = a_1 r^4 = (a_1 r)r^3 = -18r^3 = \dfrac{2}{3} \implies r = -\dfrac{1}{3}$

    $a_1 = \dfrac{-18}{r} = \dfrac{-18}{-1/3} = 54$

    $a_6 = a_1 r^5 = 54\left(\dfrac{-1}{3}\right)^5 = -\dfrac{54}{243} = -\dfrac{2}{9}$

39. $a_n = 18\left(\frac{2}{3}\right)^{n-1}$

$r = \frac{2}{3} < 1$, so the sequence is decreasing.

Matches (a).

41. $a_n = 18\left(\frac{3}{2}\right)^{n-1}$

$r = \frac{3}{2} > 1$, so the sequence is increasing.

Matches (b).

43. $a_n = 12(-0.75)^{n-1}$

45. $a_n = 2(1.3)^{n-1}$

47. Given real numbers r between -1 and 1, as the exponent increases, r^n approaches zero.

49. $A = P\left(1 + \dfrac{r}{n}\right)^{nt} = 1000\left(1 + \dfrac{0.10}{n}\right)^{n(10)}$

(a) $n = 1$, $A = 1000(1 + 0.10)^{10} \approx \$2593.74$

(b) $n = 2$, $A = 1000\left(1 + \dfrac{0.10}{2}\right)^{2(10)} \approx \$2653.30$

(c) $n = 4$, $A = 1000\left(1 + \dfrac{0.10}{4}\right)^{4(10)} \approx \$2685.06$

(d) $n = 12$, $A = 1000\left(1 + \dfrac{0.10}{12}\right)^{12(10)} \approx \$2707.04$

(e) $n = 365$, $A = 1000\left(1 + \dfrac{0.10}{365}\right)^{365(10)} \approx \$2717.91$

51. $V_5 = 135,000(0.70)^5 = \$22,689.45$

53. $8, -4, 2, -1, \frac{1}{2}, \ldots$

$S_1 = 8$

$S_2 = 8 + (-4) = 4$

$S_3 = 8 + (-4) + 2 = 6$

$S_4 = 8 + (-4) + 2 + (-1) = 5$

55. $\displaystyle\sum_{n=1}^{9} 2^{n-1} \implies a_1 = 1, \ r = 2$

$S_9 = \dfrac{1(1 - 2^9)}{1 - 2} = 511$

57. $\displaystyle\sum_{i=1}^{7} 64\left(-\dfrac{1}{2}\right)^{i-1} \implies a_1 = 64, \ r = -\dfrac{1}{2}$

$S_7 = 64\left[\dfrac{1 - \left(-\frac{1}{2}\right)^7}{1 - \left(-\frac{1}{2}\right)}\right] = \dfrac{128}{3}\left[1 - \left(-\dfrac{1}{2}\right)^7\right] = 43$

59. $\displaystyle\sum_{n=0}^{20} 3\left(\dfrac{3}{2}\right)^n = \sum_{n=1}^{21} 3\left(\dfrac{3}{2}\right)^{n-1} \implies a_1 = 3, \ r = \dfrac{3}{2}$

$S_{21} = 3\left[\dfrac{1 - \left(\frac{3}{2}\right)^{21}}{1 - \frac{3}{2}}\right] = -6\left[1 - \left(\dfrac{3}{2}\right)^{21}\right] \approx 29,921.31$

61. $\displaystyle\sum_{i=1}^{10} 8\left(-\tfrac{1}{4}\right)^{i-1} \implies a_1 = 8, \; r = -\tfrac{1}{4}$

$$S_{10} = 8\left[\frac{1 - \left(-\tfrac{1}{4}\right)^{10}}{1 - \left(-\tfrac{1}{4}\right)}\right] = \frac{32}{5}\left[1 - \left(-\tfrac{1}{4}\right)^{10}\right] \approx 6.4$$

63. $\displaystyle\sum_{n=0}^{5} 300(1.06)^n = \sum_{n=1}^{6} 300(1.06)^{n-1} \implies a_1 = 300, \; r = 1.06$

$$S_6 = 300\left[\frac{1 - (1.06)^6}{1 - 1.06}\right] \approx 2092.60$$

65. $5 + 15 + 45 + \cdots + 3645$

$r = 3$ and $3645 = 5(3)^{n-1} \implies n = 7$

Thus, the sum can be written as $\displaystyle\sum_{n=1}^{7} 5(3)^{n-1}$.

67. $\displaystyle A = \sum_{n=1}^{60} 100\left(1 + \frac{0.10}{12}\right)^n = 100\left(1 + \frac{0.10}{12}\right) \cdot \frac{\left[1 - \left(1 + \dfrac{0.10}{12}\right)^{60}\right]}{\left[1 - \left(1 + \dfrac{0.10}{12}\right)\right]} \approx \$7808.24$

69. Let $N = 12t$ be the total number of deposits.

$$A = P\left(1 + \frac{r}{12}\right) + P\left(1 + \frac{r}{12}\right)^2 + \cdots + P\left(1 + \frac{r}{12}\right)^N$$

$$= \left(1 + \frac{r}{12}\right)\left[P + P\left(r + \frac{r}{12}\right) + \cdots + P\left(1 + \frac{r}{12}\right)^{N-1}\right]$$

$$= P\left(1 + \frac{r}{12}\right)\sum_{n=1}^{N}\left(1 + \frac{r}{12}\right)^{n-1}$$

$$= P\left(1 + \frac{r}{12}\right)\frac{1 - \left(1 + \dfrac{r}{12}\right)^N}{1 - \left(1 + \dfrac{r}{12}\right)}$$

$$= P\left(1 + \frac{r}{12}\right)\left(-\frac{12}{r}\right)\left[1 - \left(1 + \frac{r}{12}\right)^N\right]$$

$$= P\left(\frac{12}{r} + 1\right)\left[-1 + \left(1 + \frac{r}{12}\right)^N\right]$$

$$= P\left[\left(1 + \frac{r}{12}\right)^N - 1\right]\left(1 + \frac{12}{r}\right)$$

$$= P\left[\left(1 + \frac{r}{12}\right)^{12t} - 1\right]\left(1 + \frac{12}{r}\right)$$

71. $P = \$50, \; r = 7\%, \; t = 20$ years

(a) Compounded monthly: $\displaystyle A = 50\left[\left(1 + \frac{0.07}{12}\right)^{12(20)} - 1\right]\left(1 + \frac{12}{0.07}\right) \approx \$26{,}198.27$

(b) Compounded continuously: $\displaystyle A = \frac{50e^{0.07/12}(e^{0.07(20)} - 1)}{e^{0.07/12} - 1} \approx \$26{,}263.88$

73. $P = \$100$, $r = 10\%$, $t = 40$ years

(a) Compounded monthly: $A = 100\left[\left(1 + \dfrac{0.10}{12}\right)^{12(40)} - 1\right]\left(1 + \dfrac{12}{0.10}\right) \approx \$637{,}678.02$

(b) Compounded continuously: $A = \dfrac{100e^{0.10/12}(e^{(0.10)(40)} - 1)}{e^{0.10/12} - 1} \approx \$645{,}861.43$

75. $P = W\displaystyle\sum_{n=1}^{12t}\left[\left(1 + \dfrac{r}{12}\right)^{-1}\right]^{n}$

$= W\left(1 + \dfrac{r}{12}\right)^{-1}\left[\dfrac{1 - \left(1 + \dfrac{r}{12}\right)^{-12t}}{1 - \left(1 - \dfrac{r}{12}\right)^{-1}}\right]$

$= W\left(\dfrac{1}{1 + \dfrac{r}{12}}\right)\dfrac{\left[1 - \left(1 + \dfrac{r}{12}\right)^{-12t}\right]}{1 - \dfrac{1}{\left(1 + \dfrac{r}{12}\right)}}$

$= W\dfrac{\left[1 - \left(1 + \dfrac{r}{12}\right)^{-12t}\right]}{\left(1 + \dfrac{r}{12}\right) - 1}$

$= W\left(\dfrac{12}{r}\right)\left[1 - \left(1 - \dfrac{r}{12}\right)^{-12t}\right]$

77. $64 + 32 + 16 + 8 + 4 + 2 = 126$
Total area of shaded region is
approximately 126 square inches.

79. $S_n = \displaystyle\sum_{i=1}^{n} 0.01(2)^{i-1}$

$S_{29} = \$5{,}368{,}709.11$
$S_{30} = \$10{,}737{,}418.23$
$S_{31} = \$21{,}474{,}836.47$

81. $a_1 = 1$, $r = \dfrac{1}{2}$

$\displaystyle\sum_{n=0}^{\infty}\left(\dfrac{1}{2}\right)^{n} = \dfrac{a_1}{1 - r} = \dfrac{1}{1 - (1/2)} = 2$

83. $a_1 = 1$, $r = -\dfrac{1}{2}$

$\displaystyle\sum_{n=1}^{\infty}\left(-\dfrac{1}{2}\right)^{n-1} = \dfrac{a_1}{1 - r} = \dfrac{1}{1 - (-1/2)} = \dfrac{2}{3}$

85. $a_1 = 4$, $r = \dfrac{1}{4}$

$\displaystyle\sum_{n=0}^{\infty} 4\left(\dfrac{1}{4}\right)^{n} = \dfrac{a_1}{1 - r} = \dfrac{4}{1 - (1/4)} = \dfrac{16}{3}$

87. $8 + 6 + \dfrac{9}{2} + \dfrac{27}{8} + \cdots = \displaystyle\sum_{n=0}^{\infty} 8\left(\dfrac{3}{4}\right)^{n} = \dfrac{8}{1 - 3/4} = 32$

89. $0.\overline{36} = \displaystyle\sum_{n=0}^{\infty} 0.36(0.01)^{n} = \dfrac{0.36}{1 - 0.01} = \dfrac{0.36}{0.99} = \dfrac{36}{99} = \dfrac{4}{11}$

91. $0.3\overline{18} = 0.3 + \displaystyle\sum_{n=0}^{\infty} 0.018(0.01)^n = \dfrac{3}{10} + \dfrac{0.018}{1 - 0.01}$

$\phantom{0.3\overline{18}} = \dfrac{3}{10} + \dfrac{0.018}{0.99} = \dfrac{3}{10} + \dfrac{18}{990} = \dfrac{3}{10} + \dfrac{2}{110}$

$\phantom{0.3\overline{18}} = \dfrac{35}{110} = \dfrac{7}{22}$

93. $f(x) = 6\left[\dfrac{1 - (0.5)^x}{1 - (0.5)}\right], \displaystyle\sum_{n=0}^{\infty} 6\left(\dfrac{1}{2}\right)^n = \dfrac{6}{1 - 1/2} = 12$

The horizontal asymptote of $f(x)$ is $y = 12$. This corresponds to the sum of the series.

95. (a) Total distance $= \left[\displaystyle\sum_{n=0}^{\infty} 32(0.81)^n\right] - 16 = \dfrac{32}{1 - 0.81} - 16 \approx 152.42$ feet

(b) $t = 1 + 2\displaystyle\sum_{n=1}^{\infty} (0.9)^n = 1 + 2\left[\dfrac{0.9}{1 - 0.9}\right] = 19$ seconds

Section 9.4   Mathematical Induction

- You should be sure that you understand the principle of mathematical induction. If P_n is a statement involving the positive integer n, where P_1 is true and the truth of P_k implies the truth of P_{k+1}, then P_n is true for all positive integers n.
- You should be able to verify (by induction) the formulas for the sums of powers of integers and be able to use these formulas.

Solutions to Odd-Numbered Exercises

1. $P_k = \dfrac{5}{k(k + 1)}$

$P_{k+1} = \dfrac{5}{(k + 1)((k + 1) + 1)} = \dfrac{5}{(k + 1)(k + 2)}$

3. $P_k = \dfrac{k^2(k + 1)^2}{4}$

$P_{k+1} = \dfrac{(k + 1)^2((k + 1) + 1)^2}{4} = \dfrac{(k + 1)^2(k + 2)^2}{4}$

5. 1. When $n = 1$, $S_1 = 2 = 1(1 + 1)$.

2. Assume that

$S_k = 2 + 4 + 6 + 8 + \cdots + 2k = k(k + 1)$.

Then,

$S_{k+1} = 2 + 4 + 6 + 8 + \cdots + 2k + 2(k + 1)$

$\phantom{S_{k+1}} = S_k + 2(k + 1) = k(k + 1) + 2(k + 1) = (k + 1)(k + 2).$

We conclude by mathematical induction that the formula is valid for all positive integer values of n.

7. 1. When $n = 1$, $S_1 = 2 = \frac{1}{2}(5(1) - 1)$.

   2. Assume that
   $$S_k = 2 + 7 + 12 + 17 + \cdots + (5k - 3) = \frac{k}{2}(5k - 1).$$
   Then,
   $$S_{k+1} = 2 + 7 + 12 + 17 + \cdots + (5k - 3) + [5(k + 1) - 3]$$
   $$= S_k + (5k + 5 - 3) = \frac{k}{2}(5k - 1) + 5k + 2$$
   $$= \frac{5k^2 - k + 10k + 4}{2} = \frac{5k^2 + 9k + 4}{2}$$
   $$= \frac{(k + 1)(5k + 4)}{2} = \frac{(k + 1)}{2}[5(k + 1) - 1].$$

   We conclude by mathematical induction that the formula is valid for all positive integer values of n.

9. 1. When $n = 1$, $S_1 = 1 = 2^1 - 1$.

   2. Assume that
   $$S_k = 1 + 2 + 2^2 + 2^3 + \cdots + 2^{k-1} = 2^k - 1.$$
   Then,
   $$S_{k+1} = 1 + 2 + 2^2 + 2^3 + \cdots + 2^{k-1} + 2^k$$
   $$= S_k + 2^k = 2^k - 1 + 2^k = 2(2^k) - 1 = 2^{k+1} - 1.$$

   Therefore, by mathematical induction, the formula is valid for all positive integer values of n.

11. 1. When $n = 1$, $S_1 = 1 = \frac{1(1 + 1)}{2}$.

   2. Assume that
   $$S_k = 1 + 2 + 3 + 4 + \cdots + k = \frac{k(k + 1)}{2}.$$
   Then,
   $$S_{k+1} = 1 + 2 + 3 + 4 + \cdots + k + (k + 1)$$
   $$= S_k + (k + 1) = \frac{k(k + 1)}{2} + \frac{2(k + 1)}{2} = \frac{(k + 1)(k + 2)}{2}.$$

   Therefore, we conclude that this formula holds for all positive integer values of n.

13. 1. When $n = 1$, $S_1 = 1^3 = 1 = \frac{1(1 + 1)^2}{4}$.

   2. Assume that
   $$S_k = 1^3 + 2^3 + 3^3 + 4^3 + \cdots + k^3 = \frac{k^2(k + 1)^2}{4}.$$
   Then,
   $$S_{k+1} = 1^3 + 2^3 + 3^3 + 4^3 + \cdots + k^3 + (k + 1)^3$$
   $$= S_k + (k + 1)^3 = \frac{k^2(k + 1)^2}{4} + (k + 1)^3 = \frac{k^2(k + 1)^2 + 4(k + 1)^3}{4}$$
   $$= \frac{(k + 1)^2[k^2 + 4(k + 1)]}{4} = \frac{(k + 1)^2(k^2 + 4k + 4)}{4} = \frac{(k + 1)^2(k + 2)^2}{4}.$$

   Therefore, we conclude that this formula holds for all positive integer values of n.

15. 1. When $n = 1$, $S_1 = 1 = \dfrac{(1)^2(1 + 1)^2(2(1)^2 + 2(1) - 1)}{12}$.

2. Assume that

$$S_k = \sum_{i=1}^{k} i^5 = \frac{k^2(k + 1)^2(2k^2 + 2k - 1)}{12}.$$

Then,

$$S_{k+1} = \sum_{i=1}^{k+1} i^5 = \sum_{i=1}^{k} i^5 + (k + 1)^5$$

$$= \frac{k^2(k + 1)^2(2k^2 + 2k - 1)}{12} + \frac{12(k + 1)^5}{12}$$

$$= \frac{(k + 1)^2[k^2(2k^2 + 2k - 1) + 12(k + 1)^3]}{12}$$

$$= \frac{(k + 1)^2[2k^4 + 2k^3 - k^2 + 12(k^3 + 3k^2 + 3k + 1)]}{12}$$

$$= \frac{(k + 1)^2[2k^4 + 14k^3 + 35k^2 + 36k + 12]}{12}$$

$$= \frac{(k + 1)^2(k^2 + 4k + 4)(2k^2 + 6k + 3)}{12}$$

$$= \frac{(k + 1)^2(k + 2)^2[2(k + 1)^2 + 2(k + 1) - 1]}{12}.$$

Therefore, we conclude that this formula holds for all positive integer values of n.

17. 1. When $n = 1$, $S_1 = 2 = \dfrac{1(2)(3)}{3}$.

2. Assume that,

$$S_k = 1(2) + 2(3) + 3(4) + \cdots + k(k + 1) = \frac{k(k + 1)(k + 2)}{3}.$$

Then,

$$S_{k+1} = 1(2) + 2(3) + 3(4) + \cdots + k(k + 1) + (k + 1)(k + 2)$$

$$= S_k + (k + 1)(k + 2) = \frac{k(k + 1)(k + 2)}{3} + \frac{3(k + 1)(k + 2)}{3}$$

$$= \frac{(k + 1)(k + 2)(k + 3)}{3}.$$

Thus, this formula is valid for all positive integer values of n.

19. $\sum_{n=1}^{20} n = \dfrac{20(20 + 1)}{2} = 210$

21. $\sum_{n=1}^{6} n^2 = \dfrac{6(6 + 1)(2(6) + 1)}{6} = 91$

23. $\sum_{n=1}^{5} n^4 = \dfrac{5(5 + 1)(2(5) + 1)(3(5)^2 + 3(5) - 1)}{30} = 979$

25. $\sum_{n=1}^{6}(n^2 - n) = \sum_{n=1}^{6} n^2 - \sum_{n=1}^{6} n = \dfrac{6(6 + 1)(2(6) + 1)}{6} - \dfrac{6(6 + 1)}{2} = 91 - 21 = 70$

27. $\displaystyle\sum_{i=1}^{6}(6i - 8i^3) = 6\sum_{i=1}^{6}i - 8\sum_{i=1}^{6}i^3 = 6\left[\frac{6(6+1)}{2}\right] - 8\left[\frac{(6)^2(6+1)^2}{4}\right] = 6(21) - 8(441) = -3402$

29. $1 + 5 + 9 + 13 + \cdots = n(2n - 1)$

31. $1 + \frac{9}{10} + \frac{81}{100} + \frac{729}{1000} + \cdots = 10 - 10\left(\frac{9}{10}\right)^n$

33. $\dfrac{1}{4} + \dfrac{1}{12} + \dfrac{1}{24} + \dfrac{1}{40} + \cdots + \dfrac{1}{2n(n-1)} + \cdots = \dfrac{n}{2(n+1)}$

35. 1. When $n = 4$, $4! = 24$ and $2^4 = 16$, thus $4! > 2^4$.

     2. Assume

       $k! > 2^k,\ k > 4.$

       Then,

       $(k + 1)! = k!(k + 1) > 2^k(2)$ since $k + 1 > 2$.

       Thus, $(k + 1)! > 2^{k+1}$.

Therefore, by mathematical induction, the formula is valid for all integers n such that $n \geq 4$.

37. 1. When $n = 2$, $\dfrac{1}{\sqrt{1}} + \dfrac{1}{\sqrt{2}} \approx 1.707$ and $\sqrt{2} \approx 1.414$, thus $\dfrac{1}{\sqrt{1}} + \dfrac{1}{\sqrt{2}} > \sqrt{2}$.

     2. Assume

$$\frac{1}{\sqrt{1}} + \frac{1}{\sqrt{2}} + \frac{1}{\sqrt{3}} + \cdots + \frac{1}{\sqrt{k}} > \sqrt{k},\, k > 2.$$

       Then,

$$\frac{1}{\sqrt{1}} + \frac{1}{\sqrt{2}} + \frac{1}{\sqrt{3}} + \cdots + \frac{1}{\sqrt{k}} + \frac{1}{\sqrt{k+1}} > \sqrt{k} + \frac{1}{\sqrt{k+1}}.$$

       Now we need to show that

$$\sqrt{k} + \frac{1}{\sqrt{k+1}} > \sqrt{k+1},\ k > 2.$$

       This is true since

$$\sqrt{k(k+1)} > k$$
$$\sqrt{k(k+1)} + 1 > k + 1$$
$$\frac{\sqrt{k(k+1)} + 1}{\sqrt{k+1}} > \frac{k+1}{\sqrt{k+1}}$$
$$\sqrt{k} + \frac{1}{\sqrt{k+1}} > \sqrt{k+1}.$$

       Therefore,

$$\frac{1}{\sqrt{1}} + \frac{1}{\sqrt{2}} + \frac{1}{\sqrt{3}} + \ldots + \frac{1}{\sqrt{k}} + \frac{1}{\sqrt{k+1}} > \sqrt{k+1}.$$

Therefore, by mathematical induction, the formula is valid for all integers n such that $n \geq 2$.

39. 1. When $n = 1$, $(ab)^1 = a^1 b^1 = ab$.

2. Assume that $(ab)^k = a^k b^k$.

Then, $(ab)^{k+1} = (ab)^k (ab)$

$$= a^k b^k ab$$

$$= a^{k+1} b^{k+1}.$$

Thus, $(ab)^n = a^n b^n$.

41. 1. When $n = 1$, $(x_1)^{-1} = x_1^{-1}$.

2. Assume that

$$(x_1 x_2 x_3 \cdots x_k)^{-1} = x_1^{-1} x_2^{-1} x_3^{-1} \cdots x_k^{-1}.$$

Then,

$$(x_1 x_2 x_3 \cdots x_k x_{k+1})^{-1} = [(x_1 x_2 x_3 \cdots x_k) x_{k+1}]^{-1}$$

$$= (x_1 x_2 x_3 \dots x_k)^{-1} x_{k+1}^{-1}$$

$$= x_1^{-1} x_2^{-1} x_3^{-1} \cdots x_k^{-1} x_{k+1}^{-1}.$$

Thus, the formula is valid.

43. 1. When $n = 1$, $x(y_1) = xy_1$.

2. Assume that

$$x(y_1 + y_2 + \cdots + y_k) = xy_1 + xy_2 + \cdots + xy_k.$$

Then,

$$xy_1 + xy_2 + \cdots + xy_k + xy_{k+1} = x(y_1 + y_2 + \cdots + y_k) + xy_{k+1}$$

$$= x[(y_1 + y_2 + \cdots + y_k) + y_{k+1}]$$

$$= x(y_1 + y_2 + \cdots + y_k + y_{k+1}).$$

Hence, the formula holds.

45. 1. When $n = 1$, $\sin(x + n) = (-1)^1 \sin x$

2. Assume that $\sin(x + k\pi) = (-1)^k \sin x$

Then, $\sin[x + (k + 1)\pi] = \sin[(x + k\pi) + \pi] = (-1)^1 \sin(x + k\pi)$

$$= (-1)^1 (-1)^k \sin x = (-1)^{k+1} \sin x.$$

Thus, the formula is valid for all positive interger values of n.

47. 1. When $n = 1$, $(1^3 + 3(1)^2 + 2(1)) = 6$ and 3 is a factor.

2. Assume that 3 is a factor of $(k^3 + 3k^2 + 2k)$.

Then,

$$[(k + 1)^3 + 3(k + 1)^2 + 2(k + 1)]$$

$$= k^3 + 3k^2 + 3k + 1 + 3k^2 + 6k + 3 + 2k + 2$$

$$= (k^3 + 3k^2 + 2k) + (3k^2 + 9k + 6)$$

$$= (k^3 + 3k^2 + 2k) + 3(k^2 + 3k + 2).$$

Since 3 is a factor of $(k^3 + 3k^2 + 2k)$, our assumption, and 3 is a factor of $3(k^2 + 3k + 2)$, then 3 is a factor of the whole sum.

Thus, 3 is a factor of $(n^3 + 3n^2 + 2n)$ for every positive integer n.

49. See page 622 in the textbook.

51. $a_0 = 1, a_n = a_{n-1} + 2$

$a_0 = 1$

$a_1 = a_0 + 2 = 1 + 2 = 3$

$a_2 = a_1 + 2 = 3 + 2 = 5$

$a_3 = a_2 + 2 = 5 + 2 = 7$

$a_4 = a_3 + 2 = 7 + 2 = 9$

53. $a_0 = 4, a_1 = 2, a_n = a_{n-1} - a_{n-2}$

$a_0 = 4$

$a_1 = 2$

$a_2 = a_1 - a_0 = 2 - 4 = -2$

$a_3 = a_2 - a_1 = -2 - 2 = -4$

$a_4 = a_3 - a_2 = -4 - (-2) = -2$

55. $f(1) = 0, a_n = a_{n-1} + 3$

$a_1 = f(1) = 0$

$a_2 = a_1 + 3 = 0 + 3 = 3$

$a_3 = a_2 + 3 = 3 + 3 = 6$

$a_4 = a_3 + 3 = 6 + 3 = 9$

$a_5 = a_4 + 3 = 9 + 3 = 12$

Since the first differences are equal, the sequence has a linear model.

57. $f(1) = 3, a_n = a_{n-1} - n$

$a_1 = f(1) = 3$

$a_2 = a_1 - 2 = 3 - 2 = 1$

$a_3 = a_2 - 3 = 1 - 3 = -2$

$a_4 = a_3 - 4 = -2 - 4 = -6$

$a_5 = a_4 - 5 = -6 - 5 = -11$

Since the second differences are all the same, the sequence has a quadratic model.

59. $a_0 = 0, a_n = a_{n-1} + n$

$a_0 = 0$

$a_1 = a_0 + 1 = 0 + 1 = 1$

$a_2 = a_1 + 2 = 1 + 2 = 3$

$a_3 = a_2 + 3 = 3 + 3 = 6$

$a_4 = a_3 + 4 = 6 + 4 = 10$

Since the second differences are equal, the sequence has a quadratic model.

61. $f(1) = 2, a_n = a_{n-1} + 2$

$a_1 = f(1) = 2$

$a_2 = a_1 + 2 = 2 + 2 = 4$

$a_3 = a_2 + 2 = 4 + 2 = 6$

$a_4 = a_3 + 2 = 6 + 2 = 8$

$a_5 = a_4 + 2 = 8 + 2 = 10$

Since the first differences are equal, the sequence has a linear model.

63. $a_0 = 1, a_n = a_{n-1} + n^2$

$a_0 = 1$

$a_1 = 1 + 1^2 = 2$

$a_2 = 2 + 2^2 = 6$

$a_3 = 6 + 3^2 = 15$

$a_4 = 15 + 4^2 = 31$

Since neither the first differences nor the second differences are equal, the sequence does not have a linear or a quadratic model.

65. $a_0 = 3, a_1 = 3, a_4 = 15$

Let $a_n = an^2 + bn + c$.

Thus: $a_0 = a(0)^2 + b(0) + c = 3 \implies c = 3$

$a_1 = a(1)^2 + b(1) + c = 3 \implies a + b + c = 3$

$a + b = 0$

$a_4 = a(4)^2 + b(4) + c = 15 \implies 16a + 4b + c = 15$

$16a + 4b = 12$

$4a + b = 3$

By elimination: $-a - b = 0$

$\underline{4a + b = 3}$

$3a = 3$

$a = 1 \implies b = -1$

Thus, $a_n = n^2 - n + 3$.

67. $a_0 = -3, a_2 = 1, a_4 = 9$

Let $a_n = an^2 + bn + c$.

Then: $a_0 = a(0)^2 + b(0) + c = -3 \implies c = -3$

$a_2 = a(2)^2 + b(2) + c = 1 \implies 4a + 2b + c = 1$

$4a + 2b = 4$

$2a + b = 2$

$a_4 = a(4)^2 + b(4) + c = 9 \implies 16a + 4b + c = 9$

$16a + 4b = 12$

$4a + b = 3$

By elimination: $-2a - b = -2$

$\underline{4a + b = 3}$

$2a = -1$

$a = \frac{1}{2} \implies b = 1$

Thus, $a_n = \frac{1}{2}n^2 + n - 3$.

69. $y = x^2$

$-3x + 2y = 2 \implies -3x + 2x^2 = 2$

$2x^2 - 3x - 2 = 0$

$(2x + 1)(x - 2) = 0$

$x = -\frac{1}{2} \quad \text{or} \quad x = 2$

$y = \frac{1}{4} \qquad y = 4$

Points of intersection: $\left(-\frac{1}{2}, \frac{1}{4}\right), (2, 4)$

71. $x - y \qquad = -1$

$\qquad x + 2y - 2z = \quad 3$

$\quad 3x - y + 2z = \quad 3$

Using an augmented matrix, we have:

$$\begin{bmatrix} 1 & -1 & 0 & \vdots & -1 \\ 1 & 2 & -2 & \vdots & 3 \\ 3 & -1 & 2 & \vdots & 3 \end{bmatrix}$$

$$\begin{matrix} \\ -R_1 + R_2 \rightarrow \\ -3R_1 + R_3 \rightarrow \end{matrix} \begin{bmatrix} 1 & -1 & 0 & \vdots & -1 \\ 0 & 3 & -2 & \vdots & 4 \\ 0 & 2 & 2 & \vdots & 6 \end{bmatrix}$$

$$\begin{matrix} \\ -R_3 + R_2 \rightarrow \\ \tfrac{1}{2}R_3 \rightarrow \end{matrix} \begin{bmatrix} 1 & -1 & 0 & \vdots & -1 \\ 0 & 1 & -4 & \vdots & -2 \\ 0 & 1 & 1 & \vdots & 3 \end{bmatrix}$$

$$\begin{matrix} R_2 + R_1 \rightarrow \\ \\ -R_2 + R_3 \rightarrow \end{matrix} \begin{bmatrix} 1 & 0 & -4 & \vdots & -3 \\ 0 & 1 & -4 & \vdots & -2 \\ 0 & 0 & 5 & \vdots & 5 \end{bmatrix}$$

$$\begin{matrix} 4R_3 + R_1 \rightarrow \\ 4R_3 + R_2 \rightarrow \\ \tfrac{1}{5}R_3 \rightarrow \end{matrix} \begin{bmatrix} 1 & 0 & 0 & \vdots & 1 \\ 0 & 1 & 0 & \vdots & 2 \\ 0 & 0 & 1 & \vdots & 1 \end{bmatrix}$$

Thus, $x = 1, y = 2, z = 1$.

Answer: $(1, 2, 1)$

Section 9.5   The Binomial Theorem

■ You should be able to use the formula

$$(x + y)^n = x^n + nx^{n-1}y + \frac{n(n-1)}{2!}x^{n-2}y^2 + \cdots + {}_nC_r x^{n-r}y^r + \cdots + y^n$$

where ${}_nC_r = \dfrac{n!}{(n-r)!r!}$, to expand $(x + y)^n$.

■ You should be able to use Pascal's Triangle in binomial expansion.

Solutions to Odd-Numbered Exercises

1. ${}_5C_3 = \dfrac{5!}{3!2!} = \dfrac{5 \cdot 4}{2 \cdot 1} = 10$

3. ${}_{12}C_0 = \dfrac{12!}{0!12!} = 1$

5. ${}_{20}C_{15} = \dfrac{20!}{15!5!} = \dfrac{20 \cdot 19 \cdot 18 \cdot 17 \cdot 16}{5 \cdot 4 \cdot 3 \cdot 2 \cdot 1} = 15{,}504$

7. ${}_{100}C_{98} = \dfrac{100!}{98!2!} = \dfrac{100 \cdot 99}{2 \cdot 1} = 4950$

9. ${}_{100}C_2 = \dfrac{100!}{2!98!} = \dfrac{100 \cdot 99}{2 \cdot 1} = 4950$

11. The first and last number in each row is 1. Every other number is found by adding the two numbers immediately above it.

13.

```
              1
            1   1
          1   2   1
        1   3   3   1
      1   4   6   4   1
    1   5  10  10   5   1
  1   6  15  20  15   6   1
1   7  21  35 (35) 21   7   1
```

$_7C_4 = 35$, the 5th entry in the 8th row.

15.

```
                1
              1   1
            1   2   1
          1   3   3   1
        1   4   6   4   1
      1   5  10  10   5   1
    1   6  15  20  15   6   1
  1   7  21  35  35  21   7   1
1   8  28  56  70 (56) 28   8   1
```

$_8C_5 = 56$, the 6th entry in the 9th row.

17. $(x + 1)^4 = {}_4C_0x^4 + {}_4C_1x^3(1) + {}_4C_2x^2(1)^2 + {}_4C_3x(1)^3 + {}_4C_4(1)^4$

$\qquad = x^4 + 4x^3 + 6x^2 + 4x + 1$

19. $(a + 2)^3 = {}_3C_0a^3 + {}_3C_1a^2(2) + {}_3C_2a(2)^2 + {}_3C_3(2)^3$

$\qquad = a^3 + 3a^2(2) + 3a(2)^2 + (2)^3$

$\qquad = a^3 + 6a^2 + 12a + 8$

21. $(y - 2)^4 = {}_4C_0y^4 - {}_4C_1y^3(2) + {}_4C_2y^2(2)^2 - {}_4C_3y(2)^3 + {}_4C_4(2)^4$

$\qquad = y^4 - 4y^3(2) + 6y^2(4) - 4y(8) + 16$

$\qquad = y^4 - 8y^3 + 24y^2 - 32y + 16$

23. $(x + y)^5 = {}_5C_0x^5 + {}_5C_1x^4y + {}_5C_2x^3y^2 + {}_5C_3x^2y^3 + {}_5C_4xy^4 + {}_5C_5y^5$

$\qquad = x^5 + 5x^4y + 10x^3y^2 + 10x^2y^3 + 5xy^4 + y^5$

25. $(r + 3s)^6 = {}_6C_0r^6 + {}_6C_1r^5(3s) + {}_6C_2r^4(3s)^2 + {}_6C_3r^3(3s)^3 + {}_6C_4r^2(3s)^4$

$\qquad\qquad + {}_6C_5r(3s)^5 + {}_6C_6(3s)^6$

$\qquad = r^6 + 18r^5s + 135r^4s^2 + 540r^3s^3 + 1215r^2s^4 + 1458rs^5 + 729s^6$

27. $(x - y)^5 = {}_5C_0x^5 - {}_5C_1x^4y + {}_5C_2x^3y^2 - {}_5C_3x^2y^3 + {}_5C_4xy^4 - {}_5C_5y^5$

$\qquad = x^5 - 5x^4y + 10x^3y^2 - 10x^2y^3 + 5xy^4 - y^5$

29. $(1 - 2x)^3 = {}_3C_01^3 - {}_3C_11^2(2x) + {}_3C_21(2x)^2 - {}_3C_3(2x)^3$

$\qquad = 1 - 3(2x) + 3(2x)^2 - (2x)^3$

$\qquad = 1 - 6x + 12x^2 - 8x^3$

31. $(x^2 + 5)^4 = {}_4C_0(x^2)^4 + {}_4C_1(x^2)^3(5) + {}_4C_2(x^2)^2(5)^2 + {}_4C_3(x^2)(5)^3 + {}_4C_4(5)^4$

$\qquad = x^8 + 4x^6(5) + 6x^4(25) + 4x^2(125) + 625$

$\qquad = x^8 + 20x^6 + 150x^4 + 500x^2 + 625$

33. $\left(\dfrac{1}{x} + y\right)^5 = {}_5C_0\left(\dfrac{1}{x}\right)^5 + {}_5C_1\left(\dfrac{1}{x}\right)^4y + {}_5C_2\left(\dfrac{1}{x}\right)^3y^2 + {}_5C_3\left(\dfrac{1}{x}\right)^2y^3 + {}_5C_4\left(\dfrac{1}{x}\right)y^4 + {}_5C_5y^5$

$\qquad = \dfrac{1}{x^5} + \dfrac{5y}{x^4} + \dfrac{10y^2}{x^3} + \dfrac{10y^3}{x^2} + \dfrac{5y^4}{x} + y^5$

35. $2(x - 3)^4 + 5(x - 3)^2 = 2[x^4 - 4(x^3)(3) + 6(x^2)(3^2) - 4(x)(3^3) + 3^4] + 5[x^2 - 2(x)(3) + 3^2]$

$$= 2(x^4 - 12x^3 + 54x^2 - 108x + 81) + 5(x^2 - 6x + 9)$$

$$= 2x^4 - 24x^3 + 113x^2 - 246x + 207$$

37. 5th Row of Pascal's Triangle: 1   5   10   10   5   1

$(2t - s)^5 = 1(2t)^5 + 5(2t)^4(-s) + 10(2t)^3(-s)^2 + 10(2t)^2(-s)^3 + 5(2t)(-s)^4 + 1(-s)^5$

$$= 32t^5 - 80t^4s + 80t^3s^2 - 40t^2s^3 + 10ts^4 - s^5$$

39. 4th Row of Pascal's Triangle: 1   4   6   4   1

$(3 - 2z)^4 = 3^4 - 4(3)^3(2z) + 6(3)^2(2z)^2 - 4(3)(2z)^3 + (2z)^4$

$$= 81 - 216z + 216z^2 - 96z^3 + 16z^4$$

41. The term involving x^5 in the expansion of $(x + 3)^{12}$ is

$_{12}C_7 x^5(3)^7 = \dfrac{12!}{7!5!} \cdot 3^7 x^5 = 1,732,104x^5$. The coefficient is 1,732,104.

43. The term involving x^8y^2 in the expansion of $(x - 2y)^{10}$ is

$_{10}C_2 x^8(-2y)^2 = \dfrac{10!}{2!8!} \cdot 4x^8y^2 = 180x^8y^2$. The coefficient is 180.

45. The coefficient of x^4y^5 in the expansion of $(3x - 2y)^9$ is

$_9C_5(3)^4(-2)^5 = \dfrac{9!}{5!4!}(81)(-32) = -326,592$.

47. The coefficient of $x^8y^6 = (x^2)^4 y^6$ in the expansion of $(x^2 + y)^{10}$ is $_{10}C_6 = 210$.

49. There are $n + 1$ terms in the expansion of $(x + y)^n$.

51. $\left(\sqrt{x} + 3\right)^4 = \left(\sqrt{x}\right)^4 + 4\left(\sqrt{x}\right)^3(3) + 6\left(\sqrt{x}\right)^2(3)^2 + 4\left(\sqrt{x}\right)(3)^3 + (3)^4$

$$= x^2 + 12x\sqrt{x} + 54x + 108\sqrt{x} + 81$$

$$= x^2 + 12x^{3/2} + 54x + 108x^{1/2} + 81$$

53. $(x^{2/3} - y^{1/3})^3 = (x^{2/3})^3 - 3(x^{2/3})^2 (y^{1/3}) + 3(x^{2/3}) (y^{1/3})^2 - (y^{1/3})^3$

$$= x^2 - 3x^{4/3}y^{1/3} + 3x^{2/3}y^{2/3} - y$$

55. $\dfrac{f(x + h) - f(x)}{h} = \dfrac{(x + h)^3 - x^3}{h}$

$$= \dfrac{x^3 + 3x^2h + 3xh^2 + h^3 - x^3}{h}$$

$$= \dfrac{h(3x^2 + 3xh + h^2)}{h}$$

$$= 3x^2 + 3xh + h^2$$

57. $\dfrac{f(x + h) - f(x)}{h} = \dfrac{\sqrt{x + h} - \sqrt{x}}{h}$

$$= \dfrac{\sqrt{x + h} - \sqrt{x}}{h} \cdot \dfrac{\sqrt{x + h} + \sqrt{x}}{\sqrt{x + h} + \sqrt{x}}$$

$$= \dfrac{(x + h) - x}{h\left(\sqrt{x + h} + \sqrt{x}\right)}$$

$$= \dfrac{1}{\sqrt{x + h} + \sqrt{x}}$$

59. $(1 + i)^4 = {_4C_0}1^4 + {_4C_1}(1)^3 i + {_4C_2}(1)^2 i^2 + {_4C_3}1 \cdot i^3 + {_4C_4}i^4$

$$= 1 + 4i - 6 - 4i + 1$$

$$= -4$$

61. $(2 - 3i)^6 = {}_6C_02^6 - {}_6C_12^5(3i) + {}_6C_22^4(3i)^2 - {}_6C_32^3(3i)^3 + {}_6C_42^2(3i)^4 - {}_6C_52(3i)^5 + {}_6C_6(3i)^6$

$\qquad = 64 - 576i - 2160 + 4320i + 4860 - 2916i - 729$

$\qquad = 2035 + 828i$

63. $\left(-\dfrac{1}{2} + \dfrac{\sqrt{3}}{2}i\right)^3 = \dfrac{1}{8}\left(-1 + \sqrt{3}i\right)^3$

$\qquad = \dfrac{1}{8}\left[(-1)^3 + 3(-1)^2(\sqrt{3}i) + 3(-1)(\sqrt{3}i)^2 + (\sqrt{3}i)^3\right]$

$\qquad = \dfrac{1}{8}\left[-1 + 3\sqrt{3}i + 9 - 3\sqrt{3}i\right]$

$\qquad = 1$

65. ${}_7C_4\left(\dfrac{1}{2}\right)^4\left(\dfrac{1}{2}\right)^3 = 35\left(\dfrac{1}{16}\right)\left(\dfrac{1}{8}\right) \approx 0.273$

67. ${}_8C_4\left(\dfrac{1}{3}\right)^4\left(\dfrac{2}{3}\right)^4 = 70\left(\dfrac{1}{81}\right)\left(\dfrac{16}{81}\right) \approx 0.171$

69. $(1.02)^8 = (1 + 0.02)^8 = 1 + 8(0.02) + 28(0.02)^2 + 56(0.02)^3 + 70(0.02)^4 + 56(0.02)^5$

$\qquad\qquad\qquad + 28(0.02)^6 + 8(0.02)^7 + (0.02)^8$

$\qquad\qquad = 1 + 0.16 + 0.0112 + 0.000448 + \cdots \approx 1.172$

71. $(2.99)^{12} = (3 - 0.01)^{12}$

$\qquad = 3^{12} - 12(3)^{11}(0.01) + 66(3)^{10}(0.01)^2 - 220(3)^9(0.01)^3 + 495(3)^8(0.01)^4$

$\qquad\quad - 792(3)^7(0.01)^5 + 924(3)^6(0.01)^6 - 792(3)^5(0.01)^7 + 495(3)^4(0.01)^8$

$\qquad\quad - 220(3)^3(0.01)^9 + 66(3)^2(0.01)^{10} - 12(3)(0.01)^{11} + (0.01)^{12} \approx 510{,}568.785$

73. $f(x) = x^3 - 4x$

$\quad g(x) = f(x + 4)$

$\qquad = (x + 4)^3 - 4(x + 4)$

$\qquad = x^3 + 3x^2(4) + 3x(4)^2 + (4)^3 - 4x - 16$

$\qquad = x^3 + 12x^2 + 48x + 64 - 4x - 16$

$\qquad = x^3 + 12x^2 + 44x + 48$

The graph of g is the same as the graph of f shifted 4 units to the left.

75. ${}_nC_{n-r} = \dfrac{n!}{(n - (n - r))!(n - r)!}$

$\qquad = \dfrac{n!}{r!(n - r)!}$

$\qquad = \dfrac{n!}{(n - r)!r!}$

$\qquad = {}_nC_r$

77. $_nC_r + {_n}C_{r-1} = \dfrac{n!}{(n-r)!r!} + \dfrac{n!}{(n-r+1)!(r-1)!}$

$$= \dfrac{n!(n-r+1)!(r-1)! + n!(n-r)!r!}{(n-r)!r!(n-r+1)!(r-1)!}$$

$$= \dfrac{n![(n-r+1)!(r-1)! + r!(n-r)!]}{(n-r)!r!(n-r+1)!(r-1)!}$$

$$= \dfrac{n!(r-1)![(n-r+1)! + r(n-r)!]}{(n-r)!r!(n-r+1)!(r-1)!}$$

$$= \dfrac{n!(n-r)![(n-r+1) + r]}{(n-r)!r!(n-r+1)!}$$

$$= \dfrac{n![n+1]}{r!(n-r+1)!}$$

$$= \dfrac{(n+1)!}{[(n+1)-r]!r!}$$

$$= {_{n+1}}C_r$$

79. $f(t) = 0.1506t^2 + 0.7361t + 21.1374, \ 0 \le t \le 22$

(a) $g(t) = f(t+10)$

$\qquad = 0.1506(t+10)^2 + 0.7361(t+10) + 21.1374$

$\qquad = 0.1506(t^2 + 20t + 100) + 0.7361t + 7.361 + 21.1374$

$\qquad = 0.1506t^2 + 3.7481t + 43.5584$

(b)

81. $f(x) = (1-x)^3$

$\quad g(x) = 1 - 3x$

$\quad h(x) = 1 - 3x + 3x^2$

$\quad p(x) = 1 - 3x + 3x^2 - x^3$

Since $p(x)$ is the expansion of $f(x)$, they have the same graph.

83. $g(x) = f(x-3)$

$\quad g(x)$ is shifted 3 units to the right of $f(x)$.

85. $g(x) = -f(x)$

$\quad g(x)$ is the reflection of $f(x)$ in the x-axis.

Section 9.6   Counting Principles

- You should know The Fundamental Principle of Counting.

- $_nP_r = \dfrac{n!}{(n-r)!}$ is the number of permutations of n elements taken r at a time.

- Given a set of n objects that has n_1 of one kind, n_2 of a second kind, and so on, the number of distinguishable permutations is

$$\frac{n!}{n_1!n_2!\ldots n_k!}.$$

- $_nC_r = \dfrac{n!}{(n-r)!r!}$ is the number of combinations of n elements taken r at a time.

Solutions to Odd-Numbered Exercises

1. Odd integers: 1, 3, 5, 7, 9, 11
6 ways

3. Prime integers: 2, 3, 5, 7, 11
5 ways

5. Divisible by 4: 4, 8, 12
3 ways

7. Sum is 8: $1 + 7$, $2 + 6$, $3 + 5$, $4 + 4$
4 ways

9. Amplifiers: 2 choices
Compact disc players: 4 choices
Speakers: 6 choices
Total: $2 \cdot 4 \cdot 6 = 48$ ways

11. Chemist: 3 choices
Statistician: 4 choices
Total: $3 \cdot 4 = 12$ ways

13. $2^6 = 64$

15. 1st Position: 2 choices
2nd Position: 3 choices
3rd Position: 2 choices
4th Position: 1 choices
Total: $2 \cdot 3 \cdot 2 \cdot 1 = 12$ ways

Label the four people A, B, C, and D and suppose that A and B are willing to take the first position. The twelve combinations are as follows

ABCD	BACD
ABDC	BADC
ACBD	BCAD
ACDB	BCDA
ADBC	BDAC
ADCB	BDCA

17. $26 \cdot 26 \cdot 10 \cdot 10 \cdot 10 \cdot 10 = 6,760,000$

19. (a) $9 \cdot 10 \cdot 10 = 900$

    (b) $9 \cdot 9 \cdot 8 = 648$

    (c) $9 \cdot 10 \cdot 2 = 180$

    (d) $10 \cdot 10 \cdot 10 - 400 = 600$

21. $40^3 = 64{,}000$

23. (a) $6 \cdot 5 \cdot 4 \cdot 3 \cdot 2 \cdot 1 = 720$

    (b) $6 \cdot 1 \cdot 4 \cdot 1 \cdot 2 \cdot 1 = 48$

25. $_nP_r = \dfrac{n!}{(n-r)!}$

    So, $_4P_4 = \dfrac{4!}{0!} = 4! = 24.$

27. $_8P_3 = \dfrac{8!}{5!} = 8 \cdot 7 \cdot 6 = 336$

29. $_5P_4 = \dfrac{5!}{1!} = 120$

31. $14 \cdot {}_nP_3 = {}_{n+2}P_4$ Note: $n \geq 3$ for this to be defined.

$$14\left(\frac{n!}{(n-3)!}\right) = \frac{(n+2)!}{(n-2)!}$$

$14n(n-1)(n-2) = (n+2)(n+1)n(n-1)$ (We can divide here by $n(n-1)$ since $n \neq 0, n \neq 1$.)

$$14n(n-2) = (n+2)(n+1)$$
$$14n - 28 = n^2 + 3n + 2$$
$$0 = n^2 - 11n + 30$$
$$0 = (n-5)(n-6)$$
$$n = 5 \ \text{ or } \ n = 6$$

33. $_{20}P_5 = 1{,}860{,}480$

35. $_{100}P_3 = 970{,}200$

37. $_{20}C_5 = 15{,}504$

39. $_{100}P_{80} \approx 3.836 \times 10^{139}$

This number is too large for some calculators to evaluate.

41.

ABCD	BACD	CABD	DABC
ABDC	BADC	CADB	DACB
ACBD	BCAD	CBAD	DBAC
ACDB	BCDA	CBDA	DBCA
ADBC	BDAC	CDAB	DCAB
ADCB	BDCA	CDBA	DCBA

43. $5! = 120$ ways

45. $_{12}P_4 = \dfrac{12!}{8!} = 12 \cdot 11 \cdot 10 \cdot 9 = 11{,}880$ ways

47. $\dfrac{7!}{2!1!3!1!} = \dfrac{7!}{2!3!} = 420$

49. $\dfrac{7!}{2!1!1!1!1!1!} = \dfrac{7!}{2!} = 7 \cdot 6 \cdot 5 \cdot 4 \cdot 3 = 2520$

51. $_6C_2 = 15$

The 15 ways are listed below.

AB, AC, AD, AE, AF,

BC, BD, BE, BF, CD,

CE, CF, DE, DF, EF

53. $_{20}C_4 = 4845$ groups

55. $_{40}C_6 = 3,838,380$ ways

57. $_{100}C_4 = 3,921,225$ subsets

59. $_7C_2 = 21$ lines

61. (a) $_8C_4 = \dfrac{8!}{(8-4)!4!} = \dfrac{8!}{4!4!} = \dfrac{8 \cdot 7 \cdot 6 \cdot 5}{4 \cdot 3 \cdot 2} = 70$ ways

(b) $_3C_2 \cdot _5C_2 = \dfrac{3!}{(3-2)!2!} \cdot \dfrac{5!}{(5-2)!2!} = 3 \cdot 10 = 30$ ways

63. (a) $_8C_4 = \dfrac{8!}{4!4!} = 70$ ways

(b) There are 10 ways that a group of four can be formed without any couples in the group. Therefore, if at least one couple is to be in the group, there are $70 - 10 = 60$ ways that could occur.

(c) $2 \cdot 2 \cdot 2 \cdot 2 = 16$ ways

65. $_5C_2 - 5 = 10 - 5 = 5$ diagonals

67. $_8C_2 - 8 = 28 - 8 = 20$ diagonals

69. $_nP_{n-1} = \dfrac{n!}{(n-(n-1))!} = \dfrac{n!}{1!} = \dfrac{n!}{0!} = _nP_n$

71. $_nC_{n-1} = \dfrac{n!}{(n-(n-1))!(n-1)!} = \dfrac{n!}{(1)!(n-1)!} = \dfrac{n!}{(n-1)!1!} = _nC_1$

Section 9.7   Probability

You should know the following basic principles of probability.

- If an event E has $n(E)$ equally likely outcomes and its sample space has $n(S)$ equally likely outcomes, then the probability of event E is

$$P(E) = \frac{n(E)}{n(S)}, \text{ where } 0 \le P(E) \le 1.$$

- If A and B are mutually exclusive events, then $P(A \cup B) = P(A) + P(B)$.

  If A and B are not mutually exclusive events, then $P(A \cup B) = P(A) + P(B) - P(A \cap B)$.

- If A and B are independent events, then the probability that both A and B will occur is $P(A)P(B)$.

- The complement of an event E is $P(E') = 1 - P(E)$.

Solutions to Odd-Numbered Exercises

1. $\{(h, 1), (h, 2), (h, 3), (h, 4), (h, 5), (h, 6),$
$(t, 1), (t, 2), (t, 3), (t, 4), (t, 5), (t, 6)\}$

3. $\{ABC, ACB, BAC, BCA, CAB, CBA\}$

5. $\{(A, B), (A, C), (A, D), (A, E), (B, C), (B, D), (B, E), (C, D), (C, E), (D, E)\}$

7. $E = \{HHT, HTH, THH\}$

$$P(E) = \frac{n(E)}{n(S)} = \frac{3}{8}$$

9. $E = \{HHH, HHT, HTH, HTT, THH, THT, TTH\}$

$$P(E) = \frac{n(E)}{n(S)} = \frac{7}{8}$$

11. $E = \{K, K, K, K, Q, Q, Q, Q, J, J, J, J\}$

$$P(E) = \frac{n(E)}{n(S)} = \frac{12}{52} = \frac{3}{13}$$

13. $E = \{K, K, Q, Q, J, J\}$

$$P(E) = \frac{n(E)}{n(S)} = \frac{6}{52} = \frac{3}{26}$$

15. $E = \{(1, 3), (2, 2), (3, 1)\}$

$$P(E) = \frac{n(E)}{n(S)} = \frac{3}{36} = \frac{1}{12}$$

17. not $E = \{(5, 6), (6, 5), (6, 6)\}$

$$n(E) = n(S) - n(\text{not } E) = 36 - 3 = 33$$

$$P(E) = \frac{n(E)}{n(S)} = \frac{33}{36} = \frac{11}{12}$$

19. $E_3 = \{(1, 2), (2, 1)\}, \; n(E_3) = 2$

$E_5 = \{(1, 4), (2, 3), (3, 2), (4, 1)\}, \; n(E_5) = 4$

$E_7 = \{(1, 6), (2, 5), (3, 4), (4, 3), (5, 2), (6, 1)\}, \; n(E_7) = 6$

$E = E_3 \cup E_5 \cup E_7$

$n(E) = 2 + 4 + 6 = 12$

$$P(E) = \frac{n(E)}{n(S)} = \frac{12}{36} = \frac{1}{3}$$

21. $P(E) = \dfrac{_3C_2}{_6C_2} = \dfrac{3}{15} = \dfrac{1}{5}$

23. $P(E) = \dfrac{_4C_2}{_6C_2} = \dfrac{6}{15} = \dfrac{2}{5}$

25. $1 - p = 1 - 0.7 = 0.3$

27. $1 - p = 1 - 0.15 = 0.85$

29. (a) $0.37(2.5) = 0.925$ million $= 925{,}000$

(b) 18%

(c) $11\% + 6\% = 17\%$

31. (a) $\frac{290}{500} = 0.58 = 58\%$

(b) $\frac{478}{500} = 0.956 = 95.6\%$

(c) $\frac{2}{500} = 0.004 = 0.4\%$

33. (a) $\dfrac{672}{1254}$

(b) $\dfrac{582}{1254}$

(c) $\dfrac{672 - 124}{1254} = \dfrac{548}{1254}$

35. $p + p + 2p = 1$

$p = 0.25$

Taylor: $0.50 = \frac{1}{2}$

Moore: $0.25 = \frac{1}{4}$

Jenkins: $0.25 = \frac{1}{4}$

37. (a) $\dfrac{_{15}C_{10}}{_{20}C_{10}} = \dfrac{3003}{184{,}756} = \dfrac{21}{1292} \approx 0.016$

(b) $\dfrac{_{15}C_8 \cdot {_5}C_2}{_{20}C_{10}} = \dfrac{64{,}350}{184{,}756} = \dfrac{225}{646} \approx 0.348$

(c) $\dfrac{_{15}C_9 \cdot {_5}C_1}{_{20}C_{10}} + \dfrac{_{15}C_{10}}{_{20}C_{10}} = \dfrac{25{,}025 + 3003}{184{,}756} = \dfrac{28{,}028}{184{,}756} = \dfrac{49}{323} \approx 0.152$

39. Total ways to insert letters: $4! = 24$ ways

4 correct: 1 way

3 correct: not possible

2 correct: 6 ways

1 correct: 8 ways

0 correct: 9 ways

(a) $\dfrac{8}{24} = \dfrac{1}{3}$

(b) $\dfrac{8 + 6 + 1}{24} = \dfrac{15}{24} = \dfrac{5}{8}$

41. (a) $\dfrac{1}{{}_5P_5} = \dfrac{1}{120}$

(b) $\dfrac{1}{{}_4P_4} = \dfrac{1}{24}$

43. (a) $\dfrac{4}{52} \cdot \dfrac{4}{52} = \dfrac{1}{169}$

(b) $\dfrac{4}{52} \cdot \dfrac{3}{51} = \dfrac{1}{221}$

45. (a) $\dfrac{{}_9C_4}{{}_{12}C_4} = \dfrac{126}{495} = \dfrac{14}{55}$ (4 good units)

(b) $\dfrac{({}_9C_2)\,({}_3C_2)}{{}_{12}C_4} = \dfrac{108}{495} = \dfrac{12}{55}$ (2 good units)

(c) $\dfrac{({}_9C_3)({}_3C_1)}{{}_{12}C_4} = \dfrac{252}{495} = \dfrac{28}{55}$ (3 good units)

At least 2 good units: $\dfrac{12}{55} + \dfrac{28}{55} + \dfrac{14}{55} = \dfrac{54}{55}$

47. (a) $P(EE) = \dfrac{15}{30} \cdot \dfrac{15}{30} = \dfrac{1}{4}$

(b) $P(EO \text{ or } OE) = 2\left(\dfrac{15}{30}\right)\left(\dfrac{15}{30}\right) = \dfrac{1}{2}$

(c) $P(N_1 < 10, N_2 < 10) = \dfrac{9}{30} \cdot \dfrac{9}{30} = \dfrac{9}{100}$

(d) $P(N_1 N_1) = \dfrac{30}{30} \cdot \dfrac{1}{30} = \dfrac{1}{30}$

49. (a) $P(SS) = (0.985)^2 \approx 0.9702$

(b) $P(S) = 1 - P(FF) = 1 - (0.015)^2 \approx 0.9998$

(c) $P(FF) = (0.015)^2 \approx 0.0002$

51. (a) $\left(\dfrac{1}{4}\right)^5 = \dfrac{1}{1024}$

(b) $\left(\dfrac{3}{4}\right)^5 = \dfrac{243}{1024}$

(c) $1 - \dfrac{243}{1024} = \dfrac{781}{1024}$

53. $(0.32)^2 = 0.1024$

55. $1 - \dfrac{(45)^2}{(60)^2} = 1 - \left(\dfrac{45}{60}\right)^2 = 1 - \left(\dfrac{3}{4}\right)^2 = 1 - \dfrac{9}{16} = \dfrac{7}{16}$

57. (a) As you consider successive people with distinct birthdays, the probabilities must decrease to take into account the birth dates already used. Because the birth dates of people are independent events, multiply the respective probabilities of distinct birthdays.

(b) $\dfrac{365}{365} \cdot \dfrac{364}{365} \cdot \dfrac{363}{365} \cdot \dfrac{362}{365}$

(c) $P_1 = \dfrac{365}{365} = 1$

$P_2 = \dfrac{365}{365} \cdot \dfrac{364}{365} = \dfrac{364}{365} P_1 = \dfrac{365-(2-1)}{365} P_1$

$P_3 = \dfrac{365}{365} \cdot \dfrac{364}{365} \cdot \dfrac{363}{365} = \dfrac{363}{365} P_2 = \dfrac{365-(3-1)}{365} P_2$

$P_n = \dfrac{365}{365} \cdot \dfrac{364}{365} \cdot \dfrac{363}{365} \cdot \ldots \dfrac{365-(n-1)}{365} = \dfrac{365-(n-1)}{365} P_{n-1}$

(d) Q_n is the probability that the birthdays are *not* distinct which is equivalent to at least 2 people having the same birthday.

(e)

n	10	15	20	23	30	40	50
P_n	0.88	0.75	0.59	0.49	0.29	0.11	0.03
Q_n	0.12	0.25	0.41	(0.51)	0.71	0.89	0.97

(f) 23,   See the chart above.

59. $1 - 0.546 = 0.454$

Review Exercises for Chapter 9

Solutions to Odd-Numbered Exercises

1. $a_n = 2 + \dfrac{6}{n}$

$a_1 = 2 + \dfrac{6}{1} = 8$

$a_2 = 2 + \dfrac{6}{2} = 5$

$a_3 = 2 + \dfrac{6}{3} = 4$

$a_4 = 2 + \dfrac{6}{4} = \dfrac{7}{2}$

$a_5 = 2 + \dfrac{6}{5} = \dfrac{16}{5}$

3. $a_n = \dfrac{72}{n!}$

$a_1 = \dfrac{72}{1!} = 72$

$a_2 = \dfrac{72}{2!} = 36$

$a_3 = \dfrac{72}{3!} = 12$

$a_4 = \dfrac{72}{4!} = 3$

$a_5 = \dfrac{72}{5!} = \dfrac{3}{5}$

5. $a_n = \frac{3}{2}n$

7. $a_n = \frac{3n}{n+2}$

9. $\frac{1}{2(1)} + \frac{1}{2(2)} + \frac{1}{2(3)} + \cdots + \frac{1}{2(20)} = \sum_{k=1}^{20} \frac{1}{2k}$

11. $\frac{1}{2} + \frac{2}{3} + \frac{3}{4} + \cdots + \frac{9}{10} = \sum_{k=1}^{9} \frac{k}{k+1}$

13. $\sum_{i=1}^{6} 5 = 6(5) = 30$

15. $\sum_{j=1}^{4} \frac{6}{j^2} = \frac{6}{1^2} + \frac{6}{2^2} + \frac{6}{3^2} + \frac{6}{4^2} = 6 + \frac{3}{2} + \frac{2}{3} + \frac{3}{8} = \frac{205}{24}$

17. $\sum_{k=1}^{10} 2k^3 = 2(1)^3 + 2(2)^3 + 2(3)^3 + \cdots + 2(10)^3 = 6050$

19. $\sum_{n=0}^{10} (n^2 + 3) = \sum_{n=0}^{10} n^2 + \sum_{n=0}^{10} 3 = \frac{10(11)(21)}{6} + 11(3) = 418$

21. $a_1 = 3, d = 4$

$a_1 = 3$

$a_2 = 3 + 4 = 7$

$a_3 = 7 + 4 = 11$

$a_4 = 11 + 4 = 15$

$a_5 = 15 + 4 = 19$

23. $a_4 = 10 \quad a_{10} = 28$

$a_{10} = a_4 + 6d$

$28 = 10 + 6d$

$18 = 6d$

$3 = d$

$a_1 = a_4 - 3d$

$a_1 = 10 - 3(3)$

$a_1 = 1$

$a_2 = 1 + 3 = 4$

$a_3 = 4 + 3 = 7$

$a_4 = 7 + 3 = 10$

$a_5 = 10 + 3 = 13$

25. $a_1 = 35, a_{k+1} = a_k - 3$

$a_1 = 35$

$a_2 = a_1 - 3 = 35 - 3 = 32$

$a_3 = a_2 - 3 = 32 - 3 = 29$

$a_4 = a_3 - 3 = 29 - 3 = 26$

$a_5 = a_4 - 3 = 26 - 3 = 23$

$a_n = 35 + (n - 1)(-3) = 38 - 3n$

27. $a_1 = 9, a_{k+1} = a_k + 7$

$a_1 = 9$

$a_2 = a_1 + 7 = 9 + 7 = 16$

$a_3 = a_2 + 7 = 16 + 7 = 23$

$a_4 = a_3 + 7 = 23 + 7 = 30$

$a_5 = a_4 + 7 = 30 + 7 = 37$

$a_n = 9 + (n - 1)(7) = 2 + 7n$

29. $a_n = 100 + (n-1)(-3) = 103 - 3n,\ a_1 = 100,\ a_{20} = 43,\ S_{20} = \frac{20}{2}(100 + 43) = 1430$

31. $\displaystyle\sum_{j=1}^{10}(2j - 3)$ is arithmetic. Therefore, $a_1 = -1,\ a_{10} = 17,\ S_{10} = \frac{10}{2}[-1 + 17] = 80.$

33. $\displaystyle\sum_{k=1}^{11}\left(\frac{2}{3}k + 4\right)$ is arithmetic. Therefore, $a_1 = \frac{14}{3},\ a_{11} = \frac{34}{3},\ s_{11} = \frac{11}{2}\left[\frac{14}{3} + \frac{34}{3}\right] = 88.$

35. $\displaystyle\sum_{k=1}^{100} 5k$ is arithmetic. Therefore, $a_1 = 5,\ a_{100} = 500,\ s_{500} = \frac{100}{2}(5 + 500) = 25{,}250.$

37. (a) $34{,}000 + 4(2250) = \$43{,}000$

(b) $\displaystyle\sum_{k=1}^{5}[34{,}000 + (k-1)(2250)] = \sum_{k=1}^{5}(31{,}750 + 2250k) = \$192{,}500$

39. $a_1 = 4,\ r = -\frac{1}{4}$

$a_1 = 4$

$a_2 = 4\left(-\frac{1}{4}\right) = -1$

$a_3 = -1\left(-\frac{1}{4}\right) = \frac{1}{4}$

$a_4 = \frac{1}{4}\left(-\frac{1}{4}\right) = -\frac{1}{16}$

$a_5 = -\frac{1}{16}\left(-\frac{1}{4}\right) = \frac{1}{64}$

41. $a_1 = 9,\ a_3 = 4$

$a_3 = a_1 r^2$

$4 = 9r^2$

$\frac{4}{9} = r^2 \implies r = \pm\frac{2}{3}$

$a_1 = 9$	$a_1 = 9$	
$a_2 = 9\left(\frac{2}{3}\right) = 6$	$a_2 = 9\left(-\frac{2}{3}\right) = -6$	
$a_3 = 6\left(\frac{2}{3}\right) = 4$ OR	$a_3 = -6\left(-\frac{2}{3}\right) = 4$	
$a_4 = 4\left(\frac{2}{3}\right) = \frac{8}{3}$	$a_4 = 4\left(-\frac{2}{3}\right) = -\frac{8}{3}$	
$a_5 = \frac{8}{3}\left(\frac{2}{3}\right) = \frac{16}{9}$	$a_5 = -\frac{8}{3}\left(-\frac{2}{3}\right) = \frac{16}{9}$	

43. $a_1 = 120,\ a_{k+1} = \frac{1}{3}a_k$

$a_1 = 120$

$a_2 = \frac{1}{3}(120) = 40$

$a_3 = \frac{1}{3}(40) = \frac{40}{3}$

$a_4 = \frac{1}{3}\left(\frac{40}{3}\right) = \frac{40}{9}$

$a_5 = \frac{1}{3}\left(\frac{40}{9}\right) = \frac{40}{27}$

$a_n = 120\left(\frac{1}{3}\right)^{n-1}$

45. $a_1 = 25,\ a_{k+1} = -\frac{3}{5}a_k$

$a_1 = 25$

$a_2 = -\frac{3}{5}(25) = -15$

$a_3 = -\frac{3}{5}(-15) = 9$

$a_4 = -\frac{3}{5}(9) = -\frac{27}{5}$

$a_5 = -\frac{3}{5}\left(-\frac{27}{5}\right) = \frac{81}{25}$

$a_n = 25\left(-\frac{3}{5}\right)^{n-1}$

47. $a_2 = a_1 r$

$-8 = 16r$

$-\frac{1}{2} = r$

$a_n = 16\left(-\frac{1}{2}\right)^{n-1}$

$\sum_{n=1}^{20} 16\left(-\frac{1}{2}\right)^{n-1} = 16\left[\frac{1-\left(-\frac{1}{2}\right)^{20}}{1-\left(-\frac{1}{2}\right)}\right] \approx 10.67$

49. $\sum_{i=1}^{7} 2^{i-1} = \frac{1-2^7}{1-2} = 127$

51. $\sum_{i=1}^{\infty}\left(\frac{7}{8}\right)^{i-1} = \frac{1}{1-\frac{7}{8}} = 8$

53. $\sum_{k=1}^{\infty} 4\left(\frac{2}{3}\right)^{k-1} = \frac{4}{1-\frac{2}{3}} = 12$

55. $\sum_{i=1}^{10} 10\left(\frac{3}{5}\right)^{i-1} \approx 24.849$

57. (a) $a_t = 120{,}000(0.7)^t$

(b) $a_5 = 120{,}000(0.7)^5 = \$20{,}168.40$

59. $A = \sum_{i=1}^{24} 200\left(1 + \frac{0.06}{12}\right)^i \approx \$5111.82$

61. 1. When $n = 1,\ 1 = \frac{1}{2}(3(1) - 1)$.

2. Assume that

$S_k = 1 + 4 + \cdots + (3k - 2) = \frac{k}{2}(3k - 1)$.

Then,

$S_{k+1} = 1 + 4 + \cdots + (3k - 2) + (3(k + 1) - 2) = S_k + (3k + 1)$

$= \frac{k}{2}(3k - 1) + (3k + 1) = \frac{k(3k - 1) + 2(3k + 1)}{2}$

$= \frac{3k^2 + 5k + 2}{2} = \frac{(k + 1)(3k + 2)}{2} = \frac{(k + 1)}{2}(3(k + 1) - 1)$.

Therefore, by mathematical induction, the formula is valid for all positive integer values of n.

63. 1. When $n = 1$, $a = a\left(\dfrac{1 - r}{1 - r}\right)$.

2. Assume that

$$S_k = \sum_{i=0}^{k-1} ar^i = \frac{a(1 - r^k)}{1 - r}$$

Then,

$$S_{k+1} = \sum_{i=0}^{k} ar^i = \sum_{i=0}^{k-1} ar^i + ar^k = \frac{a(1 - r^k)}{1 - r} + ar^k$$

$$= \frac{a(1 - r^k + r^k - r^{k+1})}{1 - r} = \frac{a(1 - r^{k+1})}{1 - r}.$$

Therefore, by mathematical induction, the formula is valid for all positive integer values of n.

65. $_6C_4 = \dfrac{6!}{2!\,4!} = 15$

67. $_8P_5 = \dfrac{8!}{3!} = 6720$

69. $\left(\dfrac{x}{2} + y\right)^4 = \left(\dfrac{x}{2}\right)^4 + 4\left(\dfrac{x}{2}\right)^3 y + 6\left(\dfrac{x}{2}\right)^2 y^2 + 4\left(\dfrac{x}{2}\right) y^3 + y^4$

$$= \frac{x^4}{16} + \frac{x^3 y}{2} + \frac{3x^2 y^2}{2} + 2xy^3 + y^4$$

71. $\left(\dfrac{2}{x} - 3x\right)^6 = \left(\dfrac{2}{x}\right)^6 + 6\left(\dfrac{2}{x}\right)^5 (-3x) + 15\left(\dfrac{2}{x}\right)^4 (-3x)^2 + 20\left(\dfrac{2}{x}\right)^3 (-3x)^3$

$$+ 15\left(\dfrac{2}{x}\right)^2 (-3x)^4 + 6\left(\dfrac{2}{x}\right)(-3x)^5 + (-3x)^6$$

$$= \frac{64}{x^6} - \frac{576}{x^4} + \frac{2160}{x^2} - 4320 + 4860x^2 - 2916x^4 + 729x^6$$

73. $(5 + 2i)^4 = (5)^4 + 4(5)^3(2i) + 6(5)^2(2i)^2 + 4(5)(2i)^3 + (2i)^4$

$$= 625 + 1000i + 600i^2 + 160i^3 + 16i^4$$

$$= 625 + 1000i - 600 - 160i + 16 = 41 + 840i$$

75. $(26)\,(26)\,(10)\,(26)\,(26)\,(26) = 118{,}813{,}760$

77. $\dfrac{10}{10} \cdot \dfrac{1}{9} = \dfrac{1}{9}$

79. Chance of rolling a 3 with one die is $\frac{1}{6}$. With two dice

$E = \{(1, 5),\ (2, 4),\ (3, 3),\ (4, 2),\ (5, 1)\}$ and $P(E) = \frac{5}{36}$.

The probability of rolling a 3 with one die is higher.

81. $1 - P(HHHHH) = 1 - \left(\dfrac{1}{2}\right)^5 = \dfrac{31}{32}$

83. $P(\text{2 pairs}) = \dfrac{(_{13}C_2)(_4C_2)(_4C_2)(_{44}C_1)}{(_{52}C_5)} = 0.0475$

☐ Practice Test for Chapter 9

1. Write out the first five terms of the sequence $a_n = \dfrac{2n}{(n+2)!}$.

2. Write an expression for the nth term of the sequence $\left\{\dfrac{4}{3}, \dfrac{5}{9}, \dfrac{6}{27}, \dfrac{7}{81}, \dfrac{8}{243}, \ldots\right\}$.

3. Find the sum $\displaystyle\sum_{i=1}^{6}(2i-1)$.

4. Write out the first five terms of the arithmetic sequence where $a_1 = 23$ and $d = -2$.

5. Find a_n for the arithmetic sequence with $a_1 = 12$, $d = 3$, and $n = 50$.

6. Find the sum of the first 200 positive integers.

7. Write out the first five terms of the geometric sequence with $a_1 = 7$ and $r = 2$.

8. Evaluate $\displaystyle\sum_{n=0}^{9}6\left(\dfrac{2}{3}\right)^n$.

9. Evaluate $\displaystyle\sum_{n=0}^{\infty}(0.03)^n$.

10. Use mathematical induction to prove that $1 + 2 + 3 + 4 + \cdots + n = \dfrac{n(n+1)}{2}$.

11. Use mathematical induction to prove that $n! > 2^n$, $n \geq 4$.

12. Evaluate $_{13}C_4$.

13. Expand $(x+3)^5$.

14. Find the term involving x^7 in $(x-2)^{12}$.

15. Evaluate $_{30}P_4$.

16. How many ways can six people sit at a table with six chairs?

17. Twelve cars run in a race. How many different ways can they come in first, second, and third place? (Assume that there are no ties.)

18. Two six-sided dice are tossed. Find the probability that the total of the two dice is less than 5.

19. Two cards are selected at random form a deck of 52 playing cards without replacement. Find the probability that the first card is a King and the second card is a black ten.

20. A manufacturer has determined that for every 1000 units it produces, 3 will be faulty. What is the probability that an order of 50 units will have one or more faulty units?

C H A P T E R   1 0
Topics in Analytic Geometry

C H A P T E R 1 0
Topics in Analytic Geometry

Section 10.1 Lines

■ The **inclination** of a non-horizontal line is the positive angle θ ($\theta < 180°$) measured counterclockwise from the x-axis to the line. A horizontal line has an inclination of zero.

■ If a nonvertical line has inclination of θ and slope m, then $m = \tan \theta$.

■ If two non-perpendicular lines have slopes m_1 and m_2, then the angle between the lines is given by

$$\tan \theta = \left| \frac{m_2 - m_1}{1 + m_1 m_2} \right|.$$

■ The distance between a point (x_1, y_1) and a line $Ax + By + C = 0$ is given by

$$d = \frac{|Ax_1 + By_1 + C|}{\sqrt{A^2 + B^2}}.$$

Solutions to Odd-Numbered Exercises

1. $m = \tan 30° = \dfrac{\sqrt{3}}{3}$

3. $m = \tan 135° = -1$

5. $m = \tan 38.2° \approx 0.7869$

7. $m = \tan 110° \approx -2.7475$

9. $m = -1$

$-1 = \tan \theta$

$\theta = 180° + \arctan(-1) = 135°$

11. $m = \frac{3}{4}$

$\frac{3}{4} = \tan \theta$

$\theta = \arctan\left(\frac{3}{4}\right) \approx 36.9°$

13. $(6, 1), (10, 8)$

$m = \dfrac{8 - 1}{10 - 6} = \dfrac{7}{4}$

$\dfrac{7}{4} = \tan \theta$

$\theta = \arctan\left(\dfrac{7}{4}\right) \approx 60.3°$

15. $(-2, 20), (10, 0)$

$m = \dfrac{0 - 20}{10 - (-2)} = -\dfrac{20}{12} = -\dfrac{5}{3}$

$-\dfrac{5}{3} = \tan \theta$

$\theta = 180° + \arctan\left(-\dfrac{5}{3}\right) \approx 121.0°$

17. $5x - y + 3 = 0$

$y = 5x + 3 \Rightarrow m = 5$

$5 = \tan \theta$

$\theta = \arctan 5 \approx 78.7°$

19. $5x + 3y = 0$

$y = -\frac{5}{3}x \Rightarrow m = -\frac{5}{3}$

$-\frac{5}{3} = \tan \theta$

$\theta = 180° + \arctan\left(-\frac{5}{3}\right) \approx 121.0°$

21. Slope: $m = \tan 6.5° \approx 0.1139$

Change in elevation: $\dfrac{x}{2(5280)} = \sin 6.5°$

$$x = 10{,}560 \sin 6.5°$$

$$x \approx 1195 \text{ feet}$$

23. (a) $\tan \theta = \dfrac{1}{3}$

$\theta = \arctan\left(\dfrac{1}{3}\right) \approx 18.4°$

(b) $\dfrac{5}{x} = \sin 18.4°$

$x = \dfrac{5}{\sin 18.4°}$

$x \approx 15.8 \text{ meters}$

25. $2x + y = 4 \Rightarrow y = -2x + 4 \Rightarrow m_1 = -2$

$x - y = 2 \Rightarrow y = x - 2 \Rightarrow m_2 = 1$

$\tan \theta = \left|\dfrac{1 - (-2)}{1 + (-2)(1)}\right| = 3$

$\theta = \arctan 3 \approx 71.6°$

27. $x - y = 0 \Rightarrow y = x \Rightarrow m_1 = 1$

$3x - 2y = -1 \Rightarrow y = \dfrac{3}{2}x + \dfrac{1}{2} \Rightarrow m_2 = \dfrac{3}{2}$

$\tan \theta = \left|\dfrac{(3/2) - 1}{1 + (1)(3/2)}\right| = \dfrac{1}{5}$

$\theta = \arctan\left(\dfrac{1}{5}\right) \approx 11.3°$

29. $x - 2y = 5 \Rightarrow y = \dfrac{1}{2}x - \dfrac{5}{2} \Rightarrow m_2 = \dfrac{1}{2}$

$6x + 2y = 7 \Rightarrow y = -3x + \dfrac{7}{2} \Rightarrow m_2 = -3$

$\tan \theta = \left|\dfrac{-3 - (1/2)}{1 + (1/2)(-3)}\right| = 7$

$\theta = \arctan 7 \approx 81.9°$

31. $x + 2y = 4 \Rightarrow y = -\dfrac{1}{2}x + 2 \Rightarrow m_1 = -\dfrac{1}{2}$

$x - 2y = 1 \Rightarrow y = \dfrac{1}{2}x - \dfrac{1}{2} \Rightarrow m_2 = \dfrac{1}{2}$

$\tan \theta = \left|\dfrac{(1/2) - (-1/2)}{1 + (-1/2)(1/2)}\right| = \dfrac{4}{3}$

$\theta = \arctan\left(\dfrac{4}{3}\right) \approx 53.1°$

33. $0.05x - 0.03y = 0.21 \Rightarrow y = \dfrac{5}{3}x - 7 \Rightarrow m_1 = \dfrac{5}{3}$

$0.07x - 0.02y = 0.16 \Rightarrow y = -\dfrac{7}{2}x + 8 \Rightarrow m_2 = -\dfrac{7}{2}$

$\tan \theta = \left|\dfrac{(-7/2) - (5/3)}{1 + (5/3)(-7/2)}\right| = \dfrac{31}{29}$

$\theta = \arctan\left(\dfrac{31}{29}\right) \approx 46.9°$

35. Let $A = (2, 1)$, $B = (4, 4)$, and $C = (6, 2)$.

Slope of *AB:* $m_1 = \dfrac{1 - 4}{2 - 4} = \dfrac{3}{2}$

Slope of *BC:* $m_2 = \dfrac{4 - 2}{4 - 6} = -1$

Slope of *AC:* $m_3 = \dfrac{1 - 2}{2 - 6} = \dfrac{1}{4}$

$\tan A = \left| \dfrac{(1/4) - (3/2)}{1 + (3/2)(1/4)} \right| = \dfrac{5/4}{11/8} = \dfrac{10}{11}$

$A = \arctan\left(\dfrac{10}{11}\right) \approx 42.3°$

$\tan B = \left| \dfrac{(3/2) - (-1)}{1 + (-1)(3/2)} \right| = \dfrac{5/2}{1/2} = 5$

$B = \arctan 5 \approx 78.7°$

$\tan C = \left| \dfrac{-1 - (1/4)}{1 + (1/4)(-1)} \right| = \dfrac{5/4}{3/4} = \dfrac{5}{3}$

$C = \arctan\left(\dfrac{5}{3}\right) \approx 59.0°$

37. Let $A = (-4, -1)$, $B = (3, 2)$, and $C = (1, 0)$.

Slope of *AB:* $m_1 = \dfrac{-1 - 2}{-4 - 3} = \dfrac{3}{7}$

Slope of *BC:* $m_2 = \dfrac{2 - 0}{3 - 1} = 1$

Slope of *AC:* $m_3 = \dfrac{-1 - 0}{-4 - 1} = \dfrac{1}{5}$

$\tan A = \left| \dfrac{(1/5) - (3/7)}{1 + (3/7)(1/5)} \right| = \dfrac{8/35}{38/35} = \dfrac{4}{19}$

$A = \arctan\left(\dfrac{4}{19}\right) \approx 11.9°$

$\tan B = \left| \dfrac{1 - (3/7)}{1 + (3/7)(1)} \right| = \dfrac{4/7}{10/7} = \dfrac{2}{5}$

$B = \arctan\left(\dfrac{2}{5}\right) \approx 21.8°$

$C = 180° - A - B$
$\approx 180° - 11.9° - 21.8° = 146.3°$

39. (a) $m_1 = \tan 48°$

$m_2 = \tan(180° - 63°) = \tan 117°$

$\tan \theta = \left| \dfrac{\tan 117° - \tan 48°}{1 + \tan 48° \tan 117°} \right|$

$\theta = 69°$

(b) $\dfrac{x}{6700} = \sin 63°$

$x = 6700 \sin 63°$

≈ 5970 feet

$\dfrac{x}{3250} = \sin 48°$

$x = 3250 \sin 48°$

≈ 2415 feet

41. $(0, 0) \Rightarrow x_1 = 0$ and $y_1 = 0$

$4x + 3y = 0 \Rightarrow A = 4, B = 3,$ and $C = 0$

$d = \dfrac{|4(0) + 3(0) + 0|}{\sqrt{4^2 + 3^2}} = \dfrac{0}{5} = 0$

Note: The point is *on* the line.

43. $(2, 3) \Rightarrow x_1 = 2$ and $y_1 = 3$

$4x + 3y - 10 = 0 \Rightarrow A = 4, B = 3,$ and $C = -10$

$d = \dfrac{|4(2) + 3(3) + (-10)|}{\sqrt{4^2 + 3^2}} = \dfrac{7}{5} = 1.4$

45. $(6, 2) \Rightarrow x_1 = 6$ and $y_1 = 2$

$x + 1 = 0 \Rightarrow A = 1, B = 0,$ and $C = 1$

$d = \dfrac{|1(6) + 0(2) + 1|}{\sqrt{1^2 + 0^2}} = 7$

47. $(0, 8) \Rightarrow x_1 = 0$ and $y_1 = 8$

$6x - y = 0 \Rightarrow A = 6, B = -1,$ and $C = 0$

$d = \dfrac{|6(0) + (-1)(8) + 0|}{\sqrt{6^2 + (-1)^2}}$

$= \dfrac{8}{\sqrt{37}} = \dfrac{8\sqrt{37}}{37} \approx 1.3152$

49. (a) The slope of the line through AC is $m = \dfrac{0 - 1}{0 - 3} = \dfrac{1}{3}$.

The equation of the line is $y - 0 = \dfrac{1}{3}(x - 0) \Rightarrow \dfrac{1}{3}x - y = 0$.

The distance between the line and $B = (1, 5)$ is $d = \dfrac{|(1/3)(1) + (-1)(5) + 0|}{\sqrt{(1/3)^2 + (-1)^2}} = \dfrac{14/3}{\sqrt{10}/3} = \dfrac{7\sqrt{10}}{5}$.

(b) The distance between A and C is $d = \sqrt{(0 - 3)^2 + (0 - 1)^2} = \sqrt{10}$.

$A = \dfrac{1}{2}(\sqrt{10})\left(\dfrac{7\sqrt{10}}{5}\right) = 7$ square units

51. (a) The slope of the line through AC is $m = \dfrac{(1/2) - 0}{(-1/2) - (5/2)} = -\dfrac{1}{6}$.

The equation of the line through AC is $y - 0 = -\dfrac{1}{6}\left(x - \dfrac{5}{2}\right) \Rightarrow 2x + 12y - 5 = 0$.

The distance between the line and $B = (2, 3)$ is $d = \dfrac{|2(2) + 12(3) + (-5)|}{\sqrt{2^2 + 12^2}} = \dfrac{35}{\sqrt{148}} = \dfrac{35\sqrt{37}}{74}$.

(b) The distance between A and C is $d = \sqrt{\left[\left(-\dfrac{1}{2}\right) - \left(\dfrac{5}{2}\right)\right]^2 + \left[\left(\dfrac{1}{2}\right) - 0\right]^2} = \dfrac{\sqrt{37}}{2}$.

$A = \dfrac{1}{2}\left(\dfrac{\sqrt{37}}{2}\right)\left(\dfrac{35\sqrt{37}}{74}\right) = \dfrac{35}{8}$ square units

53. $x + y = 1 \Rightarrow (0, 1) \Rightarrow x_1 = 0$ and $y_1 = 1$

$x + y = 5 \Rightarrow A = 1, B = 1,$ and $C = -5$

$d = \dfrac{|1(0) + 1(1) + (-5)|}{\sqrt{1^2 + 1^2}} = \dfrac{4}{\sqrt{2}} = 2\sqrt{2} \approx 2.8284$

55. (a) $(0, 0) \Rightarrow x_1 = 0$ and $y_1 = 0$

$y = mx + 4 \Rightarrow 0 = mx - y + 4$

$d = \dfrac{|m(0) + (-1)(0) + 4|}{\sqrt{m^2 + (-1)^2}} = \dfrac{4}{\sqrt{m^2 + 1}}$

(b)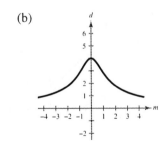

(c) The maximum distance of 4 occurs when the slope m is 0 and the line through $(0, 4)$ is horizontal.

(d) The graph has a horizontal asymptote at $d = 0$. As the slope becomes larger, the distance between the origin and the line, $y = mx + 4$, becomes smaller and approaches 0.

Section 10.2   Introduction to Conics: Parabolas

■ A **parabola** is the set of all points *(x, y)* that are equidistant from a fixed line (**directrix**) and a fixed point (**focus**) not on the line.

■ The standard equation of a parabola with vertex *(h, k)* and:
   (a) Vertical axis $x = h$ and directrix $y = k - p$ is:
       $(x - h)^2 = 4p(y - k), p \neq 0$
   (b) Horizontal axis $y = k$ and directrix $x = h - p$ is:
       $(y - k)^2 = 4p(x - h), p \neq 0$

■ The tangent line to a parabola at a point *P* makes **equal angles** with:
   (a) the line through *P* and the focus
   (b) the axis of the parabola

Solutions to Odd-Numbered Exercises

1. $y^2 = -4x$

Vertex: $(0, 0)$

Opens to the left since p is negative.

Matches graph (e).

3. $x^2 = -8y$

Vertex: $(0, 0)$

Opens downward since p is negative.

Matches graph (d).

5. $(y - 1)^2 = 4(x - 3)$

Vertex: $(3, 1)$

Opens to the right since p is positive.

Matches graph (a).

7. $y = \frac{1}{2}x^2$

$x^2 = 2y$

$x^2 = 4\left(\frac{1}{2}\right)y \Rightarrow h = 0, k = 0, p = \frac{1}{2}$

Vertex: $(0, 0)$

Focus: $\left(\frac{1}{2}, 0\right)$

Directrix: $y = -\frac{1}{2}$

9. $y^2 = -6x$

$y^2 = 4\left(-\frac{3}{2}\right)x \Rightarrow h = 0, k = 0, p = -\frac{3}{2}$

Vertex: $(0, 0)$

Focus: $\left(-\frac{3}{2}, 0\right)$

Directrix: $x = \frac{3}{2}$

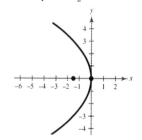

11. $x^2 + 8y = 0$

$x^2 = 4(-2)y \Rightarrow h = 0, k = 0, p = -2$

Vertex: $(0, 0)$

Focus: $(0, -2)$

Directrix: $y = 2$

13. $(x - 1)^2 + 8(y + 2) = 0$

$\qquad (x - 1)^2 = 4(-2)(y + 2)$

$h = 1, k = -2, p = -2$

Vertex: $(1, -2)$

Focus: $(1, -4)$

Directrix: $y = 0$

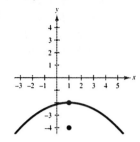

15. $\left(y + \frac{1}{2}\right)^2 = 2(x - 5)$

$\qquad = 4\left(\frac{1}{2}\right)(x - 5)$

$h = 5, k = -\frac{1}{2}, p = \frac{1}{2}$

Vertex: $\left(5, -\frac{1}{2}\right)$

Focus: $\left(\frac{11}{2}, -\frac{1}{2}\right)$

Directrix: $x = \frac{9}{2}$

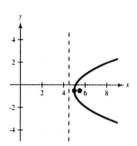

17. $\qquad y = \frac{1}{4}(x^2 - 2x + 5)$

$4y - 4 = (x - 1)^2$

$(x - 1)^2 = 4(1)(y - 1)$

$h = 1, k = 1, p = 1$

Vertex: $(1, 1)$

Focus: $(1, 2)$

Directrix: $y = 0$

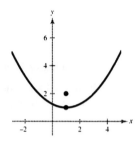

19. $y^2 + 6y + 8x + 25 = 0$

$\qquad y^2 + 6y + 9 = -8x - 25 + 9$

$\qquad (y + 3)^2 = 4(-2)(x + 2)$

$h = -2, k = -3, p = -2$

Vertex: $(-2, -3)$

Focus: $(-4, -3)$

Directrix: $x = 0$

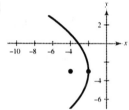

21. $\qquad y = -\frac{1}{6}(x^2 + 4x - 2)$

$\qquad -6y = x^2 + 4x - 2$

$-6y + 2 + 4 = x^2 + 4x + 4$

$\qquad -6y + 6 = (x + 2)^2$

$\qquad (x + 2)^2 = -6(y - 1)$

$\qquad (x + 2)^2 = 4\left(-\frac{3}{2}\right)(y - 1)$

$h = -2, k = 1, p = -\frac{3}{2}$

Vertex: $(-2, 1)$

Focus: $\left(-2, -\frac{1}{2}\right)$

Directrix: $y = \frac{5}{2}$

23. $y^2 + x + y = 0$

$\qquad y^2 + y + \frac{1}{4} = -x + \frac{1}{4}$

$\qquad \left(y + \frac{1}{2}\right)^2 = 4\left(-\frac{1}{4}\right)\left(x - \frac{1}{4}\right)$

$h = \frac{1}{4}, k = -\frac{1}{2}, p = -\frac{1}{4}$

Vertex: $\left(\frac{1}{4}, -\frac{1}{2}\right)$

Focus: $\left(0, -\frac{1}{2}\right)$

Directrix: $x = \frac{1}{2}$

To use a graphing calculator, enter:

$y_1 = -\frac{1}{2} + \sqrt{\frac{1}{4} - x}$

$y_2 = -\frac{1}{2} - \sqrt{\frac{1}{4} - x}$

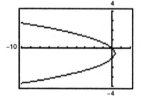

25. $y^2 - 8x = 0 \Rightarrow y = \pm\sqrt{8x}$

$\quad x - y + 2 = 0 \Rightarrow y = x + 2$

The point of tangency is $(2, 4)$.

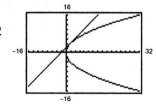

27. $x^2 = 4py \implies y = \dfrac{x^2}{4p}$

(a)
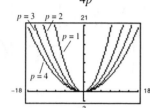

(b) $p = 1$: focus $(0, 1)$
$p = 2$: focus $(0, 2)$
$p = 3$: focus $(0, 3)$
$p = 4$: focus $(0, 4)$

As p increases, the parabola opens wider.

(c)

p-value	Length of chord
1	4
2	8
3	12
4	16

In general, the chord through the focus parallel to the directrix has a length of $4p$.

(d) Once the focus is located, move $2|p|$ units in both directions from the focus parallel to the directrix. This yields two points on the graph of the parabola, as shown in the following figures.

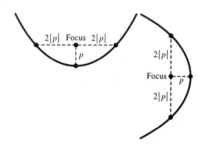

29. Vertex: $(0, 0) \implies h = 0, k = 0$

Graph opens upward.

$x^2 = 4py$

Point on graph: $(3, 6)$

$3^2 = 4p(6)$

$9 = 24p$

$\frac{3}{8} = p$

Thus, $x^2 = 4\left(\frac{3}{8}\right)y \implies y = \frac{2}{3}x^2$.

31. Vertex: $(0, 0) \implies h = 0, k = 0$

Focus: $\left(0, -\frac{3}{2}\right) \implies p = -\frac{3}{2}$

$(x - h)^2 = 4p(y - k)$

$x^2 = 4\left(-\frac{3}{2}\right)y$

$x^2 = -6y$

33. Vertex: $(0, 0) \implies h = 0, k = 0$

Focus: $(-2, 0) \implies p = -2$

$(y - k)^2 = 4p(x - h)$

$y^2 = 4(-2)x$

$y^2 = -8x$

35. Vertex: $(0, 0) \implies h = 0, k = 0$

Directrix: $y = -1 \implies p = 1$

$(x - h)^2 = 4p(y - k)$

$(x - 0)^2 = 4(1)(y - 0)$

$x^2 = 4y$ or $y = \frac{1}{4}x^2$

37. Vertex: $(0, 0) \Rightarrow h = 0, k = 0$
Directrix: $y = 2 \Rightarrow p = -2$
$(x - h)^2 = 4p(y - k)$
$(x - 0)^2 = 4(-2)(y - 0)$
$\quad x^2 = -8y$ or $y = -\frac{1}{8}x^2$

39. Vertex: $(0, 0) \Rightarrow h = 0, k = 0$
Horizontal axis and passes through the point $(4, 6)$
$(y - k)^2 = 4p(x - h)$
$(y - 0)^2 = 4p(x - 0)$
$\quad\quad y^2 = 4px$
$\quad\quad 6^2 = 4p(4)$
$\quad\quad 36 = 16p \Rightarrow p = \frac{9}{4}$
$\quad\quad y^2 = 4\left(\frac{9}{4}\right)x$
$\quad\quad y^2 = 9x$

41. Vertex: $(3, 1)$ and opens downward. Passes through $(2, 0)$ and $(4, 0)$.
$y = -(x - 2)(x - 4)$
$\quad = -x^2 + 6x - 8$
$\quad = -(x - 3)^2 + 1$
$(x - 3)^2 = -(y - 1)$

43. Vertex: $(-2, 0)$ and opens to the right. Passes through $(0, 2)$.
$(y - 0)^2 = 4p(x + 2)$
$\quad\quad 2^2 = 4p(0 + 2)$
$\quad\quad \frac{1}{2} = p$
$\quad\quad y^2 = 4\left(\frac{1}{2}\right)(x + 2)$
$\quad\quad y^2 = 2(x + 2)$

45. Vertex: $(3, 2)$
Focus: $(1, 2)$
Horizontal axis
$p = 1 - 3 = -2$
$(y - 2)^2 = 4(-2)(x - 3)$
$(y - 2)^2 = -8(x - 3)$

47. Vertex: $(0, 4)$
Directrix: $y = 2$
Vertical axis
$p = 4 - 2 = 2$
$(x - 0)^2 = 4(2)(y - 4)$
$\quad\quad x^2 = 8(y - 4)$

49. Focus: $(2, 2)$
Directrix: $x = -2$
Horizontal axis
Vertex: $(0, 2)$
$p = 2 - 0 = 2$
$(y - 2)^2 = 4(2)(x - 0)$
$(y - 2)^2 = 8x$

51. $(y - 3)^2 = 6(x + 1)$
For the upper half of the parabola:
$y - 3 = +\sqrt{6(x + 1)}$
$\quad\quad y = \sqrt{6(x + 1)} + 3$

53. Vertex: $(0, 0) \Rightarrow h = 0, k = 0$
Focus: $(0, 3.5) \Rightarrow p = 3.5$
$(x - h)^2 = 4p(y - k)$
$(x - 0)^2 = 4(3.5)(y - 0)$
$\quad\quad x^2 = 14y$ or $y = \frac{1}{14}x^2$

55. (a) Converting 16 meters to 1600 centimeters, and superimposing the coordinate plane over the parabola so that its vertex is $(0, 0)$, shows us that the points $(\pm 800, 3)$ are on the parabola.
$(x - 0)^2 = 4p(y - 0)$
$\quad\quad x^2 = 4py$

At $(\pm 800, 3)$ we have:
$640,000 = 12p$
$\quad\quad p = \dfrac{640,000}{12}$
$\quad\quad x^2 = 4\left(\dfrac{640,000}{12}\right)y$
$\quad\quad y = \dfrac{3x^2}{640,000}$

—CONTINUED—

55. —CONTINUED—

(b) Let $y = 1$, then:

$$1 = \frac{3x^2}{640{,}000}$$

$$x^2 = \frac{640{,}000}{3}$$

$$x = \frac{800\sqrt[3]{3}}{3} \approx 462 \text{ centimeters}$$

57. $R = 375x - \frac{3}{2}x^2$

The revenue is maximum when $x = 125$ units.

59. $y = -0.08x^2 + x + 4$

(a)

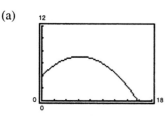

(b) The maximum occurs at the point (6.25, 7.125) and the graph crosses the x-axis when $x \approx 15.69$ feet.

61. The slope of the line $y - y_1 = \frac{x_1}{2p}(x - x_1)$

is $m = \frac{x_1}{2p}$.

63. $x^2 = 2y \Rightarrow p = \frac{1}{2}$

Point: $(x_1, y_1) = (4, 8)$

Use: $y - y_1 = \frac{x_1}{2p}(x - x_1)$

$$y - 8 = \frac{4}{2(1/2)}(x - 4)$$

$$y - 8 = 4x - 16$$

$$y = 4x - 8 \Rightarrow 0 = 4x - y - 8$$

x-intercept: $(2, 0)$

65. $y = -2x^2 \Rightarrow x^2 = -\frac{1}{2}y \Rightarrow p = -\frac{1}{8}$

Point: $(x_1, y_1) = (-1, -2)$

Use: $y - y_1 = \frac{x_1}{2p}(x - x_1)$

$$y + 2 = \frac{-1}{2(-1/8)}(x + 1)$$

$$y + 2 = 4(x + 1)$$

$$y = 4x + 2 \Rightarrow 0 = 4x - y + 2$$

x-intercept: $\left(-\frac{1}{2}, 0\right)$

67. $f(x) = (x - 3)[x - (2 + i)][x - (2 - i)]$

$$= (x - 3)(x - 2 - i)(x - 2 + i)$$

$$= (x - 3)(x^2 - 4x + 5)$$

$$= x^3 - 7x^2 + 17x - 15$$

69. $g(x) = 6x^4 + 7x^3 - 29x^2 - 28x + 20$

Possible rational roots: $\pm 1, \pm 2, \pm 4, \pm 5, \pm 10, \pm 20,$
$\pm\frac{1}{2}, \pm\frac{5}{2}, \pm\frac{1}{3}, \pm\frac{2}{3}, \pm\frac{4}{3}, \pm\frac{5}{3}, \pm\frac{10}{3}, \pm\frac{20}{3}, \pm\frac{1}{6}, \pm\frac{5}{6}$

$x = \pm 2$ are both solutions.

2	6	7	−29	−28	20
		12	38	18	−20
−2	6	19	9	−10	0
		−12	−14	10	
	6	7	−5	0	

$g(x) = (x - 2)(x + 2)(6x^2 + 7x - 5)$

$$= (x - 2)(x + 2)(2x - 1)(3x + 5)$$

The zeros of $g(x)$ are $x = \pm 2$, $x = \frac{1}{2}$, $x = -\frac{5}{3}$.

Section 10.3   Ellipses

- An **ellipse** is the set of all points *(x, y)* the sum of whose distances from two distinct fixed points (**foci**) is constant.
- The standard equation of an ellipse with center *(h, k)* and major and minor axes of lengths 2a and 2b is:

  (a) $\dfrac{(x-h)^2}{a^2} + \dfrac{(y-k)^2}{b^2} = 1$ if the major axis is horizontal.

  (b) $\dfrac{(x-h)^2}{b^2} + \dfrac{(y-k)^2}{a^2} = 1$ if the major axis is vertical.

- $c^2 = a^2 - b^2$ where *c* is the distance from the center to a focus.

- The eccentricity of an ellipse is $e = \dfrac{c}{a}$

Solutions to Odd-Numbered Exercises

1. $\dfrac{x^2}{4} + \dfrac{y^2}{9} = 1$

Center: $(0, 0)$

$a = 3, b = 2$

Vertical major axis

Matches graph (b).

3. $\dfrac{x^2}{4} + \dfrac{y^2}{25} = 1$

Center: $(0, 0)$

$a = 5, b = 2$

Vertical major axis

Matches graph (d).

5. $\dfrac{(x-2)^2}{16} + (y+1)^2 = 1$

Center: $(2, -1)$

$a = 4, b = 1$

Horizontal major axis

Matches graph (a).

7. $\dfrac{x^2}{25} + \dfrac{y^2}{16} = 1$

Center: $(0, 0)$

$a = 5, b = 4, c = 3$

Foci: $(\pm 3, 0)$

Vertices: $(\pm 5, 0)$

$e = \dfrac{3}{5}$

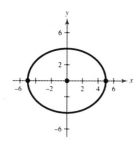

9. $\dfrac{x^2}{16} + \dfrac{y^2}{25} = 1$

$a = 5, b = 4, c = 3$

Center: $(0, 0)$

Foci: $(0, \pm 3)$

Vertices: $(0, \pm 5)$

$e = \dfrac{3}{5}$

11. $\dfrac{x^2}{9} + \dfrac{y^2}{5} = 1$

Center: $(0, 0)$

$a = 3, b = \sqrt{5}, c = 2$

Foci: $(\pm 2, 0)$

Vertices: $(\pm 3, 0)$

$e = \dfrac{2}{3}$

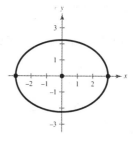

13. $\dfrac{(x-1)^2}{9} + \dfrac{(y-5)^2}{25} = 1$

$a = 5, b = 3, c = 4$

Center: $(1, 5)$

Foci: $(1, 9), (1, 1)$

Vertices: $(1, 10), (1, 0)$

$e = \dfrac{4}{5}$

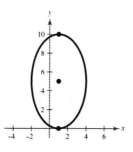

15. $9x^2 + 4y^2 + 36x - 24y + 36 = 0$

$9(x^2 + 4x + 4) + 4(y^2 - 6y + 9) = -36 + 36 + 36$

$$\frac{(x + 2)^2}{4} + \frac{(y - 3)^2}{9} = 1$$

$a = 3, b = 2, c = \sqrt{5}$

Center: $(-2, 3)$

Foci: $\left(-2, 3 \pm \sqrt{5}\right)$

Vertices: $(-2, 6), (-2, 0)$

$e = \dfrac{\sqrt{5}}{3}$

17. $16x^2 + 25y^2 - 32x + 50y + 16 = 0$

$16(x^2 - 2x + 1) + 25(y^2 + 2y + 1) = -16 + 16 + 25$

$$\frac{(x - 1)^2}{25/16} + (y + 1)^2 = 1$$

$a = \dfrac{5}{4}, b = 1, c = \dfrac{3}{4}$

Center: $(1, -1)$

Foci: $\left(\dfrac{7}{4}, -1\right), \left(\dfrac{1}{4}, -1\right)$

Vertices: $\left(\dfrac{9}{4}, -1\right), \left(-\dfrac{1}{4}, -1\right)$

$e = \dfrac{3}{5}$

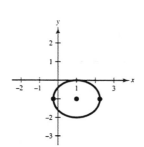

19. $5x^2 + 3y^2 = 15$

$$\frac{x^2}{3} + \frac{y^2}{5} = 1$$

Center: $(0, 0)$

$a = \sqrt{5}, b = \sqrt{3}, c = \sqrt{2}$

Foci: $\left(0, \pm\sqrt{2}\right)$

Vertices: $\left(0, \pm\sqrt{5}\right)$

To graph, solve for y.

$$y^2 = \frac{15 - 5x^2}{3}$$

$$y_1 = \sqrt{\frac{15 - 5x^2}{3}}$$

$$y_2 = -\sqrt{\frac{15 - 5x^2}{3}}$$

21. $12x^2 + 20y^2 - 12x + 40y - 37 = 0$

$12\left(x^2 - x + \dfrac{1}{4}\right) + 20(y^2 + 2y + 1) = 37 + 3 + 20$

$$\frac{[x - (1/2)]^2}{5} + \frac{(y + 1)^2}{3} = 1$$

$a = \sqrt{5}, b = \sqrt{3}, c = \sqrt{2}$

Center: $\left(\dfrac{1}{2}, -1\right)$

Foci: $\left(\dfrac{1}{2} \pm \sqrt{2}, -1\right)$

Vertices: $\left(\dfrac{1}{2} \pm \sqrt{5}, -1\right)$

$e = \dfrac{\sqrt{10}}{5}$

To graph, solve for y.

$$(y + 1)^2 = 3\left[1 - \frac{(x - 0.5)^2}{5}\right]$$

$$y_1 = -1 + \sqrt{3\left[1 - \frac{(x - 0.5)^2}{5}\right]}$$

$$y_2 = -1 - \sqrt{3\left[1 - \frac{(x - 0.5)^2}{5}\right]}$$

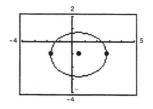

23. For the right half of the ellipse, solve for x and use the positive square root.

$$\frac{(x-3)^2}{9} + \frac{y^2}{4} = 1$$

$$4(x-3)^2 + 9y^2 = 36$$

$$4(x-3)^2 = 36 - 9y^2$$

$$(x-3)^2 = \frac{9(4-y^2)}{4}$$

$$x - 3 = \frac{2}{3}\sqrt{4-y^2}$$

$$x = 3 + \frac{2}{3}\sqrt{4-y^2}$$

$$= \frac{3}{2}\left(2 + \sqrt{4-y^2}\right)$$

25. Center: $(0,0)$

$a = 2, b = 1$

Vertical major axis

$$\frac{(x-h)^2}{b^2} + \frac{(y-k)^2}{a^2} = 1$$

$$\frac{x^2}{1} + \frac{y^2}{4} = 1$$

27. Vertices: $(\pm 5, 0)$

$a = 5, c = 2 \Rightarrow b = \sqrt{21}$

Foci: $(\pm 2, 0)$

Horizontal major axis

Center: $(0,0)$

$$\frac{(x-h)^2}{a^2} + \frac{(y-k)^2}{b^2} = 1$$

$$\frac{x^2}{25} + \frac{y^2}{21} = 1$$

29. Foci: $(\pm 5, 0) \Rightarrow c = 5$

Center: $(0,0)$

Horizontal major axis

Major axis of length $12 \Rightarrow 2a = 12$

$$a = 6$$

$$6^2 - b^2 = 5^2 \Rightarrow b^2 = 11$$

$$\frac{(x-h)^2}{a^2} + \frac{(y-k)^2}{b^2} = 1$$

$$\frac{x^2}{36} + \frac{y^2}{11} = 1$$

31. Vertices: $(0, \pm 5) \Rightarrow a = 5$

Center: $(0,0)$

Vertical major axis

$$\frac{(x-h)^2}{b^2} + \frac{(y-k)^2}{a^2} = 1$$

$$\frac{x^2}{b^2} + \frac{y^2}{25} = 1$$

Point: $(4, 2)$

$$\frac{4^2}{b^2} + \frac{2^2}{25} = 1$$

$$\frac{16}{b^2} = 1 - \frac{4}{25} = \frac{21}{25}$$

$$400 = 21b^2$$

$$\frac{400}{21} = b^2$$

$$\frac{x^2}{400/21} + \frac{y^2}{25} = 1$$

$$\frac{21x^2}{400} + \frac{y^2}{25} = 1$$

33. Center: $(2, 3)$

$a = 3, \quad b = 1$

Vertical major axis

$$\frac{(x-h)^2}{b^2} + \frac{(y-k)^2}{a^2} = 1$$

$$\frac{(x-2)^2}{1} + \frac{(y-3)^2}{9} = 1$$

35. Center: $(2, 2)$

$a = 3, \quad b = 2$

Horizontal major axis

$$\frac{(x-h)^2}{a^2} + \frac{(y-k)^2}{b^2} = 1$$

$$\frac{(x-2)^2}{9} + \frac{(y-2)^2}{4} = 1$$

37. Vertices: $(0, 2), (4, 2) \Rightarrow a = 2$

Minor axis of length $2 \Rightarrow b = 1$

Center: $(2, 2) = (h, k)$

$$\frac{(x - h)^2}{a^2} + \frac{(y - k)^2}{b^2} = 1$$

$$\frac{(x - 2)^2}{4} + \frac{(y - 2)^2}{1} = 1$$

39. Foci: $(0, 0), (0, 8) \Rightarrow c = 4$

Major axis of length $16 \Rightarrow a = 8$

$b^2 = a^2 - c^2 = 64 - 16 = 48$

Center: $(0, 4) = (h, k)$

$$\frac{(x - h)^2}{b^2} + \frac{(y - k)^2}{a^2} = 1$$

$$\frac{x^2}{48} + \frac{(y - 4)^2}{64} = 1$$

41. Vertices: $(3, 1), (3, 9) \Rightarrow a = 4$

Center: $(3, 5)$

Minor axis of length $6 \Rightarrow b = 3$

Vertical major axis

$$\frac{(x - h)^2}{b^2} + \frac{(y - k)^2}{a^2} = 1$$

$$\frac{(x - 3)^2}{9} + \frac{(y - 5)^2}{16} = 1$$

43. Center: $(0, 4)$

Vertices: $(-4, 4), (4, 4) \Rightarrow a = 4$

$a = 2c \Rightarrow 4 = 2c \Rightarrow c = 2$

$2^2 = 4^2 - b^2 \Rightarrow b^2 = 12$

Horizontal major axis

$$\frac{(x - h)^2}{a^2} + \frac{(y - k)^2}{b^2} = 1$$

$$\frac{x^2}{16} + \frac{(y - 4)^2}{12} = 1$$

45. (a) The length of the string is $2a$.

(b) The path is an ellipse because the sum of the distances from the two thumbtacks is always the length of the string, that is, it is constant.

47.

49. $\dfrac{x^2}{a^2} + \dfrac{y^2}{b^2} = 1$

(a) $a + b = 20 \Rightarrow b = 20 - a$

$A = \pi ab = \pi a(20 - a)$

(b) $264 = \pi a(20 - a)$

$0 = -\pi a^2 + 20\pi a - 264$

$0 = \pi a^2 - 20\pi a + 264$

$a = 14$ or $a = 6$. The equation of an ellipse with an area of 264 is $\dfrac{x^2}{196} + \dfrac{y^2}{36} = 1$.

(c)

a	8	9	10	11	12	13
A	301.6	311.0	314.2	311.0	301.6	285.9

The area is maximum when $a = 10$ and the ellipse is a circle.

(d)

The area is maximum (314.16) when $a = b = 10$ and the ellipse is a circle.

51. Vertices: $(\pm 5, 0) \Rightarrow a = 5$

Eccentricity: $\dfrac{3}{5} \Rightarrow c = \dfrac{3}{5} a = 3$

$b^2 = a^2 - c^2 = 25 - 9 = 16$

Center: $(0, 0) = (h, k)$

$$\frac{(x - h)^2}{a^2} + \frac{(y - k)^2}{b^2} = 1$$

$$\frac{x^2}{25} + \frac{y^2}{16} = 1$$

53. $2a = 36.18 \Rightarrow a = 18.09$

$e = \dfrac{c}{a} = 0.97 \Rightarrow c = (18.09)(0.97) = 17.5473$

$b^2 = a^2 - c^2 = (18.09)^2 - (17.5473)^2 \approx 19.34$

The equation of the ellipse is:

$$\frac{x^2}{(18.09)^2} + \frac{y^2}{19.34} = 1$$

$$\frac{x^2}{327.25} + \frac{y^2}{19.34} = 1$$

55. apogee $= 938 + 6378 = 7316$

perigee $= 212 + 6378 = 6590$

$$e = \frac{7316 - 6590}{7316 + 6590} \approx 0.052$$

57. False: The graph of $\dfrac{x^2}{4} + y^4 = 1$ is not an ellipse.

The degree on y is 4, not 2.

59. $\dfrac{x^2}{4} + \dfrac{y^2}{1} = 1$

$a = 2, b = 1, c = \sqrt{3}$

Points on the ellipse: $(\pm 2, 0), (0, \pm 1)$

Length of latus recta: $\dfrac{2b^2}{a} = \dfrac{2(1)^2}{2} = 1$

Additional points: $\left(-\sqrt{3}, \pm\dfrac{1}{2} \right), \left(\sqrt{3}, \pm\dfrac{1}{2} \right)$

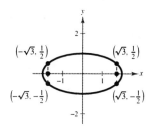

61. $9x^2 + 4y^2 = 36$

$\dfrac{x^2}{4} + \dfrac{y^2}{9} = 1$

$a = 3, b = 2, c = \sqrt{5}$

Points on the ellipse: $(\pm 2, 0), (0, \pm 3)$

Length of latus recta: $\dfrac{2b^2}{a} = \dfrac{2 \cdot 2^2}{3} = \dfrac{8}{3}$

Additional points: $\left(\pm\dfrac{4}{3}, -\sqrt{5} \right), \left(\pm\dfrac{4}{3}, \sqrt{5} \right)$

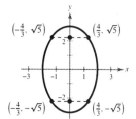

Section 10.4   Hyperbolas

- A **hyperbola** is the set of all points *(x, y)* the difference of whose distances from two distinct fixed points **(foci)** is constant.

- The standard equation of a hyperbola with center *(h, k)* and transverse and conjugate axes of lengths $2a$ and $2b$ is:

    (a) $\dfrac{(x - h)^2}{a^2} - \dfrac{(y - k)^2}{b^2} = 1$ if the traverse axis is horizontal.

    (b) $\dfrac{(y - k)^2}{a^2} - \dfrac{(x - h)^2}{b^2} = 1$ if the traverse axis is vertical.

- $c^2 = a^2 + b^2$ where c is the distance fromthe center to a focus.

- The asymptotes of a hyperbola are:

    (a) $y = k \pm \dfrac{b}{a}(x - h)$ if the transverse axis is horizontal.

    (b) $y = k \pm \dfrac{a}{b}(x - h)$ the transverse axis is vertical.

- The eccentricity of a hyperbola is $e = \dfrac{c}{a}$.

- To classify a nondegenerate conic from its general equation $Ax^2 + Cy^2 + Dx + Ey + F = 0$:
    (a) If $A = C$ $(A \neq 0, C \neq 0)$, then it is a circle.
    (b) If $AC = 0$ $(A = 0$ or $C = 0$, but not both), then it is a parabola.
    (c) If $AC > 0$, then it is an ellipse.
    (d) If $AC < 0$, then it is a hyperbola.

Solutions to Odd Numbered Exercises

1. $\dfrac{x^2}{16} - \dfrac{y^2}{4} = 1$

Center: $(0, 0)$

$a = 4, b = 2$

Horizontal transverse axis

Matches graph (b).

3. $\dfrac{y^2}{9} - \dfrac{x^2}{16} = 1$

Center: $(0, 0)$

$a = 3, b = 4$

Vertical transverse axis

Matches graph (e).

5. $\dfrac{(x - 1)^2}{16} - \dfrac{y^2}{4} = 1$

Center: $(1, 0)$

$a = 4, b = 2$

Horizontal transverse axis

Matches graph (a).

7. $x^2 - y^2 = 1$

$a = 1, b = 1, c = \sqrt{2}$

Center: $(0, 0)$

Vertices: $(\pm 1, 0)$

Foci: $\left(\pm \sqrt{2}, 0\right)$

Asymptotes: $y = \pm x$

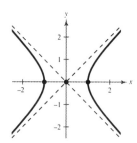

9. $\dfrac{y^2}{1} - \dfrac{x^2}{4} = 1$

$a = 1, b = 2, c = \sqrt{5}$

Center: $(0, 0)$

Vertices: $(0, \pm 1)$

Foci: $\left(0, \pm \sqrt{5}\right)$

Asymptotes: $y = \pm \dfrac{1}{2} x$

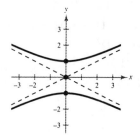

11. $\dfrac{y^2}{25} - \dfrac{x^2}{144} = 1$

$a = 5, b = 12, c = 13$

Center: $(0, 0)$

Vertices: $(0, \pm 5)$

Foci: $(0, \pm 13)$

Asymptotes: $y = \pm \dfrac{5}{12} x$

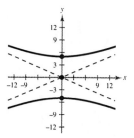

13. $\dfrac{(x - 1)^2}{4} - \dfrac{(y + 2)^2}{1} = 1$

$a = 2, b = 1, c = \sqrt{5}$

Center: $(1, -2)$

Vertices: $(-1, -2), (3, -2)$

Foci: $\left(1 \pm \sqrt{5}, -2\right)$

Asymptotes: $y = -2 \pm \dfrac{1}{2}(x - 1)$

15. $(y + 6)^2 - (x - 2)^2 = 1$

$a = 1, b = 1, c = \sqrt{2}$

Center: $(2, -6)$

Vertices: $(2, -5), (2, -7)$

Foci: $\left(2, -6 \pm \sqrt{2}\right)$

Asymptotes: $y = -6 \pm (x - 2)$

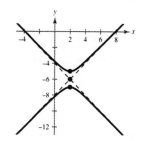

17. $9x^2 - y^2 - 36x - 6y + 18 = 0$

$9\left(x^2 - 4x + 4\right) - \left(y^2 + 6y + 9\right) = -18 + 36 - 9$

$\dfrac{(x - 2)^2}{1} - \dfrac{(y + 3)^2}{9} = 1$

$a = 1, b = 3, c = \sqrt{10}$

Center: $(2, -3)$

Vertices: $(1, -3), (3, -3)$

Foci: $\left(2 \pm \sqrt{10}, -3\right)$

Asymptotes: $y = -3 \pm 3(x - 2)$

19.
$$x^2 - 9y^2 + 2x - 54y - 80 = 0$$
$$(x^2 + 2x + 1) - 9(y^2 + 6y + 9) = 80 + 1 - 81$$
$$(x + 1)^2 - 9(y + 3)^2 = 0$$
$$y + 3 = \pm\frac{1}{3}(x + 1)$$

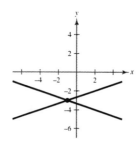

Degenerate hyperbola is two lines intersecting at $(-1, -3)$.

21. $2x^2 - 3y^2 = 6$

$$\frac{x^2}{3} - \frac{y^2}{2} = 1$$

$a = \sqrt{3}, b = \sqrt{2}, c = \sqrt{5}$

Center: $(0, 0)$

Vertices: $(\pm\sqrt{3}, 0)$

Foci: $(\pm\sqrt{5}, 0)$

Asymptotes: $y = \pm\sqrt{\frac{2}{3}}\, x$

To use a graphing calculator, solve first for y.

$$y^2 = \frac{2x^2 - 6}{3}$$

$$\left.\begin{array}{l} y_1 = \sqrt{\dfrac{2x^2 - 6}{3}} \\[2em] y_2 = -\sqrt{\dfrac{2x^2 - 6}{3}} \end{array}\right\} \text{Hyperbola}$$

$$\left.\begin{array}{l} y_3 = \sqrt{\dfrac{2}{3}}\, x \\[2em] y_4 = -\sqrt{\dfrac{2}{3}}\, x \end{array}\right\} \text{Asymptotes}$$

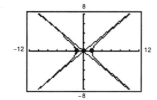

23.
$$9y^2 - x^2 + 2x + 54y + 62 = 0$$
$$9(y^2 + 6y + 9) - (x^2 - 2x + 1) = -62 - 1 + 81$$
$$\frac{(y + 3)^2}{2} - \frac{(x - 1)^2}{18} = 1$$

$a = \sqrt{2}, b = 3\sqrt{2}, c = 2\sqrt{5}$

Center: $(1, -3)$

Vertices: $(1, -3 \pm \sqrt{2})$

Foci: $(1, -3 \pm 2\sqrt{5})$

Asymptotes: $y = -3 \pm \frac{1}{3}(x - 1)$

To use a graphing calculator, solve for y first.

$$9(y + 3)^2 = 18 + (x - 1)^2$$

$$y = -3 \pm \sqrt{\frac{18 + (x - 1)^2}{9}}$$

$$\left.\begin{array}{l} y_1 = -3 + \dfrac{1}{3}\sqrt{18 + (x - 1)^2} \\[2em] y_2 = -3 - \dfrac{1}{3}\sqrt{18 + (x - 1)^2} \end{array}\right\} \text{Hyperbola}$$

$$\left.\begin{array}{l} y_3 = -3 + \dfrac{1}{3}(x - 1) \\[2em] y_4 = -3 - \dfrac{1}{3}(x - 1) \end{array}\right\} \text{Asymptotes}$$

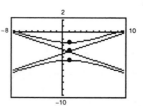

25. Vertices: $(0, \pm 3) \Rightarrow a = 3$

Solution point: $(-2, 5)$

Center: $(0, 0) = (h, k)$

$$\frac{(y - k)^2}{a^2} - \frac{(x - h)^2}{b^2} = 1$$

$$\frac{y^2}{9} - \frac{x^2}{b^2} = 1 \Rightarrow b^2 = \frac{9x^2}{y^2 - 9} = \frac{9(-2)^2}{5^2 - 9} = \frac{36}{16} = \frac{9}{4}$$

$$\frac{y^2}{9} - \frac{x^2}{9/4} = 1$$

27. Vertices: $(0, \pm 2) \Rightarrow a = 2$

Foci: $(0, \pm 4) \Rightarrow c = 4$

$b^2 = c^2 - a^2 = 16 - 4 = 12$

Center: $(0, 0) = (h, k)$

$\dfrac{(y - k)^2}{a^2} - \dfrac{(x - h)^2}{b^2} = 1$

$\dfrac{y^2}{4} - \dfrac{x^2}{12} = 1$

29. Vertices: $(\pm 1, 0) \Rightarrow a = 1$

Asymptotes: $y = \pm 3x \Rightarrow \dfrac{b}{a} = 3, b = 3$

Center: $(0, 0) = (h, k)$

$\dfrac{(x - h)^2}{a^2} - \dfrac{(y - k)^2}{b^2} = 1$

$\dfrac{x^2}{1} - \dfrac{y^2}{9} = 1$

31. Foci: $(0, \pm 8) \Rightarrow c = 8$

Asymptotes: $y = \pm 4x \Rightarrow \dfrac{a}{b} = 4 \Rightarrow a = 4b$

Center: $(0, 0) = (h, k)$

$c^2 = a^2 + b^2 \Rightarrow 64 = 16b^2 + b^2$

$\dfrac{64}{17} = b^2 \Rightarrow a^2 = \dfrac{1024}{17}$

$\dfrac{(y - k)^2}{a^2} - \dfrac{(x - h)^2}{b^2} = 1$

$\dfrac{y^2}{1024/17} - \dfrac{x^2}{64/17} = 1$

$\dfrac{17y^2}{1024} - \dfrac{17x^2}{65} = 1$

33. Vertices: $(0, 0), (0, 2) \Rightarrow a = 1$

Solution point: $\left(\sqrt{3}, 3 \right)$

Center: $(0, 1) = (h, k)$

$\dfrac{(y - k)^2}{a^2} - \dfrac{(x - h)^2}{b^2} = 1$

$(y - 1)^2 - \dfrac{x^2}{b^2} = 1 \Rightarrow 4 - \dfrac{3}{b^2} = 1 \Rightarrow b^2 = 1$

$(y - 1)^2 - x^2 = 1$

35. Center: $(3, 2) = (h, k)$

Vertices: $(1, 2), (5, 2) \Rightarrow a = 2$

Solution point: $(0, 0)$

$\dfrac{(x - h)^2}{a^2} - \dfrac{(y - k)^2}{b^2} = 1$

$\dfrac{(x - 3)^2}{4} - \dfrac{(y - 2)^2}{b^2} = 1 \Rightarrow \dfrac{9}{4} - \dfrac{4}{b^2} = 1 \Rightarrow b^2 = \dfrac{16}{5}$

$\dfrac{(x - 3)^2}{4} - \dfrac{(y - 2)^2}{16/5} = 1$

37. Vertices: $(2, 0), (6, 0) \Rightarrow a = 2$

Foci: $(0, 0), (8, 0) \Rightarrow c = 4$

$b^2 = c^2 - a^2 = 16 - 4 = 12$

Center: $(4, 0) = (h, k)$

$$\frac{(x - h)^2}{a^2} - \frac{(y - k)^2}{b^2} = 1$$

$$\frac{(x - 4)^2}{4} - \frac{y^2}{12} = 1$$

39. Vertices: $(4, 1), (4, 9) \Rightarrow a = 4$

Foci: $(4, 0), (4, 10) \Rightarrow c = 5$

$b^2 = c^2 - a^2 = 25 - 16 = 9$

Center: $(4, 5) = (h, k)$

$$\frac{(y - k)^2}{a^2} - \frac{(x - h)^2}{b^2} = 1$$

$$\frac{(y - 4)^2}{16} - \frac{(x - 4)^2}{9} = 1$$

41. Vertices: $(2, 3), (2, -3) \Rightarrow a = 3$

Solution point: $(0, 5)$

Center: $(2, 0) = (h, k)$

$$\frac{(y - k)^2}{a^2} - \frac{(x - h)^2}{b^2} = 1$$

$$\frac{y^2}{9} - \frac{(x - 2)^2}{b^2} = 1 \Rightarrow b^2 = \frac{9(x - 2)^2}{y^2 - 9} = \frac{9(-2)^2}{25 - 9} = \frac{36}{16} = \frac{9}{4}$$

$$\frac{y^2}{9} - \frac{(x - 2)^2}{9/4} = 1$$

43. Vertices: $(0, 2), (6, 2) \Rightarrow a = 3$

Asymptotes: $y = \frac{2}{3}x, y = 4 - \frac{2}{3}x$

$\dfrac{b}{a} = \dfrac{2}{3} \Rightarrow b = 2$

Center: $(3, 2) = (h, k)$

$$\frac{(x - h)^2}{a^2} - \frac{(y - k)^2}{b^2} = 1$$

$$\frac{(x - 3)^2}{9} - \frac{(y - 2)^2}{4} = 1$$

45. $x = 3 - \dfrac{2}{3}\sqrt{1 + (y - 1)^2}$ represents the left branch of the hyperbola.

47. Since $\overline{AB} = 1100$ feet and the sound takes one second longer to reach B than A, the explosion must occur on the vertical line through A and B below A.

Foci: $(\pm 4400, 0) \Rightarrow c = 4400$

Center: $(0, 0) = (h, k)$

$$\frac{\overline{CE}}{1100} - \frac{\overline{AE}}{1100} = 5 \Rightarrow 2a = 5500, a = \frac{5500}{2} = 2750$$

$b^2 = c^2 - a^2 = (4400)^2 - (2750)^2 = 11{,}797{,}500$

$$\frac{x^2}{(2750)^2} - \frac{y^2}{11{,}797{,}500} = 1$$

$$y^2 = 11{,}797{,}500\left(\frac{x^2}{(2750)^2} - 1\right)$$

$$y^2 = 11{,}797{,}500\left(\frac{(4400)^2}{(2750)^2} - 1\right) = 18{,}404{,}100$$

$$y = -4290$$

The explosion occurs at $(4400, -4290)$.

49. Center: $(0, 0) = (h, k)$

Focus: $(24, 0) \Rightarrow c = 24$

Solution point: $(24, 24)$

$24^2 = a^2 + b^2 \Rightarrow b^2 = 24^2 - a^2$

$\dfrac{(x - h)^2}{a^2} - \dfrac{(y - k)^2}{b^2} = 1$

$\dfrac{x^2}{a^2} - \dfrac{y^2}{24^2 - a^2} = 1 \Rightarrow \dfrac{24^2}{a^2} - \dfrac{24^2}{24^2 - a^2} = 1$

Solving yields $a^2 = \dfrac{\left(3 - \sqrt{5}\right)24^2}{2} \approx 220.0124$ and $b^2 \approx 355.9876$.

Thus, we have $\dfrac{x^2}{220.0124} - \dfrac{y^2}{355.9876} = 1$.

The right vertex is at $(a, 0) \approx (14.83, 0)$.

51. $x^2 + y^2 - 6x + 4y + 9 = 0$

$A = 1, C = 1$

$A = C \Rightarrow$ Circle

53. $4x^2 - y^2 - 4x - 3 = 0$

$A = 4, C = -1$

$AC = 4(-1)$

$\quad = -4 < 0 \Rightarrow$ Hyperbola

55. $4x^2 + 3y^2 + 8x - 24y + 51 = 0$

$A = 4, C = 3$

$AC = 4(3) = 12 > 0 \Rightarrow$ Ellipse

57. $25x^2 - 10x - 200y - 119 = 0$

$A = 25, C = 0$

$AC = 25(0) = 0 \Rightarrow$ Parabola

59. $\left(x^3 - 3x^2\right) - \left(6 - 2x - 4x^2\right) = x^3 - 3x^2 - 6 + 2x + 4x^2$

$\qquad\qquad\qquad\qquad\qquad = x^3 + x^2 + 2x - 6$

61.
$$x + 2 \overline{)\, x^3 + 0x^2 - 3x + 4} \quad\quad x^2 - 2x + 1 + \frac{2}{x + 2}$$

$$\underline{x^3 + 2x^2}$$
$$-2x^2 - 3x$$
$$\underline{-2x^2 - 4x}$$
$$x + 4$$
$$\underline{x + 2}$$
$$2$$

Thus, $\dfrac{x^3 - 3x + 4}{x + 2} = x^2 - 2x + 1 + \dfrac{2}{x + 2}$.

Section 10.5   Rotation of Conics

■   The general second-degree equation $Ax^2 + Bxy + Cy^2 + Dx + Ey + F = 0$ can be rewritten as $A'(x')^2 + C'(y')^2 + D'x' + E'y' + F' = 0$ by rotating the coordinate axes through the angle θ, where $\cot 2\theta = (A - C)/B$.

■ $x = x' \cos \theta - y' \sin \theta$
    $y = x' \sin \theta + y' \cos \theta$

■   The graph of the nondegenerate equation $Ax^2 + Bxy + Cy^2 + Dx + Ey + F = 0$ is:

   (a)   An ellipse or circle if $B^2 - 4AC < 0$.

   (b)   A parabola if $B^2 - 4AC = 0$.

   (c)   A hyperbola if $B^2 - 4AC > 0$.

Solutions to Odd-Numbered Exercises

1. $\theta = 90°$; Point: $(0, 3)$

   $x' = x \cos \theta - y \sin \theta = 0(\cos 90°) - 3(\sin 90°) = -3$

   $y' = x \sin \theta + y \cos \theta = 0(\sin 90°) + 3(\cos 90°) = 0$

   Thus, $(x', y') = (-3, 0)$.

3. $\theta = 30°$; Point: $(1, 4)$

   $x' = x \cos \theta - y \sin \theta = 1(\cos 30°) - 4(\sin 30°) = \dfrac{\sqrt{3}}{2} - \dfrac{4}{2} = \dfrac{1}{2}(\sqrt{3} - 4)$

   $y' = x \sin \theta + y \cos \theta = 1(\sin 30°) + 4(\cos 30°) = \dfrac{1}{2} + \dfrac{4\sqrt{3}}{2} = \dfrac{1}{2}(1 + 4\sqrt{3})$

   Thus, $(x', y') = \left(\dfrac{1}{2}(\sqrt{3} - 4), \dfrac{1}{2}(1 + 4\sqrt{3}) \right)$.

5. $xy + 1 = 0$

   $A = 0, B = 1, C = 0$

   $\cot 2\theta = \dfrac{A - C}{B} = 0 \Rightarrow 2\theta = \dfrac{\pi}{2} \Rightarrow \theta = \dfrac{\pi}{4}$

   $x = x' \cos \dfrac{\pi}{4} - y' \sin \dfrac{\pi}{4}$ $y = x' \sin \dfrac{\pi}{4} + y' \cos \dfrac{\pi}{4}$

   $\quad = x'\left(\dfrac{\sqrt{2}}{2} \right) - y'\left(\dfrac{\sqrt{2}}{2} \right)$ $\quad = x'\left(\dfrac{\sqrt{2}}{2} \right) + y'\left(\dfrac{\sqrt{2}}{2} \right)$

   $\quad = \dfrac{x' - y'}{\sqrt{2}}$ $\quad = \dfrac{x' + y'}{\sqrt{2}}$

   $xy + 1 = 0$

   $\left(\dfrac{x' - y'}{\sqrt{2}} \right)\left(\dfrac{x' + y'}{\sqrt{2}} \right) + 1 = 0$

   $\dfrac{(y')^2}{2} - \dfrac{(x')^2}{2} = 1$

7. $x^2 - 10xy + y^2 + 1 = 0$

$A = 1, B = -10, C = 1$

$\cot 2\theta = \dfrac{A - C}{B} = 0 \Rightarrow 2\theta = \dfrac{\pi}{2} \Rightarrow \theta = \dfrac{\pi}{4}$

$x = x'\cos\dfrac{\pi}{4} - y'\sin\dfrac{\pi}{4}$

$\qquad = x'\left(\dfrac{\sqrt{2}}{2}\right) - y'\left(\dfrac{\sqrt{2}}{2}\right)$

$\qquad = \dfrac{x' - y'}{\sqrt{2}}$

$y = x'\sin\dfrac{\pi}{4} + y'\cos\dfrac{\pi}{4}$

$\qquad = x'\left(\dfrac{\sqrt{2}}{2}\right) + y'\left(\dfrac{\sqrt{2}}{2}\right)$

$\qquad = \dfrac{x' + y'}{\sqrt{2}}$

$x^2 - 10xy + y^2 + 1 = 0$

$$\left(\dfrac{x' - y'}{\sqrt{2}}\right)^2 - 10\left(\dfrac{x' - y'}{\sqrt{2}}\right)\left(\dfrac{x' + y'}{\sqrt{2}}\right) + \left(\dfrac{x' + y'}{\sqrt{2}}\right)^2 + 1 = 0$$

$$\dfrac{(x')^2}{2} - x'y' + \dfrac{(y')^2}{2} - 5(x')^2 + 5(y')^2 + \dfrac{(x')^2}{2} + x'y' + \dfrac{(y')^2}{2} + 1 = 0$$

$$-4(x')^2 + 6(y')^2 = -1$$

$$\dfrac{(x')^2}{1/4} - \dfrac{(y')^2}{1/6} = 1$$

9. $xy - 2y - 4x = 0$

$A = 0, B = 1, C = 0$

$\cot 2\theta = \dfrac{A - C}{B} = 0 \Rightarrow 2\theta = \dfrac{\pi}{2} \Rightarrow \theta = \dfrac{\pi}{4}$

$x = x'\cos\dfrac{\pi}{4} - y'\sin\dfrac{\pi}{4}$

$\qquad = x'\left(\dfrac{\sqrt{2}}{2}\right) - y'\left(\dfrac{\sqrt{2}}{2}\right)$

$\qquad = \dfrac{x' - y'}{\sqrt{2}}$

$y = x'\sin\dfrac{\pi}{4} + y'\cos\dfrac{\pi}{4}$

$\qquad = x'\left(\dfrac{\sqrt{2}}{2}\right) + y'\left(\dfrac{\sqrt{2}}{2}\right)$

$\qquad = \dfrac{x' + y'}{\sqrt{2}}$

$xy - 2y - 4x = 0$

$$\left(\dfrac{x' - y'}{\sqrt{2}}\right)\left(\dfrac{x' + y'}{\sqrt{2}}\right) - 2\left(\dfrac{x' + y'}{\sqrt{2}}\right) - 4\left(\dfrac{x' - y'}{\sqrt{2}}\right) = 0$$

$$\dfrac{(x')^2}{2} - \dfrac{(y')^2}{2} - \sqrt{2}x' - \sqrt{2}y' - 2\sqrt{2}x' + 2\sqrt{2}y' = 0$$

$$\left[(x')^2 - 6\sqrt{2}x' + (3\sqrt{2})^2\right] - \left[(y')^2 - 2\sqrt{2}y' + (\sqrt{2})^2\right] = 0 + (3\sqrt{2})^2 - (\sqrt{2})^2$$

$$(x' - 3\sqrt{2})^2 - (y' - \sqrt{2})^2 = 16$$

$$\dfrac{(x' - 3\sqrt{2})^2}{16} - \dfrac{(y' - \sqrt{2})^2}{16} = 1$$

11. $5x^2 - 2xy + 5y^2 - 12 = 0$

$A = 5, B = -2, C = 5$

$\cot 2\theta = \dfrac{A - C}{B} = 0 \Rightarrow 2\theta = \dfrac{\pi}{2} \Rightarrow \theta = \dfrac{\pi}{4}$

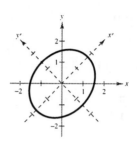

$x = x'\cos\dfrac{\pi}{4} - y'\sin\dfrac{\pi}{4} \qquad y = x'\sin\dfrac{\pi}{4} + y'\cos\dfrac{\pi}{4}$

$\quad = x'\left(\dfrac{\sqrt{2}}{2}\right) - y'\left(\dfrac{\sqrt{2}}{2}\right) \qquad\quad = x'\left(\dfrac{\sqrt{2}}{2}\right) + y'\left(\dfrac{\sqrt{2}}{2}\right)$

$\quad = \dfrac{x' - y'}{\sqrt{2}} \qquad\qquad\qquad\quad = \dfrac{x' + y'}{\sqrt{2}}$

$$5x^2 - 2xy + 5y^2 - 12 = 0$$

$$5\left(\dfrac{x' - y'}{\sqrt{2}}\right)^2 - 2\left(\dfrac{x' - y'}{\sqrt{2}}\right)\left(\dfrac{x' + y'}{\sqrt{2}}\right) + 5\left(\dfrac{x' + y'}{\sqrt{2}}\right)^2 - 12 = 0$$

$$\dfrac{5(x')^2}{2} - 5x'y' + \dfrac{5(y')^2}{2} - (x')^2 + (y')^2 + \dfrac{5(x')^2}{2} + 5x'y' + \dfrac{5(y')^2}{2} - 12 = 0$$

$$4(x')^2 + 6(y')^2 = 12$$

$$\dfrac{(x')^2}{3} + \dfrac{(y')^2}{2} = 1$$

13. $3x^2 - 2\sqrt{3}xy + y^2 + 2x + 2\sqrt{3}y = 0$

$A = 3, B = -2\sqrt{3}, C = 1$

$\cot 2\theta = \dfrac{A - C}{B} = -\dfrac{1}{\sqrt{3}} \Rightarrow \theta = 60°$

$x = x'\cos 60° - y'\sin 60° \qquad\qquad y = x'\sin 60° + y'\cos 60°$

$\quad = x'\left(\dfrac{1}{2}\right) - y'\left(\dfrac{\sqrt{3}}{2}\right) = \dfrac{x' - \sqrt{3}y'}{2} \qquad = x'\left(\dfrac{\sqrt{3}}{2}\right) + y'\left(\dfrac{1}{2}\right) = \dfrac{\sqrt{3}x' - y'}{2}$

$$3x^2 - 2\sqrt{3}xy + y^2 + 2x + 2\sqrt{3}y = 0$$

$$3\left(\dfrac{x' - \sqrt{3}y'}{2}\right)^2 - 2\sqrt{3}\left(\dfrac{x' - \sqrt{3}y'}{2}\right)\left(\dfrac{\sqrt{3}x' + y'}{2}\right) + \left(\dfrac{\sqrt{3}x' + y'}{2}\right)^2 + 2\left(\dfrac{x' - \sqrt{3}y'}{2}\right) + 2\sqrt{3}\left(\dfrac{\sqrt{3}x' + y'}{2}\right) = 0$$

$$\dfrac{3(x')^2}{4} - \dfrac{6\sqrt{3}x'y'}{4} + \dfrac{9(y')^2}{4} - \dfrac{6(x')^2}{4} + \dfrac{4\sqrt{3}x'y'}{4} + \dfrac{6(y')^2}{4} + \dfrac{3(x')^2}{4} + \dfrac{2\sqrt{3}x'y'}{4} + \dfrac{(y')^2}{4}$$

$$+ x' - \sqrt{3}y' + 3x' + \sqrt{3}y' = 0$$

$$4(y')^2 + 4x' = 0$$

$$x' = -(y')^2$$

15. $9x^2 + 24xy + 16y^2 + 90x - 130y = 0$

$A = 9, B = 24, C = 16$

$\cot 2\theta = \dfrac{A - C}{B} = -\dfrac{7}{24} \Rightarrow \theta \approx 53.13°$

$\cos 2\theta = -\dfrac{7}{25}$

$\sin\theta = \sqrt{\dfrac{1 - \cos\theta}{2}} = \sqrt{\dfrac{1 - (-7/25)}{2}} = \dfrac{4}{5}$

$\cos\theta = \sqrt{\dfrac{1 + \cos 2\theta}{2}} = \sqrt{\dfrac{1 + (-7/25)}{2}} = \dfrac{3}{5}$

$x = x'\cos\theta - y'\sin\theta$ $y = x'\sin\theta + y'\cos\theta$

$= x'\left(\dfrac{3}{5}\right) - y'\left(\dfrac{4}{5}\right) = \dfrac{3x' - 4y'}{5}$ $= x'\left(\dfrac{4}{5}\right) + y'\left(\dfrac{3}{5}\right)$

$= \dfrac{4x' + 3y'}{5}$

$9x^2 + 24xy + 16y^2 + 90x - 130y = 0$

$9\left(\dfrac{3x' - 4y'}{5}\right)^2 + 24\left(\dfrac{3x' - 4y'}{5}\right)\left(\dfrac{4x' + 3y'}{5}\right) + 16\left(\dfrac{3x' - 4y'}{5}\right)^2 + 90\left(\dfrac{3x' - 4y'}{5}\right) - 130\left(\dfrac{4x' + 3y'}{5}\right) = 0$

$\dfrac{81(x')^2}{25} - \dfrac{216x'y'}{25} + \dfrac{144(y')^2}{25} + \dfrac{288(x')^2}{25} - \dfrac{168x'y'}{25} - \dfrac{288(y')^2}{25} + \dfrac{256(x')^2}{25} + \dfrac{384x'y'}{25}$

$+ \dfrac{144(y')^2}{25} + 54x' - 72y' - 104x' - 78y' = 0$

$25(x')^2 - 50x' - 150y' = 0$

$(x')^2 - 2x' + 1 = 6y' + 1$

$y' = \dfrac{(x')^2}{6} - \dfrac{x'}{3}$

17. $x^2 + xy + y^2 = 10$

$\cot 2\theta = \dfrac{A - C}{B} = \dfrac{1 - 1}{0} = 0 \Rightarrow \theta = \dfrac{\pi}{4}$ or $45°$

To graph the conic using a graphing calculator, we need to solve for y in terms of x.

$y^2 + xy = 10 - x^2$

$y^2 + xy + \dfrac{x^2}{4} = 10 - x^2 + \dfrac{x^2}{4}$

$\left(y + \dfrac{x}{2}\right)^2 = \dfrac{40 - 3x^2}{4}$

$y = -\dfrac{x}{2} \pm \dfrac{\sqrt{40 - 3x^2}}{2}$

Enter $y_1 = \dfrac{-x + \sqrt{40 - 3x^2}}{2}$

and $y_2 = \dfrac{-x - \sqrt{40 - 3x^2}}{2}$.

19. $17x^2 + 32xy - 7y^2 = 75$

$$\cot 2\theta = \frac{A - C}{B} = \frac{17 + 7}{32} = \frac{24}{32} = \frac{3}{4} \Rightarrow \theta \approx 26.57°$$

Solve for y in terms of x by completing the square.

$$-7y^2 + 32xy = -17x^2 + 75$$

$$y^2 - \frac{32}{7}xy = \frac{17}{7}x^2 - \frac{75}{7}$$

$$y^2 - \frac{32}{7}xy + \frac{256}{49}x^2 = \frac{119}{49}x^2 - \frac{525}{49} + \frac{256}{49}x^2$$

$$\left(y - \frac{16}{7}x\right)^2 = \frac{375x^2 - 525}{49}$$

$$y = \frac{16}{7}x \pm \sqrt{\frac{375x^2 - 525}{49}}$$

$$y = \frac{16x \pm 5\sqrt{15x^2 - 21}}{7}$$

Use $y_1 = \dfrac{16x + 5\sqrt{15x^2 - 21}}{7}$

and $y_2 = \dfrac{16x - 5\sqrt{15x^2 - 21}}{7}$.

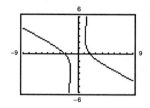

21. $32x^2 + 50xy + 7y^2 = 52$

$$\cot 2\theta = \frac{A - C}{B} = \frac{32 - 7}{50} = \frac{1}{2} \Rightarrow \theta \approx 31.72°$$

Solve for y in terms of x by completing the square.

$$7y^2 + 50xy = 52 - 32x^2$$

$$y^2 + \frac{50}{7}xy = \frac{52 - 32x^2}{7}$$

$$y^2 + \frac{50}{7}xy + \frac{625}{49}x^2 = \frac{52 - 32x^2}{7} + \frac{625x^2}{49}$$

$$\left(y + \frac{25}{7}x\right)^2 = \frac{364 + 401x^2}{49}$$

$$y = -\frac{25x}{7} \pm \frac{\sqrt{364 + 401x^2}}{7}$$

Enter $y_1 = \dfrac{-25x + \sqrt{364 + 401x^2}}{7}$

and $y_2 = \dfrac{-25x - \sqrt{364 + 401x^2}}{7}$.

23. $xy + 3 = 0$

$B^2 - 4AC = 1 \Rightarrow$ The graph is a hyperbola.

$$\cot 2\theta = \frac{A - C}{B} = 0 \Rightarrow \theta = 45°$$

Matches graph (e).

25. $-2x^2 + 3xy + 2y^2 + 3 = 0$

$B^2 - 4AC = (3)^2 - 4(-2)(2) = 25 \Rightarrow$ The graph is a hyperbola.

$\cot 2\theta = \dfrac{A - C}{B} = -\dfrac{4}{3} \Rightarrow \theta \approx -18.43°$

Matches graph (b).

27. $3x^2 + 2xy + y^2 - 10 = 0$

$B^2 - 4AC = (2)^2 - 4(3)(1) = -8 \Rightarrow$ The graph is an ellipse or circle.

$\cot 2\theta = \dfrac{A - C}{B} = 1 \Rightarrow \theta = 22.5°$

Matches graph (d).

29. $16x^2 - 24xy + 9y^2 - 30x - 40y = 0$

$B^2 - 4AC = (-24)^2 - 4(16)(9) = 0$

Parabola

31. $13x^2 - 8xy + 7y^2 - 45 = 0$

$B^2 - 4AC = (-8)^2 - 4(13)(7) = -300$

Ellipse or circle

33. $x^2 - 6xy - 5y^2 + 4x - 22 = 0$

$B^2 - 4AC = (-6)^2 - 4(1)(-5) = 56$

Hyperbola

35. $x^2 + 4xy + 4y^2 - 5x - y - 3 = 0$

$B^2 - 4AC = (4)^2 - 4(1)(4) = 0$

Parabola

37. $y^2 - 4x^2 = 0$

$\qquad y^2 = 4x^2$

$\qquad y = \pm 2x$

Two intersecting lines

39. $x^2 + 2xy + y^2 - 1 = 0$

$\qquad (x + y)^2 - 1 = 0$

$\qquad (x + y)^2 = 1$

$\qquad x + y = \pm 1$

$\qquad y = -x \pm 1$

Two parallel lines

41.
$$-x^2 + y^2 + 4x - 6y + 4 = 0 \Rightarrow (y - 3)^2 - (x - 2)^2 = 1$$
$$\underline{x^2 + y^2 - 4x - 6y + 12 = 0 \Rightarrow (x - 2)^2 + (y - 3)^2 = 1}$$
$$2y^2 - 12y + 16 = 0$$
$$2(y - 2)(y - 4) = 0$$
$$y = 2 \text{ or } y = 4$$

For $y = 2$: $x^2 + 2^2 - 4x - 6(2) + 12 = 0$

$\qquad\qquad\qquad x^2 - 4x + 4 = 0$

$\qquad\qquad\qquad (x - 2)^2 = 0$

$\qquad\qquad\qquad x = 2$

For $y = 4$: $x^2 + 4^2 - 4x - 6(4) + 12 = 0$

$\qquad\qquad\qquad x^2 - 4x + 4 = 0$

$\qquad\qquad\qquad (x - 2)^2 = 0$

$\qquad\qquad\qquad x = 2$

The points of intersection are $(2, 2)$ and $(2, 4)$.

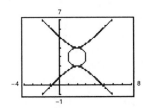

43. $-4x^2 - y^2 - 32x + 24y - 64 = 0$

$\underline{4x^2 + y^2 + 56x - 24y + 304 = 0}$

$24x + 240 = 0$

$x = -10$

When $x = -10$: $4(-10)^2 + y^2 + 56(-10) - 24y + 304 = 0$

$y^2 - 24y + 144 = 0$

$(y - 12)^2 = 0$

$y = 12$

The point of intersection is $(-10, 12)$.
In standard form the equations are:

$$\frac{(x + 4)^2}{36} + \frac{(y - 12)^2}{144} = 1$$

$$\frac{(x + y)^2}{9} + \frac{(y - 12)^2}{36} = 1$$

45. $x^2 - y^2 - 12x + 12y - 36 = 0$

$\underline{x^2 + y^2 - 12x - 12y + 36 = 0}$

$2x^2 - 24x = 0$

$2x(x - 12) = 0$

$x = 0$ or $x = 12$

When $x = 0$: $y^2 - 12y + 36 = 0$

$(y - 6)^2 = 0$

$y = 6$

When $x = 12$: $12^2 + y^2 - 12(12) - 12y + 36 = 0$

$y^2 - 12y + 36 = 0$

$(y - 6)^2 = 0$

$y = 6$

The points of intersection are $(0, 6)$ and $(12, 6)$.
In standard form the equations are:

$$\frac{(x - 6)^2}{36} + \frac{(y - 6)^2}{36} = 1$$

$$(x - 6)^2 + (y - 6)^2 = 36$$

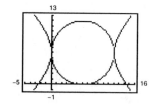

47. $-16x^2 - y^2 + 24y - 80 = 0$

$\underline{16x^2 + 25y^2 - 400 = 0}$

$24y^2 + 24y - 480 = 0$

$24(y + 5)(y - 4) = 0$

$y = -5$ or $y = 4$

When $y = -5$: $16x^2 + 25(-5)^2 - 400 = 0$

$16x^2 = -225$

No real solution

When $y = 4$: $16x^2 + 25(4)^2 - 400 = 0$

$16x^2 = 0$

$x = 0$

The point of intersection is $(0, 4)$.
In standard form the equations are:

$$\frac{x^2}{4} + \frac{(y - 12)^2}{64} = 1$$

$$\frac{x^2}{25} + \frac{y^2}{16} = 1$$

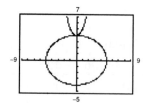

49. $x^2 + y^2 - 25 = 0 \Rightarrow y^2 = 25 - x^2$

$\quad 9x - 4y^2 = 0 \Rightarrow 9x - 4(25 - x^2) = 0$

$\qquad\qquad\qquad\quad 4x^2 + 9x - 100 = 0$

$\qquad\qquad\qquad\quad (4x + 25)(x - 4) = 0$

$\qquad\qquad\qquad\qquad x = -\frac{25}{4} \text{ or } x = 4$

When $x = -\frac{25}{4}$: $y^2 = 25 - \left(-\frac{25}{4}\right)^2$

$\qquad\qquad\qquad y^2 = -\frac{225}{16}$

$\qquad\qquad$ No real solution

When $x = 4$: $y^2 = 25 - 4^2$

$\qquad\qquad y^2 = 9$

$\qquad\qquad y = \pm 3$

The points of intersection are $(4, 3)$, $(4, -3)$.

In standard form the equations are:

$\qquad x^2 + y^2 = 25$

$\qquad\qquad y^2 = \frac{9}{4}x$

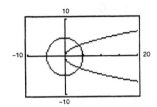

51. $\qquad\qquad x^2 + 2y^2 - 4x + 6y - 5 = 0$

$\qquad\qquad\qquad\quad x + y + 5 = 0 \Rightarrow y = -x - 5$

$\quad x^2 + 2(-x - 5)^2 - 4x + 6(-x - 5) - 5 = 0$

$x^2 + 2x^2 + 20x + 50 - 4x - 6x - 30 - 5 = 0$

$\qquad\qquad\qquad\quad 3x^2 + 10x + 15 = 0$

No real solution

No points of intersection

In standard form we have:

$$\frac{(x - 2)^2}{27/2} + \frac{(y + 3/2)^2}{27/4} = 1$$

$$x + y = -5$$

53. $\qquad\qquad xy + x - 2y + 3 = 0 \Rightarrow y = \frac{-x - 3}{x - 2}$

$\qquad\qquad\qquad x^2 + 4y^2 - 9 = 0$

$\qquad\qquad\quad x^2 + 4\left(\frac{-x - 3}{x - 2}\right)^2 = 9$

$\qquad\quad x^2(x - 2)^2 + 4(-x - 3)^2 = 9(x - 2)^2$

$x^2(x^2 - 4x + 4) + 4(x^2 + 6x + 9) = 9(x^2 - 4x + 4)$

$x^4 - 4x^3 + 4x^2 + 4x^2 + 24x + 36 = 9x^2 - 36x + 36$

$\qquad\qquad x^4 - 4x^3 - x^2 + 60x = 0$

$\qquad\qquad x(x + 3)(x^2 - 7x + 20) = 0$

$\qquad\qquad\qquad\quad x = 0 \text{ or } x = -3$

Note: $x^2 - 7x + 20 = 0$ has no real solution.

When $x = 0$: $\quad y = \frac{-0 - 3}{0 - 2} = \frac{3}{2}$

When $x = -3$: $y = \frac{-(-3) - 3}{-3 - 2} = 0$

The points of intersection are $\left(0, \dfrac{3}{2}\right)$, $(-3, 0)$.

55. $(x')^2 + (y')^2 = (x \cos\theta + y \sin\theta)^2 + (y \cos\theta - x \sin\theta)^2$

$\qquad\qquad = x^2 \cos^2\theta + 2xy \cos\theta \sin\theta + y^2 \sin^2\theta + y^2 \cos^2\theta - 2xy \cos\theta \sin\theta + x^2 \sin^2\theta$

$\qquad\qquad = x^2(\cos^2\theta + \sin^2\theta) + y^2(\sin^2\theta + \cos^2\theta) = x^2 + y^2 = r^2$

57. $g(x) = \dfrac{2}{2 - x}$

y-intercept: (0, 1)

Vertical asymptote: $x = 2$

Horizontal asymptote: $y = 0$

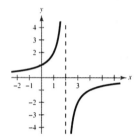

59. $h(t) = \dfrac{t^2}{2 - t} = -t - 2 + \dfrac{4}{2 - t}$

Intercept: (0, 0)

Vertical asymptote: $t = 2$

Slant asymptote: $y = -t - 2$

Section 10.6   Parametric Equations

- If f and g are continuous functions of t on an interval I, then the set of ordered pairs $(f(t), g(t))$ is a *plane curve C*. The equations $x = f(t)$ and $y = g(t)$ are *parametric equations* for C and t is the *parameter*.
- To eliminate the parameter:
  (a) Solve for t in one equation and substitute into the second equation.
  (b) Use trigonometric identities.
- You should be able to find the parametric equations for a graph.

Solutions to Odd-Numbered Exercises

1. $x = \sqrt{t}, y = 1 - t$

(a)

t	0	1	2	3	4
x	0	1	$\sqrt{2}$	$\sqrt{3}$	2
y	1	0	-1	-2	-3

(b)

(c) $x = \sqrt{t} \Rightarrow x^2 = t$
     $y = 1 - t \Rightarrow y = 1 - x^2$

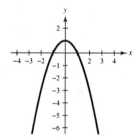

The graph of the parametric equations only shows the right half of the parabola, whereas the rectangular equation yields the entire parabola.

3. $x = t$

$\quad y = -2t \implies y = -2x$

$\qquad 2x + y = 0$

5. $x = 3t - 1 \implies t = \dfrac{x + 1}{3}$

$\quad y = 2t + 1 \implies y = 2\left(\dfrac{x + 1}{3}\right) + 1$

$\qquad 2x - 3y + 5 = 0$

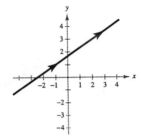

7. $x = \frac{1}{4}t \implies t = 4x$

$\quad y = t^2 \implies y = 16x^2$

9. $x = t + 1 \implies t = x - 1$

$\quad y = t^2 \quad\implies y = (x - 1)^2$

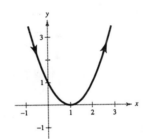

11. $x = t^3 \implies t = x^{1/3}$

$\quad y = \frac{1}{2}t^2 \implies y = \frac{1}{2}x^{2/3}$

$\qquad\qquad y = \frac{1}{2}\sqrt[3]{x^2}$

13. $\qquad x = 2t \implies t = \dfrac{x}{2}$

$\quad y = |t - 2| \implies y = \left|\dfrac{x}{2} - 2\right|$

$\qquad\qquad y = \dfrac{1}{2}|x - 4|$

15. $x = 3\cos\theta \implies \left(\dfrac{x}{3}\right)^2 = \cos^2\theta$

$\quad y = 3\sin\theta \implies \left(\dfrac{y}{3}\right)^2 = \sin^2\theta$

$\quad \left(\dfrac{x}{3}\right)^2 + \left(\dfrac{y}{3}\right)^2 = 1$

$\qquad\qquad x^2 + y^2 = 9$

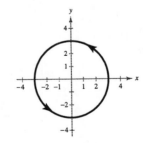

17. $x = 4 \sin 2\theta \Rightarrow \left(\dfrac{x}{4}\right)^2 = \sin^2 2\theta$

$y = 2 \cos 2\theta \Rightarrow \left(\dfrac{y}{2}\right)^2 = \cos^2 2\theta$

$\left(\dfrac{x}{4}\right)^2 + \left(\dfrac{y}{3}\right)^2 = 1$

$\dfrac{x^2}{16} + \dfrac{y^2}{4} = 1$

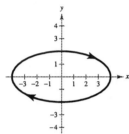

19. $x = 4 + 2 \cos \theta \Rightarrow \left(\dfrac{x-4}{2}\right)^2 = \cos^2 \theta$

$y = -1 + \sin \theta \Rightarrow (y+1)^2 = \sin^2 \theta$

$\dfrac{(x-4)^2}{4} + \dfrac{(y+1)^2}{1} = 1$

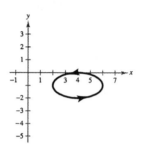

21. $x = 4 + 2 \cos \theta \Rightarrow \left(\dfrac{x-4}{2}\right)^2 = \cos^2 \theta$

$y = -1 + 4 \sin \theta \Rightarrow \left(\dfrac{y+1}{4}\right)^2 = \sin^2 \theta$

$\dfrac{(x-4)^2}{4} + \dfrac{(y+1)^2}{16} = 1$

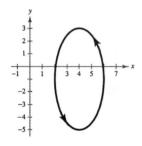

23. $x = 4 \sec \theta \Rightarrow \left(\dfrac{x}{4}\right)^2 = \sec^2 \theta$

$y = 3 \tan \theta \Rightarrow \left(\dfrac{y}{3}\right)^2 = \tan^2 \theta$

$1 + \left(\dfrac{y}{3}\right)^2 = \left(\dfrac{x}{4}\right)^2$

$\dfrac{x^2}{16} - \dfrac{y^2}{9} = 1$

25. $x = e^{-1} \Rightarrow \dfrac{1}{x} = e^t$

$y = e^{3t} \Rightarrow y = (e^t)^3$

$y = \left(\dfrac{1}{x}\right)^3$

$y = \dfrac{1}{x^3}, \ x > 0, y > 0$

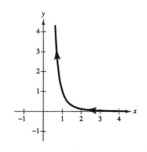

27. $x = t^3 \qquad \Rightarrow x^{1/3} = t$

$y = 3 \ln t \Rightarrow y = \ln t^3$

$y = \ln(x^{1/3})^3$

$y = \ln x$

29. By eliminating the parameter, each curve becomes $y = 2x + 1$.

(a) $x = t$

$y = 2t + 1$

There are no restrictions on x and y.

Domain: $(-\infty, \infty)$

Orientation: Left to right

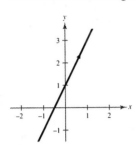

(b) $x = \cos \theta \qquad \Rightarrow -1 \le x \le 1$

$y = 2 \cos \theta + 1 \Rightarrow -1 \le y \le 3$

The graph oscillates.

Domain: $[-1, 1]$

Orientation: Depends on θ

(c) $x = e^{-t} \qquad \Rightarrow x > 0$

$y = 2e^{-t} + 1 \Rightarrow y > 1$

Domain: $(0, \infty)$

Orientation: Downward or right to left

(d) $x = e^{t} \qquad \Rightarrow x > 0$

$y = 2e^{t} + 1 \Rightarrow y > 1$

Domain: $(0, \infty)$

Orientation: Upward or left to right

31. (a) $x = \cos \theta$

$y = \sin \theta$

$x^2 + y^2 = 1$

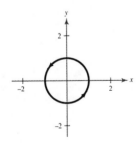

Oriented counterclockwise

(b) $x = \sin \theta$

$y = \cos \theta$

$x^2 + y^2 = 1$

Oriented clockwise

—CONTINUED—

31. —CONTINUED—

(c) $x = \sin^2 \theta$

$y = \cos^2 \theta$

$x + y = 1, 0 \le x \le 1, 0 \le y \le 1$

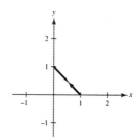

Oscillates

(d) $x = -\cos \theta$

$y = \sin \theta$

$x^2 + y^2 = 1$

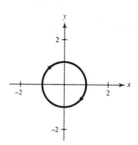

Oriented clockwise

33. $x = x_1 + t(x_2 - x_1), y = y_1 + t(y_2 - y_1)$

$\dfrac{x - x_1}{x_2 - x_1} = t$

$y = y_1 + \left(\dfrac{x - x_1}{x_2 - x_1}\right)(y_2 - y_1)$

$y - y_1 = \dfrac{y_2 - y_1}{x_2 - x_1}(x - x_1) = m(x - x_1)$

35. $x = h + a \cos \theta, y = k + b \sin \theta$

$\dfrac{x - h}{a} = \cos \theta, \dfrac{y - k}{b} = \sin \theta$

$\dfrac{(x - h)^2}{a^2} + \dfrac{(y - k)^2}{b^2} = 1$

37. From Exercise 33 we have:

$x = 0 + t(5 - 0) = 5t$

$y = 0 + t(-2 - 0) = -2t$

39. From Exercise 34 we have:

$x = 2 + 4 \cos \theta$

$y = 1 + 4 \sin \theta$

41. Vertices: $(\pm 5, 0) \Rightarrow (h, k) = (0, 0)$ and $a = 5$

Foci: $(\pm 4, 0) \Rightarrow c = 4$

$c^2 = a^2 - b^2 \Rightarrow 16 = 25 - b^2 \Rightarrow b = 3$

From Exercise 35 we have:

$x = 5 \cos \theta$

$y = 3 \sin \theta$

43. Vertices: $(\pm 4, 0) \Rightarrow (h, k) = (0, 0)$ and $a = 4$

Foci: $(\pm 5, 0) \Rightarrow c = 5$

$c^2 = a^2 + b^2 \Rightarrow 25 = 16 + b^2 \Rightarrow b = 3$

From Exercise 36 we have:

$x = 4 \sec \theta$

$y = 3 \tan \theta$

45. $y = 3x - 2$

Examples

$x = t, \qquad y = 3t - 2$

$x = \dfrac{t}{3}, \qquad y = t - 2$

$x = \dfrac{t + 2}{3}, \quad y = t$

$x = 2t, \qquad y = 6t - 2$

47. $y = x^3$

Examples

$x = t, \qquad y = t^3$

$x = \sqrt[3]{t}, \qquad y = t$

$x = \tan t, \quad y = \tan^3 t$

49. $x = 2(\theta - \sin \theta)$
$y = 2(1 - \cos \theta)$

51. $x = \theta - \dfrac{3}{2} \sin \theta$

$y = 1 - \dfrac{3}{2} \cos \theta$

53. $x = 3 \cos^3 \theta$
$y = 3 \sin^3 \theta$

55. $x = 2 \cot \theta$
$y = 2 \sin^2 \theta$

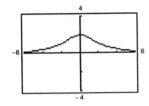

57. $x = 2 \cos \theta \Rightarrow -2 \le x \le 2$
$y = \sin 2\theta \Rightarrow -1 \le y \le 1$
Matches graph (b).
Domain: $[-2, 2]$
Range: $[-1, 1]$

59. $x = \dfrac{1}{2}(\cos \theta + \theta \sin \theta)$

$y = \dfrac{1}{2}(\sin \theta - \theta \cos \theta)$

Matches graph (d).
Domain: $(-\infty, \infty)$
Range: $(-\infty, \infty)$

61. $x = (v_0 \cos \theta)t$
$y = h + (v_0 \sin \theta)t - 16t^2$

(a) $\theta = 20°$, $v_0 = 88$ ft/sec
Maximum height: 14.2 ft
Range: 155.6 ft

(b) $\theta = 20°$, $v_0 = 132$ ft/sec
Maximum height: 31.8 ft
Range: 350.0 ft

(c) $\theta = 245°$, $v_0 = 88$ ft/sec
Maximum height: 60.5 ft
Range: 242.0 ft

(d) $\theta = 45°$, $v_0 = 132$ ft/sec
Maximum height: 136.1 ft
Range: 544.5 ft

494 Chapter 10 Topics in Analytic Geometry

63. (a) $100 \text{ miles per hour} = 100\left(\dfrac{5280}{3600}\right) \text{ ft/sec} = \dfrac{440}{3} \text{ ft/sec}$

$$x = \left(\dfrac{440}{3}\cos\theta\right)t \approx (146.67\cos\theta)t$$

$$y = 3 + \left(\dfrac{440}{3}\sin\theta\right)t - 16t^2 \approx 3 + (146.67\sin\theta)t - 16t^2$$

(b) For $\theta = 15°$, we have:

$$x = \left(\dfrac{440}{3}\cos 15°\right)t \approx 141.7t$$

$$y = 3 + \left(\dfrac{440}{3}\sin 15°\right)t - 16t^2 \approx 3 + 38.0t - 16t^2$$

The ball hits the ground inside the ballpark, so it is not a home run.

(c) For $\theta = 23°$, we have:

$$x = \left(\dfrac{440}{3}\cos 23°\right)t \approx 135.0t$$

$$y = 3 + \left(\dfrac{440}{3}\sin 23°\right)t - 16t^2 \approx 3 + 57.3t - 16t^2$$

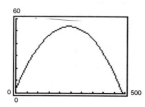

The ball easily clears the 10-foot fence at 400 feet so it is a home run.

(d) Find θ so that $y = 10$ when $x = 400$ by graphing the parametric equations for θ values between $15°$ and $23°$. This occurs when $\theta \approx 19.4°$.

65. $x = (v_0 \cos\theta)t \implies t = \dfrac{x}{v_0 \cos\theta}$

$y = h + (v_0 \sin\theta)t - 16t^2$

$ = h + (v_0 \sin\theta)\left(\dfrac{x}{v_0 \cos\theta}\right) - 16\left(\dfrac{x}{v_0 \cos\theta}\right)^2$

$ = h + (\tan\theta)x - \dfrac{16x^2}{v_0^2 \cos^2\theta}$

$ = -\dfrac{16\sec^2\theta}{v_0^2}x^2 + (\tan\theta)x + h$

67. When the circle has rolled θ radians, the center is at $(a\theta, a)$.

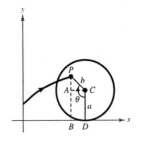

$$\sin \theta = \sin(180° - \theta)$$

$$= \frac{|AC|}{b} = \frac{|BD|}{b} \Rightarrow |BD| = b \sin \theta$$

$$\cos \theta = -\cos(180° - \theta)$$

$$= \frac{|AP|}{-b} \Rightarrow |AP| = -b \cos \theta$$

Therefore, $x = a\theta - b \sin \theta$ and $y = a - b \cos \theta$.

69. $x = t$

$y = t^2 + 1 \Rightarrow y = x^2 + 1$

$x = 3t$

$y = 9t^2 + 1 \Rightarrow y = x^2 + 1$

True

71.
$$\begin{array}{rcl} 5x - 7y = & 11 & \Rightarrow \quad 5x - 7y = \quad 11 \\ -3x + \ y = -13 & \Rightarrow & \underline{-21x + 7y = -91} \\ & & -16x \qquad = -80 \\ & & x = 5 \\ & & 5(5) - 7y = \quad 11 \Rightarrow y = 2 \end{array}$$

Solution: $(5, 2)$

73.
$$\begin{array}{rcl} 3a - 2b + \ c = & 8 \Rightarrow & 9a - 6b + 3c = \ 24 \\ 2a + \ b - 3c = & -3 \Rightarrow & \underline{2a + \ b - 3c = -3} \\ & & 11a - 5b \quad = \ 21 \end{array}$$

$$\begin{array}{rcl} 2a + \ b - 3c = & -3 \Rightarrow & 6a + 3b - 9c = -9 \\ a - 3b + 9c = & 16 \Rightarrow & \underline{a - 3b + 9c = \ 16} \\ & & 7a \qquad = \ 7 \\ & & a \qquad = \ 1 \end{array}$$

$a = 11(1) - 5b = 21 \Rightarrow b = -2$

$3(1) - 2(-2) + c = 8 \Rightarrow c = 1$

Solution: $(1, -2, 1)$

Section 10.7   Polar Coordinates

- In polar coordinates you do not have unique representation of points. The point (r, θ) can be repsresented by $(r, \theta \pm 2n\pi)$ or by $(-r, \theta \pm (2n + 1)\pi)$ where n is any integer. The pole is represented by $(0, \theta)$ where θ is any angle.

- To convert from polar coordinates to rectangular coordinates, use the following relationships.
  $$x = r \cos \theta$$
  $$y = r \sin \theta$$

- To convert from rectangular coordinates to polar coordinates, use the following relationships.
  $$r = \pm\sqrt{x^2 + y^2}$$
  $$\tan \theta = y/x$$
  If θ is in the same quadrant as the point (x, y), then r is positive. If θ is in the opposite quadrant as the point (x, y), then r is negative.

- You should be able to convert rectangular equations to polar form and vice versa.

Solutions to Odd-Numbered Exercises

1. Polar coordinates: $\left(4, \dfrac{3\pi}{6}\right)$

$x = 4 \cos\left(\dfrac{3\pi}{6}\right) = 0, \ y = 4 \sin\left(\dfrac{3\pi}{6}\right) = 4$

Rectangular coordinates: $(0, 4)$

3. Polar coordinates: $\left(-1, \dfrac{5\pi}{4}\right)$

$x = -1 \cos\left(\dfrac{5\pi}{4}\right) = \dfrac{\sqrt{2}}{2}, \ y = -1 \sin\left(\dfrac{5\pi}{4}\right) = \dfrac{\sqrt{2}}{2}$

Rectangular coordinates: $\left(\dfrac{\sqrt{2}}{2}, \dfrac{\sqrt{2}}{2}\right)$

5. Polar coordinates: $\left(4, -\dfrac{\pi}{3}\right)$

$x = 4\cos\left(-\dfrac{\pi}{3}\right) = 2, \ y = 4\sin\left(-\dfrac{\pi}{3}\right) = -2\sqrt{3}$

Rectangular coordinates: $(2, -2\sqrt{3})$

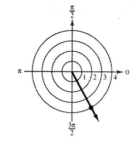

7. Polar coordinates: $\left(0, -\dfrac{7\pi}{6}\right)$

$x = 0\cos\left(-\dfrac{7\pi}{6}\right) = 0, \ y = 0\sin\left(-\dfrac{7\pi}{6}\right) = 0$

Rectangular coordinates: $(0, 0)$

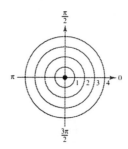

9. Polar coordinates: $\left(\sqrt{2}, 2.36\right)$

$x = \sqrt{2}\cos(2.36) \approx -1.004$

$y = \sqrt{2}\sin(2.36) \approx 0.996$

Rectangular coordinates: $(-1.004, 0.996)$

11. Polar coordinates: $\left(2, \dfrac{3\pi}{4}\right)$

$\left(2 < \dfrac{3\pi}{4}\right) \blacktriangleright \text{Rec}$

$\approx (-1.4142, 1.4142)$

$= \left(-\sqrt{2}, \sqrt{2}\right)$

13. Polar coordinates: $(-4.5, 1.3)$

$(-4.5 < 1.3) \blacktriangleright \text{Rec}$

$\approx (-1.204, -4.336)$

15. Rectangular coordinates: $(1, 1)$

$r = \pm\sqrt{2}, \ \tan\theta = 1, \ \theta = \dfrac{\pi}{4} \text{ or } \dfrac{5\pi}{4}$

Polar coordinates: $\left(\sqrt{2}, \dfrac{\pi}{4}\right), \left(-\sqrt{2}, \dfrac{5\pi}{4}\right)$

17. Rectangular coordinates: $(-6, 0)$

$r = \pm 6, \ \tan\theta = 0, \ \theta = 0 \text{ or } \pi$

Polar coordinates: $(6, \pi), (-6, 0)$

19. Rectangular coordinates: $(-3, 4)$

$r = \pm\sqrt{9 + 16} = \pm 5$, $\tan \theta = -\dfrac{4}{3}$, $\theta \approx 2.214, 5.356$

Polar coordinates: $(5, 2.214)$, $(-5, 5.356)$

23. Rectangular coordinates: $(4, 6)$

$r = \pm\sqrt{4^2 + 6^2} = \pm\sqrt{52} = \pm 2\sqrt{13}$

$\tan \theta = \dfrac{6}{4} \Rightarrow \theta \approx 0.983, 4.124$

Polar coordinates: $\left(2\sqrt{13}, 0.983\right)$, $\left(-2\sqrt{13}, 4.124\right)$

21. Rectangular coordinates: $\left(-\sqrt{3}, -\sqrt{3}\right)$

$r = \pm\sqrt{3 + 3} = \pm\sqrt{6}$, $\tan \theta = 1$, $\theta = \dfrac{\pi}{4}$ or $\dfrac{5\pi}{4}$

Polar coordinates: $\left(\sqrt{6}, \dfrac{5\pi}{4}\right), \left(-\sqrt{6}, \dfrac{\pi}{4}\right)$

25. Rectangular: $(3, -2)$

$(3, -2) \blacktriangleright$ Pol

$\approx (3.606, -0.588)$

31. True, $|r_1| = |r_2|$

27. Rectangular: $\left(\sqrt{3}, 2\right)$

$\left(\sqrt{3}, 2\right) \blacktriangleright$ Pol

$\approx (2.646, 0.857)$

33. $x^2 + y^2 = 9$

$r = 3$

29. Rectangular: $\left(\frac{5}{2}, \frac{4}{3}\right)$

$\left(\frac{5}{2}, \frac{4}{3}\right) \blacktriangleright$ Pol

$\approx (2.833, 0.490)$

35. $x^2 + y^2 - 2ax = 0$

$r^2 - 2ar\cos\theta = 0$

$r(r - 2a\cos\theta) = 0$

$r = 2a\cos\theta$

37. $y = 4$

$r\sin\theta = 4$

$r = 4\csc\theta$

41. $3x - y + 2 = 0$

$3r\cos\theta - r\sin\theta + 2 = 0$

$r(3\cos\theta - \sin\theta) = -2$

$r = \dfrac{-2}{3\cos\theta - \sin\theta}$

45. $\left(x^2 + y^2\right)^2 - 9\left(x^2 - y^2\right) = 0$

$\left(r^2\right) - 9\left(r^2\cos^2\theta - r^2\sin^2\theta\right) = 0$

$r^2\left[r^2 - 9(\cos 2\theta)\right] = 0$

$r^2 = 9\cos 2\theta$

39. $x = 10$

$r\cos\theta = 10$

$r = 10\sec\theta$

43. $xy = 4$

$(r\cos\theta)(r\sin\theta) = 4$

$r^2 = 4\sec\theta\csc\theta = 8\csc 2\theta$

47. $r = 4\sin\theta$

$r^2 = 4r\sin\theta$

$x^2 + y^2 = 4y$

$x^2 + y^2 - 4y = 0$

49.
$$\theta = \frac{\pi}{6}$$
$$\tan \theta = \frac{\sqrt{3}}{3}$$
$$\frac{y}{x} = \frac{\sqrt{3}}{3}$$
$$y = \frac{\sqrt{3}}{3}x$$
$$\sqrt{3}\,x - 3y = 0$$

51.
$$r = 2\csc\theta$$
$$r\sin\theta = 2$$
$$y = 2$$

53.
$$r = 2\sin 3\theta$$
$$r = 2(3\sin\theta - 4\sin^3\theta)$$
$$r^4 = 6r^3\sin\theta - 8r^3\sin^3\theta$$
$$(x^2 + y^2)^2 = 6(x^2 + y^2)y - 8y^3$$
$$(x^2 + y^2)^2 = 6x^2y - 2y^3$$

55.
$$r = \frac{6}{2 - \sin\theta}$$
$$r(2 - \sin\theta) = 6$$
$$2r = 6 + r\sin\theta$$
$$2\left(\pm\sqrt{x^2 + y^2}\right) = 6 + 3y$$
$$4(x^2 + y^2) = (6 + 3y)^2$$
$$4x^2 + 4y^2 = 36 + 36y + 9y^2$$
$$4x^2 - 5y^2 - 36y - 36 = 0$$

57.
$$r = 3$$
$$r^2 = 9$$
$$x^2 + y^2 = 9$$

59.
$$\theta = \frac{\pi}{4}$$
$$\tan\theta = \tan\frac{\pi}{4}$$
$$\frac{y}{x} = 1$$
$$y = x$$
$$x - y = 0$$

61.
$$r = 3\sec\theta$$
$$r\cos\theta = 3$$
$$x = 3$$
$$x - 3 = 0$$

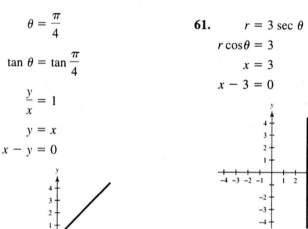

63.
$$r = 2(h\cos\theta + k\sin\theta)$$
$$r = 2\left(h\left(\frac{x}{r}\right) + k\left(\frac{y}{r}\right)\right)$$
$$r = \frac{2hx + 2ky}{r}$$
$$r^2 = 2hx + 2ky$$
$$x^2 + y^2 = 2hx + 2ky$$
$$x^2 - 2hx + y^2 - 2ky = 0$$
$$(x^2 - 2hx + h^2) + (y^2 - 2ky + k^2) = h^2 + k^2$$
$$(x - h)^2 + (y - k)^2 = h^2 + k^2$$

Center: *(h, k)*

Radius: $\sqrt{h^2 + k^2}$

65. (a) $(r_1, \theta_1) = (x_1, y_1)$ where $x_1 = r_1 \cos \theta_1$ and $y_1 = r_1 \sin \theta_1$.

$(r_2, \theta_2) = (x_2, y_2)$ where $x_2 = r_2 \cos \theta_2$ and $y_2 = r_2 \sin \theta_2$.

$$
\begin{aligned}
d &= \sqrt{(x_1 - x_2)^2 + (y_1 - y_2)^2} \\
&= \sqrt{x_1{}^2 - 2x_1 x_2 + x_2{}^2 + y_1{}^2 - 2y_1 y_2 + y_2{}^2} \\
&= \sqrt{(x_1{}^2 + y_1{}^2) + (x_2{}^2 + y_2 + y_2{}^2) - 2(x_1 x_2 + y_1 y_2)} \\
&= \sqrt{r_1{}^2 + r_2{}^2 - 2\,(r_1 r_2 \cos \theta_1 \cos \theta_2 + r_1 r_2 \sin \theta_1 \sin \theta_2)} \\
&= \sqrt{r_1{}^2 + r_2{}^2 - 2r_1 r_2 \cos(\theta_1 - \theta_2)}
\end{aligned}
$$

(b) If $\theta_1 = \theta_2$, then

$$
\begin{aligned}
d &= \sqrt{r_1{}^2 + r_2{}^2 - 2r_1 r_2} \\
&= \sqrt{(r_1 - r_2)^2} \\
&= |r_1 - r_2|.
\end{aligned}
$$

This represents the distance between two points on the line $\theta = \theta_1 = \theta_2$.

(c) If $\theta_1 - \theta_2 = 90°$, then

$$d = \sqrt{r_1{}^2 + r_2{}^2}.$$

This is the result of the Pythagorean Theorem.

(d) The results should be the same. For example, use the points

$$\left(3, \frac{\pi}{6}\right) \text{ and } \left(4, \frac{\pi}{3}\right).$$

The distance is $d \approx 2.053$.
Now use the representations

$$\left(-3, \frac{7\pi}{6}\right) \text{ and } \left(-4, \frac{4\pi}{3}\right).$$

The distance is still $d \approx 2.053$.

67. $5x - 7y = -11$

$-3x + y = -3$

By Cramer's Rule we have:

$$x = \frac{\begin{vmatrix} -11 & -7 \\ -3 & 1 \end{vmatrix}}{\begin{vmatrix} 5 & -7 \\ -3 & 1 \end{vmatrix}} = \frac{-32}{-16} = 2$$

$$y = \frac{\begin{vmatrix} 5 & -11 \\ -3 & -3 \end{vmatrix}}{\begin{vmatrix} 5 & -7 \\ -3 & 1 \end{vmatrix}} = \frac{-48}{-16} = 3$$

Solution: $(2, 3)$

69. $3a - 2b + c = 0$

$2a + b - 3c = 0$

$a - 3b + 9c = 8$

$$\begin{vmatrix} 3 & -2 & 1 \\ 2 & 1 & -3 \\ 1 & -3 & 9 \end{vmatrix} = 35$$

By Cramer's Rule we have:

$$x = \frac{\begin{vmatrix} 0 & -2 & 1 \\ 0 & 1 & -3 \\ 8 & -3 & 9 \end{vmatrix}}{35} = \frac{40}{35} = \frac{8}{7}$$

$$y = \frac{\begin{vmatrix} 3 & 0 & 1 \\ 2 & 0 & -3 \\ 1 & 8 & 9 \end{vmatrix}}{35} = \frac{88}{35}$$

$$z = \frac{\begin{vmatrix} 3 & -2 & 0 \\ 2 & 1 & 0 \\ 1 & -3 & 8 \end{vmatrix}}{35} = \frac{56}{35} = \frac{8}{5}$$

Solution: $\left(\frac{8}{7}, \frac{88}{35}, \frac{8}{5}\right)$

71. $x + y + z - 3w = -8$

$3x - y - 2z + w = 7$

$-x + y - z + 2w = -2$

$2y + w = -6$

$$\begin{vmatrix} 1 & 1 & 1 & -3 \\ 3 & -1 & -2 & 1 \\ -1 & 1 & -1 & 2 \\ 0 & 2 & 0 & 1 \end{vmatrix} = 20$$

By Cramer's Rule we have:

$$x = \frac{\begin{vmatrix} -8 & 1 & 1 & -3 \\ 7 & -1 & -2 & 1 \\ -2 & 1 & -1 & 2 \\ -6 & 2 & 0 & 1 \end{vmatrix}}{20} = \frac{20}{20} = 1$$

$$z = \frac{\begin{vmatrix} 1 & 1 & -8 & -3 \\ 3 & -1 & 7 & 1 \\ -1 & 1 & -2 & 2 \\ 0 & 2 & -6 & 1 \end{vmatrix}}{20} = \frac{20}{20} = 1$$

$$y = \frac{\begin{vmatrix} 1 & -8 & 1 & -3 \\ 3 & 7 & -2 & 1 \\ -1 & -2 & -1 & 2 \\ 0 & -6 & 0 & 1 \end{vmatrix}}{20} = \frac{-80}{20} = -4$$

$$w = \frac{\begin{vmatrix} 1 & 1 & 1 & -8 \\ 3 & -1 & -2 & 7 \\ -1 & 1 & -1 & -2 \\ 0 & 2 & 0 & -6 \end{vmatrix}}{20} = \frac{40}{20} = 2$$

Solution: $(1, -4, 1, 2)$

Section 10.8   Graphs of Polar Equations

■   When graphing polar equations:

1. Test for symmetry
   (a) $\theta = \pi/2$: Replace (r, θ) by $(r, \pi - \theta)$ or $(-r, -\theta)$.
   (b) Polar axis: Replace (r, θ) by $(r, -\theta)$ or $(-r, \pi - \theta)$.
   (c) Pole: Replace (r, θ) by $(r, \pi + \theta)$ or $(-r, \theta)$.
   (d) $r = f(\sin \theta)$ is symmetric with repsect to the line $\theta = \pi/2$.
   (e) $r = f(\cos \theta)$ is symmetric with respect to the polar axis.

2. Find the θ values for which $|r|$ is maximum.

3. Find the θ values for which $r = 0$.

4. Know the different types of polar graphs.
   (a) Limacons
   $$r = a \pm b \cos \theta$$
   $$r = a \pm b \sin \theta$$
   (b) Rose Curves, $n \geq 2$
   $$r = a \cos n\theta$$
   $$r = a \sin n\theta$$
   (c) Circles
   $$r = a \cos \theta$$
   $$r = a \sin \theta$$
   $$r = a$$
   (d) Lemniscates
   $$r^2 = a^2 \cos 2\theta$$
   $$r^2 = a^2 \sin 2\theta$$

5. Plot additional points.

Solutions to Odd-Numbered Exercises

1. $r = 3 \cos 2\theta$

Rose curve with 4 petals

3. $r = 2 - \cos \theta$

Convex limaçon

5. $r = 6 \sin 2\theta$

Rose curve with 4 petals

7. $r = 10 + 6 \cos \theta$

$\theta = \dfrac{\pi}{2}$: $-r = 10 + 6 \cos(-\theta)$

$\qquad -r = 10 + 6 \cos \theta$

Not an equivalent equation

Polar $r = 10 + 6 \cos(-\theta)$

axis: $r = 10 + 6 \cos \theta$

Equivalent equation

Pole: $-r = 10 + 6 \cos \theta$

Not an equivalent equation

Answer: Symmetric with respect to polar axis

9. $r = \dfrac{2}{1 + \sin \theta}$

$\theta = \dfrac{\pi}{2}$: $r = \dfrac{2}{1 + \sin(\pi - \theta)}$

$\qquad r = \dfrac{2}{1 + \sin \pi \cos \theta - \cos \pi \sin \theta}$

$\qquad r = \dfrac{2}{1 + \sin \theta}$

Equivalent equation

Polar $r = \dfrac{2}{1 + \sin(-\theta)}$

axis: $r = \dfrac{2}{1 - \sin \theta}$

Not an equivalent equation

Pole: $-r = \dfrac{2}{1 + \sin \theta}$

Answer: Symmetric with respect to $\theta = \pi/2$

11. $r = 4 \sec \theta \csc \theta$

$\theta = \dfrac{\pi}{2}$: $-r = 4 \sec(-\theta) \csc(-\theta)$

$\qquad -r = -4 \sec \theta \csc \theta$

$\qquad r = 4 \sec \theta \csc \theta$

Equivalent equation

Polar $-r = 4 \sec(\pi - \theta) \csc(\pi - \theta)$

axis: $-r = 4(-\sec \theta) \csc \theta$

$\qquad r = 4 \sec \theta \csc \theta$

Equivalent equation

Pole: $r = 4 \sec(\pi + \theta) \csc(\pi + \theta)$

$\qquad r = 4(-\sec \theta)(-\csc \theta)$

$\qquad r = 4 \sec \theta \csc \theta$

Equivalent equation

Answer: Symmetric with respect to $\theta = \pi/2$, polar axis, and pole

13. $|r| = |10(1 - \sin \theta)| = 10|1 - \sin \theta| \le 10(2) = 20$

$|1 - \sin \theta| = 2$

$1 - \sin \theta = 2$ or $1 - \sin \theta = -2$

$\sin \theta = -1$ $\sin \theta = 3$

$\theta = \dfrac{3\pi}{2}$ Not possible

Maximum: $|r| = 20$ when $\theta = \dfrac{3\pi}{2}$.

$0 = 10(1 - \sin \theta)$

$\sin \theta = 1$

$\theta = \dfrac{\pi}{2}$

Zero: $r = 0$ when $\theta = \dfrac{\pi}{2}$.

15. $|r| = |4 \cos 3\theta| = 4|\cos 3\theta| \le 4$

$|\cos 3\theta| = 1$

$\cos 3\theta = \pm 1$

$\theta = 0, \dfrac{\pi}{3}, \dfrac{2\pi}{3}$

Maximum: $|r| = 4$ when $\theta = 0, \dfrac{\pi}{3}, \dfrac{2\pi}{3}$.

$0 = 4 \cos 3\theta$

$\cos 3\theta = 0$

$\theta = \dfrac{\pi}{6}, \dfrac{\pi}{2}, \dfrac{5\pi}{6}$

Zero: $r = 0$ when $\theta = \dfrac{\pi}{6}, \dfrac{\pi}{2}, \dfrac{5\pi}{6}$.

19. Circle: $r = \dfrac{\pi}{6}$

23. $r = 3 - 3 \cos \theta$

Symmetric with respect to polar axis

$\dfrac{a}{b} = \dfrac{3}{3} = 1 \Rightarrow$ Cardioid

$|r| = 6$ when $\theta = \pi$.

$r = 0$ when $\pi = 0$.

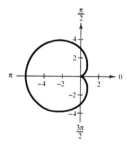

17. Circle: $r = 5$

21. $r = 3 \sin \theta$

Symmetric with respect to $\theta = \dfrac{\pi}{2}$

Circle with a radius of $\dfrac{3}{2}$

25. $r = 4 + 4 \sin \theta$

Symmetric with respect to

$\theta = \dfrac{\pi}{2}$

$\dfrac{a}{b} = \dfrac{4}{4} = 1 \Rightarrow$ Cardioid

$|r| = 8$ when $\theta = \dfrac{\pi}{2}$.

$r = 0$ when $\theta = \dfrac{3\pi}{2}$.

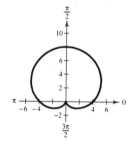

27. $r = 3 - 2\cos\theta$

Symmetric with respect to polar axis

$\dfrac{a}{b} = \dfrac{3}{2} > 1 \implies$ Dimpled limaçon

$|r| = 5$ when $\theta = \pi$.

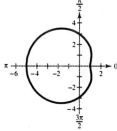

29. $r = 2 + \sin\theta$

Symmetric with respect to $\theta = \dfrac{\pi}{2}$

$\dfrac{a}{b} = \dfrac{2}{1} \geq 2 \implies$ Convex limaçon

$|r| = 3$ when $\theta = \dfrac{\pi}{2}$.

31. $r = 2 + 4\sin\theta$

Symmetric with respect to $\theta = \dfrac{\pi}{2}$

$\dfrac{a}{b} = \dfrac{2}{4} < 1 \implies$ Limaçon with inner loop

$|r| = 6$ when $\theta = \dfrac{\pi}{2}$.

$r = 0$ when $\theta = \dfrac{7\pi}{6}, \dfrac{11\pi}{6}$.

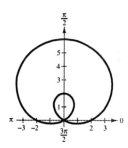

33. $r = 3 - 4\cos\theta$

Symmetric with respect to polar axis

$\dfrac{a}{b} = \dfrac{2}{4} < 1 \implies$ Limaçon with inner loop

$|r| = 7$ when $\theta = \pi$.

$r = 0$ when $\cos\theta = \dfrac{3}{4}$ or

$\theta \approx 0.723, 5.560$

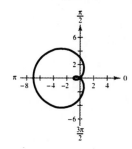

35. $r = 2\cos 3\theta$

Symmetric with respect to polar axis

Rose curve ($n = 3$) with 3 petals

$|r| = 2$ when $\theta = 0, \dfrac{2\pi}{3}, \dfrac{4\pi}{3}$.

$r = 0$ when $\theta = \dfrac{\pi}{6}, \dfrac{\pi}{2}, \dfrac{5\pi}{6}$.

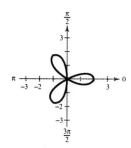

37. $r = 3 \sin 2\theta$

Symmetric with respect to $\theta = \dfrac{\pi}{2}$

Rose curve ($n = 2$) with 4 petals

$|r| = 3$ when $\theta = \dfrac{\pi}{4}, \dfrac{3\pi}{4}, \dfrac{5\pi}{4}, \dfrac{7\pi}{4}.$

$r = 0$ when $\theta = 0, \dfrac{\pi}{2}, \pi.$

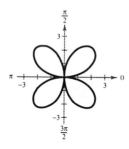

39. $r = 2 \sec \theta$

$r = \dfrac{2}{\cos \theta}$

$r \cos \theta = 2$

$x = 2 \implies$ Line

41. $r = \dfrac{3}{\sin \theta - 2 \cos \theta}$

$r(\sin \theta - 2 \cos \theta) = 3$

$y - 2x = 3$

$y = 2x + 3 \implies$ Line

43. $r^2 = 4 \cos 2\theta$

Symmetric with respect to polar axis

Lemniscate

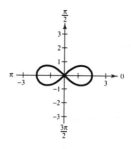

45. $r = \dfrac{\theta}{2}$

Symmetric with respect to $\theta = \dfrac{\pi}{2}$

Spiral

47. $r = 6 \cos \theta$

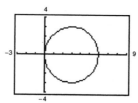

49. $r = 3(2 - \sin \theta)$

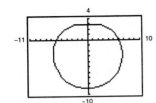

51. $r = 4 \sin \theta \cos^2 \theta$

53. $r = 2 \csc \theta + 5 = \dfrac{2}{\sin \theta} + 5$

55. $r = 3 - 4 \cos \theta$
$0 \le \theta < 2\pi$

57. $r = 2 + \sin \theta$
$0 \le \theta < 2\pi$

59. $r = 2 \cos\left(\dfrac{3\theta}{2}\right)$

$0 \le \theta < 4\pi$

61. $r^2 = 4 \sin 2\theta$
$0 \le \theta < \pi$

63.

$$r = 2 - \sec \theta = 2 - \frac{1}{\cos \theta}$$

$$r \cos \theta = 2 \cos \theta - 1$$

$$r(r \cos \theta) = 2r \cos \theta - r$$

$$\left(\pm\sqrt{x^2 + y^2}\right)x = 2x - \left(\pm\sqrt{x^2 + y^2}\right)$$

$$\left(\pm\sqrt{x^2 + y^2}\right)(x + 1) = 2x$$

$$\left(\pm\sqrt{x^2 + y^2}\right) = \frac{2x}{x + 1}$$

$$x^2 + y^2 = \frac{4x^2}{(x + 1)^2}$$

$$y^2 = \frac{4x^2}{(x + 1)^2} - x^2$$

$$= \frac{4x^2 - x^2(x + 1)^2}{(x + 1)^2} = \frac{4x^2 - x^2(x^2 + 2x + 1)}{(x + 1)^2}$$

$$= \frac{-x^4 - 2x^3 + 3x^2}{(x + 1)^2} = \frac{-x^2(x^2 + 2x - 3)}{(x + 1)^2}$$

$$y = \pm\sqrt{\frac{x^2(3 - 2x - x^2)}{(x + 1)^2}} = \pm\left|\frac{x}{x + 1}\right|\sqrt{3 - 2x - x^2}$$

The graph has an asymptote at $x = -1$.

65. $r = \dfrac{2}{\theta}$

$\theta = \dfrac{2}{r} = \dfrac{2\sin\theta}{r\sin\theta} = \dfrac{2\sin\theta}{y}$

$y = \dfrac{2\sin\theta}{\theta}$

As $\theta \Rightarrow 0, y \Rightarrow 2.$

67. $r = 4\sin\theta$

(a) $0 \le \theta \le \dfrac{\pi}{2}$

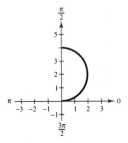

Right half of the circle

(b) $\dfrac{\pi}{2} \le \theta \le \pi$

Left half of the circle

(c) $-\dfrac{\pi}{2} \le \theta \le \dfrac{\pi}{2}$

Entire circle

(d) $\dfrac{\pi}{4} \le \theta \le \dfrac{3\pi}{4}$

Top half of the circle

69. Let the curve $r = f(\theta)$ be rotated by ϕ to form the curve $r = g(\theta)$. If (r_1, θ_1) is a point on $r = f(\theta)$, then $(r_1, \theta_1 + \phi)$ is on $r = g(\theta)$. That is, $g(\theta_1 + \phi) = r_1 = f(\theta_1)$. Letting $\theta = \theta_1 + \phi$, or $\theta_1 = \theta - \phi$, we see that $g(\theta) = g(\theta_1 + \phi) = f(\theta_1) = f(\theta - \phi).$

71. (a) $r = 2 - \sin\left(\theta - \dfrac{\pi}{4}\right)$

$\quad = 2 - \dfrac{\sqrt{2}}{2}(\sin\theta - \cos\theta)$

(c) $r = 2 - \sin(\theta - \pi)$

$\quad = 2 + \sin\theta$

(b) $r = 2 - \sin\left(\theta - \dfrac{\pi}{2}\right)$

$\quad = 2 + \cos\theta$

(d) $r = 2 - \sin\left(\theta - \dfrac{3\pi}{2}\right)$

$\quad = 2 - \cos\theta$

73. (a) $r = 1 - \sin \theta$

(b) $r = 1 - \sin\left(\theta - \dfrac{\pi}{4}\right)$

Rotate the graph in part (a) through the angle $\dfrac{\pi}{4}$.

75. $r = 2 + k \cos \theta$

$k = 0:\ r = 2$

    Circle

$k = 2:\ r = 2 + 2 \cos \theta$

    Cardioid

$k = 1:\ r = 2 + \cos \theta$

    Convex limaçon

$k = 3:\ r = 2 + 3 \cos \theta$

    Limaçon with
    inner loop

Section 10.9   Polar Equations of Conics

- The graph of a polar equation of the form

$$r = \frac{ep}{1 \pm e \cos \theta} \quad \text{or} \quad r = \frac{ep}{1 \pm e \sin \theta}$$

  is a conic, *where $e > 0$ is the eccentricity and $|p|$ is the distance between the focus (pole) and the directrix.*
  (a) If $e < 1$, the graph is an ellipse.
  (b) If $e = 1$, the graph is a parabola.
  (c) If $e > 1$, the graph is a hyperbola.

- Guidelines for finding polar equations of conics:

  (a) Horizontal directrix above the pole: $r = \dfrac{ep}{1 + e \sin \theta}$

  (b) Horizontal directrix below the pole: $r = \dfrac{ep}{1 - e \sin \theta}$

  (c) Vertical directrix to the right of the pole: $r = \dfrac{ep}{1 + e \cos \theta}$

  (d) Vertical directrix to the left of the pole: $r = \dfrac{ep}{1 - e \cos \theta}$

Solutions to Odd-Numbered Exercises

1. $r = \dfrac{2e}{1 + e \cos \theta}$

    (a) $e = 1$, $r = \dfrac{2}{1 + \cos \theta}$, parabola

    (b) $e = 0.5$, $r = \dfrac{1}{1 + 0.5 \cos \theta} = \dfrac{2}{2 + \cos \theta}$, ellipse

    (c) $e = 1.5$, $r = \dfrac{3}{1 + 1.5 \cos \theta} = \dfrac{6}{2 + 3 \cos \theta}$, hyperbola

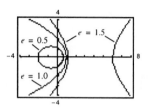

3. $r = \dfrac{2e}{1 - e \sin \theta}$

    (a) $e = 1$, $r = \dfrac{2}{1 - \sin \theta}$, parabola

    (b) $e = 0.5$, $r = \dfrac{1}{1 - 0.5 \sin \theta} = \dfrac{2}{2 - \sin \theta}$, ellipse

    (c) $e = 1.5$, $r = \dfrac{3}{1 - 1.5 \sin \theta} = \dfrac{6}{2 - 3 \sin \theta}$, hyperbola

5. $r = \dfrac{4}{1 - \cos \theta}$

$e = 1 \Rightarrow$ Parabola

Vertical directrix to the left of the pole
Matches graph (b).

7. $r = \dfrac{3}{1 + 2 \sin \theta}$

$e = 2 \Rightarrow$ Hyperbola
Matches graph (d).

9. $r = \dfrac{2}{1 - \cos \theta}$

$e = 1$, the graph is a parabola.

Vertex: $(1, \pi)$

11. $r = \dfrac{5}{1 + \sin \theta}$

$e = 1$, the graph is a parabola.

Vertex: $\left(\dfrac{5}{2}, \dfrac{\pi}{2}\right)$

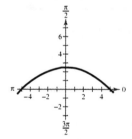

13. $r = \dfrac{2}{2 - \cos \theta} = \dfrac{1}{1 - \frac{1}{2} \cos \theta}$

$e = \dfrac{1}{2} < 1$, the graph is an ellipse.

Vertices: $(2, 0), \left(\dfrac{2}{3}, \pi\right)$

15. $r = \dfrac{4}{2 + \sin \theta} = \dfrac{2}{1 + \frac{1}{2} \sin \theta}$

$e = \dfrac{1}{2} < 1$, the graph is an ellipse.

Vertices: $\left(\dfrac{4}{3}, \dfrac{\pi}{2}\right), \left(4, \dfrac{3\pi}{2}\right)$

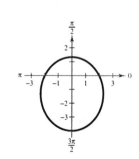

17. $r = \dfrac{3}{2 + 4 \sin \theta} = \dfrac{3/2}{1 + 2 \sin \theta}$

$e = 2 > 1$, the graph is a hyperbola.

Vertices: $\left(\dfrac{1}{2}, \dfrac{\pi}{2}\right), \left(-\dfrac{3}{2}, \dfrac{3\pi}{2}\right)$

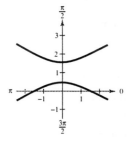

19. $r = \dfrac{3}{2 - 6 \cos \theta} = \dfrac{3/2}{1 - 3 \cos \theta}$

$e = 3 > 1$, the graph is a hyperbola.

Vertices: $\left(-\dfrac{3}{4}, 0\right), \left(\dfrac{3}{8}, \pi\right)$

21. $r = \dfrac{6}{2 - \cos \theta} = \dfrac{3}{1 - \frac{1}{2} \cos \theta}$

$e = \dfrac{1}{2} < 1$, the graph is an ellipse.

Vertices: $(6, 0), (2, \pi)$

23. $r = \dfrac{-1}{1 - \sin \theta}$

$e = 1 \Rightarrow$ Parabola

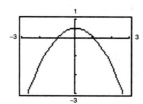

25. $r = \dfrac{3}{-4 + 2 \cos \theta}$

$e = \dfrac{1}{2} \Rightarrow$ Ellipse

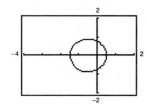

27. $r = \dfrac{2}{1 - \cos(\theta - \pi/4)}$

Rotate the graph in Exercise 9 through the angle $\dfrac{\pi}{4}$.

29. $r = \dfrac{4}{2 + \sin(\theta + \pi/6)}$

Rotate the graph in Exercise 15 through the angle $-\pi/6$.

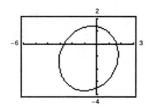

31. Parabola: $e = 1$

Directrix: $x = -1$

Vertical directrix to the left of the pole

$r = \dfrac{1(1)}{1 - 1 \cos \theta} = \dfrac{1}{1 - \cos \theta}$

33. Ellipse: $e = \dfrac{1}{2}$

Directrix: $y = 1$

$\qquad\qquad p = 1$

Horizontal directrix above the pole

$$r = \frac{\frac{1}{2}(1)}{1 + \frac{1}{2}\sin\theta} = \frac{1}{2 + \sin\theta}$$

37. Parabola

Vertex: $\left(1, -\dfrac{\pi}{2}\right) \Rightarrow e = 1, p = 2$

Horizontal directrix below the pole

$$r = \frac{1(2)}{1 - 1\sin\theta} = \frac{2}{1 - \sin\theta}$$

41. Ellipse: Vertices $(2, 0)$, $(8, \pi)$

Center: $(3, \pi)$; $c = 3$, $a = 5$, $e = \dfrac{3}{5}$

Vertical directrix to the right of the pole

$$r = \frac{\frac{3}{5}p}{1 + \frac{3}{5}\cos\theta} = \frac{3p}{5 + 3\cos\theta}$$

$$2 = \frac{3p}{5 + 3\cos 0}$$

$$p = \frac{16}{3}$$

$$r = \frac{3\left(\frac{16}{3}\right)}{5 + 3\cos\theta} = \frac{16}{5 + 3\cos\theta}$$

45. Hyperbola: Vertices $\left(1, \dfrac{3\pi}{2}\right)$, $\left(9, \dfrac{3\pi}{2}\right)$

Center: $\left(5, \dfrac{3\pi}{2}\right)$; $c = 5$, $a = 4$, $e = \dfrac{5}{4}$

Horizontal directrix below the pole

$$r = \frac{5/4p}{1 - 5/4\sin\theta} = \frac{5p}{4 - 5\sin\theta}$$

$$1 = \frac{5p}{4 - 5\sin(3\pi/2)}$$

$$p = \frac{9}{5}$$

$$r = \frac{5(9/5)}{4 - 5\sin\theta} = \frac{9}{4 - 5\sin\theta}$$

35. Hyperbola: $e = 2$

Directrix: $x = 1$

$\qquad\qquad p = 1$

Vertical directrix to the right of the pole

$$r = \frac{2(1)}{1 + 2\cos\theta} = \frac{2}{1 + 2\cos\theta}$$

39. Parabola

Vertex: $(5, \pi) \Rightarrow e = 1, p = 10$

Vertical directrix to the left of the pole

$$r = \frac{1(10)}{1 - 1\cos\theta} = \frac{10}{1 - \cos\theta}$$

43. Ellipse: Vertices $(20, 0)$, $(4, \pi)$

Center: $(8, 0)$; $c = 8$, $a = 12$, $e = \dfrac{2}{3}$

Vertical directrix to the left of the pole

$$r = \frac{\frac{2}{3}p}{1 - \frac{2}{3}\cos\theta} = \frac{2p}{3 - 2\cos\theta}$$

$$20 = \frac{2p}{3 - 2\cos 0}$$

$$p = 10$$

$$r = \frac{2(10)}{3 - 2\cos\theta} = \frac{20}{3 - 2\cos\theta}$$

47.

$$\frac{x^2}{a^2} + \frac{y^2}{b^2} = 1$$

$$\frac{r^2\cos^2\theta}{a^2} + \frac{r^2\sin^2\theta}{b^2} = 1$$

$$\frac{r^2\cos^2\theta}{a^2} + \frac{r^2(1 - \cos^2\theta)}{b^2} = 1$$

$$r^2b^2\cos^2\theta + r^2a^2 - r^2a^2\cos^2\theta = a^2b^2$$

$$r^2(b^2 - a^2)\cos^2\theta + r^2a^2 = a^2b^2$$

$$b^2 - a^2 = -c^2$$

$$-r^2c^2\cos^2\theta + r^2a^2 = a^2b^2$$

$$-r^2\left(\frac{c}{a}\right)^2\cos^2\theta + r^2 = b^2, e = \frac{c}{a}$$

$$-r^2e^2\cos^2\theta + r^2 = b^2$$

$$r^2(1 - e^2\cos^2\theta) = b^2$$

$$r^2 = \frac{b^2}{1 - e^2\cos^2\theta}$$

49. $\dfrac{x^2}{169} + \dfrac{y^2}{144} = 1$

$a = 13, b = 12, c = 5, e = \dfrac{5}{13}$

$r^2 = \dfrac{144}{1 - \left(\frac{25}{169}\right)\cos^2\theta} = \dfrac{24{,}336}{169 - 25\cos^2\theta}$

51. $\dfrac{x^2}{9} - \dfrac{y^2}{16} = 1$

$a = 3, b = 4, c = 5, e = \dfrac{5}{3}$

$r^2 = \dfrac{-16}{1 - \left(\frac{25}{9}\right)\cos^2\theta} = \dfrac{144}{25\cos^2\theta - 9}$

53. One focus: $\left(5, \dfrac{\pi}{2}\right)$

Vertices: $\left(4, \dfrac{\pi}{2}\right), \left(4, -\dfrac{\pi}{2}\right)$

$a = 4, c = 5 \Rightarrow b = 3$ and $e = \dfrac{5}{4}$

$$\dfrac{y^2}{16} - \dfrac{x^2}{9} = 1$$

$$\dfrac{r^2\sin^2\theta}{16} - \dfrac{r^2\cos^2\theta}{9} = 1$$

$$9r^2\sin^2\theta - 16r^2(1 - \sin^2\theta) = 144$$

$$25r^2\sin^2\theta - 16r^2 = 144$$

$$r^2 = \dfrac{144}{25\sin^2\theta - 16} = \dfrac{-144}{16 - 25\sin^2\theta}$$

55. When $\theta = 0$, $r = c + a = ea + a = a(1 + e)$.
Therefore,

$$a(1 + e) = \dfrac{ep}{1 - e\cos\theta}$$

$$a(1 + e)(1 - e) = ep$$

$$a(1 - e^2) = ep.$$

Thus, $r = \dfrac{ep}{1 - e\cos\theta} = \dfrac{(1 - e^2)a}{1 - e\cos\theta}$.

57. $r = \dfrac{[1 - (0.0167)^2](92.957 \times 10^6)}{1 - 0.0167\cos\theta}$

$\approx \dfrac{9.2931 \times 10^7}{1 - 0.0167\cos\theta}$

Perihelion distance:
$r = 92.957 \times 10^6(1 - 0.0167) \approx 9.1405 \times 10^7$

Aphelion distance:
$r = 92.957 \times 10^6(1 + 0.0167) \approx 9.4509 \times 10^7$

59. $r = \dfrac{[1 - (0.2481)^2](5.9 \times 10^9)}{1 - 0.2481\cos\theta}$

$\approx \dfrac{5.5368 \times 10^9}{1 - 0.2481\cos\theta}$

Perihelion distance:
$r = 5.9 \times 10^9(1 - 0.2481) \approx 4.4362 \times 10^9$

Aphelion distance:
$r = 5.9 \times 10^9(1 + 0.2481) \approx 7.3638 \times 10^9$

61. Vertex: $\left(4100, \dfrac{\pi}{2}\right)$

Focus: $(0, 0)$

$e = 1, p = 8200$

$r = \dfrac{ep}{1 + e\sin\theta} = \dfrac{8200}{1 + \sin\theta}$

When $\theta = 30°$, $r = 8200/1.5 \approx 5466.67$.
Distance between the surface of the earth
and the satellite is $r - 4000 \approx 1467$ miles.

63. $f(x) = 4^{x-2}$

Exponential function

x	0	1	2	3
y	$\frac{1}{16}$	$\frac{1}{4}$	1	4

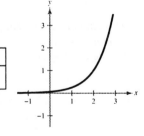

65. $h(t) = \log_4(t - 2)$

Logarithmic function

$$4^y = t - 2$$

$$4^y + 2 = t$$

t	$2\frac{1}{4}$	3	6
y	-1	0	1

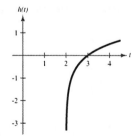

Vertical asymptote: $t = 2$

Review Exercises for Chapter 10

Solutions to Odd-Numbered Exercises

1. $m = \tan 120°$

$= -\sqrt{3}$

3. $y = -x + 10$

$m = -1 = \tan \theta$

$\theta = \arctan(-1) = 135°$

5. $(1, 2) \Rightarrow x_1 = 1, y_1 = 2$

$x - y - 3 = 0 \Rightarrow A = 1, B = -1, C = -3$

$d = \dfrac{|1(1) + (-1)(2) + (-3)|}{\sqrt{1^2 + (-1)^2}} = \dfrac{4}{\sqrt{2}} = 2\sqrt{2}$

7. $4x^2 + y^2 = 4$

$\dfrac{x^2}{1} + \dfrac{y^2}{4} = 1$

Ellipse with center $(0, 0)$ and a vertical major axis
Matches graph (g).

9. $4x^2 - y^2 = 4$

$\dfrac{x^2}{1} - \dfrac{y^2}{4} = 1$

Hyperbola with center $(0, 0)$ and
a horizontal transverse axis
Matches graph (f).

11. $x^2 + 4y^2 = 4$

$\dfrac{x^2}{4} + \dfrac{y^2}{1} = 1$

Ellipse with center $(0, 0)$ and a horizontal
major axis.
Matches graph (d)

13. $x^2 = -6y$

$y = -\dfrac{1}{6}x^2$

Parabola with vertex $(0, 0)$ and opening downward
Matches graph (b).

15. $x^2 - 5y^2 = -5$

$\dfrac{y^2}{1} - \dfrac{x^2}{5} = 1$

Hyperbola with center $(0, 0)$ and a vertical
transverse axis
Matches graph (h).

17. $4x - y^2 = 0$

$y^2 = 4x$

The graph is a parabola.
Vertex: $(0, 0)$

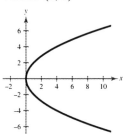

19. $x^2 - 6x + 2y + 9 = 0$

$(x - 3)^2 = -2y$

The graph is a parabola.
Vertex: $(3, 0)$

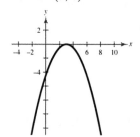

21. $x^2 + y^2 - 2x - 4y + 5 = 0$

$(x - 1)^2 + (y - 2)^2 = 0$

The graph is a degenerate circle. $(1, 2)$ is the only
point that satisfies this equation.

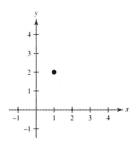

23. $4x^2 + y^2 = 16$

$\dfrac{x^2}{4} + \dfrac{y^2}{16} = 1$

The graph is an ellipse.
Center: $(0, 0)$
Vertices: $(0, \pm 4)$

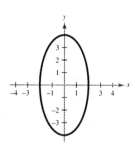

25. $x^2 + 9y^2 + 10x - 18y + 25 = 0$

$$(x + 5)^2 + 9(y - 1)^2 = 9$$

$$\frac{(x + 5)^2}{9} + \frac{(y - 1)^2}{1} = 1$$

The graph is an ellipse.

Center: $(-5, 1)$

Vertices: $(-8, 1)\ (-2, 1)$

27. $5y^2 - 4x^2 = 20$

$$\frac{y^2}{4} - \frac{x^2}{5} = 1$$

The graph is a hyperbola.

Center: $(0, 0)$

Vertices: $(\pm 2, 0)$

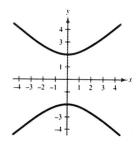

29. $B^2 - 4AC = 2^2 - 4(1)(1) = 0$

The graph is a parabola.

$$\cot 2\theta = \frac{A - C}{B} = 0 \implies 2\theta = \frac{\pi}{2} \implies \theta = \frac{\pi}{4}$$

$$x = x' \cos \frac{\pi}{4} - y' \sin \frac{\pi}{4} = \frac{x' - y'}{\sqrt{2}}$$

$$y = x' \sin \frac{\pi}{4} + y' \cos \frac{\pi}{4} = \frac{x' + y'}{\sqrt{2}}$$

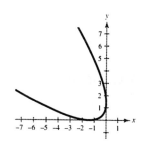

$$\left(\frac{x' - y'}{\sqrt{2}}\right)^2 + \left(\frac{x' + y'}{\sqrt{2}}\right)^2 + 2\left(\frac{x' - y'}{\sqrt{2}}\right)\left(\frac{x' + y'}{\sqrt{2}}\right) + 2\sqrt{2}\left(\frac{x' - y'}{\sqrt{2}}\right) - 2\sqrt{2}\left(\frac{x' + y'}{\sqrt{2}}\right) + 2 = 0$$

$$2(x')^2 - 4y' + 2 = 0$$

$$(x')^2 = 2y' - 1$$

Vertex: $(x', y') = \left(0, \frac{1}{2}\right)$, $\theta = 45°$

31. $AC = 3(2) = 6 > 0$

The graph is an ellipse.

$$3x^2 + 2y^2 - 12x + 12y + 29 = 0$$

$$\frac{(x - 2)^2}{1/3} + \frac{(y + 3)^2}{1/2} = 1$$

Center: $(2, -3)$

Vertices: $\left(2, -3 \pm \frac{\sqrt{2}}{2}\right)$

To use a graphing calculator, we need to solve for y in terms of x.

$$2(y + 3)^2 = 1 - 3(x - 2)^2|$$

$$y = -3 \pm \sqrt{\frac{1 - (x - 2)^2}{2}}$$

33. $x^2 - 10xy + y^2 + 1 = 0$

Since $B^2 - 4AC = (-10)^2 - 4(1)(1) > 0$, the graph is a hyperbola.

To use a graphing calculator, we need to solve for y in terms of x.

$$(y^2 - 10xy + 25x^2) = -x^2 - 1 + 25x^2$$
$$(y - 5x)^2 = 24x^2 - 1$$
$$y = 5x \pm \sqrt{24x^2 - 1}$$

35. Vertex: $(4, 2) = (h, k)$

Focus: $(4, 0) \Rightarrow p = -2$

$(x - h)^2 = 4p(y - k)$

$(x - 4)^2 = -8(y - 2)$

37. Vertex: $(0, 2) = (h, k)$

Directrix: $x = -3 \Rightarrow p = 3$

$(y - k^2) = 4p(x - h)$

$(y - 2)^2 = 12x$

39. Vertices: $(-3, 0), (7, 0) \Rightarrow a = 5$
     $(h, k) = (2, 0)$

Foci: $(0, 0), (4, 0) \Rightarrow c = 2$

$b^2 = a^2 - c^2 = 25 - 4 = 21$

$$\frac{(x - h)^2}{a^2} + \frac{(y - k)^2}{b^2} = 1$$

$$\frac{(x - 2)^2}{25} + \frac{y^2}{.21} = 1$$

41. Vertices: $(0, \pm 6) \Rightarrow a = 6, (h, k) = (0, 0)$

Passes through $(2, 2)$

$$\frac{(x - h)^2}{b^2} + \frac{(y - k)^2}{a^2} = 1$$

$$\frac{x^2}{b^2} + \frac{y^2}{36} = 1 \Rightarrow b^2 = \frac{36(4)}{36 - 4} = \frac{36x^2}{36 - y^2} = \frac{9}{2}$$

$$\frac{x^2}{9/2} + \frac{y^2}{36} = 1$$

$$\frac{2x^2}{9} + \frac{y^2}{36} = 1$$

43. Vertices: $(0, \pm 1) \Rightarrow a = 1, (h, k) = (0, 0)$

Foci: $(0, \pm 3) \Rightarrow c = 3$

$b^2 = c^2 - a^2 = 9 - 1 = 8$

$$\frac{(y - k)^2}{a^2} - \frac{(x - h)^2}{b^2} = 1$$

$$y^2 - \frac{x^2}{8} = 1$$

45. Foci: $(0, 0), (8, 0) \Rightarrow c = 4, (h, k) = (4, 0)$

Asymptotes: $y = \pm 2(x - 4) \Rightarrow \dfrac{b}{a} = 2, b = 2a$

$b^2 = c^2 - a^2 \Rightarrow 4a^2 = 16 - a^2 \Rightarrow a^2 = \dfrac{16}{5},$

$b^2 = \dfrac{64}{5}$

$$\frac{(x - h)^2}{a^2} - \frac{(y - k)^2}{b^2} = 1$$

$$\frac{(x - 4)^2}{16/5} - \frac{y^2}{64/5} = 1$$

$$\frac{5(x - 4)^2}{16} - \frac{5y^2}{64} = 1$$

47. Parabola

Opens downward

Vertex: $(0, 12)$

$$(x - h)^2 = 4p(y - k)$$
$$x^2 = 4p(y - 12)$$

Solution points: $(\pm 4, 10)$

$$16 = 4p(10 - 12)$$
$$16 = -8p$$
$$-2 = p$$
$$x^2 = -8(y - 12)$$

To find the x-intercepts, let $y = 0$.

$$x^2 = 96$$
$$x = \pm\sqrt{96} = \pm 4\sqrt{6}$$

At the base,z the archway is $2\left(4\sqrt{6}\right) = 8\sqrt{6}$ meters wide.

49. $BD = AD + 6\left(\dfrac{1100}{5280}\right)$

$$CD = AD + 8\left(\frac{1100}{5280}\right)$$

$$2a = CD - BD = 2\left(\frac{1100}{5280}\right)$$

$$a = \frac{5}{24}, c = 2 \implies b^2 = \frac{2279}{576}$$

Thus, we have $\dfrac{576x^2}{25} - \dfrac{576y^2}{2279} = 1$ OR:

$$CD = AD + 8\left(\frac{1100}{5280}\right)$$

$$BD = AD + 6\left(\frac{1100}{5280}\right)$$

$$2a = BD - AD = 6\left(\frac{1100}{5280}\right)$$

$$a = 3\left(\frac{5}{24}\right) = \frac{5}{8}, c = 1 \implies b^2 = \frac{39}{64}$$

Center: $(1, 0)$

$$\frac{64(x - 1)^2}{25} - \frac{64y^2}{39} = 1$$

$$CD - 8\left(\frac{1100}{5280}\right) = AD$$

$$BD = CD - 8\left(\frac{1100}{5280}\right) + 6\left(\frac{1100}{5280}\right) = CD - 2\left(\frac{1100}{5280}\right)$$

Thus, the friend to the west hears the explosion two seconds after the friend to the east.

51. $x = 2t \Rightarrow \dfrac{x}{2} = t$

$y = 4t \Rightarrow y = 4\left(\dfrac{x}{2}\right) = 2x$

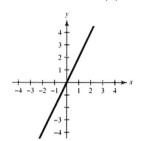

53. $x = 1 + 4t, \ y = 2 - 3t$

$t = \dfrac{x - 1}{4}$

$y = 2 - 3\left(\dfrac{x - 1}{4}\right)$

$3x + 4y = 11$

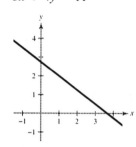

55. $x = \dfrac{1}{t}, \ y = t^2$

$t = \dfrac{1}{x}$

$y = \dfrac{1}{x^2}$

57. $x = 6 \cos \theta, \ y = 6 \sin \theta$

$\cos \theta = \dfrac{x}{6}, \ \sin \theta = \dfrac{y}{6}$

$\dfrac{x^2}{36} + \dfrac{y^2}{36} = 1$

$x^2 + y^2 = 36$

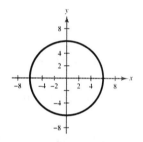

59. $(h, k) = (-3, 4)$

$2a = 8 \Rightarrow a = 4$

$2b = 6 \Rightarrow b = 3$

$\dfrac{(x + 3)^2}{16} + \dfrac{(y - 4)^2}{9} = 1$

$x = -3 + 4 \cos \theta$

$y = 4 + 3 \sin \theta$

This solution is not unique.

61. $x = \cos 3\theta + 5 \cos \theta$

$y = \sin 3\theta + 5 \sin \theta$

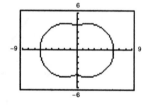

63. $r = 3 \cos \theta$

$r^2 = 3r \cos \theta$

$x^2 + y^2 = 3x$

65. $r^2 = \cos 2\theta$

$r^2 = 1 - 2 \sin^2 \theta$

$r^4 = r^2 - 2r^2 \sin^2 \theta$

$(x^2 + y^2)^2 = x^2 + y^2 - 2y^2$

$(x^2 + y^2)^2 - x^2 + y^2 = 0$

67. $(x^2 + y^2)^2 = ax^2y$

$(r^2)^2 = ar^2 \cos^2 \theta \, r \sin \theta$

$r = a \cos^2 \theta \sin \theta$

69. $r = 4$

Circle of radius 4 centered at the pole

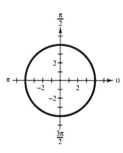

71. $r = 4 \sin 2\theta$

Symmetric with respect to $\theta = \pi/2$

Rose curve ($n = 2$) with 4 petals

73. $r = -2 - 2\cos\theta$

Symmetric with respect to polar axis

$\dfrac{a}{b} = \dfrac{2}{2} = 1 \Rightarrow$ Cardioid

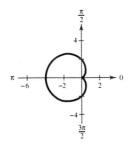

75. $r = 4 - 3\cos\theta$

Symmetric with respect to polar axis

$\dfrac{a}{b} = \dfrac{4}{3} > 0 \Rightarrow$ Dimpled limaçon

77. $r = -3\cos 2\theta$

Symmetric with respect to the polar axis, $\theta = \pi/2$, and the pole

Rose curve with 4 petals

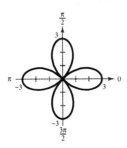

79. $r = \dfrac{2}{1 - \sin\theta}$, $e = 1$

Parabola symmetric with $\theta = \pi/2$ and the vertex at $(1, 3\pi/2)$

81. $r^2 = 4\sin^2 2\theta \Rightarrow r = \pm 2\sin 2\theta$

Symmetric with respect to $\theta = \pi/2$, polar axis, and pole

Rose curve ($n = 2$) with 4 petals

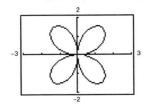

83. $r = \dfrac{3}{\cos(\theta - \pi/4)}$

The graph is a line.

85. Center: $(5, \pi/2)$

Solution point: $(0, 0) \Rightarrow$ Radius $= 5 \Rightarrow a = 10$

$r = a\sin\theta$

$r = 10\sin\theta$

87. Parabola: $r = \dfrac{ep}{1 - e\cos\theta}$, $e = 1$

Vertex: $(2, \pi)$

Focus: $(0, 0) \Rightarrow p = 4$

$r = \dfrac{4}{1 - \cos\theta}$

89. Ellipse: $r = \dfrac{ep}{1 - e\cos\theta}$; Vertices: $(5, 0), (1, \pi) \Rightarrow a = 3$; One focus: $(0, 0) \Rightarrow c = 2$

$e = \dfrac{c}{a} = \dfrac{2}{3}, p = \dfrac{5}{2}$

$r = \dfrac{(2/3)(5/2)}{1 - (2/3)\cos\theta} = \dfrac{5/3}{1 - (2/3)\cos\theta} = \dfrac{5}{3 - 2\cos\theta}$

❑ Practice Test for Chapter 10

1. Find the angle, θ, between the lines $3x + 4y = 12$ and $4x - 3y = 12$.

2. Find the distance between the point $(5, -9)$ and the line $3x - 7y = 21$.

3. Find the vertex, focus and directrix of the parabola $x^2 - 6x - 4y + 1 = 0$.

4. Find an equation of the parabola with its vertex at $(2, -5)$ and focus at $(2, -6)$.

5. Find the center, foci, vertices, and eccentricity of the ellipse $x^2 + 4y^2 - 2x + 32y + 61 = 0$.

6. Find an equation of the ellipse with vertices $(0, \pm6)$ and eccentricity $e = \frac{1}{2}$.

7. Find the center, vertices, foci, and asymptotes of the hyperbola $16y^2 - x^2 - 6x - 128y + 231 = 0$.

8. Find an equation of the hyperbola with vertices at $(\pm3, 2)$ and foci at $(\pm5, 2)$.

9. Rotate the axes to eliminate the xy-term. Sketch the graph of the resulting equation, showing both sets of axes.

   $5x^2 + 2xy + 5y^2 - 10 = 0$

10. Use the discriminant to determine whether the graph of the equation is a parabola, ellipse, or hyperbola.

    (a) $6x^2 - 2xy + y^2 = 0$ (b) $x^2 + 4xy + 4y^2 - x - y + 17 = 0$

11. Convert the polar point $\left(\sqrt{2}, (3\pi)/4\right)$ to rectangular coordinates.

12. Convert the rectangular point $\left(\sqrt{3}, -1\right)$ to polar coordinates.

13. Convert the rectangular equation $4x - 3y = 12$ to polar form.

14. Convert the polar equation $r = 5 \cos \theta$ to rectangular form.

15. Sketch the graph of $r = 1 - \cos \theta$.

16. Sketch the graph of $r = 5 \sin 2\theta$.

17. Sketch the graph of $r = \dfrac{3}{6 - \cos \theta}$.

18. Find a polar equation of the parabola with its vertex at $\left(6, \pi/2\right)$ and focus at $(0, 0)$.

For Exercises 19 and 20, eliminate the parameter and write the corresponding rectangular equation.

19. $x = 3 - 2 \sin \theta, y = 1 + 5 \cos \theta$ 20. $x = e^{2t}, y = e^{4t}$

❑ Chapter P Practice Test Solutions

1. $\dfrac{|-42|-20}{15-|-4|} = \dfrac{42-20}{15-4} = \dfrac{22}{11} = 2$

2. $\dfrac{x}{z} - \dfrac{z}{y} = \dfrac{x}{z}\cdot\dfrac{y}{y} - \dfrac{z}{y}\cdot\dfrac{z}{z} = \dfrac{xy - z^2}{yz}$

3. $|x - 7| \le 4$

4. $10(-5)^3 = 10(-125) = -1250$

5. $(-4x^3)(-2x^{-5})\left(\dfrac{1}{16}x\right) = (-4)(-2)\left(\dfrac{1}{16}\right)x^{3+(-5)+1} = \dfrac{8}{16}x^{-1} = \dfrac{1}{2x}$

6. $0.0000412 = 4.12 \times 10^{-5}$

7. $125^{2/3} = \left(\sqrt[3]{125}\right)^2 = (5)^2 = 25$

8. $\sqrt[4]{64x^7y^9} = \sqrt[4]{16 \cdot 4x^4x^3y^8y} = 2xy^2\sqrt[4]{4x^3y}$

9. $\dfrac{6}{\sqrt{12}} = \dfrac{6}{2\sqrt{3}}\cdot\dfrac{\sqrt{3}}{\sqrt{3}} = \dfrac{6\sqrt{3}}{6} = \sqrt{3}$

10. $3\sqrt{80} - 7\sqrt{500} = 3(4\sqrt{5}) - 7(10\sqrt{5}) = 12\sqrt{5} - 70\sqrt{5} = -58\sqrt{5}$

11. $(8x^4 - 9x^2 + 2x - 1) - (3x^3 + 5x + 4) = 8x^4 - 3x^3 - 9x^2 - 3x - 5$

12. $(x - 3)(x^2 + x - 7) = x^3 + x^2 - 7x - 3x^2 - 3x + 21 = x^3 - 2x^2 - 10x + 21$

13. $[(x - 2) - y]^2 = (x - 2)^2 - 2y(x - 2) + y^2$
$$= x^2 - 4x + 4 - 2xy + 4y + y^2 = x^2 + y^2 - 2xy - 4x + 4y + 4$$

14. $16x^4 - 1 = (4x^2 + 1)(4x^2 - 1) = (4x^2 + 1)(2x + 1)(2x - 1)$

15. $6x^2 + 5x - 4 = (2x - 1)(3x + 4)$

16. $x^3 - 64 = x^3 - 4^3 = (x - 4)(x^2 + 4x + 16)$

17. $-\dfrac{3}{x} + \dfrac{x}{x^2 + 2} = \dfrac{-3(x^2 + 2) + x^2}{x(x^2 + 2)} = \dfrac{-2x^2 - 6}{x(x^2 + 2)} = \dfrac{-2(x^2 + 3)}{x(x^2 + 2)}$

18. $\dfrac{x - 3}{4x} \div \dfrac{x^2 - 9}{x^2} = \dfrac{x - 3}{4x} \cdot \dfrac{x^2}{(x + 3)(x - 3)} = \dfrac{x}{4(x + 3)}$

19. $\dfrac{1 - \dfrac{1}{x}}{1 - \dfrac{1}{1 - (1/x)}} = \dfrac{\dfrac{x - 1}{x}}{1 - \dfrac{1}{(x - 1)/x}} = \dfrac{\dfrac{x - 1}{x}}{1 - \dfrac{x}{x - 1}} = \dfrac{\dfrac{x - 1}{x}}{\dfrac{-1}{x - 1}} = \dfrac{x - 1}{x} \cdot \dfrac{x - 1}{-1} = \dfrac{-(x - 1)^2}{x}$

20. (a)

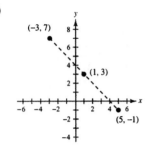

(b) $d = \sqrt{[5 - (-3)]^2 + (-1 - 7)^2}$

$= \sqrt{(8)^2 + (-8)^2}$

$= \sqrt{64 + 64}$

$= \sqrt{128}$

$= 8\sqrt{2}$

(c) $\left(\dfrac{-3 + 5}{2}, \dfrac{7 + (-1)}{2} \right)$

$= (1, 3)$

21. (a) $x^2 - 2x - 35 = 0$

$(x - 7)(x + 5) = 0$

$x - 7 = 0 \text{ or } x + 5 = 0$

$x = 7 \text{ or } \quad x = -5$

(b) $x^2 - 2x - 35 = 0$

$x^2 - 2x = 35$

$x^2 - 2x + 1 = 35 + 1$

$(x - 1)^2 = 36$

$x - 1 = \pm\sqrt{36}$

$x = 1 \pm 6$

$x = 7 \text{ or } x = -5$

(c) $x^2 - 2x - 35 = 0$

$x = \dfrac{-(-2) \pm \sqrt{(-2)^2 - 4(1)(-35)}}{2(1)}$

$= \dfrac{2 \pm \sqrt{4 + 140}}{2}$

$= \dfrac{2 \pm 12}{2}$

$= 1 \pm 6$

Thus, $x = 7$ or $x = -5$.

22.

$x^5 - 5x^3 + 4x = 0$

$x(x^4 - 5x^2 + 4) = 0$

$x(x^2 - 1)(x^2 - 4) = 0$

$x(x + 1)(x - 1)(x + 2)(x - 2) = 0$

$x = 0, x = \pm 1, x = \pm 2$

23. $x = 2\sqrt{x + 3}$

$x^2 = 4(x + 3)$

$x^2 = 4x + 12$

$x^2 - 4x - 12 = 0$

$(x - 6)(x + 2) = 0$

$x - 6 = 0 \Rightarrow x = 6$

$x + 2 = 0 \Rightarrow x = -2, \text{ extraneous}$

24. $x^2 - 16 \le 0$

$(x + 4)(x - 4) \le 0$

Critical numbers: $x = \pm 4$

Test intervals: $(-\infty, -4), (-4, 4), (4, \infty)$

Test: Is $(x + 4)(x - 4) \le 0$?

Solution set: $[-4, 4]$

25. $\left| \dfrac{4 - x}{3} \right| > 2$

$\dfrac{4 - x}{3} < -2 \quad \text{or} \quad \dfrac{4 - x}{3} > 2$

$4 - x < -6 \qquad\quad 4 - x > 6$

$-x < -10 \qquad\quad -x > 2$

$x > 10 \qquad\qquad x < -2$

❏ Chapter 1 Practice Test Solutions

1. $y = \sqrt{7 - x}$

x	7	6	3	-2
y	0	1	2	3

2. $y = \sqrt{25 - x^2}$

Domain: $25 - x^2 \geq 0$

$\qquad (5 - x)(5 + x) \geq 0$

Critical numbers: $x = \pm 5$

Test intervals: $(-\infty, -5), (-5, 5), (5, \infty)$

Solution set: $[-5, 5]$

3. $[x - (-3)]^2 + (y - 5)^2 = 6^2$

$\qquad (x + 3)^2 + (y - 5)^2 = 36$

4. $m = \dfrac{-1 - 4}{3 - 2} = -5$

$y - 4 = -5(x - 2)$

$y - 4 = -5x + 10$

$\quad\; y = -5x + 14$

5. $y = \dfrac{4}{3}x - 3$

6. $2x + 3y = 0$

$y = -\dfrac{2}{3}x$

$m_1 = -\dfrac{2}{3}$

$\perp m_2 = \dfrac{3}{2}$ through $(4, 1)$

$y - 1 = \dfrac{3}{2}(x - 4)$

$y - 1 = \dfrac{3}{2}x - 6$

$\quad\; y = \dfrac{3}{2}x - 5$

7. $(5, 32)$ and $(9, 44)$

$m = \dfrac{44 - 32}{9 - 5} = \dfrac{12}{4} = 3$

$y - 32 = 3(x - 5)$

$y - 32 = 3x - 15$

$\quad\; y = 3x + 17$

When $x = 20$, $y = 3(20) + 17$

$\qquad\qquad y = \$77.$

8. $f(x - 3) = (x - 3)^2 - 2(x - 3) + 1$

$\qquad\qquad = x^2 - 6x + 9 - 2x + 6 + 1$

$\qquad\qquad = x^2 - 8x + 16$

9. $f(3) = 12 - 11 = 1$

$\dfrac{f(x) - f(3)}{x - 3} = \dfrac{(4x - 11) - 1}{x - 3}$

$\qquad\qquad = \dfrac{4x - 12}{x - 3}$

$\qquad\qquad = \dfrac{4(x - 3)}{x - 3} = 4, x \neq 3$

10. $f(x) = \sqrt{36 - x^2} = \sqrt{(6 + x)(6 - x)}$

Domain: $[-6, 6]$

Range: $[0, 6]$, because

$(6 + x)(6 - x) \geq 0$ on this interval

11. (a) $6x - 5y + 4 = 0$

$$y = \frac{6x + 4}{5} \text{ is a function of } x.$$

(b) $x^2 + y^2 = 9$

$$y = \pm\sqrt{9 - x^2} \text{ is not a function of } x.$$

(c) $y^3 = x^2 + 6$

$$y = \sqrt[3]{x^2 + 6} \text{ is a function of } x.$$

12. Parabola

Vertex: $(0, -5)$

Intercepts: $(0, -5),\ \left(\pm\sqrt{5}, 0\right)$

y-axis symmetry

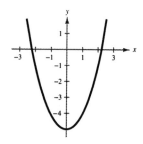

13. Intercepts: $(0, 3),\ (-3, 0)$

x	0	1	-1	2	-2	-3	-4
y	3	4	2	5	1	0	1

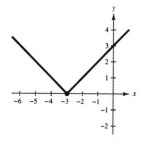

14.

x	0	1	2	3	-1	-2	-3
y	1	3	5	7	2	6	12

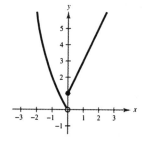

15. (a) $f(x + 2)$

Horizontal shift two units to the left

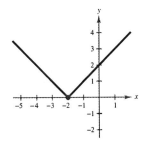

(b) $-f(x) + 2$

Reflection in the x-axis and a vertical shift two units upward

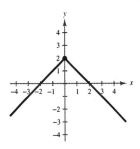

16. (a) $(g - f)(x) = g(x) - f(x)$

$$= (2x^2 - 5) - (3x + 7)$$

$$= 2x^2 - 3x - 12$$

(b) $(fg)(x) = f(x)g(x)$

$$= (3x + 7)(2x^2 - 5)$$

$$= 6x^3 + 14x^2 - 15x - 35$$

17. $f(g(x)) = f(2x + 3)$

$$= (2x + 3)^2 - 2(2x + 3) + 16$$

$$= 4x^2 + 12x + 9 - 4x - 6 + 16$$

$$= 4x^2 + 8x + 19$$

18. $f(x) = x^3 + 7$

$$y = x^3 + 7$$

$$x = y^3 + 7$$

$$x - 7 = y^3$$

$$\sqrt[3]{x - 7} = y$$

$$f^{-1}(x) = \sqrt[3]{x - 7}$$

19. (a) $f(x) = |x - 6|$ does not have an inverse. Its graph does not pass the horizontal line test.

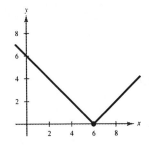

(b) $f(x) = ax + b, a \neq 0$ does have an inverse.

$$y = ax + b$$

$$x = ay + b$$

$$\frac{x - b}{a} = y$$

$$f^{-1}(x) = \frac{x - b}{a}$$

(c) $f(x) = x^3 - 19$ does have an inverse.

$$y = x^3 - 19$$

$$x = y^3 - 19$$

$$x + 19 = y^3$$

$$\sqrt[3]{x + 19} = y$$

$$f^{-1}(x) = \sqrt[3]{x + 19}$$

20. $f(x) = \sqrt{\dfrac{3-x}{x}}, \ 0 < x \le 3, y \ge 0$

$$y = \sqrt{\dfrac{3-x}{x}}$$

$$x = \sqrt{\dfrac{3-y}{y}}$$

$$x^2 = \dfrac{3-y}{y}$$

$$x^2 y = 3 - y$$

$$x^2 y + y = 3$$

$$y(x^2 + 1) = 3$$

$$y = \dfrac{3}{x^2 + 1}$$

$$f^{-1}(x) = \dfrac{3}{x^2 + 1}, \ x \ge 0$$

21. False. The slopes of 3 and $\frac{1}{3}$ are not **negative** reciprocals.

22. True. Let $y = (f \circ g)(x)$. Then $x = (f \circ g)^{-1}(y)$.

Also,

$$(f \circ g)(x) = y$$

$$f(g(x)) = y$$

$$g(x) = f^{-1}(y)$$

$$x = g^{-1}(f^{-1}(y))$$

$$x = (g^{-1} \circ f^{-1})(y)$$

Since $x = x$, we have $(f \circ g)^{-1}(y) = (g^{-1} \circ f^{-1})(y)$.

23. True. It must pass the vertical line test to be a function and it must pass the horizontal line test to have an inverse.test to have an inverse.

24. $z = \dfrac{cx^3}{\sqrt{y}}$

$$-1 = \dfrac{c(-1)^3}{\sqrt{25}}$$

$$-1 = \dfrac{-c}{5}$$

$$5 = c$$

$$z = \dfrac{5x^3}{\sqrt{y}}$$

25. $y \approx 0.669x + 2.669$

❏ Chapter 2 Practice Test Solutions

1. *x*-intercepts: $(1, 0)$, $(5, 0)$

   y-intercepts: $(0, 5)$

   Vertex: $(3, -4)$

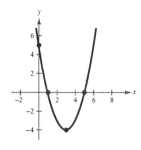

2. $a = 0.01$, $b = -90$

   $$\frac{-b}{2a} = \frac{90}{2(.01)} = 4500 \text{ units}$$

3. Vertex $(1, 7)$ opening downward through $(2, 5)$

   $y = a(x - 1)^2 + 7$ Standard form

   $5 = a(2 - 1)^2 + 7$

   $5 = a + 7$

   $a = -2$

   $y = -2(x - 1)^2 + 7$

   $\quad = -2(x^2 - 2x + 1) + 7$

   $\quad = -2x^2 + 4x + 5$

4. $y = \pm a(x - 2)(3x - 4)$ where *a* is any real number

   $y = \pm(3x^2 - 10x + 8)$

5. Leading coefficient: -3

   Degree: 5

   Moves down to the right and up to the left

6. $0 = x^5 - 5x^3 + 4x$

   $\quad = x(x^4 - 5x^2 + 4)$

   $\quad = x(x^2 - 1)(x^2 - 4)$

   $\quad = x(x + 1)(x - 1)(x + 2)(x - 2)$

   $x = 0, x = \pm 1, x = \pm 2$

7. $f(x) = x(x - 3)(x + 2)$

   $\quad = x(x^2 - x - 6)$

   $\quad = x^3 - x^2 - 6x$

8. Intercepts: $(0, 0)$, $\left(\pm 2\sqrt{3}, 0\right)$

   Moves up to the right.

   Moves down to the left.

x	-2	-1	0	1	2
y	16	11	0	-11	-16

9.
$$
x - 3 \overline{\smash{\big)}\ 3x^4 + 0x^3 - 7x^2 + 2x - 10}
$$

quotient written above: $3x^3 + 9x^2 + 20x + 62 + \dfrac{176}{x - 3}$

$$
\begin{array}{r}
3x^4 - 9x^3 \\ \hline
9x^3 - 7x^2 \\
9x^3 - 27x^2 \\ \hline
20x^2 + 2x \\
20x^2 - 60x \\ \hline
62x - 10 \\
62x - 186 \\ \hline
176
\end{array}
$$

10.
$$
x^2 + 2x - 1 \overline{\smash{\big)}\ x^3 + 0x^2 + 0x - 11}
$$

quotient written above: $x - 2 + \dfrac{5x - 13}{x^2 + 2x - 1}$

$$
\begin{array}{r}
x^3 + 2x^2 - x \\ \hline
-2x^2 + x - 11 \\
-2x^2 - 4x + 2 \\ \hline
5x - 13
\end{array}
$$

11.

$$
\begin{array}{r|rrrrrr}
-5 & 3 & 13 & 0 & 0 & 12 & -1 \\
   &   & -15 & 10 & -50 & 250 & -1310 \\ \hline
   & 3 & -2 & 10 & -50 & 262 & -1311
\end{array}
$$

$$
\frac{3x^5 + 13x^4 + 12x - 1}{x + 5} = 3x^4 - 2x^3 + 10x^2 - 50x + 262 - \frac{1311}{x + 5}
$$

12.

$$
\begin{array}{r|rrrr}
-6 & 7 & 40 & -12 & 15 \\
   &   & -42 & 12 & 0 \\ \hline
   & 7 & -2 & 0 & 15
\end{array}
$$

$$f(-6) = 15$$

13. $0 = x^3 - 19x - 30$

Possible rational roots: $\pm 1, \pm 2, \pm 3, \pm 5, \pm 6, \pm 10, \pm 15, \pm 30$

$$
\begin{array}{r|rrrr}
-2 & 1 & 0 & -19 & -30 \\
   &   & -2 & 4 & 30 \\ \hline
   & 1 & -2 & -15 & 0
\end{array}
$$

$x = -2$ is a zero.

$$0 = (x + 2)(x^2 - 2x - 15)$$
$$0 = (x + 2)(x + 3)(x - 5)$$

Zeros: $x = -2, x = -3, x = 5$

14. $0 = x^4 + x^3 - 8x^2 - 9x - 9$

Possible rational roots: $\pm 1, \pm 3, \pm 9$

$$
\begin{array}{r|rrrr}
3 & 1 & 1 & -8 & -9 & -9 \\
  &   & 3 & 12 & 12 & 9 \\
\hline
  & 1 & 4 & 4 & 3 & 0
\end{array}
\quad x = 3 \text{ is a zero.}
$$

$0 = (x - 3)(x^3 + 4x^2 + 4x + 3)$

Possible Rational Roots of $x^3 + 4x^2 + 4x + 3$: $\pm 1, \pm 3$

$$
\begin{array}{r|rrrr}
-3 & 1 & 4 & 4 & 3 \\
   &   & -3 & -3 & -3 \\
\hline
   & 1 & 1 & 1 & 0
\end{array}
\quad x = -3 \text{ is a zero.}
$$

$0 = (x - 3)(x + 3)(x^2 + x + 1)$

The zeros of $x^2 + x + 1$ are $x = \dfrac{-1 \pm \sqrt{3}i}{2}$.

Zeros: $x = 3, x = -3, x = -\dfrac{1}{2} + \dfrac{\sqrt{3}}{2}i, x = -\dfrac{1}{2} - \dfrac{\sqrt{3}}{2}i$

15. $0 = 6x^3 - 5x^2 + 4x - 15$

Possible rational roots: $\pm 1, \pm 3, \pm 5, \pm 15, \pm \frac{1}{2}, \pm \frac{3}{2}, \pm \frac{5}{2}, \pm \frac{15}{2}, \pm \frac{1}{3}, \pm \frac{5}{3}, \pm \frac{1}{6}, \pm \frac{5}{6}$

16. $0 = x^3 - \frac{20}{3}x^2 + 9x - \frac{10}{3}$

$0 = 3x^3 - 20x^2 + 27x - 10$

Possible Rational Roots: $\pm 1, \pm 2, \pm 5, \pm 10, \pm \frac{1}{3}, \pm \frac{2}{3}, \pm \frac{5}{3}, \pm \frac{10}{3}$

$$
\begin{array}{r|rrrr}
1 & 3 & -20 & 27 & -10 \\
  &   & 3 & -17 & 10 \\
\hline
  & 3 & -17 & 10 & 0
\end{array}
$$

$0 = (x - 1)(3x^2 - 17x + 10)$
$0 = (x - 1)(3x - 2)(x - 5)$
Zeros: $x = 1, x = \frac{2}{3}, x = 5$

17. Possible rational roots: $\pm 1, \pm 2, \pm 5, \pm 10$

$$
\begin{array}{r|rrrrr}
1 & 1 & 1 & 3 & 5 & -10 \\
  &   & 1 & 2 & 5 & 10 \\
\hline
  & 1 & 2 & 5 & 10 & 0
\end{array}
\quad x = 1 \text{ is a zero.}
$$

$$
\begin{array}{r|rrrr}
-2 & 1 & 2 & 5 & 10 \\
   &   & -2 & 0 & -10 \\
\hline
   & 1 & 0 & 5 & 0
\end{array}
\quad x = -2 \text{ is a zero.}
$$

$f(x) = (x - 1)(x + 2)(x^2 + 5)$
$\qquad = (x - 1)(x + 2)(x + \sqrt{5}i)(x - \sqrt{5}i)$

18. $f(x) = (x - 2)[x - (3 + i)][x - (3 - i)]$

$= (x - 2)[(x - 3) - i][(x - 3) + i]$

$= (x - 2)[(x - 3)^2 - i^2]$

$= (x - 2)[x^2 - 6x + 10]$

$= x^3 - 8x^2 + 22x - 20$

19.

$$
\begin{array}{r|rrrr}
3i & 1 & 4 & 9 & 36 \\
   &   & 3i & 12i - 9 & -36 \\
\hline
   & 1 & 4 + 3i & 12i & 0
\end{array}
$$

20. Vertical asymptote: $x = 0$

Horizontal asymptote: $y = \frac{1}{2}$

x-intercept: $(1, 0)$

21. $y = 8$ is a horizontal asymptote since the degree on the numerator equals the degree of the denominator. There are no vertical asymptotes.

22. $x = 1$ is a vertical asymptote.

$$\frac{4x^2 - 2x + 7}{x - 1} = 4x + 2 + \frac{9}{x - 1}$$

so $y = 4x + 2$ is a slant asymptote.

23. (a) $(4 - 3i) - (-2 + i) = 4 - 3i + 2 - i = 6 - 4i$

(b) $(4 - 3i)(-2 + i) = -8 + 4i + 6i - 3i^2 = -8 + 10i + 3 = -5 + 10i$

(c) $\dfrac{4 - 3i}{-2 + i} = \dfrac{4 - 3i}{-2 + i} \cdot \dfrac{-2 - i}{-2 - i} = \dfrac{-8 - 4i + 6i + 3i^2}{4 + 1}$

$= \dfrac{-11 + 2i}{5} = -\dfrac{11}{5} + \dfrac{2}{5}i$

24. $\dfrac{1 - 2x}{x^2 + x} = \dfrac{1 - 2x}{x(x + 1)} = \dfrac{A}{x} + \dfrac{B}{x + 1}$

$1 - 2x = A(x + 1) + Bx$

When $x = 0$, $1 = A$.

When $x = -1$, $3 = -B \implies B = -3$.

$\dfrac{1 - 2x}{x^2 + x} = \dfrac{1}{x} - \dfrac{3}{x + 1}$

25. $\dfrac{6x - 17}{(x - 3)^2} = \dfrac{A}{x - 3} + \dfrac{B}{(x - 3)^2}$

$6x - 17 = A(x - 3) + B$

When $x = 3$, $1 = B$.

When $x = 0$, $-17 = -3A + B \implies A = 6$.

$\dfrac{6x - 17}{(x - 3)^2} = \dfrac{6}{x - 3} + \dfrac{1}{(x - 3)^2}$

❑ Chapter 3 Practice Test Solutions

1. $x^{3/5} = 8$

$\quad x = 8^{5/3} = \left(\sqrt[3]{8}\right)^5 = 2^5 = 32$

2. $3^{x-1} = \frac{1}{81}$

$\quad\quad 3^{x-1} = 3^{-4}$

$\quad\quad x - 1 = -4$

$\quad\quad\quad\quad x = -3$

3. $f(x) = 2^{-x} = \left(\frac{1}{2}\right)^x$

x	-2	-1	0	1	2
$f(x)$	4	2	1	$\frac{1}{2}$	$\frac{1}{4}$

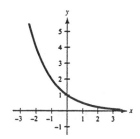

4. $g(x) = e^x + 1$

x	-2	-1	0	1	2
$g(x)$	1.14	1.37	2	3.72	8.39

5. $A = P\left(1 + \dfrac{r}{n}\right)^{nt}$ OR $A = Pe^{rt}$

(a) $A = 5000\left(1 + \dfrac{0.09}{12}\right)^{12(3)} \approx \$6543.23$

(b) $A = 5000\left(1 + \dfrac{0.09}{4}\right)^{4(3)} \approx \$6530.25$

(c) $A = 5000e^{(0.09)(3)} \approx \$6549.82$

6. $\quad 7^{-2} = \dfrac{1}{49}$

$\quad \log_7 \dfrac{1}{49} = -2$

7. $x - 4 = \log_2 \frac{1}{64}$

$\quad 2^{x-4} = \frac{1}{64}$

$\quad 2^{x-4} = 2^{-6}$

$\quad x - 4 = -6$

$\quad\quad x = -2$

8. $\log_b \sqrt[4]{\frac{8}{25}} = \frac{1}{4}\log_b \frac{8}{25}$

$\quad\quad\quad\quad = \frac{1}{4}[\log_b 8 - \log_b 25]$

$\quad\quad\quad\quad = \frac{1}{4}[\log_b 2^3 - \log_b 5^2]$

$\quad\quad\quad\quad = \frac{1}{4}[3\log_b 2 - 2\log_b 5]$

$\quad\quad\quad\quad = \frac{1}{4}[3(0.3562) - 2(0.8271)]$

$\quad\quad\quad\quad = -0.1464$

9. $5\ln x - \dfrac{1}{2}\ln y + 6\ln z = \ln x^5 - \ln \sqrt{y} + \ln z^6 = \ln\left(\dfrac{x^5 z^6}{\sqrt{y}}\right)$

10. $\log_9 28 = \dfrac{\log 28}{\log 9} \approx 1.5166$

11. $\log N = 0.6646$

$N = 10^{0.6646} \approx 4.62$

12.
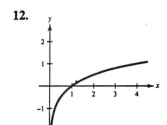

13. Domain:

$$x^2 - 9 > 0$$
$$(x + 3)(x - 3) > 0$$
$$x < -3 \text{ or } x > 3$$

14.

15. $\dfrac{\ln x}{\ln y} \neq \ln(x - y)$ since $\dfrac{\ln x}{\ln y} = \log_y x.$

16. $5^3 = 41$

$x = \log_5 41 = \dfrac{\ln 41}{\ln 5} \approx 2.3074$

17. $x - x^2 = \log_5 \frac{1}{25}$

$5^{x-x^2} = \frac{1}{25}$

$5^{x-x^2} = 5^{-2}$

$x - x^2 = -2$

$0 = x^2 - x - 2$

$0 = (x + 1)(x - 2)$

$x = -1 \text{ or } x = 2$

18. $\log_2 x + \log_2(x - 3) = 2$

$\log_2[x(x - 3)] = 2$

$x(x - 3) = 2^2$

$x^2 - 3x = 4$

$x^2 - 3x - 4 = 0$

$(x + 1)(x - 4) = 0$

$x = 4$

$x = -1 \text{ (extraneous)}$

$x = 4$ is the only solution.

19. $\dfrac{e^x + e^{-x}}{3} = 4$

$e^x(e^x + e^{-x}) = 12e^x$

$e^{2x} + 1 = 12e^x$

$e^{2x} - 12e^x + 1 = 0$

$e^x = \dfrac{12 \pm \sqrt{144 - 4}}{2}$

$e^x \approx 11.9161$ or $e^x \approx 0.0839$

$x = \ln 11.9161$ $x = \ln 0.0839$

$x \approx 2.478$ $x \approx -2.478$

20. $A = Pe^{et}$

$12{,}000 = 6000e^{0.13t}$

$2 = e^{0.13t}$

$0.13t = \ln 2$

$t = \dfrac{\ln 2}{0.13}$

$t \approx 5.3319$ years or 5 years 4 months

❏ Chapter 4 Practice Test Solutions

1. $350° = 350\left(\dfrac{\pi}{180}\right) = \dfrac{35\pi}{18}$

2. $\dfrac{5\pi}{9} = \dfrac{5\pi}{9} \cdot \dfrac{180}{\pi} = 100°$

3. $135° \, 14' \, 12'' = \left(135 + \dfrac{14}{60} + \dfrac{12}{3600}\right)°$

$\approx 135.2367°$

4. $-22.569° = -(22° + 0.569(60)')$

$= -22° \, 34.14'$

$= -(22° \, 34' + 0.14(60)'')$

$\approx -22° \, 34' \, 8''$

5. $\cos\theta = \dfrac{2}{3}$

$x = 2, \, r = 3, \, y = \pm\sqrt{9-4} = \pm\sqrt{5}$

$\tan\theta = \dfrac{y}{x} = \pm\dfrac{\sqrt{5}}{2}$

6. $\sin\theta = 0.9063$

$\theta = \arcsin(0.9063)$

$\theta = 65° = \dfrac{13\pi}{36}$

or

$\theta = 180° - 65° = 115° = \dfrac{23\pi}{36}$

7. $\tan 20° = \dfrac{35}{x}$

$x = \dfrac{35}{\tan 20°} \approx 96.1617$

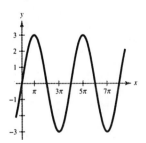

8. $\theta = \dfrac{6\pi}{5}$, θ is in Quadrant III.

Reference angle: $\dfrac{6\pi}{5} - \pi = \dfrac{\pi}{5}$ or $36°$

9. $\csc 3.92 = \dfrac{1}{\sin 3.92} \approx -1.4242$

10. $\tan\theta = 6 = \dfrac{6}{1}$, θ lies in Quadrant III.

$y = -6, \, x = -1, \, r = \sqrt{36+1} = \sqrt{37}$,

so $\sec\theta = \dfrac{\sqrt{37}}{-1} \approx -6.0828$.

11. Period: 4π

Amplitude: 3

12. Period: 2π

Amplitude: 2

13. Period: $\dfrac{\pi}{2}$

14. Period: 2π

15.

16.

17. $\theta = \arcsin 1$

$\sin \theta = 1$

$\theta = \dfrac{\pi}{2}$

18. $\theta = \arctan(-3)$

$\tan \theta = -3$

$\theta \approx -1.249 \approx -71.565°$

19. $\sin\left(\arccos \dfrac{4}{\sqrt{35}}\right)$

$\sin \theta = \dfrac{\sqrt{19}}{\sqrt{35}} \approx 0.7368$

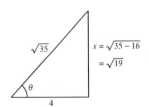

$x = \sqrt{35 - 16}$
$= \sqrt{19}$

20. $\cos\left(\arcsin \dfrac{x}{4}\right)$

$\cos \theta = \dfrac{\sqrt{16 - x^2}}{4}$

21. Given $A = 40°$, $c = 12$

$B = 90° - 40° = 50°$

$\sin 40° = \dfrac{a}{12}$

$a = 12 \sin 40° \approx 7.713$

$\cos 40° = \dfrac{b}{12}$

$b = 12 \cos 40° \approx 9.193$

22. Given $B = 6.84°$, $a = 21.3$

$A = 90° - 6.84° = 83.16°$

$\sin 83.16° = \dfrac{21.3}{c}$

$c = \dfrac{21.3}{\sin 83.16°} \approx 21.453$

$\tan 83.16° = \dfrac{21.3}{b}$

$b = \dfrac{21.3}{\tan 83.16°} \approx 2.555$

23. Given $a = 5, b = 9$

$c = \sqrt{25 + 81} = \sqrt{106} \approx 10.296$

$\tan A = \frac{5}{9}$

$A = \arctan \frac{5}{9} \approx 29.055°$

$B = 90° - 29.055° = 60.945°$

24. $\sin 67° = \frac{x}{20}$

$x = 20 \sin 67° \approx 18.41$ feet

25. $\tan 5° = \frac{250}{x}$

$x = \frac{250}{\tan 5°}$

≈ 2857.513 feet

≈ 0.541 mi

❑ Chapter 5 Practice Test Solutions

1. $\tan x = \dfrac{4}{11}$, $\sec x < 0 \implies x$ is in Quadrant III.

$y = -4$, $x = -11$, $r = \sqrt{16 + 121} = \sqrt{137}$

$$\sin x = -\frac{4}{\sqrt{137}} = -\frac{4\sqrt{137}}{137} \qquad\qquad \csc x = -\frac{\sqrt{137}}{4}$$

$$\cos x = -\frac{11}{\sqrt{137}} = -\frac{11\sqrt{137}}{137} \qquad\qquad \sec x = -\frac{\sqrt{137}}{11}$$

$$\tan x = \frac{4}{11} \qquad\qquad\qquad\qquad\qquad \cot x = \frac{11}{4}$$

2. $\dfrac{\sec^2 x + \csc^2 x}{\csc^2 x(1 + \tan^2 x)} = \dfrac{\sec^2 x + \csc^2 x}{\csc^2 x + (\csc^2 x)\tan^2 x} = \dfrac{\sec^2 x + \csc^2 x}{\csc^2 x + \dfrac{1}{\sin^2 x} \cdot \dfrac{\sin^2 x}{\cos^2 x}}$

$$= \frac{\sec^2 x + \csc^2 x}{\csc^2 x + \dfrac{1}{\cos^2 x}} = \frac{\sec^2 x + \csc^2 x}{\csc^2 x + \sec^2 x} = 1$$

3. $\ln|\tan\theta| - \ln|\cot\theta| = \ln\left|\dfrac{\tan\theta}{\cot\theta}\right| = \ln\left|\dfrac{\sin\theta/\cos\theta}{\cos\theta/\sin\theta}\right| = \ln\left|\dfrac{\sin^2\theta}{\cos^2\theta}\right| = \ln|\tan^2\theta| = 2\ln|\tan\theta|$

4. $\cos\left(\dfrac{\pi}{2} - x\right) = \dfrac{1}{\csc x}$ is true since $\cos\left(\dfrac{\pi}{2} - x\right) = \sin x = \dfrac{1}{\csc x}$.

5. $\sin^4 x + (\sin^2 x)\cos^2 x = \sin^2 x(\sin^2 x + \cos^2 x) = \sin^2 x(1) = \sin^2 x$

6. $(\csc x + 1)(\csc x - 1) = \csc^2 x - 1 = \cot^2 x$

7. $\dfrac{\cos^2 x}{1 - \sin x} \cdot \dfrac{1 + \sin x}{1 + \sin x} = \dfrac{\cos^2 x(1 + \sin x)}{1 - \sin^2 x} = \dfrac{\cos^2 x(1 + \sin x)}{\cos^2 x} = 1 + \sin x$

8. $\dfrac{1 + \cos\theta}{\sin\theta} + \dfrac{\sin\theta}{1 + \cos\theta} = \dfrac{(1 + \cos\theta)^2 + \sin^2\theta}{\sin\theta(1 + \cos\theta)}$

$$= \frac{1 + 2\cos\theta + \cos^2\theta + \sin^2\theta}{\sin\theta(1 + \cos\theta)} = \frac{2 + 2\cos\theta}{\sin\theta(1 + \cos\theta)} = \frac{2}{\sin\theta} = 2\csc\theta$$

9. $\tan^4 x + 2\tan^2 x + 1 = (\tan^2 x + 1)^2 = (\sec^2 x)^2 = \sec^4 x$

10. (a) $\sin 105° = \sin(60° + 45°) = \sin 60° \cos 45° + \cos 60° \sin 45°$

$$= \frac{\sqrt{3}}{2} \cdot \frac{\sqrt{2}}{2} + \frac{1}{2} \cdot \frac{\sqrt{2}}{2} = \frac{\sqrt{2}}{4}\left(\sqrt{3} + 1\right)$$

(b) $\tan 15° = \tan(60° - 45°) = \dfrac{\tan 60° - \tan 45°}{1 + \tan 60° \tan 45°}$

$$= \frac{\sqrt{3} - 1}{1 + \sqrt{3}} \cdot \frac{1 - \sqrt{3}}{1 - \sqrt{3}} = \frac{2\sqrt{3} - 1 - 3}{1 - 3} = \frac{2\sqrt{3} - 4}{-2} = 2 - \sqrt{3}$$

11. $(\sin 42°) \cos 38° - (\cos 42°) \sin 38° = \sin(42° - 38°) = \sin 4°$

12. $\tan\left(\theta + \dfrac{\pi}{4}\right) = \dfrac{\tan\theta + \tan(\pi/4)}{1 - (\tan\theta)\tan(\pi/4)} = \dfrac{\tan\theta + 1}{1 - \tan\theta(1)} = \dfrac{1 + \tan\theta}{1 - \tan\theta}$

13. $\sin(\arcsin x - \arccos x) = \sin(\arcsin x)\cos(\arccos x) - \cos(\arcsin x)\sin(\arccos x)$

$$= (x)(x) - \left(\sqrt{1 - x^2}\right)\left(\sqrt{1 - x^2}\right) = x^2 - (1 - x^2) = 2x^2 - 1$$

14. (a) $\cos(120°) = \cos[2(60°)] = 2\cos^2 60° - 1 = 2\left(\dfrac{1}{2}\right)^2 - 1 = -\dfrac{1}{2}$

(b) $\tan(300°) = \tan[2(150°)] = \dfrac{2\tan 150°}{1 - \tan^2 150°} = \dfrac{-2\sqrt{3}/3}{1 - (1/3)} = -\sqrt{3}$

15. (a) $\sin 22.5° = \sin\dfrac{45°}{2} = \sqrt{\dfrac{1 - \cos 45°}{2}} = \sqrt{\dfrac{1 - \sqrt{2}/2}{2}} = \dfrac{\sqrt{2 - \sqrt{2}}}{2}$

(b) $\tan\dfrac{\pi}{12} = \tan\dfrac{\pi/6}{2} = \dfrac{\sin(\pi/6)}{1 + \cos(\pi/6)} = \dfrac{1/2}{1 + \sqrt{3}/2} = \dfrac{1}{2 + \sqrt{3}} = 2 - \sqrt{3}$

16. $\sin\theta = \dfrac{4}{5}$, θ lies in Quadrant II $\implies \cos\theta = -\dfrac{3}{5}$.

$$\cos\frac{\theta}{2} = \sqrt{\frac{1 + \cos\theta}{2}} = \sqrt{\frac{1 - 3/5}{2}} = \sqrt{\frac{2}{10}} = \frac{1}{\sqrt{5}} = \frac{\sqrt{5}}{5}$$

17. $(\sin^2 x)\cos^2 x = \dfrac{1 - \cos 2x}{2} \cdot \dfrac{1 + \cos 2x}{2} = \dfrac{1}{4}[1 - \cos^2 2x] = \dfrac{1}{4}\left[1 - \dfrac{1 + \cos 4x}{2}\right]$

$$= \frac{1}{8}[2 - (1 + \cos 4x)] = \frac{1}{8}[1 - \cos 4x]$$

18. $6(\sin 5\theta)\cos 2\theta = 6\left\{\dfrac{1}{2}[\sin(5\theta + 2\theta) + \sin(5\theta - 2\theta)]\right\} = 3[\sin 7\theta + \sin 3\theta]$

19. $\sin(x + \pi) + \sin(x - \pi) = 2\left(\sin\dfrac{[(x + \pi) + (x - \pi)]}{2}\right)\cos\dfrac{[(x + \pi) - (x - \pi)]}{2} = 2\sin x \cos\pi = -2\sin x$

20. $\dfrac{\sin 9x + \sin 5x}{\cos 9x - \cos 5x} = \dfrac{2\sin 7x \cos 2x}{-2\sin 7x \sin 2x} = -\dfrac{\cos 2x}{\sin 2x} = -\cot 2x$

21. $\frac{1}{2}[\sin(u+v) - \sin(u-v)] = \frac{1}{2}\{(\sin u)\cos v + (\cos u)\sin v - [(\sin u)\cos v - (\cos u)\sin v]\}$

$$= \frac{1}{2}[2(\cos u)\sin v] = (\cos u)\sin v$$

22. $4\sin^2 x = 1$

$\sin^2 x = \dfrac{1}{4}$

$\sin x = \pm\dfrac{1}{2}$

$\sin x = \dfrac{1}{2}$ or $\sin x = -\dfrac{1}{2}$

$x = \dfrac{\pi}{6}$ or $\dfrac{5\pi}{6}$ $x = \dfrac{7\pi}{6}$ or $\dfrac{11\pi}{6}$

23. $\tan^2\theta + \left(\sqrt{3} - 1\right)\tan\theta - \sqrt{3} = 0$

$(\tan\theta - 1)(\tan\theta + \sqrt{3}) = 0$

$\tan\theta = 1$ or $\tan\theta = -\sqrt{3}$

$\theta = \dfrac{\pi}{4}$ or $\dfrac{5\pi}{4}$ $\theta = \dfrac{2\pi}{3}$ or $\dfrac{5\pi}{3}$

24. $\sin 2x = \cos x$

$2(\sin x)\cos x - \cos x = 0$

$\cos x(2\sin x - 1) = 0$

$\cos x = 0$ or $\sin x = \dfrac{1}{2}$

$x = \dfrac{\pi}{2}$ or $\dfrac{3\pi}{2}$ $x = \dfrac{\pi}{6}$ or $\dfrac{5\pi}{6}$

25. $\tan^2 x - 6\tan x + 4 = 0$

$$\tan x = \frac{-(-6) \pm \sqrt{(-6)^2 - 4(1)(4)}}{2(1)}$$

$$\tan x = \frac{6 \pm \sqrt{20}}{2} = 3 \pm \sqrt{5}$$

$\tan x = 3 + \sqrt{5}$ or $\tan x = 3 - \sqrt{5}$

$x \approx 1.3821$ or 4.5237 $x = 0.6524$ or 3.7940

❏ Chapter 6 Practice Test Solutions

1. $C = 180° - (40° + 12°) = 128°$

$a = \sin 40°\left(\dfrac{100}{\sin 12°}\right) \approx 309.164$

$c = \sin 128°\left(\dfrac{100}{\sin 12°}\right) \approx 379.012$

2. $\sin A = 5\left(\dfrac{\sin 150°}{20}\right) = 0.125$

$A \approx 7.181°$

$B \approx 180° - (150° + 7.181°) = 22.819°$

$b = \sin 22.819°\left(\dfrac{20}{\sin 150°}\right) \approx 15.513$

3. Area $= \frac{1}{2}ab\sin C$

$\quad\quad = \frac{1}{2}(3)(5)\sin 130°$

$\quad\quad \approx 5.745$ square units

4. $h = b\sin A$

$\quad\quad = 35\sin 22.5°$

$\quad\quad \approx 13.394$

$\quad a = 10$

Since $a < h$ and A is acute, the triangle has no solution.

5. $\cos A = \dfrac{(53)^2 + (38)^2 - (49)^2}{2(53)(38)} \approx 0.4598$

$\quad\quad A \approx 62.627°$

$\quad \cos B = \dfrac{(49)^2 + (38)^2 - (53)^2}{2(49)(38)} \approx 0.2782$

$\quad\quad B \approx 73.847°$

$\quad\quad C \approx 180° - (62.627° + 73.847°)$

$\quad\quad\quad = 43.526°$

6. $c^2 = (100)^2 + (300)^2 - 2(100)(300)\cos 29°$

$\quad\quad \approx 47522.8176$

$\quad c \approx 218$

$\quad \cos A = \dfrac{(300)^2 + (218)^2 - (100)^2}{2(300)(218)} \approx 0.97495$

$\quad\quad A \approx 12.85°$

$\quad\quad B \approx 180° - (12.85° + 29°) = 138.15°$

7. $s = \dfrac{a + b + c}{2} = \dfrac{4.1 + 6.8 + 5.5}{2} = 8.2$

$\quad$ Area $= \sqrt{s(s - a)(s - b)(s - c)}$

$\quad\quad = \sqrt{8.2(8.2 - 4.1)\,(8.2 - 6.8)(8.2 - 5.5)}$

$\quad\quad = 11.273$ square units

8. $x^2 = (40)^2 + (70)^2 - 2(40)(70)\cos 168°$

$\quad\quad \approx 11977.6266$

$\quad x \approx 190.442$ miles

9. $\mathbf{w} = 4(3\mathbf{i} + \mathbf{j}) - 7(-\mathbf{i} + 2\mathbf{j})$

$\quad\quad = 19\mathbf{i} - 10\mathbf{j}$

10. $\dfrac{\mathbf{v}}{\|\mathbf{v}\|} = \dfrac{5\mathbf{i} + 3\mathbf{j}}{\sqrt{25 + 9}} = \dfrac{5}{\sqrt{34}}\mathbf{i} - \dfrac{3}{\sqrt{34}}\mathbf{j}$

$\quad\quad = \dfrac{5\sqrt{34}}{34}\mathbf{i} - \dfrac{3\sqrt{34}}{34}\mathbf{j}$

11. $\mathbf{u} = 6\mathbf{i} + 5\mathbf{j} \quad\quad \mathbf{v} = 2\mathbf{i} - 3\mathbf{j}$

$\quad \mathbf{u} \cdot \mathbf{v} = 6(2) + 5(-3) = -3$

$\quad \|\mathbf{u}\| = \sqrt{61} \quad\quad \|\mathbf{v}\| = \sqrt{13}$

$\quad \cos\theta = \dfrac{-3}{\sqrt{61}\sqrt{13}}$

$\quad\quad \theta \approx 96.116°$

12. $4(\mathbf{i}\cos 30° + \mathbf{j}\sin 30°)$

$\quad = 4\left(\dfrac{\sqrt{3}}{2}\mathbf{i} + \dfrac{1}{2}\mathbf{j}\right)$

$\quad = \langle 2\sqrt{3}, 2\rangle$

13. $\text{proj}_{\mathbf{v}}\mathbf{u} = \left(\dfrac{\mathbf{u} \cdot \mathbf{v}}{\|\mathbf{v}\|^2}\right)\mathbf{v} = \dfrac{-10}{20}\langle -2, 4\rangle = \langle 1, -2\rangle$

14. $r = \sqrt{25 + 25} = \sqrt{50} = 5\sqrt{2}$

$\tan\theta = \dfrac{-5}{5} = -1$

Since z is in Quadrant IV,

$\theta = 315°$

$z = 5\sqrt{2}(\cos 315° + i \sin 315°)$.

15. $\cos 225° = -\dfrac{\sqrt{2}}{2}$ $\sin 225° = -\dfrac{\sqrt{2}}{2}$

$z = 6\left(-\dfrac{\sqrt{2}}{2} - i\dfrac{\sqrt{2}}{2}\right)$

$= -3\sqrt{2} - 3\sqrt{2}i$

16. $[7(\cos 23° + i \sin 23°)][4(\cos 7° + i \sin 7°)] = 7(4)[\cos(23° + 7°) + i \sin(23° + 7°)]$

$= 28(\cos 30° + i \sin 30°)$

17. $\dfrac{9\left(\cos\dfrac{5\pi}{4} + i \sin\dfrac{5\pi}{4}\right)}{3(\cos \pi + i \sin \pi)} = \dfrac{9}{3}\left[\cos\left(\dfrac{5\pi}{4} - \pi\right) + i \sin\left(\dfrac{5\pi}{4} - \pi\right)\right] = 3\left(\cos\dfrac{\pi}{4} + i \sin\dfrac{\pi}{4}\right)$

18. $(2 + 2i)^8 = [2\sqrt{2}(\cos 45° + i \sin 45°)]^8 = \left(2\sqrt{2}\right)^8[\cos(8)(45°) + i \sin (8)(45°)]$

$= 4096[\cos 360° + i \sin 360°] = 4096$

19. $z = 8\left(\cos\dfrac{\pi}{3} + i \sin\dfrac{\pi}{3}\right),\ n = 3$

The cube roots of z are: $\sqrt[3]{8}\left[\cos\dfrac{(\pi/3) + 2\pi k}{3} + i \sin\dfrac{(\pi/3) + 2\pi k}{3}\right],\ k = 0, 1, 2$

For $k = 0$, $\sqrt[3]{8}\left[\cos\dfrac{\pi/3}{3} + i \sin\dfrac{\pi/3}{3}\right] = 2\left(\cos\dfrac{\pi}{9} + i \sin\dfrac{\pi}{9}\right)$

For $k = 1$, $\sqrt[3]{8}\left[\cos\dfrac{\pi/3 + 2\pi}{3} + i \sin\dfrac{\pi/3 + 2\pi}{3}\right] = 2\left(\cos\dfrac{7\pi}{9} + i \sin\dfrac{7\pi}{9}\right)$

For $k = 2$, $\sqrt[3]{8}\left[\cos\dfrac{\pi/3 + 4\pi}{3} + i \sin\dfrac{\pi/3 + 4\pi}{3}\right] = 2\left(\cos\dfrac{13\pi}{9} + i \sin\dfrac{13\pi}{9}\right)$

20. $x^4 = -i = 1\left(\cos\dfrac{3\pi}{2} + i \sin\dfrac{3\pi}{2}\right)$

The fourth roots are: $\sqrt[4]{1}\left[\cos\dfrac{(3\pi/2) + 2\pi k}{4} + i \sin\dfrac{(3\pi/2) + 2\pi k}{4}\right],\ k = 0, 1, 2, 3$

For $k = 0$, $\cos\dfrac{3\pi/2}{4} + i \sin\dfrac{3\pi/2}{4} = \cos\dfrac{3\pi}{8} + i \sin\dfrac{3\pi}{8}$

For $k = 1$, $\cos\dfrac{3\pi/2 + 2\pi}{4} + i \sin\dfrac{3\pi/2 + 2\pi}{4} = \cos\dfrac{7\pi}{8} + i \sin\dfrac{7\pi}{8}$

For $k = 2$, $\cos\dfrac{3\pi/2 + 4\pi}{4} + i \sin\dfrac{3\pi/2 + 4\pi}{4} = \cos\dfrac{11\pi}{8} + i \sin\dfrac{11\pi}{8}$

For $k = 3$, $\cos\dfrac{3\pi/2 + 6\pi}{4} + i \sin\dfrac{3\pi/2 + 6\pi}{4} = \cos\dfrac{15\pi}{8} + i \sin\dfrac{15\pi}{8}$

❑ Chapter 7 Practice Test Solutions

1. $x + y = 1$
$3x - y = 15 \implies y = 3x - 15$
$x + (3x - 15) = 1$
$\qquad 4x = 16$
$\qquad x = 4$
$\qquad y = -3$
Answer: $(4, -3)$

2. $x - 3y = -3 \implies x = 3y - 3$
$x^2 + 5y = 5$
$\qquad (3y - 3)^2 + 6y = 5$
$\qquad 9y^2 - 18y + 9 + 6y = 5$
$\qquad 9y^2 - 12y + 4 = 0$
$\qquad (3y - 2)^2 = 0$
$\qquad y = \frac{2}{3}$
$\qquad x = -1$
Answer: $\left(-1, \frac{2}{3}\right)$

3. $x + y + z = 6 \implies z = 6 - x - y$
$2x - y + 3z = 0 \implies 2x - y + 3(6 - x - y) = 0 \implies -x - 4y = -18 \implies x = 18 - 4y$
$5x + 2y - z = -3 \implies 5x + 2y - (6 - x - y) = -3 \implies 6x + 3y = 3$
$6(18 - 4y) + 3y = 3$
$\qquad -21y = -105$
$\qquad y = 5$
$\qquad x = 18 - 4y = -2$
$\qquad z = 6 - x - y = 3$
Answer: $(-2, 5, 3)$

4. $x + y = 110 \implies y = 110 - x$
$xy = 2800$
$x(110 - x) = 2800$
$\qquad 0 = x^2 - 110x + 2800$
$\qquad 0 = (x - 40)(x - 70)$
$\qquad x = 40 \text{ or } x = 70$
$\qquad y = 70 \qquad y = 40$

Answer: The two numbers are 40 and 70.

5. $2x + 2y = 170 \implies y = \dfrac{170 - 2x}{2} = 85 - x$
$xy = 2800$
$x(85 - x) = 2800$
$\qquad 0 = x^2 - 85x + 2800$
$\qquad 0 = (x - 25)(x - 60)$
$\qquad x = 25 \text{ or } x = 60$
$\qquad y = 60 \qquad y = 25$

Dimensions: $60' \times 25'$

6. $2x + 15y = 4 \implies 2x + 15y = 4$
$x - 3y = 23 \implies 5x - 15y = 115$
$\qquad\qquad\qquad \overline{7x \qquad = 119}$
$\qquad\qquad\qquad x = 17$
$\qquad\qquad\qquad y = \dfrac{x - 23}{3}$
$\qquad\qquad\qquad = -2$

Answer: $(17, -2)$

7. $x + y = 2 \implies 19x + 19y = 38$
$38x - 19y = 7 \implies 38x - 19y = 7$
$\qquad\qquad\qquad \overline{57x \qquad = 45}$
$x = \dfrac{45}{57} = \dfrac{15}{19}$
$y = 2 - x = \dfrac{38}{19} - \dfrac{15}{19} = \dfrac{23}{19}$

Answer: $\left(\dfrac{15}{19}, \dfrac{23}{19}\right)$

8. $0.4x + 0.5y = 0.112 \implies 0.28x + 0.35y = 0.0784$

    $0.3x - 0.7y = -0.131 \implies 0.15x - 0.35y = -0.0655$

    $$0.43x = 0.0129$$

    $$x = \frac{0.0129}{0.43} = 0.03$$

    $$y = \frac{0.112 - 0.4x}{0.5} = 0.20$$

    Answer: (0.03, 0.20)

9. Let x = amount in 11% fund and y = amount in 13% fund.

    $$x + y = 17000 \implies y = 17000 - x$$

    $$0.11x + 0.13y = 2080$$

    $$0.11x + 0.13(17000 - x) = 2080$$

    $$-0.02x = -130$$

    $$x = \$6500 \quad \text{at } 11\%$$

    $$y = \$10{,}500 \text{ at } 13\%$$

10. $(4, 3), (1, 1), (-1, -2), (-2, -1)$

    $$n = 4, \sum_{i=1}^{4} x_i = 2, \sum_{i=1}^{4} y_i = 1, \sum_{i=1}^{4} x_i^2 = 22, \sum_{i=1}^{4} x_i y_i = 17$$

    $4b + 2a = 1 \implies 4b + 2a = 1$

    $2b + 22a = 17 \implies -4b - 44a = -34$

    $$-42a = -33$$

    $a = \frac{33}{42} = \frac{11}{14}$

    $b = \frac{1}{4}\left(1 - 2\left(\frac{33}{42}\right)\right) = -\frac{1}{7}$

    $y = ax + b = \frac{11}{14}x - \frac{1}{7}$

11. $x + y = -2 \implies -2x - 2y = 4 \qquad -9y + 3z = 45$

    $2x - y + z = 11 \qquad\qquad 2x - y + z = 11 \qquad\quad 4y - 3z = -20$

    $4y - 3z = -20 \qquad\qquad\quad -3y + z = 15 \qquad -5y = 25$

    $$y = {-5}$$

    $$x = 3$$

    $$z = 0$$

    Answer: $(3, -5, 0)$

12.

$$
\begin{array}{rcl}
4x - y + 5z = 4 & \Longrightarrow & 4x - y + 5z = 4 \\
2x + y - z = 0 & \Longrightarrow & -4x - 2y + 2z = 0 \\
2x + 4y + 8z = 0 & & \overline{-3y + 7z = 4}
\end{array}
$$

$$
\begin{array}{rcl}
2x + 4y + 8z &=& 0 \\
-2x - y + z &=& 0 \\
\hline
3y + 9z &=& 0 \\
-3y + 7z &=& 4 \\
\hline
16z &=& 4 \\
z &=& \tfrac{1}{4} \\
y &=& -\tfrac{3}{4} \\
x &=& \tfrac{1}{2}
\end{array}
$$

Answer: $\left(\tfrac{1}{2}, -\tfrac{3}{4}, \tfrac{1}{4}\right)$

13.

$$
\begin{array}{rcl}
3x + 2y - z = 5 & \Longrightarrow & 6x + 4y - 2z = 10 \\
6x - y + 5z = 2 & \Longrightarrow & -6x + y - 5z = -2 \\
& & \overline{5y - 7z = 8}
\end{array}
$$

$$
y = \frac{8 + 7z}{5}
$$

$$
\begin{array}{rcl}
3x + 2y - z &=& 5 \\
12x - 2y + 10z &=& 4 \\
\hline
15x + 9z &=& 9
\end{array}
$$

$$
x = \frac{9 - 9z}{15} = \frac{3 - 3z}{5}
$$

Let $z = a$, then $x = \dfrac{3 - 3a}{5}$ and $y = \dfrac{8 + 7a}{5}$.

Answer: $\left(\dfrac{3 - 3a}{5}, \dfrac{8 + 7a}{5}, a\right)$ where a is any real number.

14. $y = ax^2 + bx + c$ passes through $(0, -1)$, $(1, 4)$, and $(2, 13)$.

At $(0, -1)$: $-1 = a(0)^2 + b(0) + c \Longrightarrow c = -1$

At $(1, 4)$: $4 = a(1)^2 + b(1) - 1 \Longrightarrow 5 = a + b \Longrightarrow 5 = a + b$

At $(2, 13)$: $13 = a(2)^2 + b(2) - 1 \Longrightarrow 14 = 4a + 2b \Longrightarrow -7 = -2a - b$

$$
\begin{array}{rcl}
-2 &=& -a \\
a &=& 2 \\
b &=& 3
\end{array}
$$

Thus, $y = 2x^2 + 3x - 1$.

15. $s = \frac{1}{2}at^2 + v_0 t + s_0$ passes through $(1, 12)$, $(2, 5)$, and $(3, 4)$.

At $(1, 12)$: $12 = \frac{1}{2}a + v_0 + s_0$ $\implies$ $\quad 24 = \quad\; a + 2v_0 + 2s_0$

At $(2, 5)$: $5 = 2a + 2v_0 + s_0$ $\implies$ $-5 = -2a - 2v_0 - \;\; s_0$

At $(3, 4)$: $4 = \frac{9}{2}a + 3v_0 + s_0$ $\implies$ $\overline{\quad 19 = \quad -a \qquad\quad + \;\; s_0}$

$$15 = \quad 6a + 6v_0 + 3s_0$$
$$-8 = -9a - 6v_0 - 2s_0$$
$$\overline{\quad 7 = -3a \qquad\quad + \;\; s_0}$$
$$-19 = \quad\;\; a \qquad\quad - \;\; s_0$$
$$\overline{-12 = -2a}$$
$$a = 6$$
$$s_0 = 25$$
$$v_0 = -16$$

Thus, $s = \frac{1}{2}(6)t^2 - 16t + 25 = 3t^2 - 16t + 25$.

16. $x^2 + y^2 \geq 9$

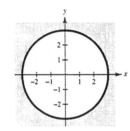

17. $x + y \leq 6$

$\qquad x \geq 2$

$\qquad y \geq 0$

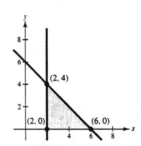

18. Line through $(0, 0)$ and $(0, 7)$:

$\quad x = 0$

Line through $(0, 0)$ and $(2, 3)$:

$\quad y = \frac{3}{2}x$ or $3x - 2y = 0$

Line through $(0, 7)$ and $(2, 3)$:

$\quad y = -2x + 7$ or $2x + y = 7$

Inequalities: $\qquad x \geq 0$

$\qquad\qquad\quad 3x - 2y \leq 0$

$\qquad\qquad\quad 2x + y \leq 7$

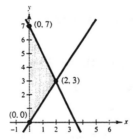

19. Vertices: $(0, 0)$, $(0, 7)$, $(6, 0)$, $(3, 5)$

$z = 30x + 26y$

At $(0, 0)$: $z = 0$

At $(0, 7)$: $z = 182$

At $(6, 0)$: $z = 180$

At $(3, 5)$: $z = 220$

The maximum value of z is 220.

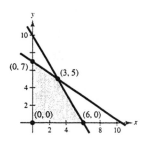

20. $x^2 + y^2 \le 4$

$(x - 2)^2 + y^2 \ge 4$

❏ Chapter 8   Practice Test Solutions

1.
$$\begin{bmatrix} 1 & -2 & 4 \\ 3 & -5 & 9 \end{bmatrix}$$

$$-3R_1 + R_2 \rightarrow \begin{bmatrix} 1 & -2 & 4 \\ 0 & 1 & -3 \end{bmatrix}$$

$$2R_2 + R_1 \rightarrow \begin{bmatrix} 1 & 0 & -2 \\ 0 & 1 & -3 \end{bmatrix}$$

2. $3x + 5y = 3$

$2x - y = -11$

$$\begin{bmatrix} 3 & 5 & \vdots & 3 \\ 2 & -1 & \vdots & -11 \end{bmatrix}$$

$$-R_2 + R_1 \rightarrow \begin{bmatrix} 1 & 6 & \vdots & 14 \\ 2 & -1 & \vdots & -11 \end{bmatrix}$$

$$-2R_1 + R_2 \rightarrow \begin{bmatrix} 1 & 6 & \vdots & 14 \\ 0 & -13 & \vdots & -39 \end{bmatrix}$$

$$-\tfrac{1}{13}R_2 \rightarrow \begin{bmatrix} 1 & 6 & \vdots & 14 \\ 0 & 1 & \vdots & 3 \end{bmatrix}$$

$$-6R_2 + R_1 \rightarrow \begin{bmatrix} 1 & 0 & \vdots & -4 \\ 0 & 1 & \vdots & 3 \end{bmatrix}$$

$x = -4, y = 3$

Answer: $(-4, 3)$

3. $2x + 3y = -3$

$\quad 3x - 2y = 8$

$\quad x + y = 1$

$$\begin{bmatrix} 2 & 3 & \vdots & -3 \\ 3 & 2 & \vdots & 8 \\ 1 & 1 & \vdots & 1 \end{bmatrix}$$

$$\begin{matrix} R_3 \to \\ \\ R_1 \to \end{matrix} \begin{bmatrix} 1 & 1 & \vdots & 1 \\ 3 & 2 & \vdots & 8 \\ 2 & 3 & \vdots & -3 \end{bmatrix}$$

$$\begin{matrix} \\ -3R_1 + R_2 \to \\ -2R_1 + R_3 \to \end{matrix} \begin{bmatrix} 1 & 1 & \vdots & 1 \\ 0 & -1 & \vdots & 5 \\ 0 & 1 & \vdots & -5 \end{bmatrix}$$

$$\begin{matrix} R_2 + R_1 \to \\ -R_2 \to \\ -R_2 + R_3 \to \end{matrix} \begin{bmatrix} 1 & 0 & \vdots & 6 \\ 0 & 1 & \vdots & -5 \\ 0 & 0 & \vdots & 0 \end{bmatrix}$$

$x = 6,\ y = -5$

Answer: $(6, -5)$

4. $\quad x + 3z = -5$

$\quad 2x + y = 0$

$\quad 3x + y - z = -3$

$$\begin{bmatrix} 1 & 0 & 3 & \vdots & -5 \\ 2 & 1 & 0 & \vdots & 0 \\ 3 & 1 & -1 & \vdots & 3 \end{bmatrix}$$

$$\begin{matrix} \\ -2R_1 + R_2 \to \\ -3R_1 + R_3 \to \end{matrix} \begin{bmatrix} 1 & 0 & 3 & \vdots & -5 \\ 0 & 1 & -6 & \vdots & 10 \\ 0 & 1 & -10 & \vdots & 18 \end{bmatrix}$$

$$\begin{matrix} \\ \\ -R_2 + R_3 \to \end{matrix} \begin{bmatrix} 1 & 0 & 3 & \vdots & -5 \\ 0 & 1 & -6 & \vdots & 10 \\ 0 & 0 & -4 & \vdots & 8 \end{bmatrix}$$

$$\begin{matrix} -3R_3 + R_1 \to \\ 6R_3 + R_2 \to \\ -\frac{1}{4}R_4 \to \end{matrix} \begin{bmatrix} 1 & 0 & 0 & \vdots & 1 \\ 0 & 1 & 0 & \vdots & -2 \\ 0 & 0 & 1 & \vdots & -2 \end{bmatrix}$$

$x = 1,\ y = -2,\ z = -2$

Answer: $(1, -2, -2)$

5. $\begin{bmatrix} 1 & 4 & 5 \\ 2 & 0 & -3 \end{bmatrix} \begin{bmatrix} 1 & 6 \\ 0 & -7 \\ -1 & 2 \end{bmatrix} = \begin{bmatrix} -4 & -12 \\ 5 & 6 \end{bmatrix}$

$\quad = \begin{bmatrix} 27 & 3 \\ -12 & 24 \end{bmatrix} - \begin{bmatrix} 30 & -10 \\ 15 & 25 \end{bmatrix}$

6. $3A - 5B = 3\begin{bmatrix} 9 & 1 \\ -4 & 8 \end{bmatrix} - 5\begin{bmatrix} 6 & -2 \\ 3 & 5 \end{bmatrix}$

$\qquad\qquad = \begin{bmatrix} -3 & 13 \\ -27 & -1 \end{bmatrix}$

7. $f(A) = \begin{bmatrix} 3 & 0 \\ 7 & 1 \end{bmatrix}^2 - 7\begin{bmatrix} 3 & 0 \\ 7 & 1 \end{bmatrix} + 8\begin{bmatrix} 1 & 0 \\ 0 & 1 \end{bmatrix}$

$\quad = \begin{bmatrix} 3 & 0 \\ 7 & 1 \end{bmatrix}\begin{bmatrix} 3 & 0 \\ 7 & 1 \end{bmatrix} - \begin{bmatrix} 21 & 0 \\ 49 & 7 \end{bmatrix} + \begin{bmatrix} 8 & 0 \\ 0 & 8 \end{bmatrix}$

$\quad = \begin{bmatrix} 9 & 0 \\ 28 & 1 \end{bmatrix} - \begin{bmatrix} 21 & 0 \\ 49 & 7 \end{bmatrix} + \begin{bmatrix} 8 & 0 \\ 0 & 8 \end{bmatrix}$

$\quad = \begin{bmatrix} -4 & 0 \\ -21 & 2 \end{bmatrix}$

8. False since

$(A + B)(A + 3B) = A(A + 3B) + B(A + 3B)$

$\qquad\qquad\qquad\quad = A^2 + 3AB + BA + 3B^2$ and, in general, $AB \neq BA$.

9.
$$\begin{bmatrix} 1 & 2 & \vdots & 1 & 0 \\ 3 & 5 & \vdots & 0 & 1 \end{bmatrix}$$

$$-3R_1 + R_2 \rightarrow \begin{bmatrix} 1 & 2 & \vdots & 1 & 0 \\ 0 & -1 & \vdots & -3 & 1 \end{bmatrix}$$

$$\begin{aligned} 2R_2 + R_1 &\rightarrow \\ -R_2 &\rightarrow \end{aligned} \begin{bmatrix} 1 & 0 & \vdots & -5 & 2 \\ 0 & 1 & \vdots & 3 & -1 \end{bmatrix}$$

$$A^{-1} = \begin{bmatrix} -5 & 2 \\ 3 & -1 \end{bmatrix}$$

10.
$$\begin{bmatrix} 1 & 1 & 1 & \vdots & 1 & 0 & 0 \\ 3 & 6 & 5 & \vdots & 0 & 1 & 0 \\ 6 & 10 & 8 & \vdots & 0 & 0 & 1 \end{bmatrix}$$

$$\begin{aligned} -3R_1 + R_2 &\rightarrow \\ -6R_1 + R_3 &\rightarrow \end{aligned} \begin{bmatrix} 1 & 1 & 1 & \vdots & 1 & 0 & 0 \\ 0 & 3 & 2 & \vdots & -3 & 1 & 0 \\ 0 & 4 & 2 & \vdots & -6 & 0 & 1 \end{bmatrix}$$

$$\begin{aligned} -R_2 + R_1 &\rightarrow \\ \tfrac{1}{3}R_2 &\rightarrow \\ -4R_2 + R_3 &\rightarrow \end{aligned} \begin{bmatrix} 1 & 0 & \tfrac{1}{3} & \vdots & 2 & -\tfrac{1}{3} & 0 \\ 0 & 1 & \tfrac{2}{3} & \vdots & -1 & \tfrac{1}{3} & 0 \\ 0 & 0 & -\tfrac{2}{3} & \vdots & -2 & -\tfrac{4}{3} & 1 \end{bmatrix}$$

$$\begin{aligned} \tfrac{1}{2}R_3 + R_1 &\rightarrow \\ R_3 + R_2 &\rightarrow \\ -\tfrac{3}{2}R_3 &\rightarrow \end{aligned} \begin{bmatrix} 1 & 0 & 0 & \vdots & 1 & -1 & \tfrac{1}{2} \\ 0 & 1 & 0 & \vdots & -3 & -1 & 1 \\ 0 & 0 & 1 & \vdots & 3 & 2 & -\tfrac{3}{2} \end{bmatrix}$$

$$A^{-1} = \begin{bmatrix} 1 & -1 & \tfrac{1}{2} \\ -3 & -1 & 1 \\ 3 & 2 & -\tfrac{3}{2} \end{bmatrix}$$

11. (a) $x + 2y = 4$
    $3x + 5y = 1$

$$\begin{bmatrix} 1 & 2 & \vdots & 1 & 0 \\ 3 & 5 & \vdots & 0 & 1 \end{bmatrix}$$

$$-3R_1 + R_2 \rightarrow \begin{bmatrix} 1 & 2 & \vdots & 1 & 0 \\ 0 & -1 & \vdots & -3 & 1 \end{bmatrix}$$

$$\begin{aligned} -2R_2 + R_1 &\rightarrow \\ -R_2 &\rightarrow \end{aligned} \begin{bmatrix} 1 & 0 & \vdots & -5 & 2 \\ 0 & 1 & \vdots & 3 & -1 \end{bmatrix}$$

$$X = A^{-1}B = \begin{bmatrix} -5 & 2 \\ 3 & -1 \end{bmatrix} \begin{bmatrix} 4 \\ 1 \end{bmatrix} = \begin{bmatrix} -18 \\ 11 \end{bmatrix}$$

$x = -18, y = 11$

Answer: $(-18, 11)$

(b) $x + 2y = 3$
    $3x + 5y = -2$

$$X = A^{-1}B = \begin{bmatrix} -5 & 2 \\ 3 & -1 \end{bmatrix} \begin{bmatrix} 3 \\ -2 \end{bmatrix} = \begin{bmatrix} -19 \\ 11 \end{bmatrix}$$

$x = -19, y = 11$

Answer: $(-19, 11)$

12. $\begin{vmatrix} 6 & -1 \\ 3 & 4 \end{vmatrix} = 24 - (-3) = 27$

13. $\begin{vmatrix} 1 & 3 & -1 \\ 5 & 9 & 0 \\ 6 & 2 & -5 \end{vmatrix} \; -1 \begin{vmatrix} 5 & 9 \\ 6 & 2 \end{vmatrix} - 5 \begin{vmatrix} 1 & 3 \\ 5 & 9 \end{vmatrix} = 74$

14. $\begin{vmatrix} 1 & 4 & 2 & 3 \\ 0 & 1 & -2 & 0 \\ 3 & 5 & -2 & 1 \\ 2 & 0 & 6 & 1 \end{vmatrix} = \begin{vmatrix} 1 & 2 & 3 \\ 3 & -1 & 1 \\ 2 & 6 & 1 \end{vmatrix} + 2 \begin{vmatrix} 1 & 4 & 3 \\ 3 & 5 & 1 \\ 2 & 0 & 1 \end{vmatrix}$

$= 51 + 2(-29) = -7$ (Expansion along Row 2.)

15. $\begin{vmatrix} 6 & 4 & 3 & 0 & 6 \\ 0 & 5 & 1 & 4 & 8 \\ 0 & 0 & 2 & 7 & 3 \\ 0 & 0 & 0 & 9 & 2 \\ 0 & 0 & 0 & 0 & 1 \end{vmatrix} = 6(5)(2)(9)(1) = 540$ (Upper triangular)

16. Area $= \dfrac{1}{2}\begin{vmatrix} 0 & 7 & 1 \\ 5 & 0 & 1 \\ 3 & 9 & 1 \end{vmatrix} = \dfrac{1}{2}(31)$

17. $\begin{vmatrix} x & y & 1 \\ 2 & 7 & 1 \\ -1 & 4 & 1 \end{vmatrix} = 3x - 3y + 15 = 0$ OR $= x - y + 5 = 0$

18. $x = \dfrac{\begin{vmatrix} 4 & -7 \\ 11 & 5 \end{vmatrix}}{\begin{vmatrix} 6 & -7 \\ 2 & 5 \end{vmatrix}} = \dfrac{97}{44}$

19. $z = \dfrac{\begin{vmatrix} 3 & 0 & 1 \\ 0 & 1 & 3 \\ 1 & -1 & 2 \end{vmatrix}}{\begin{vmatrix} 3 & 0 & 1 \\ 0 & 1 & 4 \\ 1 & -1 & 0 \end{vmatrix}} = \dfrac{14}{11}$

20. $y = \dfrac{\begin{vmatrix} 721.4 & 33.77 \\ 45.9 & 19.85 \end{vmatrix}}{\begin{vmatrix} 721.4 & -29.1 \\ 45.9 & 105.6 \end{vmatrix}} = \dfrac{12{,}769.747}{77{,}515.530} \approx 0.1647$

❑ Chapter 9 Practice Test Solutions

1. $a_n = \dfrac{2n}{(n+2)!}$

$a_1 = \dfrac{2(1)}{3!} = \dfrac{2}{6} = \dfrac{1}{3}$

$a_2 = \dfrac{2(2)}{4!} = \dfrac{4}{24} = \dfrac{1}{6}$

$a_3 = \dfrac{2(3)}{5!} = \dfrac{6}{120} = \dfrac{1}{20}$

$a_4 = \dfrac{2(4)}{6!} = \dfrac{8}{720} = \dfrac{1}{90}$

$a_5 = \dfrac{2(5)}{7!} = \dfrac{10}{5040} = \dfrac{1}{504}$

Terms: $\dfrac{1}{3}, \dfrac{1}{6}, \dfrac{1}{20}, \dfrac{1}{90}, \dfrac{1}{504}$

2. $a_n = \dfrac{n+3}{3^n}$

3. $\displaystyle\sum_{i=1}^{6}(2i-1) = 1 + 3 + 5 + 7 + 9 + 11 = 36$

4. $a_1 = 23, \ d = -2$

$a_2 = 23 + (-2) = 21$

$a_3 = 21 + (-2) = 19$

$a_4 = 19 + (-2) = 17$

$a_5 = 17 + (-2) = 15$

Terms: 23, 21, 19, 17, 15

5. $a_1 = 12, d = 3, n = 50$

$a_n = a_1 + (n - 1)d$

$a_{50} = 12 + (50 - 1)3 = 159$

6. $a_1 = 1$

$a_{200} = 200$

$S_n = \dfrac{n}{2}(a_1 + a_n)$

$S_{200} = \dfrac{200}{2}(1 + 200) = 20{,}100$

7. $a_1 = 7, \ r = 2$

$a_2 = 7(2) = 14$

$a_3 = 7(2)^2 = 28$

$a_4 = 7(2)^3 = 56$

$a_5 = 7(2)^4 = 112$

Terms: 7, 14, 28, 56, 112

8. $\displaystyle\sum_{n=0}^{9} 6\left(\dfrac{2}{3}\right)^n, \ a_1 = 6, r = \dfrac{2}{3}, n = 10$

$S_n = \dfrac{a_1(1 - r^n)}{1 - r} = \dfrac{6\left(1 - \left(\frac{2}{3}\right)^{10}\right)}{1 - \frac{2}{3}} \approx 17.6879$

9. $\displaystyle\sum_{n=0}^{\infty} (0.03)^n, \ a_1 = 1, r = 0.03$

$S = \dfrac{a_1}{1 - r} = \dfrac{1}{1 - 0.03} = \dfrac{1}{0.97} = \dfrac{100}{97} \approx 1.0309$

10. For $n = 1$, $1 = \dfrac{1(1 + 1)}{2}$.

Assume that $1 + 2 + 3 + 4 + \cdots + k = \dfrac{k(k + 1)}{2}$.

Now for $n = k + 1$,

$$1 + 2 + 3 + 4 + \cdots + k + (k + 1) = \dfrac{k(k + 1)}{2} + k + 1$$

$$= \dfrac{k(k + 1)}{2} + \dfrac{2(k + 1)}{2}$$

$$= \dfrac{(k + 1)(k + 2)}{2}.$$

Thus, $1 + 2 + 3 + 4 + \cdots + n = \dfrac{n(n + 1)}{2}$ for all integers $n \geq 1$.

11. For $n = 4$, $4! > 2^4$. Assume that $k! > 2^k$.

Then $(k + 1)! = (k + 1)(k!) > (k + 1)2^k > 2 \cdot 2^k = 2^{k+1}$.

Thus, $n! > 2^n$ for all integers $n \geq 4$.

12. $_{13}C_4 = \dfrac{13!}{(13 - 4)!4!} = 715$

13. $(x + 3)^5 = x^5 + 5x^4(3) + 10x^3(3)^2 + 10x^2(3)^3 + 5x(3)^4 + (3)^5$

$= x^5 + 15x^4 + 90x^3 + 270x^2 + 405x + 243$

14. $_{12}C_5 x^7(-2)^5 = -25{,}344x^7$

15. $_{30}P_4 = \dfrac{30!}{(30 - 4)!} = 657{,}720$

16. $6! = 720$ ways

17. $_{12}P_3 = 1320$

18. $P(2) + P(3) + P(4) = \dfrac{1}{36} + \dfrac{2}{36} + \dfrac{3}{36}$

$\qquad\qquad\qquad\qquad = \dfrac{6}{36} = \dfrac{1}{6}$

19. $P(K, B10) = \dfrac{4}{52} \cdot \dfrac{2}{51} = \dfrac{2}{663}$

20. Let A = probability of no faulty units.

$\quad P(A) = \left(\dfrac{997}{1000}\right)^{50} \approx 0.8605$

$\quad P(A') = 1 - P(A) \approx 0.1395$

❑ Chapter 10 Practice Test Solutions

1. $3x + 4y = 12 \Rightarrow y = -\frac{3}{4}x + 3 \Rightarrow m_1 = -\frac{3}{4}$

$4x - 3y = 12 \Rightarrow y = \frac{4}{3}x - 4 \Rightarrow m_2 = \frac{4}{3}$

$\tan \theta = \left| \frac{\frac{4}{3} - \left(-\frac{3}{4}\right)}{1 + \left(\frac{4}{3}\right)\left(-\frac{3}{4}\right)} \right| = \left| \frac{\frac{25}{12}}{0} \right|$

Since $\tan \theta$ is undefined, the lines are perpendicular (note that $m_2 = -1/m_1$) and $\theta = 90°$.

3. $x^2 - 6x - 4y + 1 = 0$

$x^2 - 6x + 9 = 4y - 1 + 9$

$(x - 3)^2 = 4y + 8$

$(x - 3)^2 = 4(1)(y + 2) \Rightarrow p = 1$

Vertex: $(3, -2)$

Focus: $(3, -1)$

Directrix: $y = -3$

5. $x^2 + 4y^2 - 2x + 32y + 61 = 0$

$(x^2 - 2x + 1) + 4(y^2 + 8y + 16) = -61 + 1 + 64$

$(x - 1)^2 + 4(y + 4)^2 = 4$

$\frac{(x - 1)^2}{4} + \frac{(y + 4)^2}{1} = 1$

$a = 2, b = 1, c = \sqrt{3}$

Horizontal major axis

Center: $(1, -4)$

Foci: $\left(1 \pm \sqrt{3}, -4\right)$

Vertices: $(3, -4), (-1, -4)$

Eccentricity: $e = \frac{\sqrt{3}}{2}$

2. $x_1 = 5, x_2 = -9, A = 3, B = -7, C = -21$

$d = \frac{|3(5) + (-7)(-9) + (-21)|}{\sqrt{3^2 + (-7)^2}} = \frac{57}{\sqrt{58}} \approx 7.484$

4. Vertex: $(2, -5)$

Focus: $(2, -6)$

Vertical axis; opens downward with $p = -1$

$(x - h)^2 = 4p(y - k)$

$(x - 2)^2 = 4(-1)(y + 5)$

$x^2 - 4x + 4 = -4y - 20$

$x^2 - 4x + 4y + 24 = 0$

6. Vertices: $(0, \pm 6)$

Eccentricity: $e = \frac{1}{2}$

Center: $(0, 0)$

Vertical major axis

$a = 6, e = \frac{c}{a} = \frac{c}{6} = \frac{1}{2} \Rightarrow c = 3$

$b^2 = (6)^2 - (3)^2 = 27$

$\frac{x^2}{27} + \frac{y^2}{36} = 1$

7. $16y^2 - x^2 - 6x - 128y + 231 = 0$

$16(y^2 - 8y + 16) - (x^2 + 6x + 9) = -231 + 256 - 9$

$16(y - 4)^2 - (x + 3)^2 = 16$

$\frac{(y - 4)^2}{1} - \frac{(x + 3)^2}{16} = 1$

$a = 1, b = 4, c = \sqrt{17}$

Center: $(-3, 4)$

Vertical transverse axis

Vertices: $(-3, 5), (-3, 3)$

Foci: $\left(-3, 4 \pm \sqrt{17}\right)$

Asymptotes: $y = 4 \pm \frac{1}{4}(x + 3)$

8. Vertices: $(\pm 3, 2)$

Foci: $(\pm 5, 2)$

Center: $(0, 2)$

Horizontal transverse axis

$a = 3, c = 5, b = 4$

$$\frac{(x - 0)^2}{9} - \frac{(y - 2)^2}{16} = 1$$

$$\frac{x^2}{9} - \frac{(y - 2)^2}{16} = 1$$

9. $5x^2 + 2xy + 5y^2 - 10 = 0$

$A = 5, B = 2, C = 5$

$$\cot 2\theta = \frac{5 - 5}{2} = 0$$

$$2\theta = \frac{\pi}{2} \Rightarrow \theta = \frac{\pi}{4}$$

$$x = x' \cos \frac{\pi}{4} - y' \sin \frac{\pi}{4} \qquad x = x' \cos \frac{\pi}{4} + y' \sin \frac{\pi}{4}$$

$$= \frac{x' - y'}{\sqrt{2}} \qquad\qquad = \frac{x' + y'}{\sqrt{2}}$$

$$5\left(\frac{x' - y'}{\sqrt{2}}\right)^2 + 2\left(\frac{x' - y'}{\sqrt{2}}\right)\left(\frac{x' + y'}{\sqrt{2}}\right) + 5\left(\frac{x' + y'}{\sqrt{2}}\right)^2 - 10 = 0$$

$$\frac{5(x')^2}{2} - \frac{10x'y'}{2} + \frac{5(y')^2}{2} + (x')^2 - (y')^2 + \frac{5(x')^2}{2} + \frac{10x'y'}{2} + \frac{5(y')^2}{2} - 10 = 0$$

$$6(x')^2 + 4(y')^2 - 10 = 0$$

$$\frac{3(x')^2}{5} + \frac{2(y')^2}{5} = 1$$

$$\frac{(x')^2}{5/3} + \frac{(y')^2}{5/2} = 1$$

Ellipse centered at the origin

10. (a) $6x^2 - 2xy + y^2 = 0$

$A = 6, B = -2, C = 1$

$B^2 - 4AC = (-2)^2 - 4(6)(1) = -20 < 0$

Ellipse

(b) $x^2 + 4xy + 4y^2 - x - y + 17 = 0$

$A = 1, B = 4, C = 4$

$B^2 - 4AC = (4)^2 - 4(1)(4) = 0$

Parabola

11. Polar: $\left(\sqrt{2}, \frac{3\pi}{4}\right)$

$$x = \sqrt{2} \cos \frac{3\pi}{4} = \sqrt{2}\left(-\frac{1}{\sqrt{2}}\right) = -1$$

$$y = \sqrt{2} \sin \frac{3\pi}{4} = \sqrt{2}\left(\frac{1}{\sqrt{2}}\right) = 1$$

Rectangular: $(-1, 1)$

12. Rectangular: $\left(\sqrt{3}, -1\right)$

$$r = \pm\sqrt{\left(\sqrt{3}\right)^2 + (-1)^2} = \pm 2$$

$$\tan \theta = \frac{\sqrt{3}}{-1} = -\sqrt{3}$$

$$\theta = \frac{2\pi}{3} \text{ or } \theta = \frac{5\pi}{3}$$

Polar: $\left(-2, \dfrac{2\pi}{3}\right)$ or $\left(2, \dfrac{5\pi}{3}\right)$

13. Rectangular: $4x - 3y = 12$

Polar: $4r \cos \theta - 3r \sin \theta = 12$

$$r(4 \cos \theta - 3 \sin \theta) = 12$$

14. Polar: $r = 5 \cos \theta$

$$r^2 = 5r \cos \theta$$

Rectangular: $x^2 + y^2 = 5x$

$$x^2 + y^2 - 5x = 0$$

15. $r = 1 - \cos \theta$

Cardioid

Symmetry: Polar axis

Maximum value of $|r|$: $r = 2$ when $\theta = \pi$.

Zero of r: $r = 0$ when $\theta = 0$

θ	0	$\dfrac{\pi}{2}$	π	$\dfrac{3\pi}{2}$
r	0	1	2	1

16. $r = 5 \sin 2\theta$

Rose curve with four petals

Symmetry: Polar axis, $\theta = \dfrac{\pi}{2}$, and pole

Maximum value of $|r|$: $|r| = 5$ when $\theta = \dfrac{\pi}{4}, \dfrac{3\pi}{4}, \dfrac{5\pi}{4}, \dfrac{7\pi}{4}$

Zeros of r: $r = 0$ when $\theta = 0, \dfrac{\pi}{2}, \pi, \dfrac{3\pi}{2}$

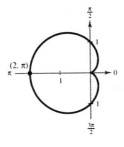

17. $r = \dfrac{3}{6 - \cos \theta}$

$$r = \frac{\frac{1}{2}}{1 - \frac{1}{6} \cos \theta}$$

$e = \dfrac{1}{6} < 1$, so the graph is an ellipse.

θ	0	$\dfrac{\pi}{2}$	π	$\dfrac{3\pi}{2}$
r	$\dfrac{3}{5}$	$\dfrac{1}{2}$	$\dfrac{3}{7}$	$\dfrac{1}{2}$

18. Parabola

Vertex: $\left(6, \dfrac{\pi}{2}\right)$

Focus: $(0, 0)$

$e = 1$

$r = \dfrac{ep}{1 + e \sin \theta}$

$r = \dfrac{p}{1 + \sin \theta}$

$6 = \dfrac{p}{1 + \sin(\pi/2)}$

$6 = \dfrac{p}{2}$

$12 = p$

$r = \dfrac{12}{1 + \sin \theta}$

20. $x = e^{2t}, y = e^{4t}$

$x > 0, y > 0$

$y = (e^{2t})^2 = (x)^2 = x^2, x < 0, y > 0$

19. $x = 3 - 2 \sin \theta, y = 1 + 5 \cos \theta$

$\dfrac{x - 3}{-2} = \sin \theta, \dfrac{y - 1}{5} = \cos \theta$

$\left(\dfrac{x - 3}{-2}\right)^2 + \left(\dfrac{y - 1}{5}\right)^2 = 1$

$\dfrac{(x - 3)^2}{4} + \dfrac{(y - 1)^2}{25} = 1$

❏ Chapter Test Solutions for Chapter P

1. $\dfrac{5}{18} \div \dfrac{15}{8} = \dfrac{\cancelto{1}{5}}{\cancelto{9}{18}} \cdot \dfrac{\cancelto{4}{8}}{\cancelto{3}{15}} = \dfrac{4}{27}$

2. $\sqrt{5} \cdot \sqrt{125} = \sqrt{625} = 25$

3. $3z^2(2z^3)^2 = 3z^2(4z^6) = 12z^8$

4. $9z\sqrt{8z} - 3\sqrt{2z^3} = 18z\sqrt{2z} - 3z\sqrt{2z} = 15z\sqrt{2z}$

5. $(x^2 + 3) - [3x + (8 - x^2)] = x^2 + 3 - 3x - 8 + x^2$
$$= 2x^2 - 3x - 5$$

6. $(3x - 2)^2 = (3x)^2 - 2(3x)(2) + (2)^2 = 9x^2 - 12x + 14$

7. $\dfrac{8x}{x-3} + \dfrac{24}{3-x} = \dfrac{8x}{x-3} - \dfrac{24}{x-3} = \dfrac{8x-24}{x-3} = \dfrac{8(x-3)}{x-3} = 8, x \neq 3$

8. $\left(\dfrac{2}{x} - \dfrac{2}{x+1}\right) \div \left(\dfrac{4}{x^2-1}\right) = \left(\dfrac{2}{x(x+1)}\right)\left(\dfrac{(x+1)(x-1)}{4}\right) = \dfrac{x-1}{2x}, x \neq \pm 1$

9. $x^3 + 2x^2 - 4x - 8 = x^2(x+2) - 4(x+2)$
$$= (x+2)(x^2-4)$$
$$= (x+2)^2(x-2)$$

10. $A = \dfrac{1}{2}(3x)(\sqrt{3}x) - \dfrac{1}{2}(2x)\left(\dfrac{2}{3}\sqrt{3}x\right)$

$\quad = \dfrac{3\sqrt{3}x^2}{2} - \dfrac{2\sqrt{3}x^2}{3} = \dfrac{9\sqrt{3}x^2 - 4\sqrt{3}x^2}{6} = \dfrac{5\sqrt{3}x^2}{6} = \dfrac{5}{6}\sqrt{3}x^2$

11. $\quad \dfrac{2}{3}(x-1) + \dfrac{1}{4}x = 10$
$$12\left[\dfrac{2}{3}(x-1) + \dfrac{1}{4}x\right] = 12(10)$$
$$8(x-1) + 3x = 120$$
$$11x - 8 = 120$$
$$11x = 128$$
$$x = \dfrac{128}{11}$$

12. $\dfrac{x-2}{x+2} + \dfrac{4}{x+2} + 4 = 0$

$$\dfrac{x+2}{x+2} + 4 = 0$$
$$5 \neq 0$$

No solution

13. $3x^2 + 6x + 2 = 0$

$\quad x = \dfrac{-6 \pm \sqrt{6^2 - 4(3)(2)}}{2(3)}$

$\quad = \dfrac{-6 \pm \sqrt{12}}{6}$

$\quad = \dfrac{-6 \pm 2\sqrt{3}}{6}$

$\quad = \dfrac{-3 \pm \sqrt{3}}{3}$

14. $x^4 + x^2 - 6 = 0$

$(x^2 - 2)(x^2 + 3) = 0$

$x^2 - 2 = 0 \Rightarrow x = \pm\sqrt{2}$

$x^2 + 3 = 0 \Rightarrow x = \pm\sqrt{3}i$

15. $2\sqrt{x} - \sqrt{2x+1} = 1$

$\qquad -\sqrt{2x+1} = 1 - 2\sqrt{x}$

$\qquad 2x + 1 = 1 - 4\sqrt{x} + 4x$

$\qquad 4\sqrt{x} = 2x$

$\qquad 16x = 4x^2$

$\qquad 16x - 4x^2 = 0$

$\qquad 4x(4 - x) = 0$

$4x = 0$ or $4 - x = 0$

$x = 0 \qquad\quad x = 4$

$x = 4$ is the only solution which checks in the orginal equation. $x = 0$ is extraneous.

17. $-3 \le 2(x + 4) < 14$

$\quad -3 \le 2x + 8 < 14$

$-11 \le 2x < 6$

$-\dfrac{11}{2} \le x < 3$

16. $|3x - 1| = 7$

$3x - 1 = -7$ or $3x - 1 = 7$

$\quad 3x = -6 \qquad\qquad 3x = 8$

$\quad x = -2 \qquad\qquad x = \dfrac{8}{3}$

18. $\qquad \dfrac{2}{x} > \dfrac{5}{x + 6}$

$\dfrac{2}{x} - \dfrac{5}{x + 6} > 0$

$\dfrac{12 - 3x}{x(x + 6)} > 0$

Critical numbers: $x = -6, x = 0, x = 4$

Test intervals: $(-\infty, -6), (-6, 0), (0, 4), (4, \infty)$

Test: Is $\dfrac{3(4 - x)}{x(x + 6)} > 0$?

Solution set: $(-\infty, -6) \cup (0, 4)$

Inequality notation: $x < -6, 0 < x < 4$

19. $(100 \text{ km/hr})\left(2\tfrac{1}{4}\text{ hr}\right) + (x \text{ km/hr})\left(1\tfrac{1}{3}\text{ hr}\right) = 350 \text{ km}$

$225 + \dfrac{4}{3}x = 250$

$\dfrac{4}{3}x = 125$

$x = \dfrac{375}{4} = 93\dfrac{3}{4} \text{ km/hr}$

20.

Midpoint: $\left(\dfrac{-2 + 6}{2}, \dfrac{5 + 0}{2}\right) = \left(2, \dfrac{5}{2}\right)$

Distance:

$d = \sqrt{(-2 - 6)^2 + (5 - 0)^2} = \sqrt{64 + 25} = \sqrt{89}$

❏ Chapter Test Solutions for Chapter 1

1. $y = 4 - \frac{3}{4}x$

No symmetry

x- intercept: $\left(\frac{16}{3}, 0\right)$

y- intercept: $(0, 4)$

2. $y = 4 - \frac{3}{4}|x|$

y- axis symmetry

x- intercepts: $\left(\pm\frac{16}{3}, 0\right)$

y- intercept: $(0, 4)$

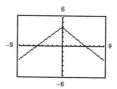

3. $y = 4 - (x - 2)^2$

Parabola; vertex: $(2, 4)$

No symmetry

x- intercepts: $(0, 0)$ and $(4, 0)$

y- intercept: $(0, 0)$

4. $y = \sqrt{3 - x}$

Domain: $x \le 3$

No symmetry

x- intercept: $(3, 0)$

y- intercept: $\left(0, \sqrt{3}\right)$

5. $m = \dfrac{2 - 6}{3 - (-3)} = \dfrac{-4}{6} = -\dfrac{2}{3}$

6. $m = \dfrac{3}{2}$

$(3 - 2, -1 - 3) = (1, -4)$

$(3 + 2, -1 + 3) = (5, 2)$

$(5 + 2, 2 + 3) = (7, 5)$

7. $5x + 2y = 3 \implies y = -\frac{5}{2}x + \frac{3}{2} \implies m_1 = -\frac{5}{2}$

Perpendicular slope: $m_2 = \frac{2}{5}$

$y - 4 = \frac{2}{5}(x - 0)$

$5y - 20 = 2x$

$0 = 2x - 5y + 20$

8. No. For some x- values there are two y- values. The graph fails the vertical line test.

9. $f(-6) = 10 - \sqrt{3 - (-6)} = 10 - 3 = 7$

10. $f(t - 3) = 10 - \sqrt{3 - (t - 3)} = 10 - \sqrt{6 - t}$

11. $3 - x \geq 0$

$-x \geq -3$

$x \leq 3$

Domain: $(-\infty, 3]$

12. $\dfrac{f(x) - f(2)}{x - 2} = \dfrac{\left(10 - \sqrt{3 - x}\right) - \left(10 - \sqrt{3 - 2}\right)}{x - 2}$

$= \dfrac{1 - \sqrt{3 - x}}{x - 2} = \dfrac{\sqrt{3 - x} - 1}{2 - x}$

13. $h(x) = \frac{1}{4}x^4 - 2x^2$

Even

Increasing on $(-2, 0), (2, \infty)$

Decreasing on $(-\infty, -2), (0, 2)$

14. $g(t) = |t + 2| - |t - 2|$

Odd

Increasing on $(-2, 2)$

Constant on $(-\infty, -2), (2, \infty)$

15. $(f - g)(x) = f(x) - g(x) = x^2 - \sqrt{2 - x}$

Domain: $(-\infty, 2]$

16. $\left(\dfrac{f}{g}\right)(x) = \dfrac{f(x)}{g(x)} = \dfrac{x^2}{\sqrt{2 - x}}$

Domain: $(-\infty, 2)$

17. $(f \circ g)(x) = f(g(x)) = f\left(\sqrt{2 - x}\right)$

$= \left(\sqrt{2 - x}\right)^2 = 2 - x$

Domain: $(-\infty, \infty)$

18. $g(x) = \sqrt{2 - x}$

Domain: $(-\infty, 2]$

Range: $[0. \infty)$

The domain of $g^{-1}(x)$ is the range of $g(x)$ and the range of $g^{-1}(x)$ is the domain of $g(x)$.

$y = \sqrt{2 - x}$

$x = \sqrt{2 - y}$

$x^2 = 2 - y$

$x^2 + 2 = y$

$g^{-1}(x) = x^2 + 2, \ x \geq 0$

Domain: $[0, \infty)$

19. (a) $\frac{1}{2}g(x - 2)$

Horizontal shift two units to the right Vertrical shrink by $\frac{1}{2}$

x	$g(x)$
-2	4
0	0
2	2
4	1

x	$\frac{1}{2}g(x - 2)$
0	2
2	0
4	1
6	$\frac{1}{2}$

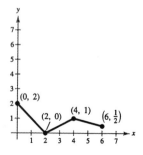

(b) $g\left(\frac{1}{2}x\right) - 1$

Change in x by a factor of $\frac{1}{2}$ Vertical shift one unit down

x	$g\left(\frac{1}{2}x\right) - 1$
-4	$4 - 1 = 3$
0	$0 - 1 = -1$
4	$2 - 1 = 1$
8	$1 - 1 = 0$

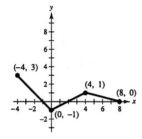

20. $d = Ks^2$

$35 = K(70)^2$

$K = \dfrac{1}{140}$

$d = \dfrac{s^2}{140}$

$d = \dfrac{(100)^2}{140} = \dfrac{500}{7} \approx 71.4$ meters

❏ Chapter Test Solutions for Chapter 2

1. $f(x) = x^2$

   (a) $g(x) = 2 - x^2$

     Reflection in the x-axis followed by a vertical shift two units upward

   (b) $h(x) = \left(x - \frac{3}{2}\right)^2$

     Horizontal shift $\frac{3}{2}$ units to the right

2. Vertex: $(3, -6)$

   $y = a(x - 3)^2 - 6$

   Point on graph: $(0, 3)$

   $3 = a(0 - 3)^2 - 6$

   $9 = 9a \implies a = 1$

   Thus, $y = (x - 3)^2 - 6$

3. $h(t) = -\frac{3}{4}t^5 + 2t^2$

   The degree is odd and the leading coefficient is negative. The graph rises to the left and falls to the right.

4.
$$\begin{array}{r} 3x + \dfrac{x - 1}{x^2 + 1} \\ x^2 + 0x + 1 \overline{)\,3x^3 + 0x^2 + 4x - 1} \\ \underline{-(3x^3 + 0x^2 + 3x)} \\ x - 1 \end{array}$$

   Thus, $\dfrac{3x^3 + 4x - 1}{x^2 + 1} = 3x + \dfrac{x - 1}{x^2 + 1}$.

5. $f(x) = x^3 + 5x^2 - 4x - 20$

   Possible rational zeros: $\pm 1, \pm 2, \pm 4, \pm 5, \pm 10, \pm 20$

   From the graph, we have $x = -5$ and $x = \pm 2$.

6. $g(t) = 2t^4 - 3t^3 + 16t - 24$

   Possible rational zeros: $\pm 1, \pm 2, \pm 3, \pm 4, \pm 6, \pm 8,$

                        $\pm 12, \pm 24, \pm \frac{1}{2}, \pm \frac{3}{2}$

   From the graph, we have $x = -2$ and $x = \frac{3}{2}$.

7. $f(x) = 3x^5 + 2x^4 - 12x - 8$

   $x \approx \pm 1.414$ and $x \approx -0.667$

8. $g(v) = 2v^3 - 11v^2 + 22v - 15$

   Possible rational zeros: $\pm 1, \pm 3, \pm 5, \pm 15, \pm \frac{1}{2}, \pm \frac{3}{2}, \pm \frac{5}{2}, \pm \frac{15}{2}$

   By checking, we find that $x = \frac{3}{2}$ is a zero.

$$\begin{array}{r|rrrr} \frac{3}{2} & 2 & -11 & 22 & -15 \\ & & 3 & -12 & 15 \\ \hline & 2 & -8 & 10 & 0 \end{array}$$

   $g(v) = \left(v - \frac{3}{2}\right)(2v^2 - 8v + 10) = (2v - 3)(x^2 - 4v + 5)$

   Using the Quadratic Formula on $v^2 - 4v + 5 = 0$ yields $v = 2 \pm i$. The zeros of $g(v)$ are $v = \frac{3}{2}$ and $v = 2 \pm i$.

9. $f(x) = \left[x - \left(1 + \sqrt{3}i\right)\right]\left[x - \left(1 - \sqrt{3}i\right)\right](x - 2)(x - 2)$

   $= \left[(x - 1) - \sqrt{3}i\right]\left[(x - 1) + \sqrt{3}i\right](x^2 - 4x + 4)$

   $= \left[(x - 1)^2 - 3i^2\right](x^2 - 4x + 4)$

   $= (x^2 - 2x + 4)(x^2 - 4x + 4)$

   $= x^4 - 6x^3 + 16x^2 - 24x + 16$

10. $x = \pm 3$ must make the demoninator zero. The numerator must have the same degree as the denominator and a leading coefficient of 4 (assuming that the leading coefficient of the denominator is one.) One possible function is

$$f(x) = \frac{4x^2}{x^2 - 9}$$

11. $h(x) = \dfrac{4}{x^2} - 1 = \dfrac{4 - x^2}{x^2}$

    Domain: all real numbers except $x = 0$

    Interval notation: $(-\infty, 0) \cup (0, \infty)$

    Vertical asymptote: $x = 0$

    Horizontal asymptote: $y = -1$

    x-intercepts: $(\pm 2, 0)$

12. $g(x) = \dfrac{x^2 + 2}{x - 1} = x + 1 + \dfrac{3}{x - 1}$

    Domain: all real numbers except $x = 1$

    Interval notation: $(-\infty, 1) \cup (1, \infty)$

    Vertical asymptote: $x = 1$

    Horizontal asymptote: None

    Slant asymptote: $y = x + 1$

    y-intercept: $(0, -2)$

13. (a) Equate the slopes.

$$\frac{y - 1}{0 - 2} = \frac{1 - 0}{2 - x}$$

$$\frac{y - 1}{-2} = \frac{1}{2 - x}$$

$$y - 1 = -2\left(\frac{1}{2 - x}\right)$$

$$y = 1 + \frac{2}{x - 2}$$

(b) $A = \dfrac{1}{2}xy = \dfrac{1}{2}x\left(1 + \dfrac{2}{x - 2}\right)$

$= \dfrac{x}{2} + \dfrac{x}{x - 2} = \dfrac{x^2}{2(x - 2)}$

In context, we have $x > 2$ for the domain.

(c)

The minimum area of $A = 4$ occurs at $x = 4$.

14. (a) $\dfrac{2x + 5}{(x - 2)(x + 1)} = \dfrac{A}{x - 2} + \dfrac{B}{x + 1}$

$$2x + 5 = A(x + 1) + B(x - 2)$$

Let $x = 2 : 9 = 3A \implies A = 3$

Let $x = -1 : 3 = -3B \implies B = -1$

Thus, $\dfrac{2x + 5}{x^2 - x - 2} = \dfrac{3}{x - 2} - \dfrac{1}{x + 1}$.

(b) $\dfrac{3x^2 - 2x + 4}{x^2(2 - x)} = \dfrac{A}{x} + \dfrac{B}{x^2} + \dfrac{C}{2 - x}$

$$3x^2 - 2x + 4 = Ax(2 - x) + B(2 - x) + Cx^2$$

Let $x = 0 : 4 = 2B \implies B = 2$

Let $x = 2 : 12 = 4C \implies C = 3$

Let $x = 1 : 5 = A + B + C \implies A = 0$

Thus, $\dfrac{3x^2 - 2x + 4}{x^2(2 - x^2)} = \dfrac{2}{x^2} + \dfrac{3}{2 - x} = \dfrac{2}{x^2} - \dfrac{3}{x - 2}$.

(c) $\dfrac{x^2 - 1}{x(x^2 + 1)} = \dfrac{A}{x} + \dfrac{Bx + C}{x^2 + 1}$

$$x^2 - 1 = A(x^2 + 1) + (Bx + C)x$$
$$= (A + B)x^2 + Cx + A$$

By equating coefficients we have:

$$1 = A + B$$
$$0 = C$$
$$-1 = A \implies B = 2$$

Thus, $\dfrac{x^2 - 1}{x^3 + x} = -\dfrac{1}{x} + \dfrac{2x}{x^2 + 1}$.

❑ Cumulative Test Solutions for Chapters 1–3

1. $x - 3y + 12 = 0$

Line

x-intercept: $(-12, 0)$

y-intercept: $(0, 4)$

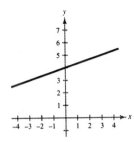

2. $h(x) = -(x^2 + 4x)$

Parabola: Vertex $(-2, 4)$

x-intercepts: $(-4, 0), (0, 0)$

3. $y = \sqrt{4 - x}$

Domain: $(-\infty, 4]$

x-intercept: $(4, 0)$

y-intercept: $(0, 2)$

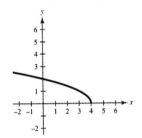

4. $y = \dfrac{2x}{x - 3}$

Vertical asymptote: $x = 3$

Horizontal asymptote: $y = 2$

Intercept: $(0, 0)$

5. $g(x) = \log_3(x - 2) \Longrightarrow 3^y + 2 = x$

Domain: $(2, \infty)$

Vertical asymptote: $x = 2$

Intercept: $(3, 0)$

6. $f(x) = 2^{-x/3}$

Exponential function

Horizontal asymptote: $x = 0$

Intercept: $(0, 1)$

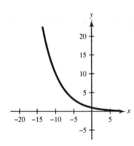

7. $m = \dfrac{8 - 1}{3 - (-1/2)} = \dfrac{7}{7/2} = 2$

$y - 8 = 2(x - 3)$

$y - 8 = 2x - 6$

$0 = 2x - y + 2$

8. $f(x) = \dfrac{x}{x - 2}$

(a) $f(6) = \dfrac{6}{6 - 2} = \dfrac{6}{4} = \dfrac{3}{2}$

(b) $f(2) = \dfrac{2}{2 - 2} = \dfrac{2}{0}$ which is undefined.

(c) $f(s + 2) = \dfrac{s + 2}{(s + 2) - 2} = \dfrac{s + 2}{s}$

9. $f(x) = x^3$

$g(x) = x^3 - 2$ is a vertical shift two units downward.

$h(x) = (x - 2)^3$ is a horizontal shift two units to the right.

10. $y = 5x - 2$

$x = 5y - 2$

$5y = x + 2$

$y = \frac{1}{5}(x + 2)$

$h^{-1}(x) = \frac{1}{5}(x + 2)$

11. $f(x) = x^3 + 2x^2 + 4x + 8$

$= x^2(x + 2) + 4(x + 2)$

$= (x + 2)(x^2 + 4)$

$x + 2 = 0 \Longrightarrow x = -2$

$x^2 + 4 = 0 \Longrightarrow x = \pm 2i$

The zeros of $f(x)$ are -2 and $\pm 2i$.

12. $200{,}000 = P\left(1 + \dfrac{0.08}{365}\right)^{(365)(20)}$

$P = \dfrac{200{,}000}{\left(1 + \dfrac{0.08}{365}\right)^{(365)(20)}} \approx \$40{,}386.38$

13. $\log_4 64 = 3$

$4^3 = 64$

14. $3 \ln z - [\ln(z + 1) + \ln(z - 1)] = \ln z^3 - \ln(z + 1)(z - 1)$

$$= \ln\left[\dfrac{z^3}{(z + 1)(z - 1)}\right]$$

15. (a) $e^{x/2} = 450$

$\dfrac{x}{2} = \ln 450$

$x = 2 \ln 450 \approx 12.218$

(b) $\left(1 + \dfrac{0.06}{4}\right)^{4t} = 3$

$(1.015)^{4t} = 3$

$\ln(1.015)^{4t} = \ln 3$

$4t \ln(1.015) = \ln 3$

$t = \dfrac{\ln 3}{4 \ln 1.015}$

≈ 18.447

(c) $5 \ln(x + 4) = 22$

$\ln(x + 4) = 4.4$

$x + 4 = e^{4.4}$

$x = -4 + e^{4.4}$

≈ 77.451

16. $C = 28{,}000$

$20{,}000 = 28{,}000e^{K(1)}$

$\dfrac{5}{7} = e^K$

$\ln\!\left(\dfrac{5}{7}\right) = K$

$y = 28{,}000e^{[\ln(5/7)](3)} \approx \$10{,}204.08$

17. $p(t) = \dfrac{1200}{1 + 3e^{-t/5}}$

(a) $p(0) = \dfrac{1200}{1 + 3(1)} = 300$

(b) $800 = \dfrac{1200}{1 + 3e^{-t/5}}$

(c) As $t \to \infty$, $p(t) \to \dfrac{1200}{1 + 3(0)} = 1200$.

$1 + 3e^{-t/5} = \dfrac{1200}{800}$

Horizontal asymptote: $p(t) = 1200$

$3e^{-t/5} = 0.5$

$-\dfrac{t}{5} = \ln\!\left(\dfrac{0.5}{3}\right)$

$t = -5\ln\!\left(\dfrac{0.5}{3}\right) \approx 8.96$ years

18. The graph has a horizontal asymptote at $y = 6$, (this eliminates (a)), and has y-axis symmetry (his eliminates (b) and (c)). The graph matches (d).

❑ Chapter Test Solutions for Chapter 4

1. $\theta = \dfrac{5\pi}{4}$

(a)

(b) $\dfrac{5\pi}{4} + 2\pi = \dfrac{13\pi}{4}$

$\dfrac{5\pi}{4} - 2\pi = -\dfrac{3\pi}{4}$

(c) $\dfrac{5\pi}{4}\left(\dfrac{180°}{\pi}\right) = 225°$

2. $90\,\dfrac{\text{km}}{\text{hr}} \times \dfrac{1\ \text{hr}}{60\ \text{min}} \times \dfrac{1000\ \text{m}}{1\ \text{km}} = 1500$ meters per minute

Circumference $= 2\pi\left(\dfrac{1}{2}\right) = \pi = \pi$ meters

$\dfrac{\text{Revolutions}}{\text{minute}} = \dfrac{1500}{\pi}$

Angular speed $= \dfrac{1500}{\pi} \cdot \pi = 1500$ radians per minute

3. $x = -2,\ y = 6$

$r = \sqrt{(-2)^2 + (6)^2} = 2\sqrt{10}$

$\sin\theta = \dfrac{y}{r} = \dfrac{6}{2\sqrt{10}} = \dfrac{3}{\sqrt{10}}$

$\cos\theta = \dfrac{x}{r} = \dfrac{-2}{2\sqrt{10}} = -\dfrac{1}{\sqrt{10}}$

$\tan\theta = \dfrac{y}{x} = \dfrac{6}{-2} = -3$

$\csc\theta = \dfrac{r}{y} = \dfrac{2\sqrt{10}}{6} = \dfrac{\sqrt{10}}{3}$

$\sec\theta = \dfrac{r}{x} = \dfrac{2\sqrt{10}}{-2} = -\sqrt{10}$

$\cot\theta = \dfrac{x}{y} = \dfrac{-2}{6} = -\dfrac{1}{3}$

4. $\sin\theta = \dfrac{\text{opp}}{\text{hyp}} = \dfrac{3}{\sqrt{13}}$

$\cos\theta = \dfrac{\text{adj}}{\text{hyp}} = \dfrac{2}{\sqrt{13}}$

$\csc\theta = \dfrac{\text{hyp}}{\text{opp}} = \dfrac{\sqrt{13}}{3}$

$\sec\theta = \dfrac{\text{hyp}}{\text{adj}} = \dfrac{\sqrt{13}}{2}$

$\cot\theta = \dfrac{\text{adj}}{\text{opp}} = \dfrac{2}{3}$

5. $\theta = 290°$

$\theta' = 360° - 290° = 70°$

6. $\sec \theta < 0$ and $\tan \theta > 0$

$\dfrac{r}{x} < 0$ and $\dfrac{y}{x} > 0$

Quadrant III

7. $\cos \theta = -\dfrac{\sqrt{3}}{2}$

Reference angle is 30° and θ is in Quadrant II or III.

$\theta = 150°$ or $210°$

8. $\csc \theta = 1.030$

$\dfrac{1}{\sin \theta} = 1.030$

$\sin \theta = \dfrac{1}{1.030}$

$\theta = \arcsin \dfrac{1}{1.030}$

$\theta \approx 1.33$ and $\pi - 1.33 \approx 1.81$

9. $g(x) = -2 \sin\left(x - \dfrac{\pi}{4}\right)$

Period: 2π

Amplitude: $|-2| = 2$

Shifted to the right by $(\pi/4)$ units and reflected in the x-axis.

x	0	$\dfrac{\pi}{4}$	$\dfrac{\pi}{2}$	$\dfrac{3\pi}{4}$	π
y	$\sqrt{2}$	0	$-\sqrt{2}$	-2	$-\sqrt{2}$

10. $f(\alpha) = \dfrac{1}{2} \tan 2\alpha$

Period: $\dfrac{\pi}{2}$

Asymptotes: $x = -\dfrac{\pi}{4}, x = \dfrac{\pi}{4}$

α	$-\dfrac{\pi}{8}$	0	$\dfrac{\pi}{8}$
$f(\alpha)$	$-\dfrac{1}{2}$	0	$\dfrac{1}{2}$

11. $y = \sin 2\pi x + 2 \cos \pi x$

Periodic: period $= 2$

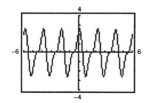

12. $y = 6e^{-0.12t} \cos(0.25t), 0 \le t \le 32$

Not periodic

13. $f(x) = a \sin(bx + c)$

Amplitude: $2 \Longrightarrow |a| = 2$

Reflected in the *x*-axis: $a = -2$

Period: $4\pi = \dfrac{2\pi}{b} \Longrightarrow b = \dfrac{1}{2}$

Phase shift: $\dfrac{c}{b} = -\dfrac{\pi}{2} \Longrightarrow c = -\dfrac{\pi}{4}$

$f(x) = -2 \sin\left(\dfrac{x}{2} - \dfrac{\pi}{4}\right)$

14. Let $u = \arccos \dfrac{2}{3}$,

$\cos u = \dfrac{2}{3}.$

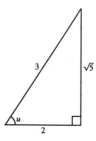

$\tan\left(\arccos \dfrac{2}{3}\right) = \tan u = \dfrac{\sqrt{5}}{2}$

15. $f(x) = 2 \arcsin\left(\dfrac{1}{2}x\right)$

Domain: $[-2, 2]$

Range: $[-\pi, \pi]$

16.

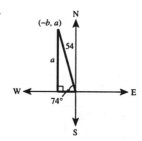

$\sin 74° = \dfrac{a}{54} \Longrightarrow a \approx 51.91$ nautical miles north

$\cos 74° = \dfrac{b}{54} \Longrightarrow b \approx 14.88$ nautical miles west

Coordinates: $(-14.88, 51.91)$

❏ Chapter Test Solutions for Chapter 5

1. $\tan \theta = \dfrac{3}{2}$ and $\cos \theta < 0$

θ is in Quadrant III.

$$\sec \theta = -\sqrt{1 + \tan^2 \theta} = -\sqrt{1 + \left(\frac{3}{2}\right)^2} = -\frac{\sqrt{13}}{2}$$

$$\cos \theta = \frac{1}{\sec \theta} = -\frac{2}{\sqrt{13}}$$

$$\sin \theta = \tan \theta \cos \theta = \left(\frac{3}{2}\right)\left(-\frac{2}{\sqrt{13}}\right) = -\frac{3}{\sqrt{13}}$$

$$\csc \theta = \frac{1}{\sin \theta} = -\frac{\sqrt{13}}{3}$$

$$\cot \theta = \frac{1}{\tan \theta} = \frac{2}{3}$$

2. $\csc^2 \beta (1 - \cos^2 \beta) = \dfrac{1}{\sin^2 \beta}(\sin^2 \beta) = 1$

3. $\dfrac{\sec^4 x - \tan^4 x}{\sec^2 x + \tan^2 x} = \dfrac{(\sec^2 x + \tan^2 x)(\sec^2 x - \tan^2 x)}{\sec^2 x + \tan^2 x}$

$$= \sec^2 x - \tan^2 x = 1$$

4. $\dfrac{\cos \theta}{\sin \theta} + \dfrac{\sin \theta}{\cos \theta} = \dfrac{\cos^2 \theta + \sin^2 \theta}{\sin \theta \cos \theta} = \dfrac{1}{\sin \theta \cos \theta}$

5. $y = \tan \theta,\ y = \sqrt{\sec^2 \theta - 1}$

$\tan \theta = -\sqrt{\sec^2 \theta - 1}$ on

$\dfrac{\pi}{2} < \theta \le \pi,\ \dfrac{3\pi}{2} < \theta < 2\pi.$

6. $y_1 = \cos x + \sin x \tan x,\ y_2 = \sec x$

It appears that $y_1 = y_2$.

$$\cos x + \sin x \tan x = \cos + \sin x \frac{\sin x}{\cos x}$$

$$= \cos + \frac{\sin^2 x}{\cos x}$$

$$= \frac{\cos^2 x + \sin^2 x}{\cos x}$$

$$= \frac{1}{\cos x} = \sec x$$

7. $\sin\theta\sec\theta = \sin\dfrac{1}{\cos\theta} = \dfrac{\sin\theta}{\cos\theta} = \tan\theta$

8. $\sec^2 x\tan^2 x + \sec^2 x = \sec^2 x(\sec^2 x - 1) + \sec^2 x$
$$= \sec^4 x - \sec^2 x + \sec^2 x$$
$$= \sec^4 x$$

9. $\dfrac{\csc\alpha + \sec\alpha}{\sin\alpha + \cos\alpha} = \dfrac{\dfrac{1}{\sin\alpha} + \dfrac{1}{\cos\alpha}}{\sin\alpha + \cos\alpha} = \dfrac{\dfrac{\cos\alpha + \sin\alpha}{\sin\alpha\cos\alpha}}{\sin\alpha + \cos\alpha} = \dfrac{1}{\sin\alpha\cos\alpha}$

$$= \dfrac{\cos^2\alpha + \sin^2\alpha}{\sin\alpha\cos\alpha} = \dfrac{\cos^2\alpha}{\sin\alpha\cos\alpha} + \dfrac{\sin^2\alpha}{\sin\alpha\cos\alpha}$$

$$= \dfrac{\cos\alpha}{\sin\alpha} + \dfrac{\sin\alpha}{\cos\alpha} = \cot\alpha + \tan\alpha$$

10. $\cos\left(x + \dfrac{\pi}{2}\right) = \cos\left(\dfrac{\pi}{2} - (-x)\right) = \sin(-x) = -\sin x$

11. $\sin(n\pi + \theta) = (-1)^n\sin\theta$, n is an integer.

For n odd: $\sin(n\pi + \theta) = \sin n\pi\cos\theta + \cos n\pi\sin\theta$
$$= (0)\cos\theta + (-1)\sin\theta = -\sin\theta$$
For n even: $\sin(n\pi + \theta) = \sin n\pi\cos\theta + \cos n\pi\sin\theta$
$$= (0)\cos\theta + (1)\sin\theta = \sin\theta$$
When n is odd, $(-1)^n = -1$. When n is even $(-1)^n = 1$. Thus, $\sin(n\pi + \theta) = (-1)^n\sin\theta$ for n is and integer.

12. $(\sin x + \cos x)^2 = \sin^2 x + 2\sin x\cos x + \cos^2 x$
$$= 1 + 2\sin x\cos x$$
$$= 1 + \sin^2 2x$$

13. $\tan^2 x + \tan x = 0$
$\tan x(1 + \tan x) = 0$
$\tan x = 0 \qquad$ or $\qquad \tan x + 1 = 0$
$x = 0,\ \pi \qquad\qquad\qquad \tan x = -1$
$$x = \dfrac{3\pi}{4}, \dfrac{7\pi}{4}$$

14. $\sin 2\alpha - \cos\alpha = 0$
$2\sin\alpha\cos\alpha - \cos\alpha = 0$
$\cos\alpha(2\sin\alpha - 1) = 0$
$\cos\alpha = 0 \qquad$ or $\qquad 2\sin\alpha - 1 = 0$
$\alpha = \dfrac{\pi}{2}, \dfrac{3\pi}{2} \qquad\qquad \sin\alpha = \dfrac{1}{2}$
$$\alpha = \dfrac{2\pi}{6}, \dfrac{5\pi}{6}$$

15. $4\cos^2 x - 3 = 0$
$$\cos^2 x = \dfrac{3}{4}$$
$$\cos x = \pm\sqrt{\dfrac{3}{4}} \pm \dfrac{\sqrt{3}}{2}$$
$$x = \dfrac{\pi}{6}, \dfrac{5\pi}{6}, \dfrac{7\pi}{6}, \dfrac{11\pi}{6}$$

16. $\csc^2 x - \csc x - 2 = 0$

$(\csc x - 2)(\csc x + 1) = 0$

$\csc x - 2 = 0$ or $\csc x + 1 = 0$

$\csc x = 2$ $\csc x = -1$

$\dfrac{1}{\sin x} = 2$ $\dfrac{1}{\sin x} = -1$

$\sin x = \dfrac{1}{2}$ $\sin x = -1$

$x = \dfrac{\pi}{6}, \dfrac{5\pi}{6}$ $x = \dfrac{3\pi}{2}$

17. $3 \cos x - x = 0$

$x \approx -2.9381, -2.6632, 1.1701$

18. $\cos^2 x + \cos x - 6 = 0$

$\cos^2 x + \cos x = 6$

But the maximum value of $\cos^2 x$ is 1 and the maximum value of $\cos x$ is 1. Thus, $|\cos^2 x + \cos x| \le 2$ for all x and $\cos^2 x + \cos x$ can never equal 6.

19. $105° = 135° - 30°$

$\cos 105° = \cos(135° - 30°)$

$= \cos 135° \cos 30° + \sin 45° \sin 30°$

$= -\cos 45° \cos 30° + \sin 45° \sin 30°$

$= \left(-\dfrac{\sqrt{2}}{2}\right)\left(\dfrac{\sqrt{3}}{2}\right) + \left(\dfrac{\sqrt{2}}{2}\right)\left(\dfrac{1}{2}\right)$

$= \dfrac{-\sqrt{6} + \sqrt{2}}{4} = \dfrac{\sqrt{2} - \sqrt{6}}{4}$

20. $\sin 2u = 2 \sin u \cos u$

$= 2\left(\dfrac{2}{\sqrt{5}}\right)\left(\dfrac{1}{\sqrt{5}}\right) = \dfrac{4}{5}$

$\tan 2u = \dfrac{2 \tan u}{1 - \tan^2 u} = \dfrac{2(2)}{1 - (2)^2} = \dfrac{4}{-3} = -\dfrac{4}{3}$

❏ Cumulative Test Solutions for Chapters 4-6

1. (a)

(b) $-120° + 360° = 240°$

(c) $-120°\left(\dfrac{\pi}{180°}\right) = -\dfrac{2\pi}{3}$

(d) $-120°$ is located in Quadrant III.

$240° - 180° = 60°$

(e) $\sin(-120°) = -\sin 60° = -\dfrac{\sqrt{3}}{2}$

$\cos(-120°) = -\cos 60° = -\dfrac{1}{2}$

$\tan(-120°) = \tan 60° = \sqrt{3}$

$\csc(-120°) = \dfrac{1}{-\sin 60°} = -\dfrac{2\sqrt{3}}{3}$

$\sec(-120°) = \dfrac{1}{-\cos 60°} = -2$

$\cot(-120°) = \dfrac{1}{\tan 60°} = \dfrac{\sqrt{3}}{3}$

2. $2.35\left(\dfrac{180°}{\pi}\right) \approx 134.6°$

3. $\tan \theta = \dfrac{y}{x} = -\dfrac{4}{3} \Rightarrow r = 5$

θ is in Quadrant IV $\Rightarrow x = 3$.

$\cos \theta = \dfrac{x}{r} = \dfrac{3}{5}$

4. (a) $f(x) = 3 - 2\sin \pi x$

Period: $\dfrac{2\pi}{\pi} = 2$

Amplitude: $|a| = |-2| = 2$

Upward shift of 3 units (reflected in x-axis prior to shift)

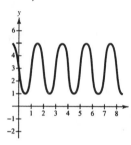

(b) $g(x) = \dfrac{1}{2}\tan\left(x - \dfrac{\pi}{2}\right)$

Period: π

Asymptotes: $x = 0, x = \pi$

5. $h(x) = a\cos(bx + c)$

Graph is reflected in x-axis.

Amplitude: $a = -3$

Period: $2 = \dfrac{2\pi}{\pi} \Rightarrow b = \pi$

No phase shift: $c = 0$

$h(x) = -3\cos(\pi x)$

6. $y = \arccos(2x)$

$\sin y = \sin(\arccos(2x)) = \sqrt{1 - 4x^2}$

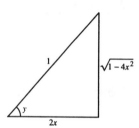

7. $\dfrac{\sin \theta - 1}{\cos \theta} - \dfrac{\cos \theta}{\sin \theta - 1} = \dfrac{\sin \theta - 1}{\cos \theta} - \dfrac{\cos \theta(\sin \theta + 1)}{\sin^2 - 1}$

$= \dfrac{\sin \theta - 1}{\cos \theta} + \dfrac{\cos \theta(\sin \theta + 1)}{\cos \theta} = \dfrac{\sin \theta - 1}{\cos \theta} - \dfrac{\sin \theta + 1}{\cos \theta} = \dfrac{2\sin \theta}{\cos \theta} = 2\tan \theta$

8. (a) $\cot^2 \alpha (\sec^2 \alpha - 1) = \cot^2 \alpha \tan^2 \alpha = 1$

(b) $\sin(x + y) \sin(x - y) = \dfrac{1}{2}[\cos(x + y - (x - y)) - \cos(x + y + x - y)]$

$$= \dfrac{1}{2}[\cos 2y - \cos 2x] = \dfrac{1}{2}[1 - 2 \sin^2 y - (1 - 2 \sin^2 x)] = \sin^2 x - \sin^2 y$$

(c) $\sin^2 x \cos^2 x = \left(\dfrac{1 - \cos 2x}{2} \right)\left(\dfrac{1 + \cos 2x}{2} \right)$

$$= \dfrac{1}{4}(1 - \cos 2x)(1 + \cos 2x)$$

$$= \dfrac{1}{4}(1 - \cos^2 2x)$$

$$= \dfrac{1}{4}\left(1 - \dfrac{1 + \cos 4x}{2} \right)$$

$$= \dfrac{1}{8}(2 - (1 + \cos 4x))$$

$$= \dfrac{1}{8}(1 - \cos 4x)$$

9. (a) $\quad 2 \cos^2 \beta - \cos \beta = 0$

$\cos \beta(2 \cos \beta - 1) = 0$

$\cos \beta = 0 \qquad\qquad 2 \cos \beta - 1 = 0$

$\beta = \dfrac{\pi}{2}, \dfrac{3\pi}{2} \qquad\qquad \cos \beta = \dfrac{1}{2}$

$\qquad\qquad\qquad\qquad \beta = \dfrac{\pi}{3}, \dfrac{5\pi}{3}$

Answer: $\dfrac{\pi}{3}, \dfrac{\pi}{2}, \dfrac{3\pi}{2}, \dfrac{5\pi}{3}$

(b) $3 \tan \theta - \cot \theta = 0$

$3 \tan \theta - \dfrac{1}{\tan \theta} = 0$

$\dfrac{3 \tan^2 \theta - 1}{\tan \theta} = 0$

$3 \tan^2 \theta - 1 = 0$

$\tan^2 \theta = \dfrac{1}{3}$

$\tan \theta = \pm\dfrac{\sqrt{3}}{3}$

$0 = \dfrac{\pi}{6}, \dfrac{5\pi}{6}, \dfrac{7\pi}{6}, \dfrac{11\pi}{6}$

10. (a) $\dfrac{\sin B}{8} = \dfrac{\sin 30}{9}$

$\sin B = \dfrac{8}{9}\left(\dfrac{1}{2}\right)$

$B = \arcsin\left(\dfrac{4}{9}\right)$

$B \approx 26.4°$

$C = 180° - A - B \approx 123.6°$

$\dfrac{c}{\sin 123.6} = \dfrac{9}{\sin 30}$

$c \approx 15.0$

(b) $a^2 = 8^2 + 10^2 - 2(8)(10) \cos 30$

$a^2 \approx 25.4$

$a \approx 5.0$

$\cos B = \dfrac{5.0^2 + 10^2 - 8^2}{2(5.0)(10)}$

$\cos B = 0.61$

$B \approx 52.4°$

$C = 180° - A - B \approx 97.6°$

11. $r = |-2 + 2i| = \sqrt{(-2)^2 + (2)^2} = 2\sqrt{2}$

$\tan \theta = \dfrac{2}{-2} = -1$

Since $\tan 135° = -1$ and $-2 + 2i$ lies in Quadrant II, $\theta = 135°$. Thus, $-2 + 2i = 2\sqrt{2}(\cos 135° + i \sin 135°)$.

12. $[4(\cos 30° + i \sin 30°)][6(\cos 120° + i \sin 120°)] = (4)(6)[\cos(30° + 120°) + i \sin(30° + 120°)]$
$$= 24(\cos 150° + i \sin 150°)$$

13. $1 = 1(\cos 0 + i \sin 0)$

$n = 3, r = 1$

$\sqrt[3]{1}\left(\cos\left(\dfrac{0 + 2\pi(0)}{3}\right) + i \sin\left(\dfrac{0 + 2\pi(0)}{3}\right)\right) = 1$

$\sqrt[3]{1}\left(\cos\left(\dfrac{0 + 2\pi(1)}{3}\right) + i \sin\left(\dfrac{0 + 2\pi(1)}{3}\right)\right) = \cos\dfrac{2\pi}{3} + i \sin\dfrac{2\pi}{3} = -\dfrac{1}{2} + \dfrac{\sqrt{3}}{2}i$

$\sqrt[3]{1}\left(\cos\left(\dfrac{0 + 2\pi(2)}{3}\right) + i \sin\left(\dfrac{0 + 2\pi(2)}{3}\right)\right) = \cos\dfrac{4\pi}{3} + i \sin\dfrac{4\pi}{3} = -\dfrac{1}{2} - \dfrac{\sqrt{3}}{2}i$

14. Height of smaller triangle:

$\tan 16° \, 45' = \dfrac{h_1}{200}$

$h_1 = 200 \tan 16.75° \approx 60.2$ feet

Height of larger triangle:

$\tan 18° = \dfrac{h_2}{200}$

$h_2 = 200 \tan 18° \approx 65.0$

Not to scale.

Height of flag:

$h_2 - h_1 = 65.0 - 60.2 \approx 5$ feet

15. $\mathbf{v}_1 = 500\langle\cos 30, \sin 30\rangle = \langle 250\sqrt{3}, 250\rangle$

$\mathbf{v}_2 = 50\langle\cos 60, \sin 60\rangle = \langle 25, 25\sqrt{3}\rangle$

$\mathbf{v} = \mathbf{v}_1 + \mathbf{v}_2 = \langle 250\sqrt{3} + 25, 250 + 25\sqrt{3}\rangle \approx \langle 458.0, 293.3\rangle$

$\|\mathbf{v}\| = \sqrt{(458.0)^2 + (293.3)^2} \approx 543.9$

$\tan \theta = \dfrac{293.3}{458.0} \approx 0.6404 \Longrightarrow \theta \approx 32.6°$

The plane is traveling N 32.6° E at 543.9 kilometers per hour.

❏ Chapter Test Solutions for Chapter 7

1. $x - y = 4 \implies y = x - 4$

$3x + 2y = 2 \implies 3x + 2(x - 4) = 2$

$$5x - 8 = 2$$

$$5x = 10$$

$$x = 2 \implies y = -2$$

Solution: $(2, -2)$

2. $\qquad y = x - 1$

$$y = (x - 1)^3$$

$$x - 1 = (x - 1)^3$$

$$x - 1 = x^3 - 3x^2 + 3x - 1$$

$$0 = x^3 - 3x^2 + 2x$$

$$0 = x(x - 1)(x - 2)$$

$$x = 0, \quad x = 1, \quad x = 2$$

$$y = -1, \quad y = 0, \quad y = 1$$

Solutions: $(0, -1), (1, 0), (2, 1)$

3. $x - y = 4 \implies x = y + 4$

$2x - y^2 = 0 \implies 2(y + 4) - y^2 = 0$

$$0 = y^2 - 2y - 8$$

$$0 = (y + 2)(y - 4)$$

$$y = -2 \quad \text{or} \quad y = 4$$

$$x = 2 \qquad x = 8$$

Solutions: $(2, -2), (8, 4)$

4. $2x - 3y = 0$

$2x + 3y = 12$

Solution: $(3, 2)$

5. $y = 9 - x^2$

$y = x + 3$

Solutions: $(-3, 0), (2, 5)$

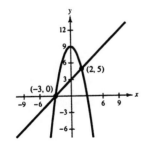

6. $y = \log_3 x \implies 3^y = x$

$y = -\frac{1}{3}x + 2$

Solutions: $(3, 1)$

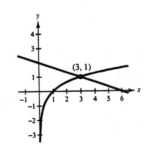

7.
$$2x + 3y = 17 \implies 8x + 12y = 68$$
$$5x - 4y = -15 \implies 15x - 12y = -45$$
$$23x = 23$$
$$x = 1 \implies y = 5$$

Solution: $(1, 5)$

8.
$$x - 2y + 3z = 11$$
$$2x \qquad - z = 3$$
$$3y + z = -8$$

$$x - 2y + 3z = 11$$
$$4y - 7z = -19 \quad -2\,\text{Eq.1} + \text{Eq. 2}$$
$$3y + z = -8$$

$$x - 2y + 3z = 11$$
$$y - 8z = -11 \quad -\text{Eq. 3} + \text{Eq. 2}$$
$$25z = 25 \implies z = 1$$
$$y - 8 = -11 \implies y = -3$$
$$x - 2(-3) + 3(1) = 11 \implies x = 2$$

Solution: $(2, -3, 1)$

9. There are infinitely many systems with the solution $\left(\frac{4}{3}, -5\right)$. One possibility is:
$$3\left(\tfrac{4}{3}\right) - (-5) = 9 \implies 3x - y = 9$$
$$6\left(\tfrac{4}{3}\right) + (-5) = 3 \implies 6x + y = 3$$

10. $y = ax^2 + bx + c$

$(0, 6)$: $\quad 6 = c$

$(-2, 2)$: $\quad 2 = 4a - 2b + c$

$\left(3, \frac{9}{2}\right)$: $\quad \frac{9}{2} = 9a + 3b + c$

Solving this system yields: $a = -\frac{1}{2}$, $b = 1$, and $c = 6$.

Thus, $y = -\frac{1}{2}x^2 + x + 6$.

11. $2x + y \le 4$

$\quad 2x - y \ge 0$

$\qquad x \ge 0$

12. $y < -x^4 + x^2 + 4$

$y > 4x$

13. Line through $(0, 15)$ and $(9, 12)$: $x + 3y = 45$

Line through $(9, 12)$ and $(12, 5)$: $7x + 3y = 99$

Line through $(12, 5)$ and $(12, 0)$: $x = 12$

Inequalities: $x + 3y \leq 45$

$7x + 3y \leq 99$

$x \leq 12$

$x \geq 0$

$y \geq 0$

14. Maximize $z = 20x + 12y$ subject to:

$x \geq 0, \quad y \geq 0$

$x + 4y \leq 32$

$3x + 2y \leq 36$

At $(0, 0)$ we have $z = 0$.

At $(0, 8)$ we have $z = 96$.

At $(8, 6)$ we have $z = 232$.

At $(12, 0)$ we have $z = 240$.

The maximum value, $z = 240$, occurs at $(12, 0)$.

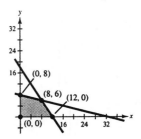

15. Maximize $P = 55x + 75y$ subject to:

$x \geq 0, \quad y \geq 0$

$x + y \leq 300$

$275x + 400y \leq 100,000$

At $(0, 0)$ we have $z = 0$.

At $(0, 250)$ we have $z = 18,750$.

At $(160, 140)$ we have $z = 19,300$.

At $(300, 0)$ we have $z = 16,500$.

The merchant should stock 160 units of the \$275 model and 140 units of the \$400 model to maximize profit.

❏ Chapter Test Solutions for Chapter 8

1.
$$\begin{bmatrix} 1 & -1 & 5 \\ 6 & 2 & 3 \\ 5 & 3 & -3 \end{bmatrix}$$

$$\begin{matrix} \\ -6R_1 + R_2 \rightarrow \\ -5R_1 + R_3 \rightarrow \end{matrix} \begin{bmatrix} 1 & -1 & 5 \\ 0 & 8 & -27 \\ 0 & 8 & -28 \end{bmatrix}$$

$$\begin{matrix} \\ \\ -R_2 + R_3 \rightarrow \end{matrix} \begin{bmatrix} 1 & -1 & 5 \\ 0 & 8 & -27 \\ 0 & 0 & -1 \end{bmatrix}$$

$$\begin{matrix} R_2 + R_1 \rightarrow \\ \frac{1}{8}R_2 \rightarrow \\ -R_3 \rightarrow \end{matrix} \begin{bmatrix} 1 & 0 & \frac{13}{8} \\ 0 & 1 & -\frac{27}{8} \\ 0 & 0 & 1 \end{bmatrix}$$

$$\begin{matrix} -\frac{13}{8}R_3 + R_1 \rightarrow \\ \frac{27}{8}R_3 + R_2 \rightarrow \\ \\ \end{matrix} \begin{bmatrix} 1 & 0 & 0 \\ 0 & 1 & 0 \\ 0 & 0 & 1 \end{bmatrix}$$

2.
$$\begin{bmatrix} 1 & 0 & -1 & 2 \\ -1 & 1 & 1 & -3 \\ 1 & 1 & -1 & 1 \\ 3 & 2 & -3 & 4 \end{bmatrix}$$

$$\begin{matrix} R_1 + R_2 \rightarrow \\ -R_1 + R_3 \rightarrow \\ -3R_1 + R_4 \rightarrow \end{matrix} \begin{bmatrix} 1 & 0 & -1 & 2 \\ 0 & 1 & 0 & -1 \\ 0 & 1 & 0 & -1 \\ 0 & 2 & 0 & -2 \end{bmatrix}$$

$$\begin{matrix} \\ \\ -R_2 + R_3 \rightarrow \\ -2R_2 + R_4 \rightarrow \end{matrix} \begin{bmatrix} 1 & 0 & -1 & 2 \\ 0 & 1 & 0 & -1 \\ 0 & 0 & 0 & 0 \\ 0 & 0 & 0 & 0 \end{bmatrix}$$

3.
$$\begin{bmatrix} 4 & 3 & -2 & \vdots & 14 \\ -1 & -1 & 2 & \vdots & -5 \\ 3 & 1 & -4 & \vdots & 8 \end{bmatrix} \rightarrow \begin{bmatrix} 1 & 0 & 0 & \vdots & 1 \\ 0 & 1 & 0 & \vdots & 3 \\ 0 & 0 & 1 & \vdots & -\frac{1}{2} \end{bmatrix}$$

Solution: $\left(1, 3, -\frac{1}{2}\right)$

4. $y = ax^2 + bx + c$

$(-2, -2)$: $-2 = 4a - 2b + c$

$(2, 2)$: $2 = 4a + 2b + c$

$(4, -2)$: $-2 = 16a + 4b + c$

Solving this system yields $a = -\frac{1}{2}$, $b = 1$, and $c = 2$.

Thus, $y = -\frac{1}{2}x^2 + x + 2$.

5. (a) $A - B = \begin{bmatrix} 5 & 4 & 4 \\ -4 & -4 & 0 \end{bmatrix} - \begin{bmatrix} 4 & -1 & 6 \\ -4 & 0 & -3 \end{bmatrix}$

$$= \begin{bmatrix} 1 & 5 & -2 \\ 0 & -4 & 3 \end{bmatrix}$$

(b) $3A = 3\begin{bmatrix} 5 & 4 & 4 \\ -4 & -4 & 0 \end{bmatrix} = \begin{bmatrix} 15 & 12 & 12 \\ -12 & -12 & 0 \end{bmatrix}$

(c) $3A - 2B = 3\begin{bmatrix} 5 & 4 & 4 \\ -4 & -4 & 0 \end{bmatrix} - 2\begin{bmatrix} 4 & -1 & 6 \\ -4 & 0 & -3 \end{bmatrix}$

$$= \begin{bmatrix} 15 & 12 & 12 \\ -12 & -12 & 0 \end{bmatrix} - \begin{bmatrix} 8 & -2 & 12 \\ -8 & 0 & -6 \end{bmatrix}$$

$$= \begin{bmatrix} 7 & 14 & 0 \\ -4 & -12 & 6 \end{bmatrix}$$

6. $\begin{bmatrix} 2 & -2 & 6 \\ 3 & -1 & 7 \\ 2 & 0 & -2 \end{bmatrix}\begin{bmatrix} 4 & 4 \\ 3 & 2 \\ 1 & -2 \end{bmatrix} = \begin{bmatrix} 8 & -8 \\ 16 & -4 \\ 6 & 12 \end{bmatrix}$

7. $\begin{bmatrix} -6 & 4 \\ 10 & -5 \end{bmatrix}^{-1} = \begin{bmatrix} \frac{1}{2} & \frac{2}{5} \\ 1 & \frac{3}{5} \end{bmatrix}$

8. $\begin{bmatrix} \frac{1}{2} & \frac{2}{5} \\ 1 & \frac{3}{5} \end{bmatrix}\begin{bmatrix} 10 \\ 20 \end{bmatrix} = \begin{bmatrix} 13 \\ 22 \end{bmatrix}$

Solution: $(13, 22)$

9. $\begin{vmatrix} 4 & 0 & 3 \\ 1 & -8 & 2 \\ 3 & 2 & 2 \end{vmatrix} = -2$

10. $A = -\frac{1}{2}\begin{vmatrix} -5 & 0 & 1 \\ 4 & 4 & 1 \\ 3 & 2 & 1 \end{vmatrix} = -\frac{1}{2}(-14) = 7$

❑ Cumulative Test Solutions for Chapters 7-9

1. $y = 3 - x^2$

$2(y - 2) = x - 1 \Longrightarrow 2(3 - x^2 - 2) = x - 1$

$\qquad\qquad\qquad\qquad 2(1 - x^2) = x - 1$

$\qquad\qquad\qquad\qquad\quad 2 - 2x^2 = x - 1$

$\qquad\qquad\qquad\qquad\qquad\quad 0 = 2x^2 + x - 3$

$\qquad\qquad\qquad\qquad\qquad\quad 0 = (2x + 3)(x - 1)$

$\qquad\qquad\qquad\qquad\qquad\quad x = -\frac{3}{2} \ \text{ or } \ x = 1$

$\qquad\qquad\qquad\qquad\qquad\quad y = \frac{3}{4} \qquad\qquad y = 2$

Solutions: $\left(-\frac{3}{2}, \frac{3}{4}\right), (1, 2)$

2. $\quad x + 3y = -1 \implies \quad 4x + 12y = -4$

$\quad 2x + 4y = \ \ \ 0 \implies -6x - 12y = \ \ \ 0$

$\qquad\qquad\qquad\qquad\qquad -2x \qquad\quad = -4$

$\qquad\qquad\qquad\qquad x = 2 \implies y = -1$

Solution: $(2, -1)$

3. $-2x + 4y - \ z = \ \ \ 3$

$\qquad x - 2y + 2z = -6$

$\qquad x - 3y - \ z = \ \ \ 1$

$-2x + 4y - \ z = \ \ \ 3$

$\qquad x - 2y + 2z = -6$

$\qquad x - 3y - \ z = \ \ \ 1$

$\qquad x - 2y + 2z = -6$

$\qquad\qquad\qquad\quad 3z = -9 \qquad 2\,\text{Eq. 1} + \text{Eq. 2}$

$\qquad\qquad -y - 3z = 7 \qquad -\text{Eq. 1} + \text{Eq. 3}$

From Equation 2 we have $z = -3$. Substituting this into Equation 3 yields $y = 2$. Using these in Equation 1 yields $x = 4$.

Solution: $(4, 2, -3)$